FASCINATING WORLD OF ANIMALS

Jellyfish of the genus *Porpita*

Gerenuk *Litocranius walleri*

READER'S DIGEST

FASCINATING WORLD OF
ANIMALS

A Unique "Safari" Through Our Strange and Surprising Animal Kingdom

THE READER'S DIGEST ASSOCIATION, INC., PLEASANTVILLE, NEW YORK
THE READER'S DIGEST ASSOCIATION (CANADA) LTD., MONTREAL

The acknowledgments that appear on pages 427–28
are hereby made a part of this copyright page.

Library of Congress Catalog Card Number: 77-161467

Printed in the United States of America

Japanese macaques *Macaca fuscata*

Reindeer *Rangifer tarandus*

Ringlet butterfly *Aphantopus hyperanthus*

Contents

Flower feeder A velvet-breasted hummingbird hovers to feed on nectar

DISCOVERING THE WORLD OF ANIMALS

Biologists now realize that no plant or animal can be
fully understood by considering it in isolation. Every living
organism plays its role in a dynamic community.
Man, one species among a million or more, is linked
with the entire animal kingdom

Primitive man was both hunter and hunted. In order
to survive, he had to study the habits of animals that
were his predators and his prey. Cave paintings dating
back 20,000 years reveal his special knowledge
of animal anatomy (see page 357).

The first Greek and Roman authors who wrote
about plants and animals copied freely from one
another. Since these authors also wrote fables, fact
and fancy were often interwoven. Yet for more than
a thousand years Western man turned to these
writings as a source of knowledge.

With the coming of the Renaissance, men began
to re-explore the world around them, relying on
their firsthand observations. The great Italian artist
and scientist Leonardo da Vinci (1452–1519) made
superb anatomical drawings of animals. Studies of
this kind led to the establishment of zoology, the
study of animals, and botany, the study of plants.

The differences between plants and animals

A complex living organism such as an ape or an oak
tree is clearly different from a nonliving block of
granite. But the distinction between living and nonliving is far less sharp when we compare the simplest
living things, such as viruses, with complex organic
chemicals, such as amino acids. This blurring of the
boundary between animate and inanimate matter, at
the borderline of life, is the basis for the view that
all life on earth originated from nonliving chemicals.

The dividing line between the simplest plants and
the simplest animals is similarly vague. We tend to
think of plants as being green and motionless, but a
fungus (usually considered a plant) has no green
parts, and a sponge (an animal) is motionless.

Green plants make their own food from simple
chemicals, using sunlight as the source of energy to
convert carbon dioxide and water into food compounds in the process known as photosynthesis.
Typically, plants grow where sunlight, air, and
water are available; and they have not evolved
means of locomotion allowing them to move if these
food and energy sources are not present in sufficient
quantities in their environment.

A typical animal, on the other hand, cannot syn-
thesize its own food, but must obtain nourishment by
eating plants or other animals. The animal must be

Burchell's zebras Herds roam undisturbed on Tanzania's Serengeti Plain

able to pursue its prey or move from plant to plant.

The first intensively studied aspect of modern biology was anatomy—how animals are put together, part by part. The invention of the microscope by the Dutch naturalist Anton van Leeuwenhoek (1632–1723), and the more recent invention of the powerful electron microscope, added impetus to the study of plant structure and animal anatomy. Anatomy paved the way for the science of physiology—the study of the ways in which living organisms function. And physiology in turn has fostered the new sciences of biochemistry, biophysics, and molecular biology.

Systematizing the living world

As more and more living organisms were studied and described, it became increasingly desirable to classify them, a scientific pursuit called taxonomy. The first to produce a generally accepted system of classification was the Swedish naturalist Karl von Linné (1707–78), or Carolus Linnaeus (the Latin version of von Linné's name). His system gave a Latin name to each species of plant and animal then known, and arranged the species in groups, based mainly on anatomical characteristics. These classification categories are described on pages 372–73, and are followed by a taxonomic survey of the animal kingdom.

The value of the Linnaean system is that it authorized a specific compound name (such as *Canis familiaris* for the domestic dog) for each species—a name which is accepted and reserved for that species alone, and which shows closely related species belonging to the same genus (such as *Canis lupus,* the timber wolf).

A key to the variety of life

The modern classification system, derived from Linnaeus, has been profoundly affected by the concept of evolution outlined by the English naturalist Charles Darwin (1809–82). His *On the Origin of Species,* published in 1859, showed how, by means of natural selection, all species living today could have evolved from preexisting forms of life.

Darwin's theory of evolution by natural selection (see pages 324–41) was extended by subsequent discoveries in the field of heredity, notably the pioneering work of Gregor Mendel (1822–84), a Moravian monk who founded the science of genetics. A basic tenet of the modern theory of evolution is that species evolve into new forms as a result of the demands (natural selection) made upon them by a changing environment. The process by which a species adjusts, over many generations, to a changing environment, is called adaptation.

And now ecology

Over the past hundred years, as understanding of the process of adaptation has grown, scientists have become increasingly interested in studying living organisms in their natural surroundings rather than as dead laboratory specimens.

The study of living things in relation to their environment is called ecology, from the Greek word *oikos,* meaning "house." All surviving wild species are (or until very recently were) adapted to their environment, which includes physical conditions—rainfall, temperature, altitude, and so on—as well as the plants and other animals that live around them. In a given location all the components of environment are considered by ecologists as a dynamically balanced whole, called an ecosystem.

In order for a species to survive, a healthy number of its individual members must be able to obtain food, escape from predators, resist parasites, and reproduce. All the other organisms in an animal's environment—plants, prey, predators, parasites, and competitors—have their own kinds of adaptation. The principal reason why so many wild species are now threatened with extinction is that man may destroy in a year—or a day—an environment to which a species may have been adapting for a million years.

Worldwide, environments can be approached in terms of certain broad and general climatic conditions, with a resulting division of the globe into wildlife regions called life zones or biomes. In these new approaches to the living world—traveled in the pages that follow—biologists see man's last best hope that we may continue to share the earth with so splendid a variety of other living creatures.

PART ONE

TEN WILDLIFE REGIONS OF THE WORLD

1
POLAR REGIONS

2
CONIFEROUS FOREST

3
TEMPERATE FORESTS

4
GRASSLANDS

The perpetual cold of the polar regions limits vegetation and land animals. Yet the oceans teem with life

Many animals sleep through the long winter in the coniferous forest. Those that remain active live on stored seeds or roots

Leaf litter in the northern deciduous forests shelters a myriad of animals. The southern temperate forests are mostly evergreen

Vast grasslands exist in both hemisphe On the African savanna great herds of pl. eaters are preyed on by flesh-eaters

Plant and animal communities

Every animal on earth is adapted to its environment, which is made up of everything that surrounds the animal: land, water, air, vegetation, and other animals. Vegetation is a major factor in animal life. Its general features in a particular area are largely determined by climate. The earth can be divided into major climatic zones, each of which supports its own specially adapted plants and animals. Ecologists call these zones biomes, and, although opinions may differ as to how many biomes there are, the most

(continued)

5 DESERTS

6 TROPICAL FORESTS

7 MOUNTAINS

8 OCEANIC ISLANDS

the scorching heat and low rainfall of the erts, animals survive by conserving water by sheltering during peak sun hours

In tropical forests the vegetation is always in leaf and producing fruit, providing for the richest variety of animal life on land

Five percent of the earth's surface is mountains. The animals are adapted to harsh conditions—thin air, low humidity, and cold

Oceanic islands support only the plants and animals able to cross the oceans and colonize them

13

9 INLAND WATERS

Inland waters range from the Caspian Sea, supporting many life forms, to rainpools containing small animals with brief lives

10 OCEANS

Oceans are the largest biome, containing the greatest number and variety of animals, all ultimately dependent on plant plankton

convenient formula recognizes ten. Six of the ten—the polar regions, coniferous forest, temperate forests, grasslands, deserts, and tropical forests—differ markedly in vegetation. In the mountains, where climate and vegetation vary with altitude, animal and plant communities are highly specialized. Oceanic islands have few climatic or vegetation characteristics in common, but, because of their isolation, are often inhabited by distinctive animal species that are not found elsewhere. The aquatic existence in the two remaining biomes, inland waters and oceans, forces upon plants and animals the highest degree of specialization.

Animals molded by their environments

The limits of the first six biomes, or life zones, are determined by particular patterns of rainfall and temperature. In addition, most life zones have their own form of seasonal change. All of these factors, in combination with others such as local soil conditions, produce characteristic types of plant life in each biome that support characteristic communities of animal life.

One combination of rainfall, temperature, and soil, for example, has produced dense tropical forests in the wet equatorial lands. Another combination has created the deserts that cover about 15 percent of the earth's land surface. In the tropical forests, taking advantage of a rich variety of habitats, live an immense number of animal species, representing most of the main groups of land animals. The scant vegetation of the deserts, on the other hand, supports relatively few animal species, representing a limited number of groups.

A single biome, such as the temperate forests, may consist of several regions, separated geographically, and each inhabited by distinctly different groups of animals. But the similar climatic influences within each region tend to lead to remarkable similarities in appearance and behavior among these different groups. Two different species of squirrels, one living in the North American temperate forest and the other in the European temperate forest, will have many physical and behavioral characteristics in common, because the conditions under which they live are so similar. (See also the map of the world's life zones on pages 16–17.)

Heating the earth The sun's rays strike the earth squarely at the equator, but obliquely at the poles. Since an oblique ray travels through more atmosphere, which disperses solar radiation, the polar regions receive less heat. Because the earth's axis is tilted 23 degrees, the sun is not perpendicular to the same place each day, but over the year shifts from the Tropic of Cancer to the Tropic of Capricorn. The variation in day length culminates at the poles in days and nights six months long

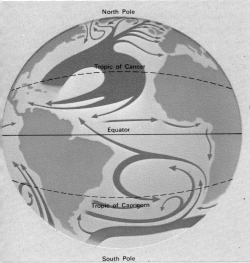

Ocean currents Prevailing winds and variations in water density create ocean currents. The earth's rotation deflects currents, causing them to move clockwise in the northern hemisphere and counterclockwise in the southern hemisphere. Ocean currents mix waters of different temperatures and of varying degrees of salinity, disperse vital chemicals, and warm and cool land masses

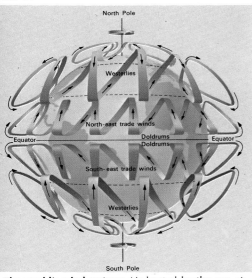

The world's wind systems Air heated by the sun at the equator expands and rises, moving at high levels. Most of it subsides around 30° N and 30° S, its weight creating high-pressure areas, which send trade winds blowing back into the tropics. Over the poles, cold air sinks and rises again at slightly lower latitudes. Between the polar and tropical wind systems are great waves of air—forming the westerlies—which rise and sink toward the tropics. Winds distribute heat from the tropics to other regions, and carry moisture inland from the oceans, bringing rain to continents

Patterns of climate

The life zones, with their characteristic plant and animal communities, are determined by climate, which varies widely over the earth

Climate, as distinguished from weather, is defined as the composite of the variety of day-to-day weather conditions in a particular area. Weather is defined as the total of the atmospheric conditions prevailing over a short period of time in a particular place. Weather, in other words, is local and short-term; climate applies to a larger area and covers a longer period of time.

The basic source of the earth's climate is radiation from the sun. Climate is created by the effect of radiation on the planet's outer coat of solids, liquids, and gases—the continents, the oceans, and the atmosphere—and is varied by the earth's daily rotation on its axis, and its year-long orbit around the sun.

The heating of the earth's surface by solar radiation also creates winds, which in turn influence ocean currents. The earth's rotation affects both winds and ocean currents, and they interact with solar radiation to bring about distribution of moisture over the planet. Basically, winds blowing off the sea carry water vapor—especially winds that pass over warm currents—while winds blowing off the land are dry.

The interaction of solar radiation, winds, and ocean currents produces the conditions in which life can develop. But radiation remains the paramount influence. Plants cannot grow without sunlight, which supplies the energy for photosynthesis, the process by which plants convert water and carbon dioxide into complex organic matter. Oxygen is a by-product of this process.

These major climatic influences combine with local factors, such as altitude and land forms, to produce a multitude of local climates.

A view from space Moisture-filled clouds, shaped by winds blowing off the sea, cover vast areas of the earth's surface. South America is near the center of this photograph, taken from a satellite 22,300 miles above the mouth of the Amazon. Africa is to the right, below cloud-covered Europe

15

Map of the world's life zones

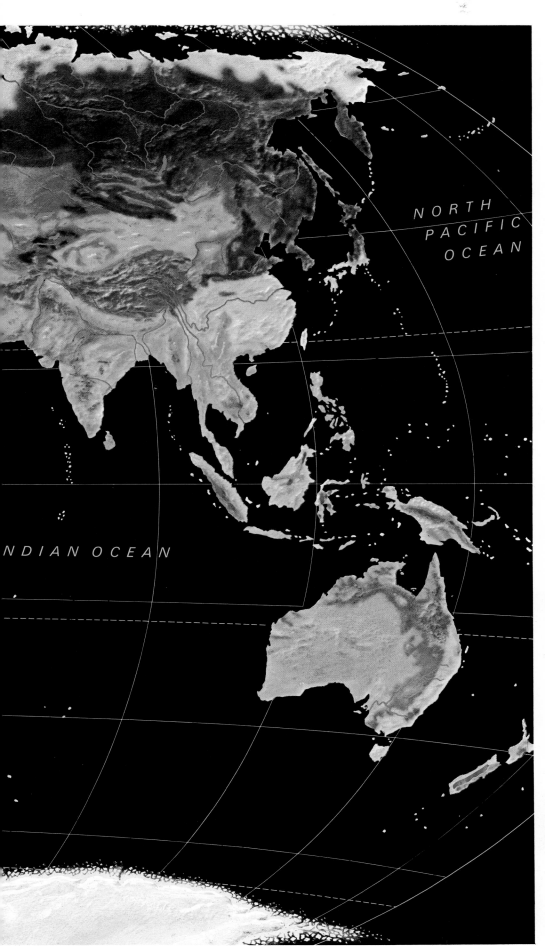

NORTH PACIFIC OCEAN

INDIAN OCEAN

Influences on the life zones

The land biomes or life zones shown on this map are greatly influenced by what geographers call relief features, such as mountains, hills, and valleys. These variations from a flat surface affect the movement of air, which in turn influences the air's moisture content and temperature.

The equator marks the world's main tropical belt, but the boundaries of the tropical zone are influenced and extended by the oceans' warm or cold currents.

Man has greatly modified many of the world's wildlife regions, especially the grasslands and forests of the northern hemisphere. Most of Europe lies within the temperate forest zone, but the land has been so intensively farmed for so long that forest survives only in isolated pockets. But if man were to disappear, most of the land area of Europe would eventually revert to forest.

Man has also had an effect on the inland waters, the tropical forests, and many oceanic islands. The polar regions and the oceans have been affected recently by the increasing demand for oil. Only the mountains have remained relatively free of man's influence.

POLAR REGIONS
Top: permanent ice
Bottom: tundra

CONIFEROUS FOREST

TEMPERATE FORESTS
Top: deciduous
Bottom: evergreen

GRASSLANDS
Top: savanna
Bottom: temperate

DESERTS

TROPICAL FORESTS
Top: rain forest
Bottom: mountain forest

MOUNTAINS

OCEANIC ISLANDS

INLAND WATERS

OCEANS

THE POLAR REGIONS

**The two polar zones occupy corresponding spots on the globe and
have a common frigid climate; but each is a different environment that supports
different species of plants and animals**

If you could watch the earth from outer space over the course of a year, you would see the brilliant Arctic ice cap gradually creep forward with the approach of winter, covering lands that had been green with summer vegetation. But the Antarctic ice in the south would stay the same all year long.

The reason? The heart of the Arctic is a permanently frozen sea surrounded by land masses that gradually merge into more temperate regions, but Antarctica is an isolated island continent. Thus the Arctic has "seasons"; the Antarctic does not.

Windy deserts of ice

Just as in desert areas, precipitation in the polar regions is scant—less than ten inches a year. But here evaporation does not exceed precipitation. When it rains on a desert the water is rapidly drawn back into the hot air. But cold temperatures prevent the air from holding much moisture, and so evaporation is limited. Over the long life of the earth, these factors have caused the creation and accumulation of the ice caps.

Both poles have permanent ice. (Antarctica carries 95 percent of the world's permanent ice.) But in the Antarctic most of it is on land, in the Arctic on water. Therefore, the effect of the ice caps on plant and animal life is entirely different.

Parts of inland Antarctica are so intensely dry that neither snow nor ice accumulates there. The soil is arid, sandy, and encrusted with salts. This picture of drought seems to contradict the vivid stories of snowstorms told by early explorers, but the wind explains the anomaly. Winds cascade off the Antarctic plateau at up to 100 miles an hour, driving snow across the land. Many blizzards consist more of drifting snow than of falling snow.

Cold and darkness inhibit life

The single most important factor permitting life on earth is the light and heat radiated by the sun. Both poles share a common feature of six months of light and six of darkness. As one moves away from the poles, these extremes are modified.

Even though there is a long period of sunlight at the poles, the angle of the sun's rays is too oblique, for most of the year, to be effective for plant growth. In the brief peak of sunlight all plant life must grow and reproduce.

Since ice and snow are highly reflective, 90 per-

cent of the solar radiation reaching the surface at any season is thrown back into space. During the short winter days, particularly, the warming effect of the sun's rays is negligible.

The polar regions are thus characterized by a monotonous cold climate. The lowest recorded temperature is −126° F. (−88° C.) in central Antarctica. In the "high polar" areas, those nearest the poles, the average temperature of the warmest month rises only a few degrees above freezing. The outer limits of both zones are delineated by a line joining those areas in which the average temperature of the warmest month reaches only 50° F. (10° C.). In the Arctic this line approximates the northern tree line, beyond which no trees can grow. Here, the coniferous forest gives way to the vast, treeless stretches of the tundra.

The Antarctic—an isolated plateau of ice

Antarctica is a disk of land with the South Pole near its center. It covers an area only a little smaller than the Arctic Ocean. In places the ice is more than 12,000 feet thick. This region today is a high plateau solely because of the ice. The altitude at the South Pole is 9200 feet above sea level, 9000 feet of which is ice.

If the ice cover disappeared, eastern Antarctica would look like a saucer of lowland surrounded by mountains. Ranges run along the shores of the Ross and Weddell seas, and there are more mountains along the eastern coast. Some peaks rise to more than 15,000 feet.

Land links in the Arctic

The core of the high Arctic is a great ocean, some 5.5 million square miles in area, covered all year by ice that drifts about the North Pole. The high Arctic contains little land—only the ice-covered mass of Greenland, smaller areas in the far north of Canada, and part of the island groups fringing Eurasia. Most of the land area of the Arctic is in the lower reaches of the polar zone. This land is not isolated, but forms the coasts of all the northern continents.

Because the Arctic has land links with the temperate zones in America and Eurasia, animals of the northern hemisphere can retreat and advance with the changes in climate. This is one reason why animal life is much more plentiful in the Arctic than in the Antarctic, which is separated from South America, the nearest continent, by 500 miles of open water, creating a barrier to the movement of land animals.

Arctic autumn As the days grow shorter, the caribou begin their annual migration southward across the meandering rivers of the tundra and into the coniferous forest

Plants in harsh climates

The longest days and nights, the lowest temperatures, and some of the strongest winds on earth dominate life in the frozen deserts of the polar regions

The land of the "high polar" regions, a cold desert with scant vegetation and few animals, contrasts with the polar oceans. It is here in the oceans that the food chain begins for most of the animals that inhabit both the north and the south polar zones.

The Antarctic seas are as rich in life as any seas of the world. Because of the Antarctic Convergence, where the warm waters of the temperate zones meet the cold currents of the Antarctic, there is a great upwelling of the water. This makes the various "layers" of water unstable and thoroughly mixes all the nutrients.

The Arctic Ocean, on the other hand, is lower in productivity, for it is extremely stable and so the supply of nutrients essential for marine plant growth is in limited supply.

An intricate web of animal life is dependent upon the abundance of phytoplankton, unicellular floating plants. These grow during the summer when the ice breaks up. There is enough light then for plant growth, and the upwelling warm currents from other regions nourish the phytoplankton with dissolved nutrients.

These plants are eaten by tiny animals, called zooplankton. In the Antarctic the most numerous of these small animals is the krill, a shrimplike crustacean. Krill is the main food supply for whales, seals, seabirds, and fish.

The chain does not stop in the seas, for marine life also enriches the land, and it is a food source to some land animals. Though seals and seabirds feed at sea, they rest and breed ashore, and their droppings supply important nutrients to the nitrogen-deficient soils. Along many coastal areas, the vegetation is much lusher than that growing inland.

The Antarctic is a continent of ice

Only 4 percent of Antarctica is free of permanent ice. On this land there is almost no topsoil, just mineral debris, so only bacteria, fungi, and microscopic plants can exist. Bacteria exist in such minimal amounts that there is only one per pint of snow. Because of the absence of a mature soil, the Antarctic lacks the vegetation that is essential for the support of animal life on land.

The principal plants of the inland mountains are about 400 species of lichens, which grow on cliffs and boulders as thin crusts or scattered tufts. Even on the warmer coasts, the ground is permanently frozen below two to three feet. Yet surface water promotes the growth of moss mats that can eventually build up into six-foot-thick layers of peat. On the whole of Antarctica there are only two flowering plants—a small grass and an inconspicuous green cushion plant. These grow low down in sunny north-facing gullies, where the soil is more mature and there is some shelter from the fierce southerly gales.

The largest Antarctic animals that do not depend on the sea for food are two wingless species of midges. These flies, less than one fifth of an inch long, are found in the same coastal areas as the flowering plants. In the interior the animal life is even sparser. But, even here, only 100 miles away from the South Pole, tiny mites have been found living on bacteria.

Ice limits and ocean currents in the polar regions

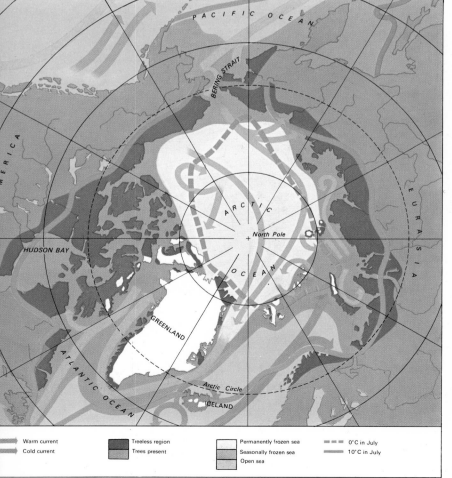

Arctic boundary The southern limit of the Arctic is delineated by the July isotherm, which is a line joining places where the sea-level temperature of the warmest month reaches 10° C. (50° F.). It approximates the tree limit

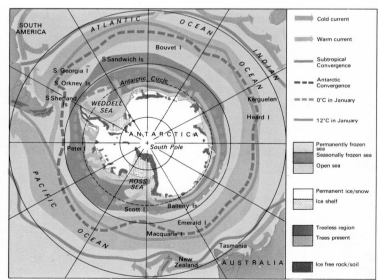

Antarctic boundary The Antarctic region is contained within the Antarctic Convergence, where there is an abrupt change from the cold Antarctic waters to warmer, saltier water. The permanent ice shelves, bordering the Ross and Weddell seas and other areas, are enormous. The Ross ice shelf is 1000 feet thick. These ice shelves have no equivalent in the Arctic

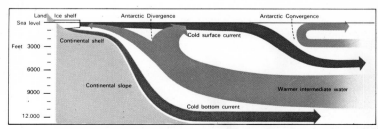

Antarctic Convergence Two cold currents flow northward from Antarctica. The surface one is diluted by melting ice, while the one on the seabed is undiluted. Between them, warmer water flows southward and wells up around the shores. This nutrient-rich water supports the plant life of the upper layers. The top cold current sinks at the Antarctic Convergence

Summer landscape Treeless, tundralike vegetation extends south of the polar zone in the Alaskan mountains. In the distance is Mount McKinley

In summer the Arctic awakens and teems with life

Along the southern reaches of the Arctic lies a kind of mid-zone between frozen and unfrozen, the land called tundra. This vast subpolar region, with the kind of life it supports, is absent in the Antarctic, where the central ice cap covers virtually the entire land mass. As summer comes to the tundra, Arctic vegetation and animal life reach their peak of development. Insect life is profuse.

The tundra lies on a permanently frozen subsoil, called permafrost, which may be 2000 feet deep. Even in summer only the few inches of topsoil thaw, but this permits the growth of more than 1000 mosses and lichens and 800 species of flowering plants.

Permafrost has several important effects on plant growth. Along with the runoff from melted surface ice, it supplies water to plants. In some places meltwater accumulates because the permafrost blocks effective drainage. The result is vast areas of mossy bogs. The root systems of Arctic plants are shallow where the permafrost presents a barrier to roots' downward growth.

The tundra soil and vegetation absorb solar heat, then disperse some of it to their immediate surroundings. Thus, the surface soil and the air around a growing plant may be 25 to 40 degrees warmer than the air a few feet above the ground. This ground-level microclimate allows Arctic plants to begin

Antarctic plants Above, left, are lichens and mosses growing together. At the right, lichens grow alone on an exposed sea cliff. All polar plants are adapted to their habitat. They are compact, wind-resistant, and able to withstand the unstable soils. The principal plants of the inland mountains of Antarctica are lichens; about 400 species grow on cliffs and boulders in thin crusts or scattered tufts. The only other plants of the interior are fungi, bacteria, and algae. Coastal growth is more luxuriant; about 75 mosses and at least 20 liverworts carpet the rocky flats and edges of glacial streams

growing even when the season is still cold.

The severe cold limits the variety of Arctic plants. All are perennials. If they were annuals, an unusually cold year could prevent seed germination and kill an entire species. A number of plants have abandoned seed altogether and reproduce by runners or tiny bulbs scattered by the wind. Their growth rate is extremely low. A bush only a few inches high, with a stem just an inch thick, may be over 100 years old.

The so-called reindeer moss, a staple food of caribou, is prominent among the Arctic lichens and may grow over large areas of the tundra.

Arctic flowers The Arctic poppy (left) has insulated hairy stems, and the moss campion (right) forms a ground-hugging cushion. These plants bring a surge of color to the Arctic spring. Polar plants flower and fruit only when exposed to the long polar days; they will not seed in temperate regions

Life in a cold climate

Warm-blooded polar animals have body systems and behavior patterns that help them survive constant near-freezing temperatures

The temperatures of the polar seas are near the freezing point of seawater, about 28° F. (−2° C.), for most of the year. The plants, invertebrate animals, and fish living in these cold waters have evolved systems that function efficiently at low temperatures. In fact, many polar species cannot tolerate higher temperatures.

On land, the plants and invertebrate animals of the polar and temperate regions become dormant when it freezes. However, they could not survive without at least a brief season of ample warmth and sunlight— the polar summer. A summer cold spell may prevent normal growth and upset the life cycle of an entire species, so that it dies before it has time to reproduce.

To stay alive, warm-blooded animals must maintain a constant warm temperature in the bulk of their body. Polar animals have effective adaptations to cope with the cold and the harsh winds.

For survival at the poles—regulated birth and behavior

Huddling to conserve heat Adélie penguin chicks stay warm in a blizzard by huddling together. This reduces the exposed surface of each bird's body, cutting the heat loss. Through huddling, some of the heat that does escape from each bird is trapped, and this creates a warmer microclimate

Protection for the newborn Ringed seal pups are born in April in an "igloo" hollowed out of snow that has drifted against columns of landfast ice. The pup is kept near the piled-up ice, where small gaps admit air. The snow traps heat radiating from the seal's body. The igloo is also heated by the warmer air rising from the water hole. Cow and pup leave this lair after a few weeks

Warm-blooded polar animals have certain behavior patterns that are linked to maintaining an internal body temperature higher than the prevailing cold. One such form of behavior is simply to move to a warmer region—migration. Some caribou move from the tundra to the coniferous forest where wind chill (wind and cold combined) is less acute and where the caribou can scrape through the lighter snow cover to the edible plants beneath. Many birds that breed in the polar regions migrate to more temperate zones in both hemispheres when winter comes.

Polar animals are also aided in conserving heat by insulating layers of fur or feathers, which prevent or moderate the transfer of heat from the animal's body to the air. It is not the fur or the feathers that provide the insulation, but the pockets of air—a poor conductor of heat—trapped between. The caribou's fur is made up of hollow tubes containing air, which give further insulation. A thicker coat of fur means more air pockets and therefore more protection. Those animals which, like the caribou, carry thick coats can stay active all winter.

Some animals escape extreme cold by taking advantage of the insulating properties of snow. Undersnow temperatures seldom drop below 19° F. (−7° C.), even though the air temperature above may be many degrees colder. Female polar bears and their small cubs survive the coldest months in dens they dig into the snow. Lemmings spend the winter in underground nests.

Birth at the best time—delayed implantation

For survival of a species, the birth of its young must occur in a season that gives the baby animals the best chance of living and maturing through their vulnerable infancy. Thus—if animals live in harsh climates—the species' time of mating and length of gestation (pregnancy) are of critical importance. Birth must coincide with a time when food is relatively plentiful and when the female can assume the biological responsibilities of mothering, such as suckling her young.

Some animals of the polar regions, including seals and polar bears, have a reproductive adaptation called delayed implantation. This is a response of the mother's internal chemistry, controlled by hormones, to the seasonal changes of her environment: the fertilized egg does not attach to the wall of the mother's uterus until her internal chemistry permits; then the fetus begins to develop.

Ways to conserve heat

Polar animals and birds are able to maintain a wide temperature difference between themselves and their environment because of the insulating properties of layers of fur or feathers. Blubber—fat beneath the skin—also provides insulation for some polar animals, such as seals and penguins. Fur and feather layers are efficient insulators on land, but lose some insulating properties when wet, so seals have blubber up to three inches thick below their hair coats.

Seal and bear pelts and penguin feathers have a greenhouse effect on sunny days. They trap the animal's surface heat, yet allow solar radiation through to warm the skin, in much the same way the glass roof and walls of a greenhouse effectively shut out the cold air while allowing the sun's rays to pass through.

No animal is completely covered with fur, feathers, or blubber; to be functional, feet, flippers, and nostrils must be relatively bare. But if large amounts of body heat were to escape through these extremities, neither mammals nor birds could survive in frigid conditions. Polar animals have evolved ways to solve even these specialized problems.

Some animals, such as gulls and penguins, avoid losing heat through their bare extremities by maintaining two body temperatures simultaneously—around 100° F. (38° C.) in the bulk of the body, and near the temperature of the environment in the extremities.

These dual temperatures are achieved by a heat-exchange system of entwined veins and arteries. Warm blood flowing from the heart heats cold blood returning from the extremities, and the cold blood in turn cools the blood flowing to the extremities. This system serves two purposes: heat can be retained in the body when the surroundings are cold, or blood can be flushed to the extremities if the animal needs to lose heat.

Impervious to cold A thick layer of blubber, combined with a tough hide, insulates the harp seal as it rests on Arctic ice. All marine mammals, even those in more temperate waters, have some blubber

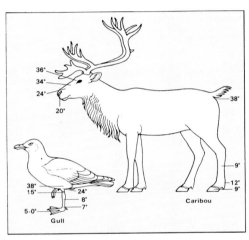

Cold feet give protection The diagram illustrates the different temperatures (in centigrade) of various parts of the gull and caribou on a typically cold day. Many other polar animals' extremities function at a

lower temperature than the rest of their body, helping to maintain an internal temperature near 38° C. (100° F.). Otherwise, swimming penguins would lose more heat through flippers than they could replace

Sizes and shapes to suit life in the polar regions

An animal's size and shape help to determine its ability to retain body heat. Heat is produced by the oxidation of glucose in the tissues and is directly related to the total bulk or volume of the animal. Yet the amount of heat an animal loses through radiation is related only to the surface area of its body, so that, in general, the bigger an animal becomes, the less surface area it has per unit of volume and the more slowly it will lose heat.

A sphere has less surface area than any other shape of the same volume. So the more nearly spherical an animal is, the better it can retain heat. Polar animals are generally chunkier and larger than their relatives in warmer climates. The polar bear, for example, is much larger and more rounded than the Asian sun bear.

Because extremities—such as ears and legs—radiate body heat, they tend to be smaller and more rounded in polar animals. Birds and mammals with the thinnest, most delicate extremities generally live in hot climates.

Smaller ears reduce heat loss The ear shapes of North American hares show how extremities tend to become smaller in successively colder climates,

reducing the heat-radiating area of the body. The varying hare and the Arctic hare turn white in winter, helping to camouflage them from predators

Walking on snow To tread on snow and ice, Arctic animals need broader, better padded feet than their relatives in warmer climates. The ptarmigan's feathered legs and toes conserve heat

Seals and the walrus

Adaptations to swimming in a cold sea make the walrus and most seals awkward on land; yet they share a common ancestry with the otter and the bear

Modern seals are thought to have evolved from land animals that lived more than 30 million years ago. Their streamlined, torpedo-shaped bodies, with all four limbs modified into flippers, are notable adaptations to a swimming life. Flippers give seals their scientific name, Pinnipedia, or "fin-footed animals." All pinnipeds must return to land to molt and give birth.

The 32 species of pinnipeds are divided among three families, distinguished by differences in their ears and flippers. True seals have only vestigial ears and are the best adapted to water. Their backward-pointing hind flippers are useless for propulsion on land. The eared seals, which form the second family, are divided into two groups: fur seals and sea lions. With more flexible hind flippers, they can move on land almost as fast as man. The walrus, the only member of the third family, can also turn its hind flippers forward, but has vestigial ears.

Five true seals inhabit the frigid Arctic ice and seas

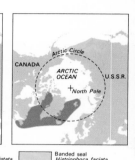

Ringed seal *Pusa hispida*	Bearded seal *Erignathus barbatus*	Harp seal *Pagophilus groenlandicus*	Hooded seal *Histriophoca cristata*	Banded seal *Histriophoca faciata*

Ranges of northern seals Banded seals and hooded seals have smaller ranges than the other species

Hooded seal pup When the young hooded seal begins to shed its dense, woolly, white coat for a grayish one, it is called a blueback by sealers

Harp seal and pup The female harp seal suckles its pup on fat-rich milk. After two to three weeks of this diet, the pup has gained about 60 pounds— most of it blubber. The mother then abandons its young on the ice, where the pup fasts for two weeks during its first molt

The ringed seal, smallest of all seals, is the most common species in the far north. Males and females are about the same size, typically five feet long and weighing 200 pounds. Ringed seals rarely congregate in groups, or migrate for any great distance. They generally stay within 15 miles of the coast, feeding on crustaceans and small fish, in those areas where the ice is locked fast all year round to the land.

Harp seals, on the other hand, breed in great aggregations—more than 1.5 million in the Gulf of St. Lawrence and 1 million off Labrador. They migrate to breed, normally on the pack ice, in February and March. Adults weigh about 400 pounds and are about six feet long.

Bearded seals, so named for their prominent bushy whiskers, also live on the edge of the ice in coastal waters. They are usually solitary, though as many as 50 may be found together in the breeding season.

A "hood" extending from above the eyes to the muzzle distinguishes the hooded or bladdernose seal ("bladdernose" referring to the seal's habit, when aroused, of inflating its hood and blowing up its nasal sac, which then resembles the skin of a brilliant red bladder or balloon). Hooded seals lead solitary lives, except when they migrate to the breeding grounds they share with harp seals. They are the largest true seals in the Arctic, weighing about 900 pounds and reaching up to 10½ feet in length.

The banded or ribbon seal, about the same size as the ringed seal, is confined to the North Pacific. It is usually a solitary creature, moving south with the ice in winter and north again in summer. The pups of this seal are thought to be born on ice floes.

Ringed seal Light-colored rings with dark centers on its back give the ringed seal its name

Banded seal Pale yellow bands on its chocolate brown coat identify the rare banded seal

Bearded seal Both sexes weigh 500 to 600 pounds and grow up to 7½ feet in length

Tusked sea monsters congregate over clam beds

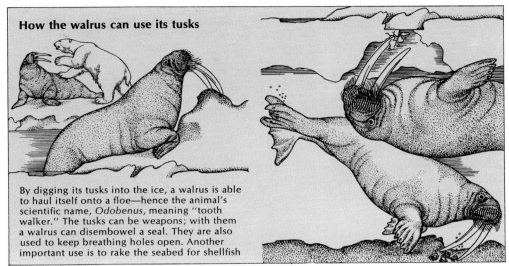

How the walrus can use its tusks

By digging its tusks into the ice, a walrus is able to haul itself onto a floe—hence the animal's scientific name, *Odobenus,* meaning "tooth walker." The tusks can be weapons; with them a walrus can disembowel a seal. They are also used to keep breathing holes open. Another important use is to rake the seabed for shellfish

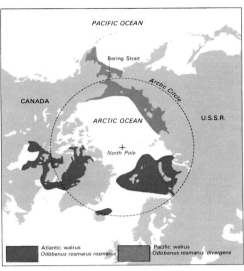

Two races Atlantic and Pacific walruses both go south to open water in autumn. Pacific herds must clear the Bering Strait before ice closes it

Basking walruses During the summer walruses haul themselves out on rocky islets and huddle together, as these bulls have done. Although mating occurs in summer, the sexes spend most of this season in separate groups. They also migrate separately, the young accompanying their mothers

Swimming with giant flippers

1. Swimming on its back, a walrus swings its hindquarters to the right as its right flipper begins to open for a new stroke

2. The walrus's left flipper is folded as its spread right flipper begins a powerful stroke to the left. The flippers may measure three feet across

3. The stroke is completed and a new one begins. Walruses are propelled mainly by the hind flippers

There is only one species of walrus, but it is separated into two races, one in the Pacific and the other in the Atlantic. The Pacific animal tends to be larger, with its nostrils placed higher on its muzzle. The habits of the two races are practically identical.

In both races a third of the animal's weight is accounted for by a layer of blubber about 2½ inches thick. This is covered by tough hide of the same thickness. The walrus remains indifferent to cold in winter. Nor does dissipation of heat in summer present any problem: in hot weather a basking walrus turns a rich rose color as blood vessels in its skin dilate to dispel body heat.

A male walrus can grow to a length of 12 feet and weigh as much as 2700 pounds. The female is usually about two feet shorter and weighs about 1200 pounds.

Both sexes have prominent tusks, but the female's are smaller. Tusks are simply highly developed canine teeth, which grow continually throughout a walrus's lifetime— around 30 years. When a walrus is one year old the tusks measure only about an inch, but they sometimes reach a length of more than three feet in mature bulls .

Walruses are restricted to a rather precise set of environmental conditions. Since their diving capacity is limited to about 12 minutes, they must find food at a depth no greater than 250 feet. Beds of edible shellfish must be extensive, since walrus herds can number in the thousands, and each member of the herd can eat 3000 clams a day. Ice or an accessible beach is also essential so that the animals can occasionally haul themselves out to rest.

Females are sexually mature at five years,

bulls at six. The pups are born on the ice —after almost a year's gestation—during the migration to the summer molting grounds in the north. A walrus calf, about four feet long and weighing about 100 pounds at birth, depends on its mother to keep it from freezing to death in the first three weeks of life, since insulation is not fully developed in this period of the walrus's life. The calf clings to its mother's neck almost constantly, even when she dives deep underwater.

A fully grown walrus is magnificently adapted to its life on the ice and in the sea. It is a strong swimmer with enormously developed hind flippers. It rakes up shellfish with its tusks or squeezes them off rocks with muscular lips. The walrus's size and mighty tusks make predators keep their distance—except for an occasional attack by a hungry killer whale or polar bear.

The polar bear

Camouflaged by its white coat, this huge, solitary creature—the most carnivorous bear—rules the northern pack ice, hunting its prey with stealth and power

The polar bear is the biggest and strongest predator of the sea ice and the windswept Arctic shoreline. No animal except man will normally attack it on land, and the polar bear fears none, except possibly an old bull walrus or a phalanx of musk-oxen.

Although the polar bear is usually found near land, members of the species probably visit most of the frozen Arctic Ocean, and may move far out to sea with the pack ice. Polar bears spread along the coasts in summer, but rarely go over 30 miles inland.

The average weight of a fully grown male polar bear is about 1000 pounds. Yet it is so agile that it can leap across a 12-foot-wide fissure in the ice. A male of this weight would be eight to nine feet long. Standing on its hind legs, such an animal could look an elephant in the eye.

In captivity, a polar bear has lived up to 40 years. Females are mature at three, males a year later.

A fabled hunter with the stealth and patience of a cat

Powerful swimming stroke

When swimming, the polar bear uses only its front legs for propulsion; the hind legs serve as a rudder. On the surface it can maintain a steady six miles an hour

Explorers and whalers tell many stories, some no doubt exaggerated, of the polar bear's hunting prowess—how a bear will break the skull of a walrus with a huge lump of ice held between its forepaws, or camouflage its black nose with snow when stalking prey, or stand on its hind legs and throw chunks of ice at a seal until the animal is knocked unconscious, an easy victim.

The polar bear is usually thought of as a rather slow and clumsy animal, but it has been observed overtaking a reindeer on land.

So powerful is the polar bear that it can drag a 200-pound ringed seal up through the seal's small breathing hole in the ice with such force that the animal's pelvis is crushed in the process.

When hunting a seal that is basking on an ice floe, the bear flattens itself, like an enormous cat, long before it is within the seal's range of vision. Hauling itself along on its side or belly, it slips from ice to water to floe, taking advantage of all cover. Then it makes a short charge to seize the seal before it can reach water, where the seal's underwater speed and endurance are far superior to the bear's. So great is this superiority in water that observers have told of ringed seals mobbing polar bears, swimming around them and even nipping at the bears' hindquarters.

The polar bear is basically a lone hunter; but females and their yearlings hunt together until the young can fend for themselves. Once the mating period is over, the male leaves the female. During the brief mating season, lasting only a few days, males often fight savagely, but at other times they ignore each other unless they come together for some rare feast of carrion, such as beluga whales or narwhals that have been trapped and asphyxiated by the enclosing ice. At this time males and groups of females and young will all eat peaceably together.

Seals—especially the ringed and bearded species—are the mainstay of the polar bear's diet and are essential to its survival. Unless it is extremely hungry, a bear will eat only the seal's guts and blubber, leaving the remains to scavengers such as the Arctic fox and the raven.

During the Arctic winter, those bears not in dens will eat anything—eggs, seaweed, wood chips, and even dead members of their own species. In summer, when they come ashore to molt, polar bears are also omnivorous, adopting the diet of their close relative, the brown bear, which gorges itself on grass, lichens, and bilberries. They also eat small animals, such as lemmings, and in Alaska when the salmon are running up the rivers, polar bears scoop them from pools and narrow channels.

Built for warmth Comparison of the polar bear with the world's smallest bear, the sun bear of Southeast Asia, shows typical cold-climate adaptations: a thicker coat, smaller ears, and a smaller ratio of body surface to volume

Waiting for prey During the winter, seals keep breathing holes in the ice. Polar bears locate the seals by scent and wait for their heads to appear, sometimes after stopping up all other holes in the vicinity. Here, a bear prepares to take a ringed seal with a lightning strike

Surefooted on ice New ice cracks beneath the mother's weight, but its spreading paws give it a strong grip on the slippery surface

Midwinter birth in a snow cavern carved by the mother bear

Although polar bears mate in April, implantation is delayed until September, and birth comes in the dead of winter, in a cavern carved out of a snowdrift by the mother. The cubs, less than a foot long and weighing under two pounds, spend the remaining winter months in the cavern with their mother, who suckles them for as long as 20 weeks, providing their only nourishment during this period. At the end of three months the cubs weigh around 22 pounds, but their mother, who has fasted all this time, may have lost half of her 700-pound weight. With the coming of warmer weather, the cubs are big enough to leave the den.

During their first months the cubs develop thick underfur and heavy guard hairs overlaying three inches of blubber.

The mother breaks out of the den and begins hunting again in March or April. Although the mother's first meal may be frozen carrion, the spring is generally a time of plentiful food, with a wealth of baby seals —especially ringed seals, born in caves beneath the snow. The bear locates them by scent. Its attack must be swift, because the seal's den is constructed over an open plunge hole. But if the bear can shatter the roof in one blow, it can take the mother seal and young together.

At this time the bear cubs get their first taste of solid food, though they may continue to suckle right through the second winter. Females breed only every third year unless they lose their cubs; if this happens, they mate sooner.

The cubs learn the lessons of survival by playing, sliding down icy slopes, and by following their mother's example in learning to swim and stalk. Mother and cubs play a sliding game for hours, and even elderly bears have been seen glissading down the flanks of ice floes, then climbing back to slide down again.

The family breaks up during the second summer, when the mother leaves the half-grown young to fend for themselves. It is then that they are most vulnerable to hunters and to the rigors of the following winter.

Man is by far the greatest threat to the polar bear population, which is now estimated at between 5000 and 18,000. The estimate is vague because it is difficult to count animals that wander over the ice and only occasionally come on land. More than 1000 polar bears are shot every year, most by trophy hunters.

Adrift on a floe Polar bears have drifted 500 miles from Greenland to Labrador

Spring outing Cubs emerge on the first warm day in spring. Triplets are rare; cubs are usually twins

A group of yearlings After this stage, polar bears avoid each other except in the mating season

Midwinter birth Cubs are born, blind and almost naked, in December or January. They are protected by the den and their mother's warm fur

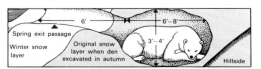

Polar bear's den Drifting snow against the slope insulates the den but does not trap the bear

Small hunting and foraging mammals

During the long winter in the far north, the coats of some predators—and their prey— turn from dark to white, camouflaging them against the snowy landscape

The growing season in the tundra is only about 60 days long, but the long hours of sunshine allow plants to grow and flower rapidly. A rich mosaic of low-growing vegetation provides food throughout the summer for the herbivores. These small animals— represented in greatest numbers by lemmings —in turn are eaten by the carnivores. When the long winter comes, many of the plants are covered by thick, crusty snow, and often much of the edible plant material is killed by the freezing conditions.

Lemmings do not hibernate, but spend the winter in tunnels beneath the snow, feeding on the roots and stems of undersnow plants. The Arctic hare and the Arctic fox, having thick fur, can endure almost continuous exposure to the cold. The fox exists by living on any animal food it can find. The hare winters on upland ridges where the wind has blown away the snow and left the scanty vegetation exposed.

Some animals profit by turning white in the winter. The snowy coats of the carnivorous short-tailed weasel and Arctic fox conceal them against the snow as they hunt for prey, while the Arctic hare's helps it to elude predators.

The Arctic fox turns scavenger when prey is scarce

Hidden hunter The Arctic fox, brown in summer, turns white in winter. Dense underhair beneath the guard hairs enables the fox to remain active in temperatures as low as −58° F. (−50° C.)

A clear view Ground squirrels, adapted for burrowing, often stand to look over obstructions

The Arctic fox lives throughout the tundra, usually in burrows on hillsides or cliff faces. It feeds on any small mammals and birds it can find, alive or dead, but its main prey is lemmings, especially in summer.

The fox forages throughout the winter and only burrows for shelter in severe blizzards. It digs through the snow to reach lemmings and, like the short-tailed weasel, stores its dead victims in the snow.

Often in winter the fox becomes a scavenger, following the polar bear onto the sea ice and living off the remains of seals killed by the bear. When food is scarce, it even eats the polar bear's droppings. Arctic foxes usually hunt alone, but sometimes they congregate to feed off carrion.

The Arctic fox breeds in March, when lemming litters provide a rich food supply for the female. The vixen gives birth in May or June to between 4 and 11 young. Both parents care for the young until the fall, when the family breaks up.

The Arctic fox is one of many predators that seek Arctic hares, which also forage throughout the winter, sheltering in crannies and hollows among the rocks. Arctic hares are usually solitary animals. Occasionally, however, many hares will congregate together when they come upon a particularly choice patch of vegetation. Arctic hares mate about April, and in late June or July the young are born, covered in gray fur which helps to make them inconspicuous among the rocks.

Two species of hares live on the tundra: *Lepus arcticus* in North America and *Lepus timidus* in Eurasia. The American Arctic hare is seldom seen except in the tundra, though in winter individuals may stray up to 100 miles southward into the coniferous forest. The Eurasian species, also known as the blue hare and the mountain hare, has a wider range and commonly reaches as far south as the Alps, feeding on exposed, low-growing vegetation.

Short-tailed weasel becomes ermine The short-tailed weasel, found throughout the tundra, is called an ermine when its red-brown summer coat turns white in winter. It is a tenacious hunter, aided by acute senses of smell and hearing, and often pursues small mammals into their burrows

The lemming's rise and fall

Brown lemmings and Arctic or collared lemmings live in most of the Arctic regions of Eurasia and North America. Arctic lemmings prefer land above the tree line having some plant cover and a sandy soil.

All species of Arctic lemmings, like the Arctic fox, grow white coats in winter. They are the only true rodents that turn white. Their third and fourth claws are much larger than their others, with strong, curved nails that aid the lemmings in digging burrows. The nails have the unusual feature of becoming thicker and less breakable as winter approaches. Lemmings' ears are small and completely hidden in their thick fur.

Fluctuating population cycles

Lemming populations fluctuate in cycles of three to four years. The cycles depend on food supply, but are also affected by predators. When lemmings abound, they provide a harvest for carnivores, such as the short-tailed weasel, the Arctic fox, and the snowy owl. When they are less numerous, their predators' populations also decrease.

Lemmings breed all year round, and a population can increase rapidly. A surge of breeding occurs when the snow begins to melt in late spring. Gestation takes only 21 days and the young are weaned after 14 days, so the summer generation of lemmings can reproduce by August or September. Reproduction during the winter occurs at a slower rate.

In winter lemmings gain protection from the cold by digging tunnels through the ground under the snow. These tunnels form extensive networks and the animals spend most of the winter there, digging for roots and stems .

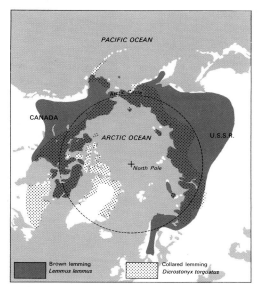

Distribution of lemmings The brown lemming lives chiefly in marshland or on ridges, especially where grass and sedge are the main vegetation. The collared lemming prefers well-drained ground, usually flats, where it can feed on cotton sedge

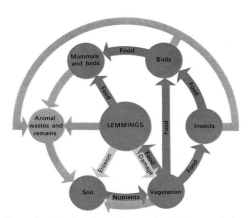

Lemmings' role Any change in their population affects the food supply of many animals. They destroy plant food and modify soil by tunneling

Brown lemmings migrate seasonally, either individually or in small groups. In spring the snow melts on their higher winter grounds, and what little vegetation remains dries out quickly. So the lemming moves away, down into valleys, in search of better pasture. In years of normal populations, these migrations are short, for the lemming can colonize near the winter grounds.

These normal migrations differ from the more dramatic huge migrations described by early observers as "suicidal."

Many small migrations

Despite a lingering popular misconception, mass migrations of lemmings are not periodic rushes to commit suicide in the sea. They are the result of population peaks, which cause both a food shortage and "overcrowding stress." The result is a forced spreading out. Although this appears to be a mass migration it is actually numerous individual ones. Lemmings appear to move in clusters merely because they follow the same trails down to the lower-lying lands. As more lemmings enter an area, competition for food and space increases. Eventually they may move off in a body to find new ground, crossing streams and small lakes as they go. However, they cannot distinguish between these and larger bodies of water, so that they drown in rivers, lakes, and the sea.

The stress caused by overcrowding results in an endocrine gland dysfunction, which interferes with reproduction. The birth rate declines. This malfunction also weakens the individual lemming and lessens its ability to withstand other stresses. Any exertion, such as in swimming or fighting to protect territorial rights, might cause death.

How the lemming population rises and falls

Year 1 High	Year 2	Year 3	Year 4 40–70 per acre
Moderate		20 per acre	
Low	1 per 10 acres		

In the first year, the numbers of lemmings decline rapidly from a summer peak. In the next two years, numbers gradually build up again. A new peak the fourth summer is followed by another steep decline, and a new cycle begins. When the population is low, lemmings are confined to the tundra; in high years they spread out. Peaks are simultaneous over a wide area

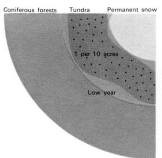

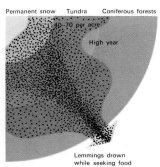

Brown lemming All lemmings have small ears hidden by thick fur. Brown lemmings retain their color all year; collared lemmings are the only rodents to turn white in winter

Wolf, musk-ox, and caribou

Wolves roam the enormous expanse of the tundra in well-organized hunting packs, preying upon the powerful musk-ox and the speedy, long-legged caribou

Throughout the year the wolf seeks the caribou and musk-ox, attacking the very young, the lame and the sick, and the very old. Wolves hunt in packs, for a lone wolf is not an easy victor.

When it locates a caribou herd, the wolf pack makes a series of test runs, watching for a calf lagging behind or a limping adult. Then the wolves concentrate on this animal, taking turns leading the pursuit, until the caribou stops, exhausted.

The sight of a wolf does not always cause immediate panic, and once a kill has been made a caribou herd stops running. The defensive behavior of both the musk-ox and the caribou is thought to be the natural result of long hunting by the wolf, but their reactions are by no means fully understood.

Compared with calf losses due to cold and hunger, the wolf's effect upon healthy animals is negligible. The overall effect of wolves on musk-oxen and caribou is beneficial. Wolves weed out the weak, deformed, and diseased animals, and help promote stronger breeds.

Highly organized wolf packs patrol tundra and forest

Gray, timber, and white wolves are all members of the same species that once lived in almost every land north of the equatorial forests. In the tundra the wolf is the largest carnivore and the only one that can successfully hunt live caribou and musk-ox.

The wolf does not hibernate and only rarely makes food caches. It survives in the Arctic mainly because of its high degree of social organization.

The basic hunting and defense unit is the pack, a family grouping of mother, father, cubs, and perhaps other relatives, numbering about ten in all. Within a pack there is usually a definite social hierarchy. Leadership is shared between a male and female, to whom animals of the second and third ranks are subordinate. At the bottom of the scale is one wolf which is just barely tolerated by the rest of the pack. This semi-outcast seems to be essential for maintaining the social order of the pack.

The size of each pack's territory depends on the number of prey within the area. In the tundra, where prey is scattered, the territory may be as large as 200 square miles. Members of the pack patrol constantly, using a wide variety of yips and howls to communicate with one another.

During the caribou migrations neighboring wolf packs come together to make mass attacks. This combining gives the young wolves an opportunity to find mates. Generally wolves mate for life. But the responsibility for the cubs' upbringing is shared among the entire group.

Preparation for hunting Wolves, like their probable descendants, domestic dogs, tussle together when young. In this way they develop hunting skills

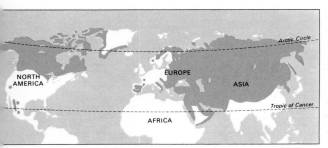

Reduced range Man has driven the wolf to the most inaccessible areas of its former range, which once covered most of the northern hemisphere

Danger signals
The wolf's hunting intentions are betrayed by its lowered head and raised shoulder ruff. If a wolf holds its head high, a herd of caribou will continue to browse without any show of alarm while the wolf walks among them

Northern wolf Some of the wolves in the northern sectors of the tundra have white coats all year

A horned phalanx of musk-oxen defeats predators

Heavy, powerful, and armed with sweeping horns, musk-oxen have little to fear from any natural enemies. Even wolves seldom attack healthy adults. Their battle formation resembles the phalanx of ancient Greece: the musk-oxen present an impenetrable walled circle of lowered horns, sheltering the young within the ring. The adult bulls constantly turn to face the point of greatest danger. A wolf hooked on the horns may be tossed back over the musk-ox's shoulder, then trampled to death by the herd.

Calves are born in April or May, when the temperature may still be as low as −20° F. (−28.9° C.). But they are born with a thick woolly coat, and within three days can keep up with the herd. They suckle for 15 months, which enables them to survive through the first winter.

In summer musk-oxen graze on grasses, sedges, and woody plants, building up stores of fat for the coming winter. Summer is also the mating season, when bulls fight for harems, charging and crashing their heads together with a thud that can be heard a mile away. These charges are repeated in a test of strength until the loser staggers away. Horn bosses, or bony shields, nine inches thick protect the animal's forehead.

As the nights lengthen, the herds move toward the winter grazing grounds. These are always in the windswept areas where snow is not deep. By scraping the surface, the oxen find frozen sedges and lichens to supplement stored fat. Even so, the animals tend to be emaciated by winter's end.

The musk-ox can withstand temperatures as low as −94° F. (−70° C.). Like those of all hooved animals, its eyes adapt well to darkness and can see in moonlight and the noon-hour twilight of midwinter.

In dry winters the musk-ox's coat gives good protection, but moisture in the pelt can freeze. Under the increasing weight of accumulating ice the ox becomes immobilized and an easy prey for wolves. But unless near starvation, wolves will attack only the weak. They will attempt to take calves from a herd only by banding together in large packs, for even the smallest group of musk-oxen will stand their ground and fight.

All-round defense Musk-oxen form a rough circle for protection against predators. In blizzards the bulls face into the wind, and the long guard hairs of the adults form a curtain around the calves

Double coat for winter The musk-ox is a short-legged, bulky animal. Its heavy coat consists of dense, soft wool overlaid by thick guard hairs reaching to the ground. The wool is shed in spring

Barren Ground caribou plod centuries-old trails

Caribou are the only species of the deer family in which both sexes have antlers. They were named by the Micmac Indians of Canada. The word means "shoveler" and refers to the way the animal uses its splayed hooves to dig through the snow to find food. Other adaptations to the Arctic are its insulating coat formed of hollow hairs, and the long, powerful legs that give the caribou mobility in deep snow and endurance on long migrations. When caribou walk they make a clicking sound, produced by a tendon sliding over a bone in the foot.

The Barren Ground caribou of the North American tundra make two journeys, averaging 700 miles, between their summer and winter grounds, following trails their ancestors have used for centuries. On these migrations they average almost 100 miles a day. In spring the females give birth on the high tundra of their northerly range, and in autumn the herd returns to mate and find winter shelter on the forest fringes.

Many animals, especially the wolf, depend on these yearly cycles. During migrations, herds of 20,000 or more caribou run the gauntlet of wolves and human predators. The great majority of healthy animals survives. Scavengers such as Arctic foxes and ravens feed on the remains of the kills.

All have antlers Caribou fight with their feet; the bulls rarely use their antlers. When they do, they may lock together. Female caribou also grow antlers. They are the only female deer to do so

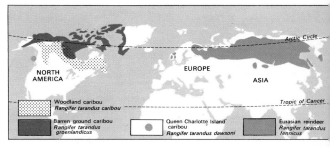

Distribution of caribou Reindeer are one of the four subspecies of caribou. Domesticated reindeer are widespread in Scandinavia

Birds of water and land

When the tundra flowers, migrant birds come to nest in this summer paradise. One species, the Arctic tern, wings all the way up from the Antarctic Ocean

A few species of birds, such as the members of the grouse family called ptarmigans, have adapted particularly well to the Arctic, and spend the whole year there. The snowy owl, which preys on the ptarmigan, is another permanent resident. But most Arctic birds are migrants, not residents. They head north to their summer breeding grounds with the approach of warmer weather, and return south when the brief Arctic summer nears its end. Since the Arctic summer is so short, birds that fly north to breed do not have lengthy courtship periods, and few species have evolved the elaborate mating rituals which are characteristic of birds in warmer zones. It is necessary for migrants to the Arctic region to nest, lay the eggs, and rear the young before the long winter night sets in.

Because of this limited season of light and warmth, many birds pair up at their winter (southern) range instead of waiting until they arrive in the Arctic. Some pair as young birds, for life. The pair may stay together when it leaves the breeding ground for the journey south, and return the next year to the same site. Geese and swans are examples of birds with long-lasting pair bonds.

As soon as the ice breaks up, seabirds arrive to feed

Snow buntings have been seen within 200 miles of the North Pole, and skuas almost as near to the South Pole. But no birds breed so near the inhospitable poles. Like mammals, however, birds are "warm-blooded," meaning that they have a relatively constant internal climate. This makes them somewhat independent of their surroundings.

Arctic seabirds, like so many polar animals, ultimately depend on the supply of microscopic sea plants and the crustaceans that feed upon them. The availability of this marine life determines how many fish will breed and be available to birds as food.

Seabirds flourish as long as the sea is free of ice. Since coastal waters become almost entirely frozen in winter, most species migrate to the open sea and some, like the Arctic skua and Arctic tern, make the longest migrations of all—12,000 miles south to Antarctica.

Murres and auks are members of the alcid family, which fills the same ecological niche in the Arctic that penguins do in the Antarctic. Superficially, they resemble penguins—both in their coloring and in their upright stance. Yet, although their wings are short, they have not reached the flightless paddle stage. Because there are many land predators in the Arctic, the alcids must still fly to escape. Only the great auk, which has been extinct for over 100 years, was completely flightless.

Alcids fly in wedge-shaped flocks to high cliffs, where they settle on small ledges. Although courtship is short, lasting only a few days, courting murres perform intricate flight displays and underwater dances.

The chicks of the razorbill and common guillemot go to sea in an unusual manner. They have not yet developed flight feathers when the time comes to leave their nests, since they have used all available energy developing waterproof feathers. With their nests on ledges sometimes 1000 feet above the sea, landing in the water presents quite a problem. The parents fly down ahead and send up a call in unison. The chicks then fling themselves over—half-parachuting, half-bouncing off ledges. The biggest danger is not the jump itself, but the hundreds of glaucous gulls waiting to catch the small birds.

When the chicks have landed safely in the water, the parents guide them out to sea. The young birds do not return to land until fully mature, around three years old.

Predatory gulls and skuas

Glaucous gulls prey on murres in much the same way skuas prey on penguins in the Antarctic. The gulls establish their colonies near alcids, especially dovekies. They feed on the eggs and chicks, and also on the adults, which are only about eight inches long. They hover over a diving bird and grab it when it surfaces. The glaucous gull also preys on the barnacle goose, which breeds on cliffs, out of reach of predators.

The kittiwake, another gull, is primarily a fish-eater. It nests higher up than any other Arctic species. The nest is secured to a narrow ledge by seaweed that dries to a cementlike hardness. The chicks are helpless before predators, since they would fall over the precipice if they moved suddenly.

Jaegers, as the smaller species of skuas are called, are also predators, but they specialize in harrying smaller seabirds, forcing them to disgorge the food they carry in their crops for their young. This lightens the bird and helps it to escape, while the jaeger abandons pursuit in exchange for the stolen food.

From Arctic to Antarctic The Arctic tern follows food-bearing currents down the coasts of Europe and Africa to the tip of South Africa, then crosses the South Atlantic. Some even reach Patagonia and Antarctica. In the spring breeding birds return to nest in the Arctic—a round trip of 24,000 miles

Spring brings waterfowl

Waterfowl leave the Arctic in September and return in mid-May, when the northern skies are dominated by ducks, swans, and especially geese, flying in undulating lines or rigid V-formations. Many species, particularly the snow geese, fly the "grand passage" route, 2000 miles nonstop from Louisiana to their tundra breeding grounds.

These birds all belong to the largest family of swimming birds, and share characteristics of buoyant, insulated bodies, webbed feet, and serrated bills. The bills of some birds enable them to sift food from the water, while the broad beak of the swan, used in conjunction with its long neck, facilitates underwater grazing. Most of these waterfowl feed in the countless large and small marsh pools of the tundra.

Geese and swans usually pair for life. Ducks do not pair for life, but they do choose a mate before leaving their wintering grounds.

Nests in varying forms are built in dry areas. The whistling swan constructs a six-foot-wide moss platform. Ducks line a clump of grass with down plucked from their own breasts. The clutch is quite large—usually not less than ten. The young are covered in down and are able to swim in a day. The chicks of loons hatch with the instinct to crawl up onto their parents' backs. When the young are hatched, the parents molt, shedding all their flight feathers, so they are flightless for a short time.

All Arctic species of loons, or divers, share the same habitat. The Arctic, common, and red-throated species breed at lake-

Arctic courtship A pair of trumpeter swans begin their graceful mating rites. Trumpeter swans now nest only in western Canada and the western United States. They make short migrations. Once heavily hunted, they are now much rarer than the whistling swans, which nest farther north

sides and eat fish, frogs, mollusks, crustaceans, and aquatic insects, taking them in dives that may last over a minute.

Many kinds of waders and sandpipers—curlew, golden plover, whimbrel, and others —patrol the shore on stiltlike legs, probing the mud for insects.

This profusion is present only during the Arctic's brief flowering. When new ice forms on the lakes, the birds fly south.

Land birds adapted to winter survival in the far north

Many small migrant birds, such as larks, buntings, and wheatears, nest in the Arctic, but there are a few land species that manage to live there the year round. These sometimes suffer from a shortage of food in the winter, and the weaker individuals perish.

The birds most obviously adapted to Arctic life are members of the grouse family—the willow ptarmigan and the rock ptarmigan. Both have feathered legs and toes, which give extra protection against the cold. The rock ptarmigan is the only bird with three seasonal plumages. In the breeding season it is brown, in autumn its dorsal plumage is gray, and in winter it is white.

Ptarmigans of both sexes help raise the young; the female parent incubates her large clutch of eggs while the male defends the nest against predators.

In the harsh Arctic winter, the ptarmigan moves to ridges where the wind has blown away the snow, leaving the vegetation exposed. The willow ptarmigan often seeks shelter among the dwarf willows and feeds mainly on the twigs and branches. The rock ptarmigan will burrow under the snow during a blizzard until hunger forces it out to search for food. The gyrfalcon and the snowy owl follow the ptarmigans, preying upon them.

Seasonal camouflage The rock ptarmigan is the only bird with three plumages. Here, in summer, it blends with the surrounding rocks and lichens

Winter dress In autumn the rock ptarmigan's primary feathers first turn gray; then the bird completely molts to winter white

The common raven is becoming rarer in Europe and North America, but it adapts well to the Arctic. Its naked legs and toes, like those of seabirds, are capable of tolerating low temperatures without affecting its metabolism.

The snowy owl preys on lemmings, mice,

Round-the-clock hunter Because of the extreme variations of light in the tundra, the snowy owl, unlike most owls, hunts by day as well as by night

and other small mammals, as well as ptarmigans. In years when the lemming population falls to a low ebb, many owls starve, and others move southward. The snowy owl is also a skillful fisherman. It lurks on the banks of rivers or lakes, waiting for fish to appear, and then seizes its victims.

Seals of the south polar waters

Several species of seals live amid the Antarctic ice throughout the year. One, the Weddell seal, dives down more than 1800 feet to the sea floor to find food

Seals and whales are the only mammals that live in the Antarctic. The five species of Antarctic seals are all members of one family, and are called earless seals. The huge elephant seal, a subfamily of its own, breeds on the sub-Antarctic shores.

The four species that breed in the high Antarctic—the Ross seal, Weddell seal, crabeater seal, and leopard seal—are all members of one subfamily. Their ranges often overlap, but competition for food is rarely a problem because their food needs are markedly different.

These seals have few natural enemies. The Antarctic has no equivalent of the Arctic polar bear, which subsists on Arctic seals. The only predators on Antarctic seals are the killer whale and the leopard seal. Seals quickly leave the water and seek refuge on land or ice when a killer whale is on the prowl. Some species may jump ten feet out of the water while fleeing a killer whale.

Beachmaster elephant seals bellow and battle for harems

The elephant seal, which lives in both the southern and northern hemispheres, is the largest of all pinnipeds—males can be 20 feet long and weigh 3½ tons.

The southern elephant seal, although it sometimes breeds on the shore-fast ice near open water, is usually found on the shores outside the ice zone.

The elephant seal's common name is derived not only from its size, but also from the adult male's short trunk, the tip of which hangs over the mouth so that the nostrils point downward. During the mating season the bull inflates his trunk, which may then reach 20 inches.

Males come ashore in September, at the beginning of the Antarctic spring. The females, pregnant from the previous year's mating, follow a few weeks later and are herded into harems by the dominant bull, known to seal hunters as the beachmaster. These harems may number as many as 100 females, but they most commonly comprise 10 to 20.

Seal pups are born in early October, and their mothers mate soon afterward. The pups are about four feet long and weigh about 80 pounds at birth, but they grow rapidly during the three weeks in which they are suckled. The mothers, which do not feed during this nursing period, lose about a third of their weight. When they are around five weeks old, the pups shed their woolly fur and are able to go to sea. The adults return to land again for their annual molt, which may last from December to February.

Elephant seals have few natural enemies —except in youth, when leopard seals and killer whales sometimes prey on them. Deaths are more often accidental; pups sink into the melting snow or get crushed when their massive elders roll on them, and adults are sometimes trapped in the muddy onshore wallows they make for themselves, which become deeper with repeated use. Elephant seals are increasing in numbers, after being hunted almost to extinction for their oil.

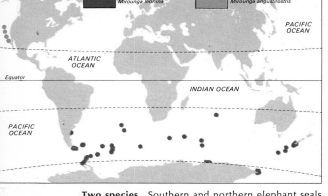

Two species Southern and northern elephant seals are almost identical. The northern species was once near extinction, but is now increasing

Threat posture The elephant seal bends its body into a U when threatening; usually, the hind flippers are raised this high only in water

Challenge for harem mastery The beachmaster elephant seal roars a warning at a bull approaching his harem. Then come these threatening postures. If the challenger remains aggressive, a fight ensues. Death seldom results, but bulls may be seriously wounded. Old bulls roar by curling their long trunks into their mouths and producing metallic snorts. Many bulls are killed by sealers before their trunks are long enough to be used this way

Seals of the pack ice

In contrast to the elephant seal, which prefers access to an ice-free shore because it hauls itself out frequently, the other seals of the Antarctic all breed on the pack ice, and only the Weddell seal has any close link with the land.

The lives of the various species of Antarctic seals differ at many points: in habitat, favorite food, and feeding methods. The swift leopard seal hunts penguins and other seals in the surface waters; while the Weddell seal, which has the greatest underwater endurance of any seal, feeds on fish and squid on the sea floor. Living amid the floating pack ice, the crabeater seal feeds on the minute crustaceans known as krill. The Ross seal, with the help of its large, protruding eyes, hunts fish and mollusks in the dim world beneath the pack ice.

Antarctic seals grow very rapidly, soon reaching a size that permits highly efficient heat retention by their bodies. For example, a Weddell seal pup weighing 64 pounds at birth grows to 250 pounds by the time it is weaned, after six weeks of nursing on its mother's rich milk.

Deep diving and underwater endurance

The Weddell seal can dive to depths of over 1800 feet, as demonstrated by pressure gauges that were attached to seals by scientific investigators. In such a dive, the seal can remain under the water for almost an hour. The underwater limit for most other seals is 20 minutes.

What makes the Weddell such a remarkable diver? All seals have more blood than land animals of comparable size, and the blood has a high oxygen storage capacity. The Weddell seal stores five times as much oxygen in its blood as a man. During a dive, the seal's oxygen consumption is reduced because the blood supply to all organs—except those which, like the brain, cannot function without an almost continuous supply—is almost shut off.

Deep-diving seal To feed on bottom-living fish and squid, the Weddell seal may dive more than 1800 feet. If its breathing hole has frozen over, the seal scrapes it open with its strong front teeth

Seals that change color Crabeater seals, also known as white seals because their coats fade, are the most common seals in the Antarctic seas

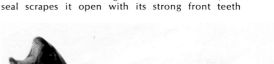

Seldom seen seal The Ross seal lives on the remote pack ice. Its large, protruding eyes help it to find cuttlefish in the dimly lit waters

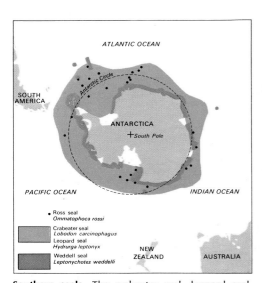

Southern seals The crabeater seal, leopard seal, and rare Ross seal are scattered throughout the pack ice. The Weddell seal keeps to the coasts

Penguin killer There are no predatory land mammals in the Antarctic except man, but there are several in the sea. One is the leopard seal. Usually a solitary hunter, it often catches penguins underwater, chasing them with great speed. It also feeds on carrion and the young of other seals

35

Penguins

The 18 species of penguins that live from Antarctica to the Galápagos Islands spend most of their lives in water, leaving it only to mate, raise young, and molt

There were penguins in the southern oceans 50 million years ago, long before the polar ice cap formed. The species that lived in the Antarctic then, when it had a temperate climate, have long since vanished, but they were similar to modern penguins.

In the course of the penguins' evolution from flying to sea-dwelling birds, their wings became smaller and smaller—an adaptation that reduces underwater drag during swimming and diving. Eventually, their wings evolved into paddles. Penguins no longer need to fly, since their entire food supply is in the water and they live on isolated coasts, protected by water and inaccessibility from land predators.

Eighteen species of penguins are found in the southern hemisphere. Only five species actually breed in Antarctica, and only one of these is confined to the continent. The remainder occupy the scattered islands of the southern Indian, South Atlantic, and Pacific oceans.

Our knowledge of their habits is largely based on observations made on land. Since penguins come ashore only to breed and molt, their world is still a mysterious one.

All penguin species are adapted for life in the sea. With their torpedo-shaped bodies, they can swim as fast as seals. Their dark-backed, white-fronted coloring camouflages them equally well, whether they are seen from above or below the water's surface. Adaptations to cold are also evident. Dense, oily feathers, as many as 70 to a square inch, are underlaid by down and blubber. These insulating tissues make the penguin so resistant to cold that when it is ashore, even in the Antarctic, dispelling heat can be almost as great a problem as retaining it.

In all penguin species, the male helps care in one way or another for the young. When baby penguins are hatched they are covered with soft down, which molts and is replaced with feathers before the young bird is ready to go to sea.

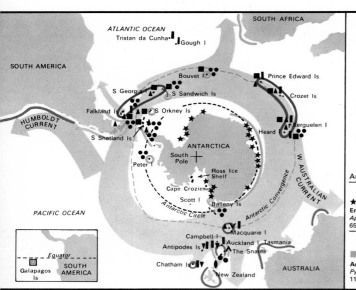

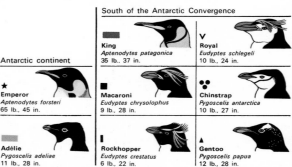

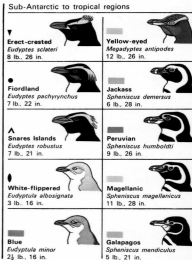

The world of penguins

The true home of penguins is the sea, and when they leave it to breed they come ashore on isolated coasts that are washed by food-rich currents. All penguins have dark backs and white fronts, but facial coloring and marking vary among species. Size also varies; average weights and body lengths—the tip of the beak to the rump—are given for each species

Antarctic continent

Emperor
Aptenodytes forsteri
65 lb., 45 in.

Adélie
Pygoscelis adeliae
11 lb., 28 in.

South of the Antarctic Convergence

King
Aptenodytes patagonica
35 lb., 37 in.

Macaroni
Eudyptes chrysolophus
9 lb., 28 in.

Royal
Eudyptes schlegeli
10 lb., 24 in.

Rockhopper
Eudyptes crestatus
6 lb., 22 in.

Chinstrap
Pygoscelis antarctica
10 lb., 27 in.

Gentoo
Pygoscelis papua
12 lb., 28 in.

Sub-Antarctic to tropical regions

Erect-crested
Eudyptes sclateri
8 lb., 26 in.

Fiordland
Eudyptes pachyrynchus
7 lb., 22 in.

Snares Islands
Eudyptes robustus
7 lb., 21 in.

White-flippered
Eudyptula albosignata
3 lb., 16 in.

Blue
Eudyptula minor
2½ lb., 16 in.

Yellow-eyed
Megadyptes antipodes
12 lb., 26 in.

Jackass
Spheniscus demersus
6 lb., 28 in.

Peruvian
Spheniscus humboldti
9 lb., 26 in.

Magellanic
Spheniscus magellanicus
11 lb., 28 in.

Galapagos
Spheniscus mendiculus
5 lb., 21 in.

Noisy colonies on the fringes of Antarctica

The most southerly penguins are the emperor and the members of the genus *Pygoscelis*—the Adélie, the chinstrap, and the gentoo. The breeding grounds of the last three extend from the shores of Antarctica to the islands of the subpolar regions. They have formed many hundreds of colonies. Large colonies are characteristic, since pygoscelid penguins are sociable—though they are also quarrelsome and vociferous.

Mating takes place when the birds come ashore in spring. Two eggs are laid in a nest, which may consist of anything from a hollow in the ground to an elaborate structure of pebbles, bones of dead animals, and sticks. Young chinstraps sometimes nest in the snow. When it melts, the bird is stuck in a water-filled hole.

Farther north, where summers are longer, penguins nest among tussocks. If skuas (see page 39) take the eggs, the female has time to lay a second clutch, and the chicks can hatch before winter comes.

The king penguin is just slightly shorter than the emperor, its closest relative, but it weighs only half as much. It breeds among the tussocks and on the barren coastal flats

King penguin colony Penguins keep together on land and in the water. The exact reason for this is not known, but a bird in a flock is generally safer from predators. This colony is on South Georgia

of the sub-Antarctic islands. King penguins do not build nests. The female lays only one egg, which both parents incubate, taking turns tucking it between their feet and abdomen. Partly because neither king nor emperor penguins have nests to defend, their colonies look and sound more peaceful than those of the smaller species.

King penguins, unlike some species, do not hop on both feet on land, but run with their bodies held upright, putting one foot in front of the other.

Emperors court in darkness

The largest of all penguins, the emperor, breeds in the coldest habitat—the sea ice and the shores of Antarctica. When on land or ice, emperor penguins normally waddle, but when alarmed they flop down on their bellies and toboggan, using their flippers to propel themselves.

Adults come out of the seas to breed in May, with the approach of the Antarctic winter. Courtship and the laying of the single egg take place in darkness. The males incubate the eggs, several thousand huddling together for warmth. So closely do the males pack together that as little as one sixth of each bird's surface is exposed to the elements. They fast throughout the long period (more than two months) of courtship and incubation. Because of this, even a male that starts with a massive fat reserve has need of physiological adjustments that serve to conserve energy. The metabolic rate of a brooding bird drops and he becomes sluggish, relying on the warmth of the huddle for survival.

The females, meanwhile, are at sea, seeking squid, a major part of the emperor's diet. They return with full crops just as the chicks are beginning to hatch. The near-starving males, which have fed any premature chicks on an oily secretion produced in the crop, relinquish their charges and go off to forage for themselves. For two or three weeks the females nourish the chicks on regurgitated food. Later, males and females alternate in feeding the chicks. By this time the sea ice is breaking up and the birds can bring freshly caught food to their young.

The chicks go to sea in December, when food is most abundant, even though they are not yet fully grown.

Protecting its young An emperor penguin chick peers from between a parent's legs. The adult's belly has a fold of skin that flops down, protecting the incubating egg and, later, the chick

Adélie penguins share parental responsibilities

The life pattern and nesting behavior of the Adélie penguin resemble those of the other pygoscelid penguins, but this species has an earlier breeding season.

Adélies come to shore in October, sometimes walking and sliding across 30 or 40 miles of sea ice to reach a colony site on land. They usually return with the same mate to the same nest site each year and begin at once to collect stones for a nest. Younger penguins find sites near the edge of the colony—often after much squabbling—but they may not breed successfully for years. Nest sites are important in courtship, for no female will accept a male that has not established one.

Partners take turns incubating the two eggs and going to sea to feed. In a cold summer late blizzards take an enormous toll of eggs and nesting birds. The ice may not break up at all, preventing the adults from feeding at sea. Hunger then forces them to abandon the eggs.

Adélies waddle slowly on land; but on snow or ice they often flop down on their bellies, propelling themselves rapidly along the surface with their flippers and feet.

Feeding the young An Adélie penguin chick reaches for food brought from the sea. Krill remains undigested in the parent's crop until the bird reaches its nest. The parent recognizes the voice of its young and will not feed another

Leaping to safety Adélie penguins can leap from the water to shore with great speed, easily clearing six feet, especially when a leopard seal is nearby. Leopard seals are the chief predators of Adélies and take enormous tolls

Birds of the far south

The birdlife of Antarctica reflects the barrenness of the land and the richness of the sea. Of 43 species that breed in the far south, 40 are seabirds

The penguins represent only 7 of the 40 species of seabirds that breed south of the Antarctic Convergence. Among the others are petrels, gulls, skuas, albatrosses, cormorants, and jaegers. All the seabirds probably had ancestors on the Antarctic coasts eons ago, before the ice cap formed. The present species evolved from birds that adapted successfully to the increasingly severe conditions.

Land birds are barred from the Antarctic continent less by the cold, to which birds could adapt, than by the lack of plant and insect food. Seabirds do not face this problem, for the Antarctic oceans abound in food, and in winter seabirds can migrate to find open water and new food supplies. The only true land bird of Antarctica is a pipit which lives on the sub-Antarctic islands. These islands are also the home of the Antarctic's only waterfowl, two species of pintail ducks.

But conditions in the Antarctic impose restrictions even on seabirds, since food must be accessible from the breeding grounds. This links the breeding season to the breakup of the sea ice, when crustaceans and other marine food become available.

Two petrels breed in the harsh interior of Antarctica

Carrion-eater The giant petrel lays a single egg in the Antarctic spring and the chick is hatched about two months later. The young bird is raised on dead pups from a nearby seal colony

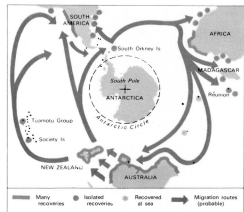

Wandering petrels The recovery of ringed birds has shown that young giant petrels may drift several times around the world, borne by the westerly winds, before returning to their breeding grounds

Petrels vary greatly in size and color, but all have a similar flight pattern. Their flight, alternating between a rapid wingbeat and gliding, resembles that of the albatross, and they skim low over the water.

The snow petrel and the Antarctic petrel experience the harshest conditions of any birds breeding in Antarctica. They breed on the coast and on mountain ranges up to 200 miles inland, nesting on ledges of cliffs. The snow petrel, the southernmost species of all, is circumpolar in its range. The Antarctic petrel breeds in a wide sector of eastern Antarctica.

Parents take turns incubating and feeding their single chick, and the "off-duty" parent makes repeated flights to and from the sea for food, which it carries back in its crop. Both species feed almost exclusively within the pack ice. Their diet probably consists mostly of crustaceans shaken loose and fish disabled by the constant jarring of the ice floes. The birds often must fly great distances before they find breaks in the ice where they can feed.

Summer blizzards may take an enormous toll. The returning parent can lose its way back in the storm, and entire nesting ledges, with chicks, may be buried.

Oil-spitting defense

Five other petrels breed on snow-free coasts, mainly north of the Antarctic Circle. The Cape pigeon and the southern fulmar nest on rocky ledges where, like all petrels, they defend themselves by spitting out a jet of stomach oil. Chicks are able to spit at 14 to 18 days old, and the parents guard them only until then. Another coastal petrel, the dove prion, nests in a burrow.

Wilson's petrel feeds on crustaceans among the floes and in the open sea. During the winter it migrates to the northern hemisphere, reaching California, Labrador, New Guinea, and Japan. In the southern spring it is back at its nesting sites in deep, protected crannies on the coasts of Antarctica and the fringing islands.

The giant petrel, a bird with an eight-foot wingspan, is known to scientists as *Macronectes giganteus* and to sailors as the stinker. This colorful common name refers to its scavenging habits—it will gorge itself on carrion until it is so full that it must vomit before takeoff.

Cliff nester The Cape pigeon breeds on ledges of cliffs, warding off intruders by spitting oil

Southern fulmar Like the Cape pigeon, this bird feeds in the open sea north of the pack ice

Snow petrel Probably the world's southernmost bird, it feeds almost exclusively within the pack ice

Shore scavengers and hunters

Gulls are outnumbered in the oceans around Antarctica by petrels and penguins, but the gull's aggressiveness and wide range of food enable it to survive where other birds would starve. Two of the gull species which breed on Antarctica are the Dominican gull and the Antarctic tern.

The sheathbill, a relative of the gulls, breeds on islands off the Antarctic Peninsula. Because its feet are only partially webbed and it feeds mainly along the shore, the sheathbill is the nearest approach to a true land bird on the continent.

During the breeding season the sheathbill scavenges among penguin colonies, eating dead chicks and taking scraps of food dropped by adults. Occasionally it will fly at a penguin that is regurgitating krill for its young, startling it into dropping morsels.

Penguin-killing skuas

Skuas are seabirds of prey. They are big, dark-colored birds with long wings, stout legs, webbed feet, and a thick, hooked beak.

Skuas cause havoc in a colony of penguins. With a wingspan up to four feet six inches, they are larger than the scavenging sheathbill and will take penguin eggs and chicks to feed themselves and their young. When penguin chicks are gathered into creches, or nurseries, skuas will swoop and dive to panic a chick away from the adult birds and into the open, where they can kill it.

Old enemies An Adélie penguin confronts two skuas. Skuas generally concentrate on the fringes of penguin colonies, where they can distract the young, inexperienced birds and steal eggs or chicks

Two species of skuas live on Antarctica, the brown skua and McCormick's skua. Nesting sites of these predatory birds vary widely, from those near penguin colonies in the coastal areas to those among the snow petrel colonies farther inland. Besides preying upon penguins and petrels, in some areas skuas scavenge for dead seals. Many also feed at sea, snatching fish and krill from the surface—or from other birds.

Skuas do not form colonies, but they have a strong territorial sense. Each pair claims an area from about 25 feet to more than 100 yards around a scrape or hollow in the ground, where the two eggs are laid. The parents stubbornly defend their territory, and a young skua that is unwary enough to stray into a neighbor's territory is often seized and eaten.

Sheathbills With their short, stubby wings, sheathbills look as if they should be weak fliers, but they sometimes migrate hundreds of miles

Pintails and pipit—birds of the sub-Antarctic islands

The sub-Antarctic islands provide a home for the only land bird and the only waterfowl in the southern polar region. These are a pipit and two pintail ducks. Some seabirds that breed mainly on the islands may extend their ranges to the northern end of the Antarctic Peninsula. One of these is the blue-eyed shag. Several sub-Antarctic island groups are the breeding grounds for many species of birds whose ranges extend northward into the southern cold temperate zone, including albatrosses, shearwaters, prions, and diving petrels.

Two natives of South Georgia

The Antarctic pipit feeds on small insects, crustaceans, and mollusks. Restricted to South Georgia in the South Atlantic, it stays close to the shore in winter and sometimes moves inland to freshwater streams and pools at other seasons.

The South Georgia pintail feeds partly in salt water. But during the breeding season, from November to February, it nests and feeds in long grass some distance inland.

The Kerguelen pintail, breeding on Kerguelen Island in the Indian Ocean, finds its food, mainly crustaceans, in freshwater ponds and on the seashore. It nests in tussocks near the water or in clefts in rocks, and in February three to six chicks are hatched.

Southernmost cormorant The blue-eyed shag is the only member of the cormorant family to reach the Antarctic. It is found primarily on the Antarctic Peninsula and the islands to the north

CONIFEROUS FOREST

**Needle-leaved conifers blanket the region between the tundra and the
more temperate areas of the northern hemisphere. This evergreen forest has been
a relatively undisturbed wildlife habitat**

A coniferous forest sweeps across northern Eurasia and North America, portions of it interweaving with the leaf-shedding trees of the temperate deciduous forests. Most dominant trees—spruce, fir, pine, and hemlock—typically retain their needle growth throughout the year and grow in dense stands that almost shut out the light. An exception is the larch, common in Siberia. It is a needle-leaved conifer that sheds its leaves and becomes dormant as a means of surviving the extremely dry, cold winter.

Covering the ground beneath the trees is a thick carpet of fallen, decaying conifer needles. Under the needles is a characteristically pale gray topsoil called podzol, from a Russian word meaning "ashes." This soil has been leached of minerals and other plant nutrients (in a process similar to filtering out) by the surface water that must drain downward because little of it can evaporate from the cool and shady forest floor. The poor topsoil and the lack of light at ground level make undergrowth scarce.

The plant and animal life of the coniferous forest is more varied than that of the tundra, but less than that of warmer regions. Alaskan tree species are similar to those in Siberia, and many of the same animal species are found throughout the biome.

Great rivers weave through the coniferous belt, flowing to the Arctic Ocean from mountain ranges such as the Urals of Russia and Canada's Mackenzies. Along the riverbanks vegetation is more abundant than in the rest of the forest, and in the sheltered river valleys conifers grow many miles north of the tree line.

The coniferous region is sometimes called by the Russian word taiga, meaning "swamp forest," because of the profusion of lakes and swamps. The swamps have formed where the shifting ice cover of the glacial period, here leveling and gouging, there picking up and dumping whole hills and ridges of earth and rock, hampered the formation of an effective river drainage system.

Coping with the harsh winter

For most of the year the ground of the coniferous forest is frozen or covered with snow. Winters are long and cold, although the air is dry and the sky usually clear. Those animal species that do not migrate have had to adapt in structure or behavior to endure the harsh climate.

Some year-round inhabitants of the coniferous forest hibernate as a means of surviving the winter

cold. Others remain active, but burrow under the snow for warmth and live on stored food. The dense winter coats of hares, wolves, moose, and foxes allow these mammals to stay active and above ground even when the air temperature falls as low as $-50°$ F. ($-45.55°$ C.).

The deep snows present another kind of problem. Huge, heavy-bodied moose, for instance, would often find themselves snowbound if they lacked their long, stiltlike legs, which permit walking through snow three feet deep. The varying hare, or snowshoe rabbit, has large tufts of fur on its feet that function like snowshoes. The wolverine, one of the most active predators of the northern woods, has toes that spread out, so it can pursue its prey over deep snow without sinking.

Conifers provide both food and shelter

Conifers are the basic source of food in the forests of the North. Their bark, buds, and seeds provide squirrels, hares, and some birds with a year-round food supply. Shelter, too, is found in and among the trees, and in rotted trunks and branches.

Among the resident birds are crossbills, hawks, owls, and grouse. In summer, insects feed on the conifers and become, in turn, the nourishment of birds that migrate north to nest and raise their young. Carnivores such as foxes, martens, and wolverines sometimes prey on these birds.

In winter, when all kinds of food are scarce, it has been observed that a particular species of animal tends to restrict its diet to just one type of food. Thus one species avoids competing for another's food supply. Beavers feed on the bark of felled trees which they stored in the fall; grouse eat conifer leaves; moose depend largely on brushwood. In summer all of these animals eat a much greater variety of foods.

Within the coniferous animal community there are fewer species, and interacting patterns of survival and behavior are less complex than those in warmer regions. Changes in the population level of certain species within the community tend to occur with great regularity. Every ten years or so, for example, the varying hare population reaches a peak. Then a combination of factors leads to mass starvation and a rapid population decline. The population cycle of the hare's main predator, the lynx, is closely related. It, too, follows a ten-year pattern, with the peak coming a year after the peak hare population. Cycles also occur in the seed production of conifers, largely because of changes in the weather, and are reflected in the fluctuating populations of seed-eating animals and birds.

The cold northern woods

Only hardy conifers and a few hardwood species can survive the harsh, usually freezing conditions of the northern forest

About 2000 miles south of the North Pole the mosses and lichens of the tundra make way for scattered groups of stunted larch, spruce, birch, and dwarf willow trees. These are outposts of the great belt of coniferous forest that extends across Eurasia and North America. In the northern part of the forest, inside the Arctic Circle, winters are long and

cold and summers short. Farther south, summers may actually be hot, but winter temperatures can still fall below −40° F. (−40° C.). Precipitation is slight throughout the region. Only conifers and a few hardwoods, such as birch and willow, can survive in these conditions.

The northern boundary of the forest is fairly distinct, but toward the south conifers and broad-leaved deciduous trees grow side by side in a wide transitional zone of mixed woodland. Broad-leaved deciduous forest ex-

tends north into the coniferous zone wherever warm ocean currents moderate the winter, while tongues of coniferous forest thrive within the deciduous belt on mountain chains, where the climate at high altitudes is similar to that of more northerly areas.

Thus, patches of coniferous forest show up on the map below in Spain, in the Pyrenees; in Japan; and in other southerly areas. Despite these geographical inconsistencies, the northern coniferous forests qualify as a distinct biome.

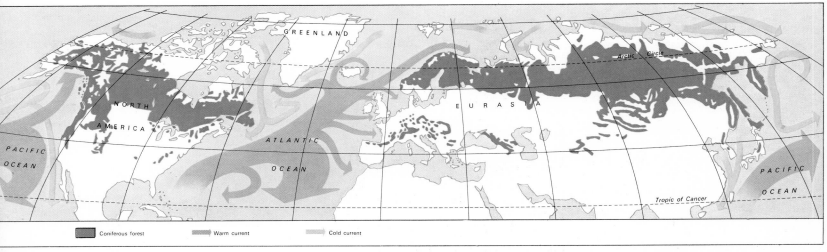

Sea's influence   Ocean currents warm Scandinavia and northwestern North America, allowing the forest to extend north into areas that otherwise would be tundra

A land of standing water and acid, infertile topsoil

Innumerable lakes and swamps dot the northern coniferous forest region. They have formed in hollows created by the ice sheet that covered the ground to a depth of thousands of feet 10,000 years ago. Scraped and flattened by that last ice age, the topography has been little affected by stream erosion. Water tends to stand, not flow, and the cold air permits little evaporation. Consequently, meltwater and the little rain that does fall are forced to drain downward, creating a permanently waterlogged soil.

There is little life in the soil. Few earthworms exist in the cold, wet conditions, and bacterial action is slow; as a result, fallen leaves and other dead vegetation decompose slowly. They do not mix in with the soil, but remain as a peaty top layer. The soil

water is acid, and as it filters downward it leaches out valuable minerals and nutrients, leaving behind the topsoil called podzol.

Sometimes the leached minerals form a hard layer in the subsoil, called an iron pan. This further impedes drainage by blocking the downward flow of water, thus adding to the swampiness of the already sodden soil and concentrating water near the surface.

Most decomposition of vegetable remains is accounted for by fungi, which thrive on dead plant matter. Fungi spread through the leaf litter and upper layer of soil as a network of interwoven threads. A cubic foot of needle-covered podzol may contain 2000 miles of fungal thread. In autumn these thread masses push their fruiting bodies, the spore-bearing toadstools, above the ground.

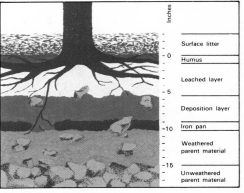

Soil structure   Beneath a thick layer of slowly decaying conifer needles and a thin layer of humus, water has leached away minerals plants need for growth, leaving the topsoil called podzol

Acid-loving lichen *Cladonia coccifera* grows in forest clearings. It thrives in acid soil

Red-top *Cladonia bellidiflora*, another lichen, is also found in coniferous forest clearings

Fungus under the pines *Hydnum auriscalpium* grows on fallen pine cones on the forest floor

Moist coniferous forest The southern Pacific coast of Vancouver Island provides an ideal climate for the growth of conifers. In winter heat is slowly transferred from the ocean to the air, moderating the island's climate. There is also abundant rainfall. Conifers reach enormous size under these conditions. The world's tallest known Douglas fir was a 305-foot giant that grew on the island. Undergrowth plants include salmonberry, blueberry, and ferns. Moss often grows on tree trunks

Snow-clad spruce Spruce and other conifers are well suited to winter conditions. Their resilient branches seldom snap under the weight of snow. In dense stands snow on the top of interwoven branches forms a protective canopy over animals

Conifers survive in a dry, cold environment

In the northern forests the season when there is sufficient warmth, light, and water for growth is so brief that most deciduous broad-leaved (hardwood) trees cannot flourish. They would lose more food material in shedding their large leaves than they could replace during the short summer. And because of the acid soil water, most mineral nutrients from their decomposing leaves would be leached from the earth before the trees could recover them through their root systems in spring.

Coniferous trees, on the other hand, are adapted to these dry, cold conditions. Unlike deciduous trees, which shed all their leaves in autumn, the conifers keep their needles throughout the winter. In this way they retain valuable nutrients and are pre-pared to start growing again with the beginning of spring. The thick outer skin of their needle-shaped leaves minimizes water loss through evaporation in frost or drought.

Resin production also helps the conifers survive. If a tree branch breaks under the weight of snow or ice, resin flows out around the break, making it difficult for disease-causing bacteria or fungi to enter the wound.

Siberia is one of the coldest portions of the coniferous belt, and a region of dry, evaporating winds. Here the larch, a deciduous conifer, predominates. Most conifers would be unable to replace water taken from their needles by the winds, even if the needles endured the intense winter cold. The larch survives the extreme conditions by shedding its needles and becoming dormant.

Mixed forest in autumn Birch, aspen, willow, and other deciduous trees thrive in river valleys. Here the silvery trunks and bright foliage of birch contrast with the dark green of the pine forest

Northern conifers and their seeds

Unlike flowering trees, whose seeds are encased in fruit, conifers produce cones in which naked seeds are enclosed by scales. The seeds, usually two in each scale, are produced by female cones that have been fertilized by pollen from male cones. As male and female cones are often on separate trees, the pollen grains of some conifers have a pair of air-filled sacs that aid their dispersal. The larch, unlike most coniferous trees, is deciduous, and each spring puts forth bright green foliage

Douglas fir
Pseudotsuga menziesii 100-300'

European larch
Larix decidua 80-150'

Lodgepole pine
Pinus contorta 70-200'

Norway spruce
Picea abies 120-150'

The beaver

A beaver dam is a marvel of engineering that can turn a stretch of river into a lake and create a new habitat for hundreds of creatures from raccoons to muskrats

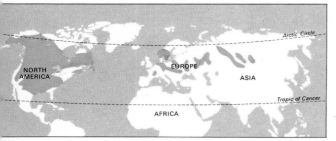

Beaver country There is one species, *Castor fiber*

The beaver, the largest rodent in the northern regions, once ranged widely throughout both North America and Eurasia, in the temperate deciduous forest and in those parts of the coniferous forest where deciduous trees grow along rivers. Today, the beaver is still widespread in North America, but in Eurasia it is now largely confined to the coniferous region. It is almost extinct in western Europe. There are a few scattered colonies in Germany, France, Poland, Russia, and Scandinavia. In some areas of the world beavers have been reintroduced, and these colonies are beginning to flourish.

The inner bark of the higher, softer branches of deciduous trees—willow, birch, aspen, and poplar—is the mainstay of the beaver's diet, though it eats a wide variety of green vegetation in summer. The beaver cannot climb to reach its favorite food, but its powerful jaws and chisel-sharp incisor teeth enable it to fell a tree and remove the branches. A pair of fully grown beavers— each about 2½ feet long and weighing 50 pounds—can gnaw through a four-inch-thick trunk in only 15 minutes.

The trees must be within easy reach of water, for the beaver is essentially an aquatic mammal, with webbed hind feet that serve as paddles and a broad, flat tail that is used as a rudder. The tail is almost hairless, and covered with large scales. The beaver often props itself up with the tail as it sits on a riverbank gnawing on sticks or chewing leaves.

Beavers store their food in water. In places

Trimming the tree Beavers often cut the trunks of trees they have felled into short lengths before transporting them to the dam site

Favorite food Beavers prefer the tender bark found on trees' topmost branches

Beaver's bite The massive jaws and prominent incisor teeth are conspicuous

Useful tail The beaver's scaly tail is a rudder in water and a prop on land

Storing food A beaver swims to its underwater food store with an aspen branch. Beavers spend the summer felling trees and storing branches for winter

where the current might wash away the branches, they build dams that stem the flow and create ponds. Most American beavers live in such ponds, in lodges they have built. Most Eurasian beavers, however, do not build dams or lodges, but live in holes with underwater entrances, often in steep banks on large rivers.

The beaver can draw on reserves of oxygen in its lungs and tissues to extend its usual five-minute dive to 15 minutes or more when there is any threat to its safety. When the beaver is submerged, its nostril and ear openings close and a transparent membrane covers its eyes. Its streamlined shape gives it added speed underwater. The beaver's water-repellent coat consists of fine underfur protected by long, coarse guard hairs.

Beavers live in pairs or family groups. A nest or lodge may be inhabited by a family of 12: parents, yearlings, and the current year's young, known as kits. On a lake which has been used by beavers over a number of years there may be a colony consisting of several lodges, whose inhabitants all contribute to the task of maintaining the dam and waterways. There seems to be no social hierarchy, however; the animals work as individuals rather than as a team.

Mating takes place in January and the young, usually three or four, are born in April or May. While the kits are being suckled the adult male lives by the lake shore in a burrow which, like a lodge, has one or more underwater entrances to tunnels that lead to a central living chamber.

After two to three months, the kits are weaned on young leaves and shoots. Soon they follow the mother wherever she goes, eating the plants she eats, and perfecting their skills in dam building and tree felling.

The young remain with the parents for two years or more after birth—much longer than the young of any other rodent—until they are driven out. Then they may travel for miles in search of a suitable site to establish their own lodge.

Marking with tell-tale scent

Beavers deposit a pungent substance called castoreum—which they manufacture in glands under the tail—on heaps of mud or stones around their dam. Apparently, the castoreum has a double function: to stake out territory and to advertise for mates.

All beavers in the colony sniff at the heaps frequently. If a beaver discovers a strange scent, the animal will try to obliterate it by leaving fresh scent. When outsiders approach the heaps they usually continue on their way if the scent deposited there is fresh.

Dangers in the forest

Many legends have grown around the beaver, crediting it with an extraordinary degree of intelligence. It has been claimed, for example, that beavers can cut a tree so as to make it fall in the precise direction they require, and that they warn each other of danger by drumming with their tails.

In fact, the trees cut by beavers fall at random, sometimes killing the very animals that felled them. And beavers often spend hours cutting through trees that cannot possibly fall because of the density of the surrounding forest.

The beaver gives an emergency signal with its tail. If a beaver is on land and senses danger it rushes to the water and swims to the deepest part. Often it dives out of sight with a loud slap of its tail on the surface. It is this noise that warns other beavers that danger is near.

Beavers as conservationists

Although beavers chop down trees for food and building materials, they actually help preserve the woodland they exploit.

Dams serve generations of beavers, but eventually a beaver-made lake may silt up, providing rich soil for vegetation. Many acres of meadows and deciduous trees owe their existence to beavers.

Beaver dams also help control spring floods, and can create marshy areas where waterfowl and other wildlife thrive.

In the United States, one soil-conservation program involves dropping beavers by parachute into mountain areas. Specially designed containers allow the beavers to escape easily when they land, and the animals then fan out and go on to build their dams, which help to prevent soil erosion.

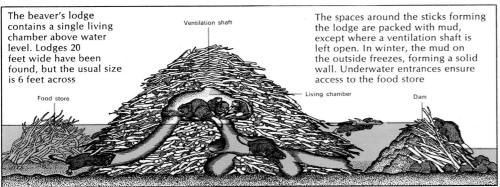

The beaver's lodge contains a single living chamber above water level. Lodges 20 feet wide have been found, but the usual size is 6 feet across

Ventilation shaft

Food store

The spaces around the sticks forming the lodge are packed with mud, except where a ventilation shaft is left open. In winter, the mud on the outside freezes, forming a solid wall. Underwater entrances ensure access to the food store

Living chamber

Dam

Dams change the landscape Beaver dams (right) create ponds, usually about three feet deep, that provide stable sites for lodges and calm waterways for transporting branches, with sufficient depth for the beaver to travel underwater, unseen by predators. Lodges are also built on the edge of ponds. Beavers sometimes fell trees right into the water, but when water is not handy they gnaw felled trees into two-to-three-foot lengths and roll or tow them to the dam. Sometimes they dig canals to transport logs. The dam is begun with stones, built up with sticks, and finished with mud and weeds. It may be a few feet to 600 yards long and up to 12 feet high. Dams, sometimes containing hundreds of tons of timber, are extended year after year

Conifer-eating birds

A dense canopy of closely woven branches shuts out the sunlight in much of the northern forest, where only certain species of birds flourish on the conifer diet

The wide range of food in broad-leaved forests provides for a great variety of birdlife. In coniferous forests the choice of food is limited, since even the more edible parts of cone-bearing trees are tough and resinous, and thus both difficult to get at and unpalatable to the majority of bird species.

The most common conifer is the spruce, except in eastern Siberia, where larches are more numerous. In North America the black and white spruces predominate. Norway spruce is the most prevalent conifer in western Europe, and the Siberian spruce in Russia and western Siberia. Firs are also common throughout the coniferous forest.

Only about 50 bird species flourish in this northern zone, and they have become specialists in feeding on conifers. Members of the finch and crow families have developed strong or specially shaped beaks that can extract seeds from cones, and some grouse can digest conifer needles and buds. The crossbill is a finch that depends mainly on the seeds of spruce, pine, and larch trees for food. It is noted for its periodic migrations when food becomes scarce in its usual habitat. These migrations are more properly called eruptions: the birds "erupt" out of their normal seasonal range.

For the seed-eating birds, a poor cone crop means starvation or massive emigration that year. But grouse can remain in the forest all year round, since they feed on the more reliable supply of conifer leaves.

Northern woodland grouse spend all day feeding

Old man of the woods A capercaillie cock crows a challenge to other males. The bird's name was originally spelled *capercailzie*—Gaelic for "old man of the woods." Capercaillies, like other grouse, perform elaborate mating displays at gatherings called leks. Each male holds his own "court" area in the lek, displaying to other males rather than to females. Females go from court to court, mating with the most demonstrative males. Unsuccessful males move to less favorable areas, and often starve

Grouse are not typically woodland dwellers, but birds of open country—moorland, desert, even the frozen tundra. Only a few species live in woodland, and of these only four species are wholly adapted to life in the coniferous forest.

The capercaillie of Europe and Siberia, the largest of all grouse, is one of the four species that can survive on the leaves and buds of conifers. The males may grow to three feet long and 17 pounds in weight. In winter capercaillies live almost entirely on conifer leaves, which have a low nutrient content. To get the nourishment they require the birds must eat so many leaves that their waking hours are almost one long meal.

The blue grouse of North America is smaller than the capercaillie, but feeds in the same way. In winter these birds may spend days stripping all the foliage from one tree.

Some grouse show a preference for particular species of trees. The spruce grouse in Canada and the Siberian sharp-winged grouse both feed exclusively on the leaves and buds of mature spruce. By contrast, the north European black grouse, which usually lives in heathland, will feed on any conifer in time of shortage.

Most male and female grouse meet only to mate, and the males take no part in raising their offspring. A male may couple with several females during the season. This promiscuous behavior has led to intense competition beween males, which are bigger than females and brighter in plumage. Competing males display flaring tails and colored wattles and make special sounds; the blue grouse hoots, and the spruce grouse drums with its wings.

After mating, the female grouse scrapes a nest in the ground and lays 6 to 15 or more eggs. The chicks feed themselves on insect pupae almost from hatching, and can survive only a few hours without food. The young have poor resistance to cold; in cold, wet weather, many chicks starve because they cannot leave the hen's warmth, and those that do venture out quickly die.

Species of grouse that live in cold climates have evolved feather-covered nostrils and legs. In winter a growth of fine feathers edges the toes of the mature grouse, giving a firm foothold on snow.

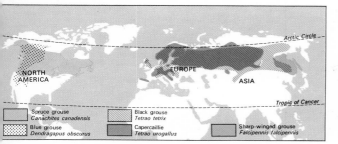

Spruce grouse *Canachites canadensis*	Black grouse *Tetrao tetrix*
Blue grouse *Dendragapus obscurus*	Capercaillie *Tetrao urogallus*
	Sharp-winged grouse *Falcipennis falcipennis*

Forest grouse In eastern Siberia the Eurasian capercaillie *Tetrao urogallus* is replaced by the smaller black-billed capercaillie *Tetrao parvirostris*

Blue grouse This grouse of the North American coniferous forest has much the same feeding and mating habits as the larger Eurasian grouse

Crossbills cut cones apart

Species of the finch family have evolved bills of different shapes to suit their particular diets. Seed-eaters usually have short, heavy beaks associated with strong jaw muscles. The edges of their beaks are sharp and often serrated inside.

The beak of several species of crossbills, members of the finch family, shows a further adaptation: the beak tips cross each other when the mouth is closed. The jaw muscles enable the beak to exert a pressure of 100 pounds per square inch at the cutting edges, so the bird can shear through the tough scales of pine cones and reach the seeds inside. This gives the crossbill an advantage over other seed-eating creatures that must wait for their food until the cones open. The bird's narrow bill, with its crossed tips, is well adapted to pick out conifer seeds from cones.

The nomadic crossbills

The red crossbill, called the common crossbill in Europe, is found in both northern and alpine coniferous forests, but the white-winged crossbill and the parrot crossbill are primarily confined to the northern forest. The last is native to Eurasia, but the other species live in both continents. There are even white-winged crossbills on Hispaniola.

All crossbills are more or less nomadic within their ranges, changing their breeding grounds with the rise and fall of the cone crop. An abundant crop often exhausts the productive capacity of trees, resulting in cone failure the next year. During such a year of plenty the bird population increases; in the following period of poverty, the surplus young birds must migrate to find food, or starve. Total failure of the crop causes occasional mass migrations, or eruptions, random and desperate searches for food during which many birds may die. Occasionally migrating birds will settle in the new area into which they have "erupted."

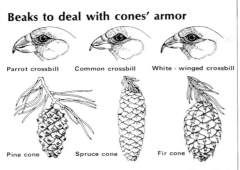

Beaks to deal with cones' armor

Parrot crossbill   Common crossbill   White-winged crossbill

Pine cone   Spruce cone   Fir cone

The parrot crossbill, feeding on thick-scaled pine cones, has the heaviest beak. The common crossbill, living among spruce, has a lighter beak. With the most slender beak of all, the white-winged crossbill feeds on the thin-scaled cones of fir trees

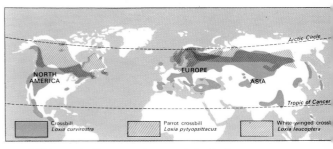

Crossbills' range Three species penetrate Arctic

Crossbill *Loxia curvirostra*   Parrot crossbill *Loxia pytyopsittacus*   White-winged crossbill *Loxia leucoptera*

Acrobatic crossbill With its ability to cling and feed at any angle, the crossbill can penetrate the densest foliage in its search for cones. The young are very resistant to cold. When the mother is absent from the nest, the chicks' metabolic rate drops, which cuts loss of body heat

The pine grosbeak hammers cones open to reach seeds

The pine grosbeak, another finch, sometimes obtains seeds by battering the cones open, using its muscular neck and thick bill. This bird, however, is much less dependent on cones than the crossbill; it also feeds on birch, sumac, and willow. In summer the pine grosbeak usually lives along the edge of a clearing in the coniferous forest. Grosbeaks are gregarious birds, and travel in search of food in flocks of up to a hundred. Like crossbills, they seem to travel only when existing food supplies in an area are exhausted.

Two species of nutcrackers hammer cones to pieces with their hard bills, in order to reach the seeds. These small crows, which store food for the winter, also eat nuts, berries, and insects. Clark's nutcracker, the North American species, has mostly gray plumage, with black-and-white wings and tail. The European nutcracker is brown.

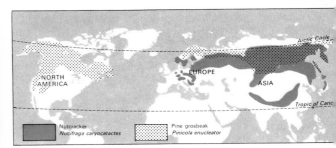

Two seed-eaters The North American Clark's nutcracker, which lives in alpine and northern forests, is a relative of the common nutcracker of Eurasia

Nutcracker *Nucifraga caryocatactes*   Pine grosbeak *Pinicola enucleator*

Common nutcracker This small member of the crow family (left) lives in the coniferous forest. Like all crows, it has adaptability and intelligence. In addition to insects, berries, and nuts, it eats pine seeds, cracking open the cones with its bill. Nutcrackers often perch on the treetops

Conifer-eating mammals

Rodent species are among the most successful on earth—hardy, remarkably fertile, and able to eat almost anything. Their prolific breeding ensures survival

Altogether there are about 1800 species of rodents—nearly equaling the total of all other species of mammals. They are found in almost every kind of habitat, from the tundra to the tropical rain forest.

Most rodents are small, the largest being the beaver—three feet long, not including the tail. Among the tiniest is the three-inch dwarf mouse of Africa.

What distinguishes rodents from other mammals are their chisellike incisor teeth, which grow throughout life, and their lack of canine teeth. Rodents are able to digest almost everything they gnaw, so they thrive under conditions which would be inhospitable to most other mammals. They are prolific breeders, often producing several large litters in a year. Within a species there is such genetic variation (because of this large population) that, if environmental conditions change, enough individuals with the newly required set of characteristics will survive to breed again.

A variety of rodents live in the northern woods, thriving on the rich harvest of conifer seeds, bark, and buds. Among the residents are red squirrels, chipmunks, flying squirrels, and porcupines.

The red squirrel—raucous rodent of the northwoods

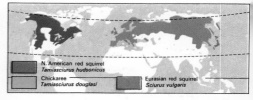

Red squirrels The Eurasian red squirrel differs so much from the two American species that it is classed as a separate genus. The three species are divided further into subspecies, according to their adaptation to the conditions of their habitats

Harvest before winter Three young Eurasian red squirrels pause to rest and eat during their late summer search for food. All squirrels have spells of great activity at this season, gathering cones, seeds, fungi, and nuts. Squirrels are not anticipating winter when they hoard food. They may "forget" where they have hidden their stores, but they hide so much food that they can hardly help finding some. Thus, though not intelligence in the human sense, this activity helps squirrels survive

Color change The coats of some races of Eurasian red squirrels are black all year. More typical members of the species change color with the season. The dark fur that follows the spring molt turns brown, then red, and finally cream

Red squirrels are active, vociferous rodents which range through most of the world's coniferous forests, and often spread south into the deciduous zones.

North America has two species of red squirrels, one known simply as the red squirrel, and the other, because of its chattering call, as the chickaree. Both are smaller and more boldly marked than the Eurasian red squirrel. Within all species there are races that differ in color and habits. For instance, the color of a Siberian squirrel's tail is determined by the type of forest in which the squirrel lives—red tails are found in pine forests, brown tails among firs and larches, and almost black tails among cedars.

The staple diet of red squirrels is conifer seeds, obtained by stripping the scales from cones. This is a time-consuming process—200 cones can yield less than a half ounce of seeds. But the squirrels do not depend entirely on the seeds; they also eat other plant food, as well as insect larvae and bird's eggs.

Squirrels are famous for storing food in preparation for winter. It is true that they gather cones, seeds, and nuts and hide them. But they are not consciously "planning" for winter. In fact, when winter comes they often forget where they have buried their stores. Seeds from the forgotten cones may sprout, and in this way squirrels inadvertently help to spread the forest.

Red squirrels often have two litters a year, especially in the south of their ranges. The number of young varies from two to six.

Cone hoarder The North American red squirrel hoards food to a greater extent than the Eurasian species. It will sometimes collect hundreds of unopened cones in a single cache

Rodents that climb, hoard, and glide among the conifers

Chipmunks are small, energetic members of the squirrel family. They live predominantly on the ground, but some species, confined to the coniferous forest, are expert climbers. The chipmunks of the northern forest eat conifer seeds and buds only to a limited extent; they depend more on the nuts and berries of other shrubs and plants.

The animals live in burrows, usually building them under rocks or logs. They line one section of the burrow with grass. This is for the two to eight young that are born in the spring, about a month after the adult chipmunks mate.

Chipmunks begin intensive hoarding of food at the onset of autumn frosts for, unlike red squirrels, they hibernate, awakening occasionally to feed from their stores. Like other squirrels, chipmunks help to spread trees, since they frequently do not find their caches, and the seeds sprout. Chipmunks molt twice a year. In summer their coat is brighter in color.

Flying squirrel: aerial acrobat

Another rodent resident of the coniferous belt is the flying squirrel. Two tiny species, both under six inches long, inhabit the northern forests. Despite their name, these creatures do not really fly, but glide from tree to tree, spreading the gliding membranes attached to the entire length of their body, from the foreleg to the hind leg. These membranes almost triple the area of its body's undersurface and help the squirrel make glides of up to 50 yards. The squirrel can even change direction during its glide by working the muscles of its membranes, like a parachutist pulling on his guidelines. In this manner it can outmaneuver the owl, its chief predator.

Stuffed chipmunk Cheek pouches, into which it can cram almost 20 hazelnuts, help the chipmunk collect its huge winter hoard of food

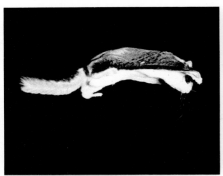
Flying squirrel It lands so that all four feet can grip the tree. Then it runs to the other side and faces downward—instinctive moves to dodge predators

Why predators leave the slow-moving porcupine alone

A single species of porcupine inhabits most of the coniferous areas of North America. It is a solitary, nocturnal, tree-climbing rodent with an armament of barbed quills. The young porcupine is well developed at birth and can climb trees when it is only a few days old.

The porcupine's quills normally lie flat, concealed by coarse back and tail hairs. When the animal is threatened, the quills become erect. They detach easily from the porcupine when it is touched, and inflict painful, festering wounds. Because of this very effective defense, most predators avoid the porcupine—which perhaps is why such a temptingly large and slow-moving rodent has managed to survive.

North American porcupine This porcupine has no counterpart in the Eurasian coniferous forest. The longer-quilled Old World porcupines, which are not closely related, are confined to warm temperate and tropical regions

Tree climber The North American porcupine is a large rodent, weighing 10 to 15 pounds. Strong, curved claws enable it to climb to its favorite food of leaves and buds. The porcupine feeds at night, hiding by day in hollow trees or holes in the ground. It does considerable damage to conifers

49

Conifer-eating insects

Many tree-eating insects lead several "lives." The spruce gall aphid progresses through five distinct forms during its complex life cycle

Few species of insects can feed successfully on conifers, which are resinous, sticky, and unpalatable. But those species that have overcome the difficulties are present in the northern forests in large numbers, feeding on every part of the trees and greatly affecting tree growth. The caterpillars of the pine-shoot moth and the spruce budworm are two of the most destructive insects.

Most insects go through a number of forms in their lives. In one type of life cycle, the eggs hatch in summer into wormlike larvae, which feed avidly until fully grown. In autumn the larvae enclose themselves in cases, or cocoons, where, as pupae, they remain inactive through the winter. During the pupal stage they undergo their fourth and final change of form, emerging in spring as adults.

There are only three stages in another type of insect life cycle. The eggs hatch into nymphs, which look rather like the adult insects. The nymphs then grow to mature form in a series of molts.

Large pine weevil A member of the beetle family, the large pine weevil eats the buds and bark of conifer shoots. The most destructive American species is the white pine weevil

Leaf-eating caterpillar The caterpillar of the panthea moth feeds on the needles of pine and larch trees, but unlike other tree-feeding species of moths, does not cause extensive damage

Pine procession caterpillars (right) They get their name from the way they follow each other along a silken thread spun by the caterpillar in front. If placed in a ring they will circle indefinitely

Sawflies, moth caterpillars, and wasps share tree food

Leaf-eaters
Sawflies, although they lack the typical "wasp waist," are members of the hymenoptera order along with ants, bees, and hymenopteran wasps. They are one of the few species of insects that feed on conifer needles. In May or June the female pine sawfly cuts a row of slits in a pine needle with its saw-toothed ovipositor and lays an egg in each slit. Over the eggs it spreads a foamy liquid, which then hardens into a solid protective cap. The larvae pupate inside this parchmentlike cocoon, and at the end of several weeks emerge by breaking open the "cap" at the end. After the young caterpillars are hatched, they begin to feed on the needles.

The caterpillars look like those of butterflies or moths, except that they have seven or eight pairs of abdominal legs instead of five. They are insatiable eaters. Each brood feeds in a colony, often stripping all the leaves from a branch.

When they are fully grown, the caterpillars descend from the trees, crawl under the soil, and spin cocoons around themselves. They remain there as pupae until spring.

The caterpillar of the spruce budworm has the dubious distinction of having been voted, by United States entomologists, one of the three most destructive North American insects. The other two are the cotton boll weevil and the corn earworm. The larvae may remove all the needles from spruce and related trees over hundreds of thousands of acres. The spruce budworm attacks fir, spruce, larch, hemlock, and pine trees. The larvae live in small silken cases on twigs near the buds. In spring, when the buds open, the caterpillar emerges and feeds on the needles for about a month.

Bud-eaters
Moth caterpillars feed in great numbers on developing buds, sometimes causing serious harm to young trees. A Eurasian species, the pine-shoot moth, has recently spread to North America and is doing extensive damage to pines. The attractive red-orange moths lay their eggs in midsummer in the buds of pines, especially red, Scotch, and Austrian pines. When the caterpillars are hatched in the spring they eat their way into the developing bud, hollowing it out and cutting off any new growth for that year. Resin spills out of the damaged buds; to prevent it from flooding their holes, the caterpillars line them with silk. If a tree is attacked by the pine-shoot moth two or three years in a row it may die. Related species of moths attack other types of pines.

Seed-eaters
Many species of seed wasps live in the northern forests, feeding on the seeds of conifers, mating on the needles, and laying their eggs in the cones.

The female seed wasp lays eggs through a long slender tube, the ovipositor, which she is able to drive through the outer scales of soft young fir cones. Usually the wasp places one egg inside each of the hundred or so seeds in the cone. When the larva hatches, it feeds on the seed for six or seven weeks, growing until it fills the husk. It normally remains inside the seed for one winter. During this time it transforms itself into a pupa, and remains inactive while it changes into a fully grown wasp.

The seed wasp's chief enemy is another wasp, the parasite *Mesopolobus spermotrophus*. To produce fertile eggs, the female must obtain protein, which is present in the seed wasp larvae. Since *Mesopolobus* does not have a long ovipositor to reach into the cones after the larvae, it must wait for the cones to open; then it creeps in between the scales. The parasitic wasp cuts a hole in a seed and sucks some of the body fluid of the larva inside. After a few days, it returns to the seed and lays an egg beside the seed wasp larva. When the egg hatches, the grub eats the larva.

Preparing to lay eggs Before it lays its eggs, the female wood wasp cuts a hole for them in a dying or fallen tree, using its long, sawlike ovipositor

Tunneling and egg laying A beetle of the genus *Dendroctonus* bores a tunnel through the bark of a pine or spruce tree. It lays eggs along the sides of the tunnel as it proceeds. This species is especially destructive to mature trees

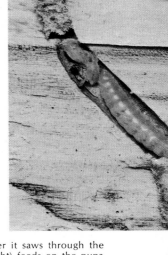

Killer wasp The female ichneumon wasp (left) explores bark in search of a wood wasp pupa, on which it will lay an egg after it saws through the wood. The hatched larva (right) feeds on the pupa

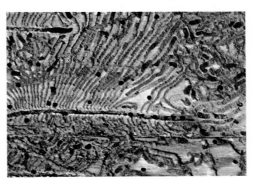

Spruce bark beetle tunnels (left) The horizontal main galleries are made by egg-laying female spruce bark beetles, the small side tunnels by the larvae. Wood dust often piles up at the base of the tree

Wood wasps and engraver beetles have a tree-boring life

Most wood-boring insects are beetles. A prominent exception is the wood wasp, or horntail, which feeds on most species of conifers. It measures about an inch long, making it one of the largest members of the sawfly group.

The female wood wasp cuts a hole in dead or dying trees with the sawlike blades of its ovipositor, and lays its eggs in the hole. It seldom attacks living trees. When the larvae are hatched, they begin eating their way through the wood, forming twisting tunnels up to 12 inches long. It takes them 2½ to 3 years to come within about an inch of the surface. Here they stop and remain inactive as pupae until they are fully grown and ready to emerge.

The wood wasp pupae's most deadly enemy is the female ichneumon wasp, which lays its eggs on the skin of the pupae.

To reach a pupa in its tunnel, the female ichneumon wasp has to saw through an inch of solid wood with its toothed ovipositor, a task it can complete in about 20 minutes. Before it begins, it carefully explores the surface of the tree to find the exact location of a pupa—apparently detected by the sense of smell. The hole it makes is rarely far from the correct spot.

When the larva hatches from the egg, it first attacks the nonvital parts of the wood wasp pupa. The wood wasp, therefore, can continue to develop. However, the parasitic ichneumon larva is also growing. As it nears the final stages of its development it attacks its host's vital tissues. When the ichneumon caterpillar emerges, the wood wasp pupa is little more than a shell.

The inside of the bark of dead spruce trees often shows a network of fine channels. These are made by the spruce bark beetle, also called the engraver beetle, as it eats its way through the bark.

The female engraver bores a vertical tunnel through the inner bark, and over a period of three to four weeks lays eggs singly at the side of the tunnel as it crawls along. When the larvae hatch, they begin boring a series of parallel side tunnels, which lead outward from the main passageway. Eventually they excavate cells between the bark and the wood, and remain there as pupae until maturity.

Engraver beetles usually bore into dead or diseased trees, since the flow of resin that would result from boring into a healthy tree would clog their tunnels.

The ambrosia beetle bores into the wood, rather than the bark, of conifers. It does not feed on the wood, but the beetle brings with it a fungus that can destroy the tree. The female ambrosia beetle first excavates a long main gallery and bores short egg galleries off it. She then prepares a bed on which she cultivates a fungus as food. Each species of ambrosia beetle cultivates a different type of fungus. Sometimes the fungus-growing gets out of hand when, for unknown reasons, the beetles are unable to control the growth and it spreads throughout the tunnels, trapping the insects in a tightly woven meshwork from which they cannot escape.

Sap-suckers

A group of gall lice feeds on the sap in conifer needles. One of these, the spruce gall aphid, abundant in both North America and Europe, has a complex life cycle extending over two years. The cycle begins when a "founding mother" lays eggs that later hatch into "immatures," or nymphs. These nymphs attack the growing tips of spruce and induce the growth of inch-high galls, called pineapple galls because of their resemblance to immature pineapples. The galls stunt the new growth of the host tree. If enough aphids attack the same tree season after season, they can kill it in a few years.

In the life cycle of the European spruce gall aphid, succeeding generations of the nymphs migrate from spruce to larch and back again. The North American species remains on the same spruce, even if a larch is nearby. Nymphs that participate in this cycle mature into females, which lay eggs that hatch only females. Males do not appear until the very end of the cycle, when both males and females hatch from the last batch of fertilized eggs. These males mate with the females, which lay fertilized eggs. The fertilized eggs hatch into founding mother nymphs, and the whole two-year cycle begins all over again.

Plant-eaters

The moose must plod through the snow in winter, searching for food, while small animals such as mice and voles forage in relative warmth beneath the snow blanket

Many of the plant-eating animals that live in this harsh land do not feed on the resinous conifers that dominate the woods. Moose, hares, woodchucks, voles, and lemmings seek instead the less abundant broad-leaved trees, as well as grasses, mosses, and herbs. They forage for these in relatively open spaces of the forest.

Winter, bringing thick snow and a scarcity of food, forces a change in the living patterns of these animals. In the spring and summer moose browse in lakes and marshes for water plants. But during the winter they must depend on berries and tree shoots, wading through deep snow on their long, stiltlike legs to find them.

For the small mammals, snow means sanctuary from predators and a protective blanket against the cold. The woodchuck hibernates, its metabolism dropping to the point where it barely sustains life. But most of the others seek a place where they can remain active but be protected from the weather.

Voles and lemmings spend the winter in the undersnow, the shallow space between the ground and snow that rests on the undergrowth and grass. In this microclimate the temperature is never more than a degree or two below freezing. Here these animals can live an active life, feeding on the roots and stems of the plants and mosses buried under the snow. When the warmer weather of spring arrives, voles and lemmings emerge to feed on the surface.

The solitary moose and its winter struggle for survival

The end of the chase A moose has been driven almost to the point of collapse by an unusually large pack of wolves. It is probably sickly; wolves do not normally attack healthy adult moose

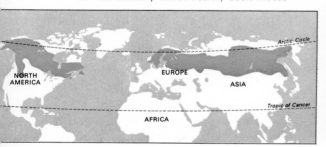

Where the moose are The moose and the slightly smaller Eurasian elk are the same species

Mother and twins Moose calves are born in May or June. One in as few as four births may be of twins. A cow moose does not abandon its calves until shortly before its next offspring are born

Food in summer The moose eats lake plants and the lakeside saplings of willow, birch, and aspen

A moose must spend almost all the hours of the long winter searching for food to fuel its vast bulk. A mature moose needs four to five tons of vegetable food simply to stay alive.

The moose and the slightly smaller Eurasian elk—they are the same species—are the largest of all deer. An adult bull moose, with antlers six feet across, may stand over six feet at the shoulder and weigh almost a ton.

In summer, moose often wade flank-deep into marshes or ponds to feed on lilies and waterweed, sometimes even submerging completely. On land they use their height and muscular lips to grasp twigs high above the ground. When a moose cannot reach tempting twigs, it simply bulldozes the sapling to the ground. In winter, they trample the snow to reach berries and willow shoots underneath, or pack it into mounds on which they stand to reach higher twigs.

Moose are normally solitary creatures, for each individual needs an extensive territory of its own over which to browse. The bulls roam the forests alone; the cows are accompanied only by their calves. But in exceptionally cold weather the territorial system breaks down and moose form groups in places where they are likely to find food.

Mating begins in September, when the bulls' antlers are fully grown and the males are ready to battle for the possession of cows. Both males and females become highly aggressive during this autumn rut, the bulls bellowing and slashing at trees with their antlers and driving away all intruders. During the mating season, the cows wander alone through the forest in search of a bull; if a cow has a calf with her from the previous year, she will reject any bull that drives it away.

The woodchuck Waking in spring after hibernating as long as eight months, the woodchuck becomes extremely active. It breeds, eats, and digs a burrow to hibernate in the following winter

Survival under the snow Two small rodents and a shrew feed beneath winter's snow blanket

How rodents live: in burrows or the undersnow

Two small rodents, the spruce vole, or mountain phenacomys, and the root vole, keep to the parts of the coniferous forest where the undergrowth is thickest. There the grasses, rushes, and other plants they eat are most plentiful and the relatively warm undersnow space is deepest and most extensive. In the undersnow, voles can travel for hundreds of yards without having to emerge to find food.

The wood lemming, the only small mammal to feed predominantly on mosses, regularly follows the same routes beneath the snow to move from one moss patch to another. When the snow melts in spring, large areas of moss may be brown where lemmings have eaten the new shoots. The wood lemming's rate of breeding is high—though lower than that of the Arctic lemming—and its effect on the environment can be great.

The American varying hare, or snowshoe rabbit, and the European blue hare adapt to winter by changing color. Their dark summer coats give way to snow-white camouflage which helps to hide them from predators, including the lynx.

The varying hare is further protected by its quick reactions and speed, which take it from rest to 30 miles an hour within a second. In winter it "snowshoes" across the snow, aided by stiff bristles that sprout on its feet in autumn.

Like most other hares, the varying hare does not dig a burrow but lies in a "form," or shallow depression in the ground. The young are born there, covered with fur and with their eyes open.

The aftermath of a population explosion

The high birthrate of varying hares leads to profound changes in its environment. Hares may produce up to five litters of three or four young a year. Although only a small proportion of these reach maturity, in a ten-year period there may be up to 4000 hares attempting to live in a square mile of forest. The females of predator species become much more fertile in response to such a glut of food and the numbers of predators—owls, minks, bobcats, and especially lynxes—increase rapidly.

After plenty comes famine. The hare birthrate and population suddenly fall, for reasons not yet fully understood. The hares may completely exhaust the food supply and starve, or they may succumb to hormone disorders caused by the stresses of overcrowding and competition for food.

The woodchuck's quiet year

One of the few animals of the northern forests to hibernate is the woodchuck, a large North American member of the squirrel family that may spend up to eight months of the year asleep in a burrow or a hollow log.

In the coldest part of the winter, the heartbeat rate of the hibernating woodchuck, which may reach 200 beats a minute when the animal is active, drops to 4 or 5 beats a minute. The animal's temperature falls, its breathing slows to as low as two breaths a minute, and the rate of consumption of stored body fat slows correspondingly. The woodchuck's level of metabolism, in fact, is no higher than is necessary to keep its vital body tissues alive. If the outside temperature drops too much, the animal's nervous system wakes it up for a few hours of heat-producing activity. Then it can return to its usual comatose state.

European blue hare Sometimes called the mountain hare, the animal is shown in its summer coat

As winter approaches Decreasing daylight triggers hormonal changes that turn the hare's fur white

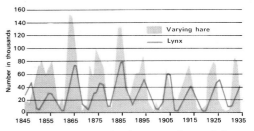

Predator and prey The lynx population follows that of the varying hare, after a slight lag

The insect-eaters

Insect-eating birds and mammals find winter prey scarce in the coniferous forest. Some migrate, others change their eating habits in order to survive

The insect life of the northern forests has two main seasons—a short summer of activity and reproduction when insects abound in the trees, and a long winter of inactivity when, their numbers greatly reduced by predators, they survive in dormant stages, underground and in crevices in bark.

No group of insectivorous animals is entirely confined to the coniferous forest, but there are certain species that are rarely found outside it.

The insect-eating animals that remain in the forest throughout the year, such as woodpeckers and shrews, manage to find sufficient food during the insects' inactive stage. In the summer, when insects are plentiful, these residents are joined by insectivorous migrants such as bats and warblers. Tits are best described as semi-migrants, remaining in their northerly haunts when winters are mild, but seeking warmer regions when the winter is unusually harsh.

Insect hunting with chisel beaks and harpoon tongues

The woodpecker's name is derived from its habit of chipping holes in trees to prey on insects or to make nesting places. It hammers at the bark and the wood with a hard, often chisel-pointed beak powered by strong neck muscles. The shock of the blows is absorbed by flexible joints connecting the skull bones. Bristly feathers surrounding the bird's nostrils filter out the wood dust that flies when a woodpecker is at work on a tree. When the hole is finished, the woodpecker probes for insects with its long, flexible tongue. Tiny barbs and sticky saliva at the end of the tongue catch the prey. Some woodpeckers feed heavily on the bark of undamaged trees; others attack mainly insect-tunneled trees.

Woodpeckers get a sure grip on the tree trunk with their sharply hooked claws, which are made more effective by an unusual arrangement of the toes—two point forward and two backward on each claw. An exception is the three-toed woodpecker, which, like most other birds, has three toes at the front of the foot and one at the back.

Woodpeckers have several interesting features. One is their habit of communicating with each other by drumming on trees in a clearly identifiable rhythm.

Northern woodpeckers The three species shown above need not migrate, since their insect food is relatively plentiful throughout the year

Pileated woodpecker *Dryocopus pileatus*

Three-toed woodpecker *Picoides tridactylus*

Black woodpecker *Dryocopus martius*

Added support A pileated woodpecker feeds its young, bracing itself against the tree with its stiff tail feathers, a mark of all true woodpeckers

The rare Kirtland's warbler follows forest fires

Kirtland's warbler The female, shown here, is better camouflaged than the male, which has a distinctive black face mask, a blue-gray back streaked with black, and a lemon yellow breast. There are more black streaks along its sides. These warblers measure almost six inches long. Most other warblers are smaller. In winter Kirtland's warbler migrates to the Bahamas

The many members of the warbler family make up a large part of the insect-eaters in the coniferous forest. In winter, when their food supply is scarce among the conifers, warblers migrate south.

Most warblers occupy a wide range, but one rare species, Kirtland's warbler, breeds only in an 85-by-100-mile area in Michigan, between Lake Huron and Lake Michigan, in those spots where jack pines are regrowing after forest fires. For a site to be acceptable, the trees must be between 5 and 15 feet high, in dense stands covering at least 80 acres. The warblers build their nests in small clearings on porous ground where drainage is good and flooding is unlikely. Cover such as grass, ferns, and bushes must be just high enough to hide the nest, but no higher.

It is probably the soil and the absence of mature trees that limit the birds to this region, since jack pines are common in North America. The comparatively barren ground also does not tend to attract predatory mammals, reptiles, and other birds. The birds can find food—caterpillars and adult ant-lions—in mature forest and open country nearby.

Kirtland's warblers must move to new breeding grounds every 20 years or so, since by then the jack pines and cover will have grown too tall to suit them. In effect, they depend on fires to clear their new home.

Residents and migrants

Tits are small, active, gregarious birds that usually remain in one locality year after year, even when temperatures drop below freezing. If they do migrate in winter, it is usually just to move from exposed ridges to sheltered valleys.

Like many birds that seek insect food, tits move in a restless, fluttering manner, with abrupt starts and halts. They keep mostly to more open forests, where they also find seeds and berries to eat.

Some of the 45 species of true tits live in pairs or groups, but join other small insect-eating birds to hunt for food in noisy parties. Most species make their nests in existing holes, from hollows in tree stumps to niches high in trees. However, some species use their stout, roughly conical beaks to carve their own nesting holes in rotten trees.

Tits typical of the coniferous forests are the crested tit, the willow tit, the boreal chickadee, and the black-capped chickadee. In summer they feed on small insects such as aphids. In winter they search for their food, including the eggs and pupae of insects, in fine crevices on tree branches.

Found in great numbers throughout the entire Eurasian taiga is the brambling, a species of finch. In summer this adaptable bird is insectivorous, and feeds in the coniferous forest. In winter it migrates south to the deciduous forest. There it becomes a vegetarian, eating seeds, such as beechnuts and grain. Occasionally millions of birds descend on a small area where food is plentiful. Bramblings often feed with chaffinches.

Willow tit This tit ranges across Eurasia. It favors swampy thickets, where it excavates nesting cavities in rotten stumps. It lives among birch, willow, and alder scrub as well as conifers

Crested tit Only 4-1/2 inches long, this is one of the smallest tits. It is distinguished by its black-pointed, white-edged crest. The crested tit is confined to the Eurasian coniferous forest

Black-capped chickadees A parent thrusts food into the gaping mouth of its offspring. Tits collect huge quantities of food for their broods, which are always large in the northern regions. Both parents help feed the young. Parents have been counted returning with insects 900 times a day

Bramblings nesting The brambling builds a deep, cuplike nest in the fork of a tree. Its brood may number as many as seven

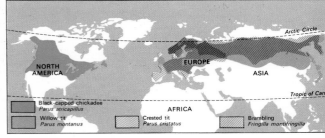

Varying ranges The North American boreal chickadee, whose range is not shown on the map above, is restricted to the coniferous forest

Tiny shrews must feed continually to stay alive

In the northern forests, as in other parts of the world, bats and shrews are the most voracious of the insect-eating mammals. However, the variety of bats decreases rapidly away from the tropics, and only a few species extend any distance into the coniferous forests, including the hoary bat in North America and the northern bat in Eurasia. Unlike other bats, these two species may rest by day on exposed tree trunks rather than in sheltered places.

Shrews, the smallest of mammals, hunt feverishly for insects in the undergrowth and leaf litter beneath the conifers. Some, particularly the smaller species, also hunt their prey in and through the burrows and tunnels of other animals.

Small animals such as shrews lose heat quickly, so they need more food in relation to their weight than large animals do. This means that shrews must eat so often that most consume their own weight in insects daily—and even up to three times their weight in spring and summer, when their insect food is plentiful.

The shrews' regular diet is beetles, spiders, and larvae, supplemented in winter by the pupae of insects which they dig out of the ground. Day and night, all year round, they have short periods of intense activity separated by longer periods of rest.

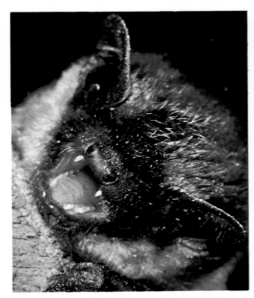

Northern bat This bat of the Eurasian coniferous forest flutters slowly through the woods at night, feeding on insects near the ground. The hoary bat, its North American counterpart, has similar habits

Keeping together Common shrews form a mouth-to-tail chain behind the mother for the first weeks

Least shrew This tiny insect-hunter weighs about 1/10 of an ounce and is about 1-1/2 inches long

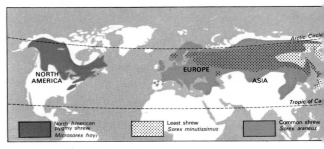

Northern shrews The 2-1/2-inch-long pygmy shrew is the North American counterpart of the least shrew

The big carnivores

The largest land carnivores are brown bears, but most items in their diet are so small that the animals must forage constantly to sustain their huge bulks

Some of the large flesh-eaters that today are confined almost entirely to the coniferous forest once had a much greater range, and are therefore not specifically adapted to life in that region. The brown bear ranged from the Arctic tundra to the Mediterranean; the North American black bear lived in all the wooded areas of North America north of central Mexico; and the lynx was found in the deciduous zones of North America and Eurasia. But as the deciduous woodlands in the south were cleared for farming and settlement, these carnivores' ranges receded into the more remote north.

Bears are more suited to the rich vegetation of the deciduous woodland, but because of their varied diet they are able to survive in the coniferous forest. Unlike the lynx, a skillful predator which eats little but flesh, the brown bear and the black bear are not strictly carnivorous. A large part of their diet consists of plants, berries, and roots. Some species, like the Kodiak Island bear, eat fish in summer.

Wolves, often thought of as typical carnivores of the coniferous forest zone, are better adapted to open country, but they too have been forced north by man.

The largest flesh-eaters of the northern forest

Learning from mother Brown bear cubs remain with their mother all during their first year

Tireless wanderer Immensely powerful brown bears of Alaska lead solitary lives, roaming the bleak land in search of food. The Kodiak Island race is the largest carnivorous land mammal

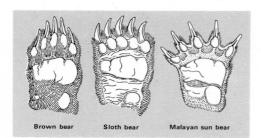

Brown bear   Sloth bear   Malayan sun bear

Walkers and climbers Ground-dwelling bears have hairier soles than those species that climb trees

NORTH AMERICA   EUROPE   ASIA   Arctic Circle   Tropic of Cancer

Brown bear *Ursus arctos arctos*
Grizzly bear *Ursus arctos horribilis*
Syrian bear *Ursus arctos syriacus*
Himalayan brown bear *Ursus arctos isabellinus*
Blue bear *Ursus arctos pruinosus*

Bear ranges Brown bears, once common in North America and Eurasia, now have a limited range

Bears have huge frames, broad heads, narrow jaws, relatively short legs, and stumpy tails. Many also have thick, shaggy coats which make them look even more heavily built than they are.

They walk on all four feet, with both soles and heels touching the ground, unlike swifter animals such as dogs, which walk on their toes. Bears move the two right limbs together, then the left limbs; this gives their gait a slow, cumbersome appearance. But they are not as slow-footed as they look—over short distances they can run about 30 miles per hour.

Most bears have a varied diet of roots, leaves, berries, nuts, insects, birds, and small mammals. They are not swift enough to prey on healthy large-hooved animals; but they will attack and kill any wounded deer or bison they manage to overtake. Some brown bears, such as the grizzly, are so strong that they can carry off a 900-pound bison.

Bears are great wanderers. Some have a home range of more than ten square miles, but they may travel far outside this area. Individuals rarely meet, except during the mating season, but they communicate their whereabouts to one another by urinating on trees and scratching and chewing the bark. They are not always aggressive. If disturbed they will either attack immediately or simply retreat. As fighters, they are most formidable when cornered or when defending their young. A mother bear is particularly dangerous when an intruder comes between her and her cubs.

Bears of the northern forest den-up in caves or holes in October and go to sleep. Scientists do not consider this long sleep hibernation in the usual sense, since bears can easily be wakened, and their body temperature falls only slightly.

Flat-footed walk Comparison of leg joints shows how a bear walks on its soles, a dog on its toes

Brown and black bears mate in spring, usually every second year. Young are born in the winter den after a gestation period which is drawn out by delayed implantation (see page 22). Cubs weigh about 12 ounces at birth. By the time they leave the den in spring they weigh five to six pounds. Both species remain with their mother at least until the autumn, and sometimes den-up with her for the following winter.

The various races of brown bear (*Ursus arctos*) are more widely distributed than the black bear (*Ursus americanus*), which is confined to North America. Brown bears vary greatly in size. Most weigh over 500 pounds, but the North American grizzly bear can weigh 1000 pounds. The largest brown bears, found on Kodiak Island in Alaska, may weigh more than 1700 pounds and measure nine feet from nose to tail. The Kodiak giants eat plant material for most of the year, and salmon in summer.

Black bears are the most numerous bears on the North American continent. They eat even less flesh than brown bears; they are also smaller, having an average mature weight of around 300 pounds. "Black" bears may be black, cinnamon brown, or almost white, and all of these colors may appear in the same litter.

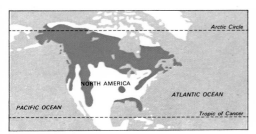

Black bear country The American black bear is capable of living outside remote wilderness

Refuge in a tree North American black bear cubs can climb trees almost as soon as they can walk.

When the mother senses danger or wants to find food, she sends the cubs scrambling up a tree

The keen-eyed lynx hunts hares in the twilight

A short body, stumpy tail, and prominent ear-tufts give the lynx a distinctive appearance, but it owes its success as a predator to its keen eyesight, strong legs, and broad, furry feet. A lynx can vault to a branch eight feet above the ground or broad-jump with lightning speed. Its large feet enable it to travel over the softest snow without sinking, and to stalk its prey without a sound. It hunts mainly at dusk, helped by its sharp eyesight

and keen senses of smell and hearing. The lynx creeps silently up on its prey until it is close enough to capture it in one pounce. Sometimes it will lie in wait, allowing its victim to come within reach before jumping.

Lynxes eat any mammal or bird they can kill, but the Canadian lynx preys mainly on the varying hare, or snowshoe rabbit. They are so dependent on the hare for food that their population cycle closely follows the ten-year cycle of the hare. When hares are scarce, lynxes often wander beyond their normal range in search of rats, squirrels, grouse, or other prey; but they are seldom seen in the open, outside the forest.

Lynx kittens are born in summer, after 60 days' gestation. They are slow developers. Even at nine months they retain their milk teeth, their claws are not fully developed, and they are unable to kill a hare. Throughout their first winter, the kittens remain almost completely dependent on their mother for food. If they become separated from her they are likely to starve.

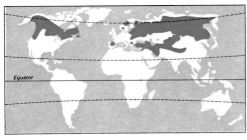

Where the lynx lives The lynx is now scarce in most of Europe except Spain

Stealthy hunter The lynx, a formidable predator, moves silently on its broad, furry feet. Keen-sighted and extremely agile, it creeps up on its victim until it can kill it in one pounce

57

Small carnivores

A family of fierce, intelligent hunters, active all year round, takes a great toll of the smaller forest animals—under the snow, on the ground, and in the trees

All the smaller carnivores of the northern forest are members of the weasel family, a group characterized by short legs, long, sinuous bodies, and highly developed scent glands. They include mink, martens, badgers, and many other species in addition to the common weasel, and are known collectively as mustelids, from the scientific name for the family, Mustelidae. All these species occur in both Eurasia and North America.

Mustelids range in size from the wolverine, more than 40 pounds, to the least weasel, the smallest flesh-eating mammal, no more than eight inches long.

All members of the family can live successfully in a wide range of habitats. The mink, an aquatic mustelid related to the polecat, digs its burrow in the banks of a tree-bordered lake, or makes a lair under tree roots or reeds. It is an expert swimmer and diver. Martens and weasels hunt in the coniferous forest, although they are also found in other zones, where their ways of living are often different. The mustelids, although primarily flesh-eating, survive by

being able to eat anything the environment offers, from birds to berries.

Mustelids do not hibernate, and most are too large to spend the winter in the undersnow. But they are small enough to find heat conservation a severe problem in winter. They combat the cold by growing dense, luxuriant winter coats.

The sable, mink, and marten, especially, have suffered from the fur trade. Early in the nineteenth century, the Hudson's Bay Company exported as many as 45,000 marten skins from Canada in a single year. More enlightened policies are now helping to ensure balanced population growth.

How competing species of weasels manage to coexist

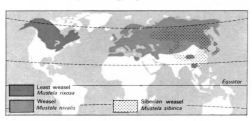

Distribution of weasels The areas where weasels live are usually inhabited by voles or mice. When prey is plentiful weasels have two litters a year

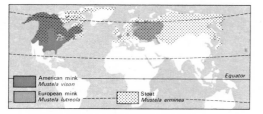

Contrasting ranges Mink are found chiefly along riverbanks. The widely distributed stoat, or short-tailed weasel, ranges far into the tundra

A list of the things weasels eat reads like a guide to the small animals of the regions they inhabit—with some plant parts thrown in. They all prey on rodents, rabbits, birds, insects, and earthworms. Some will also eat fish and reptiles and in hard times may exist almost entirely on berries. Their varied diet helps the weasels to survive throughout their wide ranges; but they are principally hunters of mammals.

The overlap between the kinds of prey they take often brings species of weasels into direct competition; but they can coexist, for each can catch prey that the other is too big or too small to cope with. In the coniferous forest, weasels are small enough—about ten inches long—to follow voles and shrews into their undersnow world, while short-tailed weasels—one and a half times as big—are large enough to kill hares.

Prey is scattered sparsely in the northern forest, so animals must establish larger hunting territories there than in other regions.

A male short-tailed weasel has a home range of about 85 acres in which to hunt rabbits. Other weasels, preying entirely on more plentiful small creatures, can find enough to eat in only two to nine acres.

Weasels are fast runners and great climbers. They pounce on their prey ferociously and will attack animals much larger than themselves. When alarmed, they eject a foul-smelling liquid from glands near the rectum.

Unlike larger carnivores in the coniferous forest, weasels grow white winter coats. The degree of whiteness increases in the more northerly latitudes and reaches full development in the coniferous forest and the tundra. The white coat helps camouflage the weasel against the snow and gives it an advantage over its predators.

The short-tailed weasel retains the black tip on its tail throughout the year. Known as the ermine when it turns white, this species has been extensively hunted for its fur, but is still abundant.

Ever-active weasel The weasel hunts anytime, day or night, in the coniferous forest. It is small enough to pursue voles through the undersnow, or it will dive directly through snow onto its prey

North American mink The mink lives near waterways, preying on fish and aquatic mammals. It will attack domestic fowl when aquatic prey is scarce. The native European species is almost identical in habits and appearance. Mink are at home in the water. They can dive to depths of 18 feet and swim underwater for 100 yards without surfacing. They live in riverbank burrows and rock crevices

Marten and victim A pine marten holds a red squirrel, killed after a chase through the branches.

Matching a squirrel's agility, it makes tremendous leaps by snapping its spine straight

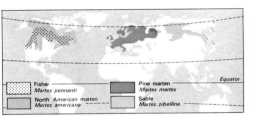

Fisher
Martes pennanti

North American marten
Martes americana

Pine marten
Martes martes

Sable
Martes zibellina

Equator

Northern martens Those of the North American and Eurasian coniferous forests are closely related

Siberian sable The sable is kept warm in its Siberian habitat by thick fur that covers even its soles

Adaptable hunter The American marten hunts with equal success in forest and on barren hillsides

Ravenous wolverine The wolverine's other common name is glutton. When it finds a dead deer it will stay with the carcass until it has eaten it all. Wolverines defend their prey against all comers

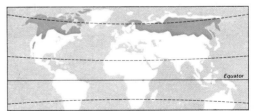

Equator

Wolverine range The wolverine, protected from cold by an ice-shedding coat, ranges into tundra

Martens and wolverines streak through the high branches in pursuit of prey

Four closely related species of martens inhabit the coniferous forest: the pine marten and the sable in Eurasia, and the American marten and the fisher in North America. The fisher, or pekan, is the largest, with an overall length of 3½ feet and a weight of 13 pounds; the other three are usually about six inches shorter and weigh only one to three pounds.

All are powerful jumpers. A pine marten has been known to leap 14 feet across a gap. The power for such leaps comes from strong muscles that can arch the flexible spine and then snap it out straight, so that the animal exerts great force against a branch.

Except during the breeding season, martens are solitary. The male's home range of one square mile may overlap the ranges of two or three solitary females. Both sexes

indicate their whereabouts, sex, and territory to each other by depositing an odorous secretion (manufactured in glands under the tail) on rocks and other flat surfaces.

As with most mustelids, implantation is delayed. In early spring, the female marten gives birth to three to six young.

Most martens of the coniferous forest stalk squirrels and birds through the high branches. The large fisher can also take bigger prey, such as varying hares and porcupines. It avoids the porcupine's quills by sheer agility until it can flip its prey over and attack its unprotected underside. The fisher's name is misleading, since it seldom catches fish.

The wolverine *Gulo gulo,* which lives in the coniferous forest and the tundra of both Eurasia and America, is a thickset animal

which contrasts with the slim martens. It is about 3½ feet long and weighs more than 40 pounds. During the last ice age the wolverine was widespread in France and England, but as the climate warmed up the animal moved north.

When hunting, the wolverine depends more on stealth than speed. It will lie on a branch and wait for a victim, such as a young deer, to pass underneath. The wolverine's usual prey is grouse. It stores dead grouse against winter shortage; up to 100 birds have been found in one cache.

But the wolverine is mainly a scavenger. Unlike most carrion-eaters, however, it does not wait for leavings, but will challenge a wolf or a bear for its kill. So ferocious is the wolverine that even a much larger animal will often abandon its prey.

Birds of prey

Small animals in the coniferous forest are never safe from birds of prey: hawks and falcons hunt by day, and at dusk the owls emerge

The birds of prey that patrol the air above the northern coniferous forest scan a harsh, bleak land where the food supply is unreliable and the choice of prey is limited.

All birds of prey are skilled killers, superbly armed with keen sight, sharp talons, and strong, hooked beaks. Some species hover to spy out prey, some dart among the treetops, and some, like the peregrine, chase their victims at speeds of up to 50 miles per hour in level flight and up to 170 miles per hour in a dive.

Birds of prey fall into two main types. Owls live among trees and hunt mainly at night, flying almost noiselessly. Nocturnal owls' wings are richly feathered, and their feet are feathered down to their toes. Even the face of an owl is heavily covered with feathers, so that the beak is almost invisible. Hawks, falcons, and their relatives hunt by day at the edge of the forest or over mountains and open ground. These birds belong to the Falconiforme order. All members have long wings, which superbly equip them for powerful and sustained flight.

The owls, night hunters, have sharp ears and can see in the dark

The eyes of an owl are highly sensitive and face forward like those of all birds of prey. Barn owls, for instance, can distinguish objects in light only 1 percent as intense as that needed by humans. The two eyes take in a total visual field of 110 degrees. The fields overlap to give a 70-degree field of binocular vision, from which the brain forms the three-dimensional images necessary for judging distances. Man and some animals possess binocular vision.

The owl resembles man in its ability to perceive objects clearly and in depth; but, unlike man, it cannot swivel its eyes to increase its field of vision. However, in most species the owl's neck is so flexible that the bird can turn its head almost completely around without moving its body.

Night owls make full use of their sharp hearing to detect the movements of rodents, small birds, and other prey. In some species the ear apertures are at different heights on each side of the head. This increases the time lag between the arrival of the same sound at each ear and helps the owl to pinpoint the source.

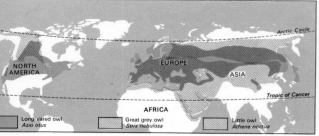

Range of owls Northern species of owls range from the coniferous forest to deciduous woodland

Long-eared owl Some owls have earlike tufts that may have nothing to do with hearing, but are probably only for display. The long-eared owl has a more flexible neck than most other owls

Little owl The stiff wing feathers of this day-hunting owl make its flight more audible than most

Saw-whet owl This handsome owl, smallest of all the northern species, lives in North America

The eyes of an owl

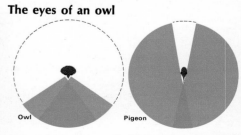

Owls' front-facing eyes have 110° visual field, narrower than birds with side-facing eyes. But an owl can turn its head through most of a circle, widening its visual field, and has a wider angle of binocular vision

Osprey landing In a manner resembling the way it plunges toward water to grab a fish, an osprey returns to its nest. Like many birds of prey, ospreys build nests of sticks high in a tree or on a ledge

Peregrine The peregrine kills a bird in midair with a blow of its talons, retrieving it on the ground

Birds of prey that hunt in broad daylight

Day-hunting birds of prey—eagles, falcons, ospreys, and hawks—include some of the largest flying birds, and others no bigger than small doves. All have keen eyes; strong, hooked beaks; long, sharp talons; and powerful wings.

Eagles have difficulty flying among close-growing trees because of their great wingspan, so the species in the coniferous forest zone, especially the golden eagle, tend to hunt over clearings, where they can dive from great heights to kill hares, rodents, grouse, and small deer.

The bald eagle, which breeds throughout North America, has become rare in most of its range. It preys on waterfowl and rabbits, and scavenges dead fish from the shore.

The peregrine, a high-flying falcon, goes into a spectacular "stoop," or dive, arching through the sky, sometimes at 170 miles an hour, to attack a flying bird. The victim drops to the ground, while the peregrine flies on. It returns to claim its prey later.

Ospreys, whose range extends far beyond the coniferous forest, feed almost entirely on fish, which they catch in a feet-first plunge.

Of all the day-flying birds of prey, the best adapted to hunting over the coniferous forest are the goshawk and the European sparrowhawk, which has a close relative, the sharp-shinned hawk, in North America. (The North American sparrowhawk is actually a small falcon.)

The goshawk's technique is to hunt at treetop level, depending upon speed and quick maneuvering to catch birds flushed from the foliage. The sparrowhawk hunts lower down, darting from the cover of bushes or hedges to surprise its prey, mostly small birds.

Goshawk at work This hunter strikes and then holds its prey, killing it with talons and ripping it apart with its beak. The goshawk attacks birds as big as itself, and even mammals such as martens

Merlin and peregrine These falcons patrol the coasts. Peregrines range north to the Arctic Circle

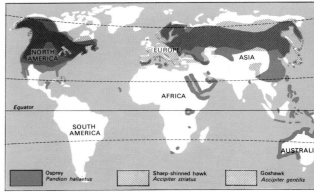

Osprey and hawks The osprey always lives near water. During winter it is found in South America

61

TEMPERATE FORESTS

**Forests in the temperate zones are extraordinarily varied: conifers
predominate in the coolest latitudes; deciduous, or leaf-shedding, trees in
warmer regions; and broad-leaved evergreens near the tropics**

Forest is the typical ground cover of the temperate zones, given sufficient moisture. However, the temperate forest biome, or life zone, cannot be strictly related to what are termed the temperate zones — that is, the areas of the globe lying between the Arctic Circle and the Tropic of Cancer in the northern hemisphere, and between the Tropic of Capricorn and the Antarctic Circle in the southern.

Indeed, what is meant by "temperate forest" is primarily deciduous, or nonconiferous, forest; but the largest area of the northern temperate zone is covered by coniferous forest, with its trees and plants adapted to long, cold winters, little available moisture, and soil leached of nutrients.

South of the northern forest, the cold-resistant conifers gradually give way to the trees of the temperate deciduous forests. Here most of the precipitation is rain, evenly distributed throughout the year. Winters are shorter, but still cold enough to affect plant processes and growth. Trees survive the winter season by shedding their leaves and becoming dormant. The leaves rot, packing down to produce a humus-rich soil which supports many plants.

From deciduous to evergreen

Temperate deciduous forests originally covered much of the eastern half of North America below the St. Lawrence River, most of Europe (except Scandinavia, the higher mountain areas, and the Mediterranean region), parts of Japan and eastern and north central Asia, and parts of southern Chile and Argentina in South America. Most of these regions have been heavily exploited by man.

Nearer the tropics deciduous forests tend to give way to warm temperate or subtropical broad-leaved forests, where the trees, though mainly broad-leaved, are often evergreen. In the woods and swamps of the Mississippi Delta, magnolia, bay, palmetto, and live oak shade an undergrowth dense with ferns and creepers.

Vegetation typical of the temperate forest also appears in the middle of the tropics, on mountain slopes where the higher altitude produces a cooler climate. In such areas, animals typical of northern latitudes may live near others that have ascended from the rain forest or the lowland savanna.

In Australia and New Zealand, plants and animals evolved in isolation. Many species in these lands bear little resemblance to those of the rest of the world. The Australian temperate forest is relatively

small, covering only 2 percent of the land mass. It is composed mainly of some 500 species of eucalyptus, which range in size from low bushes to giants 300 feet high. (The eucalyptus trees of California were transplanted by man from Australia.)

A unique forest covers a large proportion of New Zealand's two principal islands. The North Island forest is mainly a mixture of evergreen hardwood trees and conifers. In the South Island, conifers mix with evergreen beech, especially in the mountains, where tree ferns—typical of wet, warm temperate forests—flourish.

The succession of species

The term "plant succession" refers to the process in which those species that grow best in the prevailing conditions of an area become dominant, gradually superseding species that may be temporarily abundant at certain stages of the succession. The process may take hundreds or even thousands of years—the dominant sequoias and giant redwoods of California are probably several thousand years old—and the final stages in the succession are called a "climax" growth.

Each stage in plant succession presents a different range of animal habitats. As one stage succeeds another, animals unable to migrate or adapt to the changing conditions gradually become extinct.

The vanished forests

Historical records show that magnificent forests of oak, chestnut, pine, and other trees covered large areas of the Mediterranean region as recently as 2000 years ago. Such warm temperate forests still exist in a few places, but elsewhere the erosion and burning that followed the felling of the trees has led to reduced soil fertility, to which smaller trees and shrubs adapt better.

Deciduous forests throughout the temperate zones have been decimated to the point of obliteration. For 10,000 years or more these forests have been cleared to make way for farmlands and towns and to provide timber. In North America and Europe there are still large areas of northern deciduous woodland, but they are mostly either second growth or "managed" forest, cut over at intervals. Only a few small patches of the climax forests still exist.

The disappearance of the deciduous forests has been accompanied by the retreat of many large animals that once lived in them. Large carnivores such as the wolf, bear, and lynx have been driven almost entirely into coniferous forest. Other animals have adapted to the new conditions.

Deer of the deciduous forest A white-tailed deer, the most abundant species of deer in the North American deciduous forest, stands among birch trees

The yearly cycle of growth

Deciduous forests support a multitude of animals, some dependent on the burst of leaves and flowers in spring, others on the berries and nuts of autumn

The transition from coniferous forest to deciduous woodland occurs typically in areas where the annual precipitation averages 30 to 60 inches, well distributed throughout the year. The deciduous zone has less snowfall than the coniferous forest, and the snow melts faster. Although the average temperature of any winter month seldom drops below freezing, temperature differences of 100 degrees or more may occur between winter and summer. Thus, plants and animals show adaptations to the wide temperature changes rather than to a varying supply of moisture.

The typical "brown earth" of deciduous woodland results from rainwater draining down through the soil and being drawn up again by evaporation. Fallen leaves decompose into a rich layer of humus.

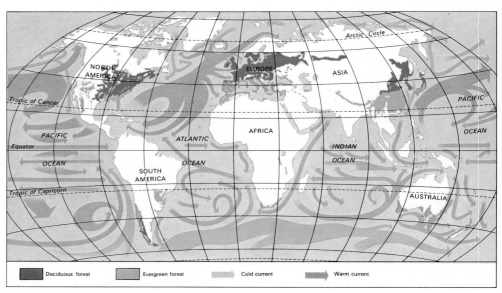

Temperate forests These forests grow in the temperate zones' warmer latitudes where rain is abundant. In the hottest parts conifers and broadleaved species mix in warm temperate forests

Limes in spring Lime trees, related to American basswood, or linden, leaf in May. Fragrant flowers follow, attracting insects that pollinate the trees

Southern beech forest This beech forest, the only large block of deciduous forest in the entire southern hemisphere, is in Argentina, near the border with Chile. Farther north on the western coast the beeches are evergreen

A rich carpet of leaves The leaf litter in this beech forest will decompose into humus, which will nourish new growth and invertebrates

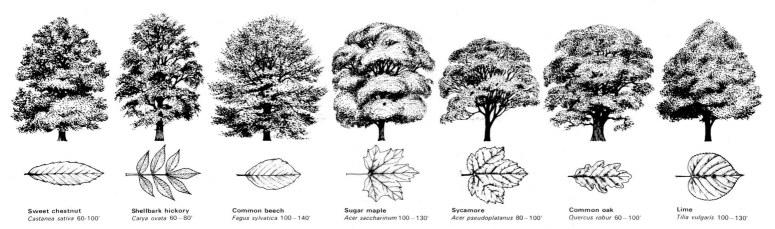

Sweet chestnut
Castanea sativa 60-100'

Shellbark hickory
Carya ovata 60-80'

Common beech
Fagus sylvatica 100-140'

Sugar maple
Acer saccharinum 100-130'

Sycamore
Acer pseudoplatanus 80-100'

Common oak
Quercus robur 60-100'

Lime
Tilia vulgaris 100-130'

Deciduous trees Similar trees grow in Eurasia and North America, but the composition of the forest varies. Oak, beech, maple, and hickory are domi-nant in eastern North America; oak, beech, chest-nut, and lime in Eurasia. Chestnut was a dominant American tree until blight destroyed vast forests. In these continents, willows coexist with these spe-cies on damp ground, and holly grows in the shade of oaks. Each tree has a distinctive form of leaf

Typical broad-leaved trees of the deciduous forest

Where the soil of the deciduous zone is rocky or porous, scrub woodland or conifers are found; where the soil is acid, or drainage is impeded, heaths and moors develop.

Deciduous forest matures in a steady suc-cession, progressing from beginnings that can be observed in abandoned farmland. The first colonists, grasses and annual and perennial weeds, are soon superseded by woody shrubs and the seedlings of trees. When the trees mature and shade the ground, a woodland is formed, and after many years, perhaps centuries, the climax forest of the area may be attained. Fire, man's interference, or local factors of soil, terrain, or climate can arrest or deflect the succession at any stage, result-ing in a mosaic of varying vegetation and animal habitats.

The broad leaves of deciduous trees allow maximum absorption of energy from sun-light. And even a relatively small oak tree with a trunk 24 inches in diameter has some 100,000 leaves to catch the summer sun-light. But the leaves' delicate structure makes them vulnerable to frost and drying winter winds. With autumn, the leaves drop off. Growth almost ceases, and the tree survives the winter on food reserves in its roots, trunk, and branches.

In spring, most large trees, such as oak, beech, and elm, produce inconspicuous flowers that are fertilized by pollen carried on the wind. Other trees, such as maple,

linden, and chestnut, grow bright or fragrant flowers which attract insects that carry the pollen from tree to tree. In autumn animals gather the products of this fertilization—seeds, fruits, and nuts—and store them away as food for the winter.

While the trees are still bare in early spring, and light can penetrate to the forest floor, primroses, violets, bluebells, and many other plants bloom, then die down and re-main dormant through the rest of the year.

In autumn the fruiting bodies of fungi appear above the damp ground or on tree trunks, providing a richly varied feast for many animals, from bears to mice. The spores and underground filaments of the fungi are food for the invertebrate inhabitants of the soil.

The oak tree plays a dominant role in the insect life of the northern deciduous forest. More than 200 species have been known to feed on a common oak. The tree reacts to the damage they do by producing a second crop of leaves in the middle of summer.

Soil structure The typical deciduous forest soils, called brown earth, occur where evaporation draws up the soil water to balance percolation downward. Moist leaf litter rapidly decomposes into humus, which worms and insects mix with the parent mate-rial, producing an even-textured soil. In water-logged soils a layer of clay, called gley, occurs

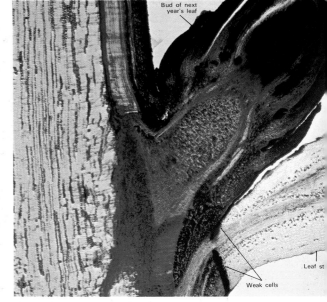

How leaves fall This twig shows the cork layer that forms in autumn, blocking nutrients from the stalk and weakening adjacent cells

Flowers and fruit mark the seasons of the year

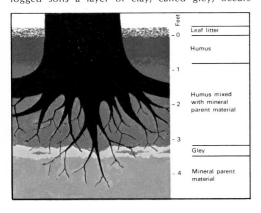

Sweet chestnuts ripen in the fall, providing food for forest animals

Lime flowers are a source of nec-tar for bees in early summer

The flowers of the American oak depend on the wind for pollination

Cantharellus cinnabarinus fungus grows in autumn in North America

A spring flower of northern woodland is *Anemone hepatica*

Coprinus disseminatus fungus grows on tree stumps in Europe

65

The leaf-eaters

A single oak tree can be host to 50,000 caterpillars; a single leaf to 500 aphids. It is these insects, not the plant-eating mammals, that are the chief leaf-destroyers

Some tree-dwelling birds and mammals eat the buds of their deciduous hosts; but none eats the opened leaves. Deer and other ground browsers only nibble at the fringes of an enormous mass of foliage.

Insects, however, eat great amounts of foliage in the deciduous forest. There are two major groups—the leaf-chewers and the sap-suckers. The leaf-chewers, typified by caterpillars, are equipped with biting jaws and can consume the entire tissue of a leaf. The sap-suckers feed by drawing in the plants' vital fluid through mouth systems that operate like hypodermic needles. Aphids, typical sap-suckers, jab into plant tissue with two sharp-tipped mandibles, after softening the tissue by injecting saliva into it.

Among the creatures that consume leaves by chewing are the caterpillars of butterflies, moths, and sawflies; the larvae of some beetles and flies; and a few species of crickets. Moth caterpillars predominate; hundreds of different species are found on the trees of the deciduous forest. Some of the caterpillars feed indiscriminately on any type of tree, but most are specialists, feeding only on a single species, and able to strip an entire tree of its foliage.

A host of insects feeds on oak trees

Tomato sphinx moth caterpillar The sphinx moths were so named because their caterpillars rest with their heads raised in a position that somewhat resembles the Egyptian sphinx

Safety in numbers Tent caterpillars cluster for protection. They spin silk continually, forming "tents"

A wasp's first home When a wasp pierces a leaf to deposit its egg, the formation of marble galls is triggered. Chemical stimulation makes the plant tissue swell, giving refuge and food to the larva

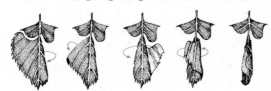

Rolling a leaf The birch leaf roller transforms a leaf into a nest. After cutting the top of a leaf, the beetle uses its legs to roll the lower part into a cone, in which it lays eggs. Then it leaves the cone, folding the tip to seal in the eggs

Mining a leaf A leaf miner burrows through the tissue (exaggerated in thickness here)

Tunnels inside a leaf Sinuous lines across this birch leaf betray the fact that a leaf miner, the caterpillar of a small moth, is at work. Other leaf miners eat out circular areas of the central tissue. Larvae of some small beetles also mine

One of these specialists is the caterpillar of the oak roller, a particularly ravenous devourer of oak leaves. The oak roller, a small green moth, flies in June and July, leaving its eggs on twigs. The caterpillars hatch from the eggs the following May, when the leaf buds have opened.

The oak is eaten by many different species of moths, and it has been estimated that a single oak tree can be host to 50,000 caterpillars at one time.

The countless numbers of caterpillars in the forest—their density has been put at 1000 in, above, and below every square yard of forest floor—provide an abundance of food for a great variety of animals, including birds, tree frogs, and parasitic insects. When caterpillars fall from the trees to the ground to pupate, they become the prey of shrews and mice.

Many species of moths spend the winter as pupae, emerging as adult moths in early summer. Others fly in autumn, leaving their eggs to hatch in spring when the new leaves are budding.

Among the leaf-eaters, there are different methods of attack. One small caterpillar, known as the leaf miner, tunnels its way through the center of the leaf without damaging the upper or lower skin. The caterpillars called leaf rollers have a different system. They roll the edges of the leaf into a tube, so that they can remain hidden from predators while feeding within the leaf. The oak roller feeds in this manner.

Some insects protect themselves by inducing trees to form galls, or swellings in the leaves or twigs. These are caused by a chemical reaction of the plant that occurs when the insect, usually a small wasp or fly, pierces the plant tissue to lay an egg. When the larva is hatched, it feeds on the tissue of the gall, pupates inside it, and finally emerges as an adult.

Although galls protect insects from large predators, they are no defense against a whole host of insect predators, including other wasps. These predatory insects cannot induce galls themselves, but invade existing galls and lay their eggs in them. The resulting larvae then prey on the original gall-makers. Other small insects that cannot make galls themselves colonize those made by other species. Galls therefore represent a whole community of interdependent species of animals.

Three conspicuous galls that appear on oak trees are oak apples, marble galls, and lentil galls. All of these are made by various species of wasps. The conspicuous red galls on sycamore leaves are the work of a mite, which is not an insect but an arachnid—a relative of the spiders.

Galls differ in appearance. One may be a smooth swelling on a twig, resembling a pea; another, on a leaf, may also be pealike but covered with a network of lines. Many large oak galls contain tannic acid, and are still used in making inks and tanning leather.

Evolution at work The dark type of peppered moth, rare 100 years ago, is less visible on sooty surfaces and is now common in industrial areas

Mimicking a twig The peppered moth caterpillar disguises itself from predators by gripping a stem and projecting itself in the shape of a twig

Camouflaged against the bark The poplar gray moth is barely visible against the lichen-covered bark. These moths fly at night during the late spring and early summer and rest on tree trunks by day. In summer they lay eggs on poplars. The caterpillars feed on leaves until they construct cocoons

Sap-suckers' surplus food forms honeydew, eaten by other insects

Greenflies and blackflies are familiar to every gardener. These two tiny plant-sucking insects are aphids. They belong to the hemipteran order, most of whose species have complex life cycles, during which there is usually a stage when several generations of females develop from unfertilized eggs. This process is known as parthenogenesis.

Most aphids cluster together on stems or leaf stalks. As many as 500 have been found on one leaf. A common European species, the sycamore aphid, has a behavioral adaptation that serves to give every individual in a group a share of sap. The aphids space themselves evenly on a leaf, each occupying a small territory about three eighths of an inch square.

Aphids need plant proteins for growth; but sap is composed mainly of sugar and water, with little protein. The aphids therefore must consume great quantities of sap to obtain enough protein for growth. Most of the sugar-water passes straight through the aphids' bodies, and this sticky liquid waste forms honeydew, which is licked off the leaves by ants and flying insects such as hoverflies and moths. It was once thought that ants "milked" aphids of their honeydew. It is now known that they only consume the sweet fluid after it leaves the aphids' bodies.

Flying insects find the proteins and sugars they need in flowers. The familiar honeybee spends its life foraging for pollen and nectar. Pollen is a source of body-building protein for the bee larvae growing back in the hive. Nectar, composed almost entirely of energy-producing sugar, provides fuel for the flying adults. The honeybee sucks up nectar through its long proboscis, and has "pollen baskets" —smooth, concave areas on the rear legs— in which the powdery pollen, molded into lumps by the legs, is taken back to the hive.

Most trees are wind-pollinated, but bees and other insects help to fertilize flowers by carrying pollen from one plant to another.

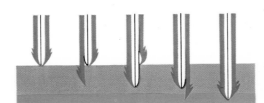

How an aphid feeds Two jagged mandibles alternately jab into the plant. These guide the entry of a tube with two ducts—one for injecting saliva to soften the plant and one for sucking the sap

Collecting eggs Worker ants are collecting the eggs of aphids to store for winter food. Aphids leave honeydew behind them as they feed on sap, and it is licked up by ants

Eaters of buds and seeds

Many species of birds and mammals find the buds and seeds of deciduous trees a constant source of protein-rich food

Many parts of a tree are edible, but buds and seeds provide the highest protein concentrations. Buds, though often available throughout the year, are most valuable as a source of nutrition in winter and early spring, when other foods are in short supply. During the winter months, buds gradually fill up with nutrients, permitting the emergence of leaves and flowers with the warmer weather of spring.

In autumn the woodlands produce a rich harvest of seeds. These remain available to animals, either as berries on the trees or as fallen nuts, far into the winter.

Many birds and mammals follow an annual pattern of feeding, eating mainly buds in spring, catching insects in summer—especially for feeding their young—and eating berries and nuts (which many species collect and store) in autumn and winter.

Strong bills that crack cherry stones and nip off buds

The temperate forests are home to one group of birds that relies almost entirely on buds and seeds—the finches. These strong-beaked songbirds are found throughout the world, but in the tropics they are outnumbered by other seed-eaters, such as the weavers. In the cooler parts of the temperate zones they usually live in open country and feed on grass seeds, but a few species are forest-dwellers. In Eurasia forest-dwelling species include the hawfinch, bullfinch, chaffinch, and greenfinch. The hawfinch can exert a force of 60 to 90 pounds at the tip of its bill to crack, for example, a cherry stone. This species spends most of its life in trees; it is seldom seen on the ground, except perhaps in winter when it feeds on fallen seeds. The grosbeaks of North America have similar feeding habits. The rose-breasted grosbeak is peculiar among small forest birds in that the male usually incubates the eggs.

Acorns are a favorite food in autumn for several of the larger forest birds, such as the jay, acorn woodpecker, and nutcracker.

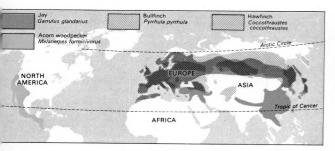

Range of tree feeders The acorn woodpecker lives in the deciduous and mixed forests of California and Mexico. The jay, an acorn-eater, is a member of the crow family and is located throughout Eurasia

Insects for the young The hawfinch collects insects for its hungry fledglings in summer. The rest of the year it has a varied diet—buds in spring, kernels of fruit pits in autumn, and seeds in winter

Bullfinches destroy buds Using their sharp, cone-shaped beaks, bullfinches nip off the buds of fruit trees in spring. One bullfinch can destroy the buds of a plum tree at the rate of 30 a minute

Acorn hoarder Acorn woodpeckers, which live in colonies, store acorns in holes they have drilled in the bark of oaks and pines. They may store as many as 50,000 acorns in a single pine tree

Jays plant acorns In autumn jays collect acorns and bury them singly and scattered in the ground. They hide more than they find again in the winter, and when the lost acorns sprout in spring, the jays dig up the seedlings before all the seeds' nourishment has been dispersed. Some escape their notice, however, and in this way oak trees are spread to new areas of the woodland

Berry-eater Bank voles relish soft, fleshy berries

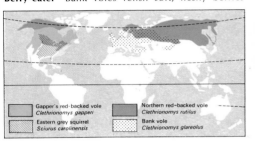

Gapper's red-backed vole
Clethrionomys gapperi

Northern red-backed vole
Clethrionomys rutilus

Eastern grey squirrel
Sciurus carolinensis

Bank vole
Clethrionomys glareolus

Squirrel and voles Best known of the many species of squirrels in the North American temperate zone is the eastern gray squirrel. The northern red-backed vole reaches the deciduous forest only in Asia

Fox squirrel at rest Usually busy and alert, fox squirrels can occasionally be seen resting on tree branches when no owls or hawks are around. They forage for food during the day, especially early in the morning. Their homes are primarily oak and hickory woods of North America; their favorite foods are acorns and hickory nuts. They spend more time on the ground than other tree squirrels

Rodents by the thousands forage at dusk for buds and seeds

Squirrels, being daytime foragers, are perhaps the most familiar consumers of buds and seeds in deciduous woodland. But of far greater importance in the food chain are the hordes of other rodents that feed at night.

Most numerous are two genera of long-tailed mice, one in North America and the other in Eurasia. The two groups resemble each other in habits and appearance, but they belong to separate families: the Eurasian wood mice to the Muridae family, which also includes house rats and mice; and the North American deer mice to the Cricetidae family, which includes voles and hamsters. The two genera provide an interesting example of convergent evolution. They have come to look alike (that is, "converge" in appearance) because over millions of years they have adapted to similar habitats.

All of these mice are good climbers. They forage in small trees and on the ground, feeding on buds and seeds, which they store near their nests. Though small, they are expert at opening nuts, using their incisor teeth —which never wear down because they grow continuously—to open even the hardest shells. They breed at any time of year except winter, and are so numerous that they form an important food source for owls, weasels, and other woodland predators.

Bank voles and red-backed voles have similar behavior patterns, but they live in shrubs such as brambles and briars, rather than in trees.

Unlike the other rodents of the temperate forest, dormice do not store food, but hibernate during winter. They fatten on the autumnal abundance of food and then withdraw to their winter hideaway, which may be a nest in the forest litter, a crevice in a rock, or the abandoned burrow of another animal. The body temperature of the dormouse drops to about 39° F. (4° C.) during its hibernation, which can last from three to seven months, depending on the climate of the habitat in which the individual lives.

Dormouse of the trees The dormouse of Europe lives and builds its nest in tree branches, although it hibernates in a hole. Rough pads on its feet give this animal a good grip for climbing

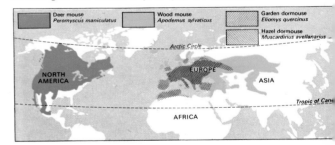

Deer mouse
Peromyscus maniculatus

Wood mouse
Apodemus sylvaticus

Garden dormouse
Eliomys quercinus

Hazel dormouse
Muscardinus avellanarius

Dormice and mice Dormice are restricted to the deciduous forests, but mice have a wider range

Nesting in the undergrowth The hazel dormouse lives in thick shrubs in the undergrowth. This cover, combined with the animal's agility, protects it against owls and other predators

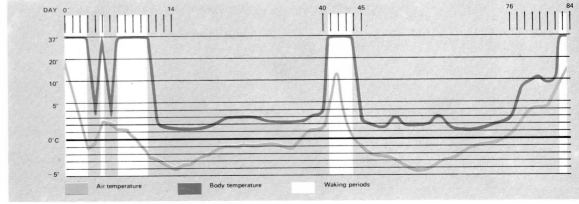

Air temperature Body temperature Waking periods

Hibernation of the hazel dormouse At winter's approach, the dormouse falls asleep, its temperature dropping rapidly to slightly above that of the air. In very cold spells, the dormouse increases its heat production, so its body temperature remains above freezing. When the air warms up, the dormouse wakes and its body temperature rises to normal. (Temperatures are given here in centigrade)

69

Deer and bison

Deer browse throughout the temperate forests of the northern hemisphere. Males are crowned with antlers that are unique in the animal kingdom

In the temperate forests of the northern hemisphere, deer are the main browsers—defined as animals that feed on the leaves of trees, rather than those that graze on grass —although deer also graze. Deer, belonging to the family of cloven-hooved animals, the Cervidae, are also found in South America and Southeast Asia.

The conspicuous feature of most males is their antlers—branches of exposed bone which are grown each summer and shed some time after the mating season, which usually occurs in October.

It is rare to find more than three species of deer in any temperate forest region. Only one species, the red deer, occurs in both Eurasia and North America; other species are limited to one continent. The red deer of Europe and the elk, or wapiti, of North America are thought by many experts to be the same species. The European race of moose is also known by the name elk.

Stags roar and fight over females in the autumn mating season

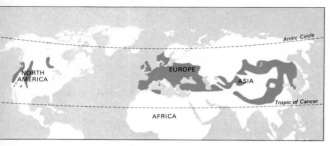

Red deer country The North American race of red deer is called elk or wapiti

Clash of antlers Wapiti stags battle for hinds, thrusting at each other with sharp-pointed antlers

A warning roar A red deer stag roars a warning to rivals to stay away from his females. During the rut, a stag moves into an area occupied by a female herd and fights off any other males

Red deer browse on the foliage of almost all species of deciduous trees, and graze on ground vegetation such as grass, sedges, lichens, and fungi. Where forests have been cleared, the deer have adapted to grazing in open country.

For most of the year, red deer stags live in separate herds from the hinds (females) and young. The herds of each sex usually number 10 to 20 in woodland.

With the arrival of the mating season, or rut—usually in October—the stag herds break up. A mature stag moves into an area occupied by a herd of females.

The stag mates several times with each hind. It eats nothing during the rut, but drinks water constantly. Its bellowing roar, a warning to rival males, can be heard two miles away. Contests between stags for females consist largely of display and bluff.

In early summer the hinds give birth, usually away from the herd. A newborn calf lies still for a few days, camouflaged in the patchy sunlight of the forest by its spotted coat. The hind stays with her calf until it is able to follow her, then both rejoin the herd.

The stag sheds its antlers in early spring. Six weeks later new antlers begin to grow. They reach full growth by the end of May, but are still covered by the membranous tissue called velvet. At this time the antlers are sensitive, and stags avoid brushing them against hard surfaces until about August, when the velvet is rubbed off.

How antlers and horns differ

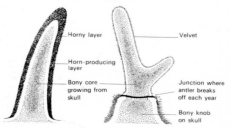

A typical horn contains a slow-growing permanent bone covered by a horny layer of hairlike substance derived from the top layer of skin. Antlers consist primarily of bone which grows yearly from knobs. Velvety skin covers antlers during growth

The growth of the red deer's antlers

Antlers grow from velvet-covered buds in spring

Full growth is reached by summer. As the bone becomes denser, the blood supply to a network of vessels beneath the velvet is cut off. The velvet, which is skin covered by fine hairs, dries up and is rubbed off. The antlers fall off in early spring

Staking out a territory

Roe deer, which browse in the dense woodlands throughout Eurasia, are smaller than red deer. A male and two or three females with their young usually remain together during the winter. These small groups split up in summer.

The male, or roebuck, sheds its antlers in midwinter. New antlers begin to grow by March, and are fully formed in June and July, when a pre-rutting period occurs during which the bucks become excited and fight. The roebuck's antlers are short and sharp-pointed and grow almost vertically from the animal's forehead.

When the actual rutting season arrives in July and August, each buck marks a piece of the forest as its own territory by scraping away the bark of young trees with its antlers and depositing on the scraped spot a secretion from a scent gland on its forehead. It fights off any rival male that intrudes into this territory.

During the rut the roebuck is attracted by the bleating of a female. The buck does not roar like the red deer stag, but makes a barking sound.

Delayed implantation (see page 22) ensures that the young, usually twins, are born in May or June, when spring foliage provides good cover and food.

The most common North American deer

White-tailed deer, also known as Virginia deer, are the most abundant and widespread deer in North America. They live in woods and thickets interspersed with meadowland, rather than in deep forest. When they are alarmed their white tails stand up over their backs like flags.

Asia has many species of deer. One, the sika, has seven races in Asia. The sika's coat is plain in winter and spotted with white in summer. Its most striking feature is a large patch of white hairs on the buttocks, which conceals its short tail.

The sika stag, which has smaller, simpler antlers than the related red deer, calls with a whistling noise during the mating season. The sika, also known as the Japanese deer, has been introduced into Europe.

Young roebucks Roe deer are timid in the presence of other large animals, and when frightened utter a barking sound. The male marks out a territory at the start of the rut in late summer and vigorously defends it against other bucks. Often fights ensue in which fatal injuries are sometimes caused by the roebuck's short, upright antlers. The bucks chase the does in excited mating play

White-tailed deer fawn The spots on the fawn's coat resemble blotches of filtered sunlight

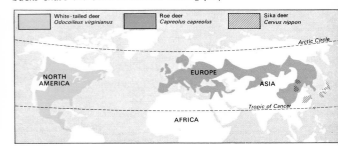

Deer of two continents The white-tailed deer's range extends from Canada to Central America

Japanese sika These deer, which live in herds deep in the forest, were once widely distributed throughout the Far East, but now flourish only in Japan and Manchuria. Other races face extinction

A huge browser, the European "buffalo," saved from extinction

The European bison, *Bison bonasus*, which stands as high as 6½ feet at the shoulder, is the largest animal in Europe. Like its American relative, *Bison bison* (see page 122), it now exists only under protection. The European bison has a smaller head and hump than the American bison.

The last wild European bisons, or wisents, were killed in Lithuania and in the Caucasus in the 1920s. However, animals from captive herds have been reintroduced to the Bialowieza Forest on the Polish-Soviet border. There they have multiplied and become reestablished as semiwild animals, browsing on oak, elm, willow, and other trees, and rarely grazing. In winter they eat acorns, shrubs such as heather, and other vegetation.

Bison of the forest The European bison is taller than the American buffalo and has heavier hindquarters

The community in the leaf litter

A million earthworms in each acre of ground are among the bottom echelons of a huge army of small animals that feed on the litter of the forest floor

In autumn the floor of the deciduous forest becomes a vast dump of natural litter, covered with dead leaves, branches, fallen trees, plant remains, and the corpses and droppings of animals. The litter on just one acre

of forest land may contain as many as 10 million leaves.

Countless small animals and plants are nourished by this litter. Fungi and bacteria are the main agents of decay, but these organisms also help to put essential chemicals back into the food cycle. Some animals, such as certain earthworms, eat the dead leaves; others depend on fungi to break down the tough tissues. The semiliquid products of

bacterial decomposition, and the bacteria themselves, are food for microscopic animals such as roundworms and rotifers. The food chains in the litter are so complex that 300 different species of invertebrates (animals that lack backbones) may feed in a square mile of forest. Predators complete the chain. They range from mammals that feed on earthworms to microscopic mites that prey on other microscopic victims.

Burrowing hordes that are nourished by decaying vegetation

Abrasive feeder The glistening slug *Arion ater* rasps its food with a long, many-toothed tongue

Protection in a ball The pill millipede *Glomeris marginata* rolls up into a tight ball when disturbed

Night browsers The garden snail *Helix aspersa* uses its rasplike tongue to feed on a wide variety

of plants, gliding out of damp corners at one inch per minute and leaving behind a glistening trail

Earthworms move through the soil by swallowing it and forcing it out behind them, digesting the edible contents of the soil as it passes through their bodies. Some of the undigested soil is passed from the worms to the surface in the form of coiled wormcasts. This process, with its tunneling and resultant soil turnover, helps make soil more fertile.

The density of earthworms in the forest can be up to one ton per acre—equivalent to a million worms per acre, or about 2000 per square yard. One patch of ground may

contain a dozen different species, including some that feed directly on fallen leaves. One species reaches out of its burrow at night and drags in leaves to eat.

Slugs, and their relatives the snails, feed on almost anything organic by using their long, rough-surfaced, strap-shaped tongues (called radulae) as rasps.

Millipedes and wood lice also feed on leaves. The pill millipede resembles a wood louse, but the two animals are not closely related. Wood lice are the largest group of

terrestrial crustaceans, while the millipedes belong to the Diplopoda class, which is more closely related to insects.

Springtails are tiny, wingless, jumping relatives of the insects. They are so minute that up to 40,000 of them can live in a square yard of moist soil, feeding on vegetation partially decomposed by other animals or fungi. Springtails are a very ancient group of land animals belonging to the Collembola class. Fossil springtails have been found in rocks 380 million years old.

How the springtail puts the spring into its tail

When the springtail is resting, a leverlike organ called a furcula is folded and clipped under its abdomen. Muscular contractions bring hard-covered segments closer together. This shortens its body and forces fluid into the furcula. Muscles release the clip, and the fluid's pressure straightens out the joint of the furcula, which then snaps downward and propels the animal into the air

In the grip of a fungus

A roundworm is caught by the fungus *Dactylaria gracilis*. A lasso (open at left) expands (center) and grips the worm until the fungus's enzymes digest it

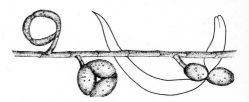

Fast-moving predators

The plant-eating animals of the deciduous litter and soil are food for the predators—vertebrate and invertebrate—that live side by side with them. The surface is patrolled by ground beetles, spiders, toads, lizards, birds, and small mammals such as mice, shrews, and hedgehogs. Some other predators live deeper in the soil; these include centipedes, pseudoscorpions, and the carnivorous roundworms.

The carnivorous invertebrate species can generally be distinguished from their prey by their greater speed and agility. The centipedes, for example, are strikingly faster in their movements than the millipedes.

Close to the surface of the soil lives *Lithobius fasciatus*, a centipede with 15 pairs of legs, which kills soft-bodied insects and worms with its poison fangs. The female lays sticky eggs and rolls them in the soil, giving them a covering which hides them from other carnivores.

Deeper in the soil live the longer, more slender centipedes. One, the luminescent *Geophilus electricum*, has about 100 pairs of legs and feeds mainly on small earthworms. Glands on the underside of its body produce a phosphorescent secretion that makes this centipede luminous.

Springtails and other small underground animals are the prey of pseudoscorpions. These hunters, less than one quarter inch long, are members of the spider class, Arachnida. The pseudoscorpions use their poison-inflicting pincers not only to kill their prey, but also to tear the victim apart and carry the pieces to their chelicerae, a smaller pair of pincers nearer the mouth. The chelicerae pour digestive juices into the prey and convert it into a liquid that the pseudoscorpion ingests; thus the prey is already partly digested before it is consumed. The chelicerae also provide silk with which the pseudoscorpion builds a complex nest, or cocoon, for egg laying, molting, or hibernation.

In mating, male and female pseudoscorpions face each other with upraised claws, moving forward and back in a kind of dance until the male places a spermatophore (package of sperm) on the ground. The male then pulls the female over the spermatophore and it passes into her genital aperture.

Antlerlike jaws Male stag beetles have enormous mandibles, but the smaller jaws of the female are less clumsy weapons

The glowworm The illumination for this photograph was provided by the cold, yellow-green light of the glowworm, which feeds on slugs and worms

Building a nest with natural bricks and silken mortar

The pseudoscorpion surrounds itself with stones and pieces of wood—the "bricks"

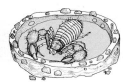

It coats the bricks with silk by brushing them against its smaller pincers, or chelicerae

As the dome rises, the pseudoscorpion leaves itself a diminishing amount of room to get out

Finally it seals itself inside the dome and lines the interior with silk before molting or laying begins

Big claws for digging The common European mole digs with its strong front feet. Its short fur permits easy movement through tunnels. Like those of all moles, its eyes are almost useless

A nose for food finding All moles depend largely on the sense of touch, but the American star-nosed mole has an extreme adaptation—a ring of fleshy tentacles around its nose. These are sensitive feelers for detecting food. Moles of the temperate regions eat mainly earthworms and beetle larvae. They store worms after injecting a paralyzing poison so their victims cannot crawl away

The insect-eaters

Insect-eating animals glut on a summer abundance of food, but many face starvation in winter. They avoid it by migrating, turning vegetarian, or going to sleep

Every winter, insect-eating animals of the deciduous forests face the challenge of a greatly reduced food supply, since insects are often hidden away as eggs or pupae.

Some species of insectivorous birds remain in the forest throughout the year. Most of these turn to seed-eating during the winter. The other main ways in which vertebrate animals overcome the seasonal shortage of insect prey are migration and hibernation. Most birds migrate south to areas where insects are active.

All the reptiles and amphibians become dormant, passing the winter in a virtual coma, without feeding. This happens because reptiles and amphibians lack the physiological adaptations that keep the internal body temperature of mammals and birds nearly constant, regardless of the outside temperature. A constant internal temperature ("warm blood") allows vital processes to continue through the winter.

Most insect-eating birds migrate south in the winter

Unwitting foster parent This willow warbler is collecting food for the young cowbird in its nest

The parasite The brown-headed cowbird lays its egg in another bird's nest. The large cowbird chick will get most of the food

The intruder A hedge sparrow feeds a young cuckoo that has hatched in its nest. The female cuckoo replaces one of the host's eggs with her own. After hatching, the cuckoo chick pushes the host's remaining eggs or any rival chicks to the side of the nest and drops them over

Among the many insect-eating birds that migrate in winter are swallows, flycatchers, vireos, and warblers. Swallows range from Scandinavia to South Africa in search of food, taking insects on the wing. A swallow will swoop through a flight of insects with its large mouth gaping open, capturing one after another. Old World flycatchers feed in a similar fashion, but some also dive to the ground to pick up prey. Vireos, found from Canada to Argentina, typically hunt for insects among the leafy foliage in tall trees.

Warblers have a diversity of songs, a type of animal communication that has important behavioral effects. The song of a willow warbler, for instance, causes another willow warbler to keep away from the singing bird's feeding territory. On the other hand, the willow warbler, which feeds low in the trees, will pay no attention to the song of the chiff-chaff, which feeds mainly in the higher branches and therefore is not in competition for the willow warbler's food supply.

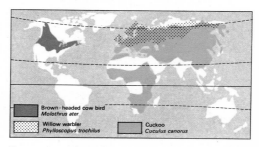

Brown-headed cow bird
Molothrus ater

Willow warbler
Phylloscopus trochilus

Cuckoo
Cuculus canorus

Squatters and a host Cuckoos and cowbirds parasitize the nests of small, insectivorous birds

Division of prey These birds can feed in the same area without competing, because their feeding habits differ

The barn swallow catches insects above the trees

The Acadian flycatcher snaps up insects on the wing within the forest canopy

The red-eyed vireo picks insects from the leaves

The brown treecreeper finds insects and their eggs and pupae on the bark

Hibernators and hunters

Bats are among the insect-eating mammals that hibernate in winter. The North American and Eurasian deciduous forests both shelter about 20 species of bats. Some, like the noctule, settle in hollow trees, while others, like the greater horseshoe bat, spend the winter in caves.

When not in hibernation, these bats feed at night, catching insects on the wing. All bats emit high-pitched squeaks in flight, whose echoes, returning to the bat's ears, help these flying mammals locate prey and avoid bumping into obstacles.

Shrews do not hibernate. A shrew that misses even one day's food is doomed. They spend the winter grubbing in the leaf litter and topsoil for dormant insects.

Shrews eat their own weight in insects and worms for a few hours, then rest for a few hours, eat again for three or four hours and so on, all day and night. Though tiny they are ferocious. Most shrews will attack members of their own species that encroach on their territory.

Reptiles and amphibians

Lizards are more plentiful in warmer regions, but some, such as the slow worm *Anguis fragilis*, a snakelike lizard whose legs remain only as vestigial shoulder and hip bones, live in the leaf litter of deciduous woodland. This slow worm is viviparous, that is, it gives birth to active young—unlike reptiles in warmer climates, which lay leathery-shelled eggs in warm places and leave them to hatch. The viviparous lizard *Lacerta vivipara* retains its young in its body until they are well developed, protected only by a thin membrane similar to the mammalian placenta. The slow worm feeds at night on insects, spiders, slugs, and earthworms.

One of the few amphibians of the Eurasian deciduous forest is the common toad, which feeds on small insects and other invertebrates at night. Toads breed in water, but outside the breeding season they are much less aquatic than frogs. Tree frogs, which can cling to the smoothest leaf with their disk-tipped digits, are represented in the North American forest by many species.

Tree frogs are often strong jumpers. From a sitting position they can lunge at an insect in one bound, gulping it down almost at the instant of landing. Despite their name, most tree frogs spawn in water, and their young go through a tadpole stage.

The web of death

Spiders abound in the deciduous forest foliage. Many species can be found on a single tree, feeding mainly on insects, which they ensnare in their sticky webs and bite with poison fangs. Some species truss their prey up in silk for storage. This technique of killing allows spiders to tackle victims larger than themselves.

The most conspicuous insect predators are dragonflies, which dart about in clearings or near water, catching insects.

Prickly protection Hedgehogs—even young ones like these—are well protected from predators by their spines. If disturbed, a hedgehog rolls into a tight ball, hiding its legs, head, and belly. When the temperature drops to about 36° F. (2° C.), the hedgehog, which is too big to tunnel under the leaf litter, hibernates in a warm, secluded spot. If there is a sudden cold spell during the winter, the hedgehog must wake up to keep its body temperature above the freezing point

Hedgehog and toad The hedgehog is virtually restricted to the deciduous forest, with two wide ranges, one stretching from Britain to western Siberia and the other in eastern Asia. Common toads live within reach of water

Defense by deception This common toad, confronted by a grass snake, is inflating its body and swaying from side to side, making itself appear larger. Other defenses used by toads include noxious secretions from glands in their skins

Lacewing A green lacewing is feeding on a cluster of aphids. Its larvae also eat aphids, seizing them with sharp jaws and sucking out body fluids

Predatory ladybug Both adults and their larvae eat aphids. These beetles, found in most parts of the world, have red, yellow, black, or blue markings

The flesh-eaters

Flesh-eating animals have suffered more from the impact of man in the deciduous forests than in any other zone; some species have adapted, many more have retreated

Man has been destroying carnivorous birds and mammals for thousands of years, in the past primarily for their depredations on domestic stock, more recently because these large species are particularly vulnerable to pressures associated with man's increasing population, such as alteration and pollution of natural environments. As the temperate forests disappear under the onslaught of civilization, the large carnivores living there have been all but wiped out. Animals such as the puma and the brown bear survive mainly in mountainous areas. But a few, more adaptable species, including the red fox and the kestrel, not only survive but have probably increased in number.

The patchwork nature of today's deciduous forest zone favors animals that are at home in open ground or at the fringes of woods, such as the birds of prey. They swoop out from their forest hiding places when they spot prey.

Some birds and small mammals have adapted to urbanization

Silent predator A tawny owl's broad wings and short, full tail are displayed as it swoops down to seize a small rodent. Mice and voles are its usual prey, but the tawny owl also feeds on fish, frogs, and insects. Like most owls, it is adapted for silent flight by the softness of its plumage and by the "furry" flight feathers that muffle sound as the bird hunts for prey at night

Hovering killer The kestrel's pointed wings and long tail allow it to hover, scrutinizing the ground for the slightest movement of a small animal. It then plummets down to seize the prey

The hobby, a European woodland falcon, catches small birds such as warblers, swallows, and finches, as well as large insects such as cicadas, as it flashes along the tops of trees or the edge of a clearing.

The hobby lays its eggs—usually about three—in an abandoned nest in the highest branches of a tree, often taking over a nest left by a crow.

The kestrel, another European species, is slightly larger than the 13-inch-long hobby and has a longer tail, which helps it to hover while it scans the ground for a movement that may betray a vole or even a large beetle.

This bird has adapted well to living in farmland and even in cities. It does not build a nest but lays its eggs in a hole in a tree, in a cliff, or in another bird's unused nest. In North America the kestrel's role in the deciduous forest community is filled by the very similar sparrowhawk. The North American counterpart of the European sparrowhawk is the sharp-shinned hawk.

Owls are the birds of prey best adapted to living in dense woodland. In North America the screech, barred, great horned, and saw-whet owls are fairly common. The most common in Europe is the tawny owl. Like most owls, it feeds at night, usually on small rodents and fish, frogs, crustaceans, and, to a lesser degree, insects.

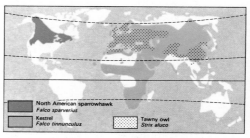

North American sparrowhawk
Falco sparverius

Kestrel
Falco tinnunculus

Tawny owl
Strix aluco

Birds of prey The sparrowhawk is similar to the kestrel of Eurasia, which favors open ground

Hobby

Sharp-shinned hawk

Wing shapes The fast-flying hobby has long wings and a short tail. For quick turns, the sharp-shinned hawk has short wings and a long tail

Semiaquatic snakes

Snakes are not common in cool temperate areas, but there are several species in North American and Eurasian deciduous forests, especially in swamps.

In North America the semiaquatic common garter snake lives in marshes and beside ponds. It feeds on frogs, mice, and invertebrates such as earthworms. In Europe the

The grass snake It is semiaquatic and is at home on land or in the water, where it seeks frogs

grass snake is similar in its habits, and there are many snakes of the same genus in North America. All are nonvenomous; but poisonous species do exist in the deciduous forest regions, notably the copperhead, the water moccasin, several species of rattlesnakes in North America, and the adder *Vipera berus* in Eurasia.

Small carnivorous mammals

One of the most widely distributed of all mammals is the red fox. It lives in tundra, coniferous and deciduous forests, steppe and mountain areas, farmland, even city suburbs. A stealthy nocturnal hunter, the fox will eat almost anything that has food value. Voles

Forest cat The wildcat is larger than domestic cats and probably arose from an African race

and mice are the mainstay of its diet, but it also eats large insects, carrion, fish, grass, and berries. Birds, especially their eggs, provide variety in summer.

The European wildcat resembles an oversize domestic cat, with black-striped yellowgray fur and a short bushy tail. It rests by day and hunts by night for small mammals, birds, frogs, and fish.

North America has no small cat that corresponds to the wildcat in the deciduous forest. But the bobcat, a lynx about 30 inches long, is found in a variety of habitats ranging from coniferous forest to desert. It is distributed throughout the United States, except some midwestern states, and in southern Canada. It has rather long, soft fur, pale to reddish brown in color, with dark streaks, and dark spots on its white underside. The feet of bobcats and lynx (which are found in northern Canada) are thickly furred, an adaptation for walking over snow. Bobcats are usually solitary, like most members of the lynx family. They are nocturnal hunters, and may cover up to 25 miles in one night, preying mainly on rabbits and hares. Mating takes place late in winter; one to four young are born after about two months' gestation.

The European polecat is a mustelid, or member of the weasel family. It is about 15 inches long—larger than the more familiar weasel but with a similar lithe build. Like the skunk of the North American temperate zones, the European polecat emits a pungent smell from scent glands under its tail when alarmed. Polecats, confined to the deciduous forest, live in hollow trees or in the abandoned burrows of other mammals.

Weasels and minks are widely distributed throughout the deciduous and the coniferous forests. Another mustelid, the beech marten, ranges south of the coniferous forests.

The Asian raccoon-dog hunts at night in the deciduous forest. It is not related to the American raccoon, but has a similar black face mask. The raccoon-dog also resembles a fox, although it is shorter in the body. It is the only member of the dog family that comes close to hibernating in winter. Although it does not become completely torpid, it is inactive and emerges only occasionally. The raccoon-dog hunts a variety of small animals but prefers fish and amphibians.

Raccoon-dog In cold areas it sleeps most of the winter and leaves its den only on warm days

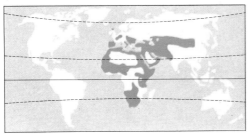

Wildcat Though primarily a forest-dweller, in Africa the wildcat's range extends into the savanna

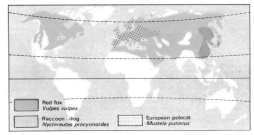

Red fox
Vulpes vulpes

Raccoon - dog
Nyctereutes procyonoides

European polecat
Mustela putorius

Widespread fox The red fox ranges widely, but the raccoon-dog and the polecat live mainly in forest

Foxes courting A male red fox and vixen in courtship play during their midwinter mating season. Three to eight cubs are born in the spring

The opportunists

Some animals eat almost anything they find, and their lack of discrimination enables them to survive where animals with specialized feeding habits would starve

Every major life zone and every broad group of animals have species that vary their feeding behavior to take advantage of whatever the seasons, local conditions, or chance may bring. Among these opportunists are many of the larger carnivorous mammals, such as bears. The size of such animals allows them to explore their environment undisturbed by predators, and their carnivorous ancestry endows them with the agility, sharp senses, and instincts of the hunter. Thus, if a favored prey animal is in short supply, an opportunist will see what other prey its environment might offer. Being an adaptable creature, it may investigate new varieties of plant food—or return to plant food after a long interval of eating meat.

Most of the opportunists in the deciduous forest are basically carnivores that eat some plant food. In addition to bears, they include raccoons and skunks in North America and badgers in Eurasia.

Raccoons, mustelids, and marsupials flourish

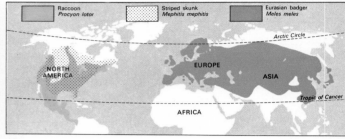

Skunk and raccoon The extensive ranges of the striped skunk and the raccoon overlap broadly in North America

The fastidious badger The European badger is extremely clean, digging holes for its droppings and changing its straw bedding regularly. If a rocky den is available badgers will use it instead of a dug-out set

A badger set The badger digs a deep set, a series of connected chambers, at the base of a tree on a slope, building up a platform of earth at the entrance. The animal sharpens its claws on the tree

Enormous numbers of raccoons have been killed for food and pelts, but the raccoon is still among the most common mammals in North America. It is a cat-size animal that makes its den in a hollow tree or a crevice in rock. Litters typically number four individuals, which become independent of their parents after a year.

The raccoon is adept at flicking crayfish and other aquatic animals out of the water with its paws, to add to its staple diet of fruit, nuts, seeds, insects, and eggs.

Raccoons in captivity appear to wash their food in water. Experts disagree as to whether this habit represents an attempt to re-create the way a raccoon catches food in water, or whether the animal really does wash its food. There have been many reports of raccoons in the wild taking nonaquatic prey down to a riverbank and dipping it in and out of the water in what looks like an attempt to wash it before eating.

Both badgers and skunks are mustelids and have scent glands with which they mark out their home ranges. But only the skunk uses the glands for defense, ejecting twin jets of foul-smelling, eye-stinging liquid that deter most attackers. The striped skunk, found only in North America, lives by foraging for insects and grubs, plus occasional mice, eggs, and carrion.

The Eurasian badger, a sturdy mustelid which resembles a small bear in appearance, uses its powerful front feet to trample to death prey such as frogs, toads, snails, mice, and moles. It also uses its feet to break into beehives, dig up larvae and worms, and excavate burrows and tunnels.

The adaptable Virginia opossum

North America's only marsupial, or pouched mammal, is the Virginia opossum. It is basically a South American animal which has spread to the temperate woodlands. The Virginia opossum is nocturnal, a versatile feeder, able to eat almost anything it finds in the undergrowth.

Protecting its young A skunk picks up one of its offspring and prepares to scurry back to its burrow. Up to ten young are born in May or June

Raccoon Preying on fish, frogs, and crayfish, the raccoon may use its paw to quickly flip its victim out of the water

The Virginia opossum lives mostly in trees. It is slow and plodding on the ground, but an expert tree climber. It can use its long, almost hairless tail to grasp—and even hang from—branches. When disturbed, the animal instinctively "plays possum," going limp and appearing to be dead. This habit—plus, perhaps, its rather repulsive smell—seems to protect it from attack. Dogs, for example, will rarely touch a Virginia opossum that is playing possum.

Wild boar and Himalayan bear

The wild boar is a vegetarian which varies its diet with animal food. In the woods of Europe and Asia, the boars leave their lairs in the evening and search for food, grubbing up roots with their snouts, eating fruits and nuts, and seizing any small animals that cross their path. They also eat carrion.

Mature males forage alone, but sows and the young travel in a group called a sounder, which may number from 6 to 50. Sounders of wild boars often destroy large areas of crops by trampling and digging.

Unlike its bulky descendant, the domestic pig, the wild boar is built for fast running and hard fighting. The male can rip open an adversary's body with the sharp tusks that grow from its lower jaw. The males fight among themselves during the mating season.

The Himalayan black bear has a much greater range than its name implies—across Asia from Iran to Manchuria and Japan. It lives high in the mountains near the upper limits of the forest. Not all individuals are black—some are red-brown—but all have a white chin and a crescent-shaped white mark on the chest. The Himalayan black bear has larger ears and a thinner muzzle than the brown bear, and is probably less carnivorous.

In winter, the Himalayan bear sleeps only for short spells in bad weather, unlike the brown bear and the North American black bear, which sleep for most of the winter.

Carrion-eaters

Man has always given crows high marks for their intelligence. They are also highly adaptable, and have a well-developed social organization. In these respects, crows represent an advanced stage in bird evolution. There is hardly anything edible that will not make a meal for them—fruit, grain, eggs, insects, small birds, mammals, or carrion. Their dietary versatility is not due simply to sturdy digestive systems, but also to adaptable patterns of behavior—for instance, they will skillfully and persistently drop shellfish onto rocks to break the shells.

Crows have survived in spite of man's constant persecution—another proof of the intelligence and adaptability of these birds. Their rate of reproduction is no higher than that of most birds; they simply make the best of any conditions in which they have to live. The female usually has one brood, laying from three to five eggs.

Himalayan black bear Growing to almost six feet long and weighing up to 265 pounds, it uses its strength to kill cattle and other domestic stock. Although more aggressive than the North American black bear, it feeds mainly on fruit, nuts, and the honey and grubs from bees' nests. An agile climber, it builds nests of sticks in the branches of trees

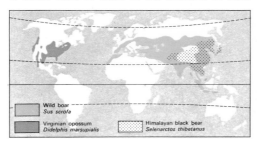

Wide-ranging wild boar Although man has extensively hunted the Eurasian wild boar for food and to protect his crops, the animal still ranges from the deciduous forests to the tropics

Fast-growing marsupial At birth Virginia opossums are smaller than honeybees. They spend two months inside the mother's pouch before venturing out and climbing onto her back

Camouflage for the young The striped backs of wild boar piglets provide effective camouflage in the woodland. The adult wild boars lack these markings

Carrion-eater This black-billed magpie is about to pick the bones of a beaver. It is a member of the crow family

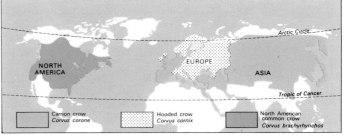

Crows The ranges of the carrion and hooded crows do not overlap in the breeding season, but where they meet is a zone, 10 to 100 miles wide, of hybrids

Animals of the maquis

Man has destroyed the original forest of the Mediterranean region and exterminated many of its animals, or confined them to isolated, mountainous pockets

The Mediterranean region supports a mixture of vegetation ranging from forest to desert plants. Much of the original forest has been destroyed by man's activities with fire, axe, and plow from very early times.

The most characteristic natural growth on the eroded land is a rather dry scrub of low trees and shrubs, known as maquis. Trees such as olive, citrus, and cork oak survive mainly in cultivation, not as descendants of the original forests.

Areas with similar climate and vegetation exist in other parts of the world, notably California, central Chile, South Africa, southern Australia, and the North Island of New Zealand. In each of these widely separated areas are found drought-resistant trees and shrubs that can survive the hot, dry summer until the warm, wet winter arrives.

In the Mediterranean region, herbaceous plants such as daffodils, tulips, and crocuses flower in spring, then die down and conserve moisture in underground bulbs or corms. These provide a source of summer food for many animals.

Wild animals have retreated from the Mediterranean area

Wild sheep Mouflons live on rocky hills in Corsica and Sardinia, browsing on shrubs and grazing

Rabbit This successful colonist will occupy any habitat that offers grazing and soil for burrowing.

Man's persecution of predatory birds and mammals has helped the rabbit to increase its range

The variety of animal life in the Mediterranean region has been greatly affected by man. Most of the large carnivores have been exterminated or forced to take refuge in the more secluded mountain areas. The few leopards left in the region are found mainly in the Atlas Mountains in Morocco; brown bears, once common over large areas, are now found only in the mountains of northwest Spain, in the Pyrenees on the Spanish-French border, and in the Balkans. Many of the larger plant-eating animals, such as sheep and goats, have for the most part been domesticated or replaced by domestic stock. Wild goats still occur from the eastern shores of the Mediterranean to West Pakistan, but most populations have been modified by interbreeding with domestic goats, so that the original characteristics of the wild goats have tended to disappear.

Wild sheep, or mouflons, still survive on the islands of Corsica and Sardinia. Other sheep, which are probably the same species, live in Asia Minor, Iran, and Mongolia. Mouflons live in small flocks, each led by an old ewe, in rough and often precipitous mountain areas. One to three lambs are born in spring after a gestation period of about six months. The lambs are able to run about their steep, rocky habitat almost immediately after birth. Mouflons are noted for their hardiness; they can go without water for long periods.

Although mouflons sometimes interbreed with domestic sheep, they have retained their own set of genetic characteristics, and when grown do not look like the domestic breed. The mouflon, unlike domestic sheep, does not have a thick, woolly coat, although in winter it does grow woolly underfur.

Fallow deer and Barbary apes

The fallow deer is one of the most familiar species of deer in the parks and open woodland of Britain and central Europe. These herds almost certainly had their origins in animals introduced from the Mediterranean region, perhaps by the Romans. Now the deer are almost extinct in much of their original range in southern Europe, and survive only in scattered populations. A species related to this deer has been reported to survive in Iraq.

Fallow deer can be recognized by the flattened antlers of the bucks. In summer the fallow deer has a light fawn coat with white spots; in winter its coat is unspotted and gray in color.

Fallow deer mate in autumn, and the fawns are born in early summer. During the mating season the males bellow to attract the females. Bucks and does often remain together outside the breeding season, especially in winter. The herd is led by a doe.

The only monkey native to the Mediterranean region is the Barbary ape. Actually about the only feature this animal shares with true apes is the lack of a tail. It is really a macaque monkey and is more closely related to the monkeys of India and Southeast Asia than to the African monkeys south of the Sahara. Like most species of monkeys, Barbary apes are sociable. They travel in small groups through rocky woodland searching for animal and vegetable food. The well-known colony of Barbary apes on the Rock of Gibraltar was probably introduced from North Africa.

Earless, eyeless burrower

Mediterranean mole-rats live almost entirely underground, only occasionally emerging from the tunnels where they feed on roots, bulbs, and tubers. They have stout, furry bodies almost 12 inches long, and their eyes and ear openings are completely covered by skin. A mole-rat identifies objects by touching them with its nose.

Mole-rats are highly adapted for burrowing. They use their huge incisor teeth to dig, and their broad, horny snouts to pack the earth as they excavate their burrows. Each burrow has several nesting chambers which are connected by passages to other chambers set aside for breeding, feeding, storage, and wastes.

The common rabbit *Oryctolagus cuniculus* is believed to have originated in Spain. ("Spain" is derived from *tsapan*, the Phoenician word for "rabbit.") It is now more widespread in northern Europe than in the Mediterranean region and has been introduced to Australia, New Zealand, and Chile.

Birds of contrasting ranges

The Mediterranean is rich in birds. Insect-eating birds are especially abundant in summer. Most species migrate to tropical Africa in winter. Among the few year-round inhabitants is the azure-winged magpie, a member of the crow family that is found in Spain and Portugal and nowhere else except the Far East. It feeds on a variety of insects and berries.

The Syrian woodpecker was restricted to the Mediterranean region until about a century ago, but in more recent times it has undergone a remarkable expansion in population and range. It has now colonized much of eastern Europe, especially in cultivated areas, where to a large extent it has replaced the indigenous great spotted woodpecker.

The reasons for this expansion are not clearly understood. But we do know that when man disturbs a natural environment the immediate effect is a reduction in the variety of flora and fauna. Yet certain species not only survive such changes but flourish in the new environment.

Scrubland partridge The red-legged partridge lives in scrub country in southwest Europe, where it replaces the closely related rock partridge, or chukar, of the eastern Mediterranean

Mediterranean mole-rat As it burrows, the blind mole-rat uses its broad snout for recognizing objects and for packing the soil

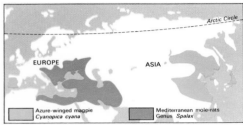

Magpies and mole-rats The azure-winged magpie has a small range in the Iberian Peninsula and a wide one in Asia, but this sedentary bird is not found anywhere else in the world. Mediterranean mole-rats have a larger and more unified distribution, taking them into deserts and grasslands

Whipsnake of southern Europe The snake is beginning to swallow a green lizard. Sometimes more than six feet long when mature, the whipsnake is one of Europe's largest snakes

Fallow deer These deer usually stay in the open woodlands, where their spotted coats become inconspicuous against the trees and shrubs. They browse on leaves and also graze on grass

Mountain- and lowland-dwellers

**Centuries of cultivation have denuded
the southern Chinese lowlands of many wild
species, but the remote mountains
harbor some of the world's rarer animals**

Southern China provides two contrasting wildlife habitats—the western mountains and the eastern lowlands. The lowlands have long been cleared of their forests and many of the animals that once flourished there are gone; but dense forests still remain in areas of the western mountains, sheltering an abundance of wildlife. Wide belts of vegetation succeed each other up the steep slopes. Broad-leaved evergreens on the foothills give way to bamboo forest at about 6000 feet; a mixture of conifers and rhododendrons begins around 8000 feet; and finally, above 11,000 feet, comes open country, with low shrubs and grass. The giant panda and the red panda are two forest-dwelling mammals of southern China.

Southern Japan has forests similar to those in southwest China, and the animal communities of the two regions show similarities. The Japanese macaque and dormouse, however, live only in Japan.

Macaque and dormouse, high-living mammals of Japan

Japanese macaques These monkeys, living high up in mountain forests and rocky hillsides of southern Japan, have dense, shaggy coats

One of the few mammals peculiar to southern Japan is the Japanese macaque, a relative of the rhesus monkey of India. Japanese macaques, the most northerly of all monkeys, live in mountain forests and rocky hillsides at altitudes over 5000 feet. Their diet varies, and may include several kinds of fruits, nuts, grasses, and insects.

Another inhabitant of the higher slopes of the mountain forests—between 1300 and 6000 feet—is the Japanese dormouse, the only dormouse in eastern Asia; its nearest relative is thousands of miles away in western Siberia. The female Japanese dormouse builds a nest in a tree, covering the nest's outside with lichen and lining the inside with bark, and gives birth to three or four young in June or July. This dormouse is one of the few mammals that are restricted to Japan.

The Japanese water shrew is found near mountain streams in southwest China and the Himalayas as well as in the hills and mountains of southern Japan. All water shrews have soft, fine fur, which is waterproof to some degree. Their ears are small, and have a flap that seals shut when the animal submerges. Some species have been observed to swim well underwater.

Mountain-dwellers Both pandas are found in the mountains of southwest China, but the red panda usually lives on the higher slopes

Giant panda
Ailuropoda melanoleuca

Red panda
Ailurus fulgens

Golden monkey
Rhinopithecus roxellanae

Japanese dormouse
Glirulus japonicus

Japanese macaque
Macaca fuscata

JAPAN

CHINA

INDIA

TAIWAN

Tropic of Cancer

Emerging to forage The Japanese dormouse rests during the day and forages at dusk. It is agile and often hangs from a branch by its hind feet

Resting by day During the day the red panda sleeps in trees, with its long, bushy tail curled around its body. At night it forages for bamboo shoots, grass, roots, acorns, and fruit. About two feet long, the red panda is much smaller than the giant panda, which is about five feet long

Bamboo-eater The giant panda chews tough bamboo with its strong teeth and powerful jaw muscles. Sometimes it eats birds and small mammals

Pandas, vegetarians of the Chinese bamboo forests

The bamboo forests of southwest China are the home of the giant panda, one of the world's rarest animals, and the red panda. Giant pandas are solitary animals which usually live on the ground. The red panda is smaller and, with its long, bushy tail and facial markings, looks more like a raccoon than the bearlike giant panda.

The two pandas have several similarities, including "sixth fingers"—pads on the front paws which help them to hold bamboo stems when feeding. They are generally classed as members of the raccoon family. Some zoologists, however, believe that the two pandas are not related and that the giant panda belongs to the bear family. Others suggest that the giant panda evolved independently, sharing a common ancestor with both bears and raccoons.

Another vegetarian of the mountain forests is the rare golden monkey, or snub-nosed langur. These animals live in troops of over 100, and eat bamboo and other plants. They sometimes have a crest of hair on the crown.

"Sixth finger" for gripping The pandas have extra pads on their forepaws which are used in opposition to the claws, to grip bamboo stems

Tibet's tufted deer have stumpy antlers, curving tusks

The tufted deer, or Tibetan muntjac, is a small, elusive animal that lives a solitary life in the dense forests of southwest China. Its antlers are little more than stumps, almost hidden in a tuft of hair on the forehead. Unlike most other present-day deer, this species has curved tusks, which protrude from its upper jaw.

Chinese muntjacs resemble tufted deer, though they are slightly smaller (18 to 23 inches high at the shoulder, compared with 20 to 28 inches). They, too, have short antlers, and the males have large tusks. They are sometimes called barking deer, because their call is similar to a dog's bark.

The Chinese water deer, a native of the Chinese lowlands, feeds on reeds, coarse grasses, and vegetables. These deer give birth to four or five young, in contrast to most other species, which bear only one or two. They are about the same size as Chinese muntjacs, and the males, like male muntjacs, have tusklike upper canine teeth. When startled, the water deer bounds off through the forest like a rabbit.

The higher, open woodlands of southwest China are the home of Thorold's deer, a large animal with spreading antlers and a white muzzle. It is rarely seen.

Rare pheasant Swinhoe's pheasant is found only in the mountain forests of Taiwan. It was once spread throughout the island, but most of its habitat has been destroyed

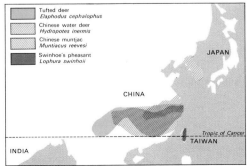

	Tufted deer *Elaphodus cephalophus*
	Chinese water deer *Hydropotes inermis*
	Chinese muntjac *Muntiacus reevesi*
	Swinhoe's pheasant *Lophura swinhoii*

Chinese deer The tufted deer and the muntjac live in forests; the water deer in open country

Chinese muntjac This small deer barks when it is frightened or detects predators

Chinese water deer Unlike other deer, it grazes on coarse grass and reeds instead of browsing

83

Mammals with pouches

Marsupials of the Australian temperate forest fill nearly all the roles played by mammals of other continents; they range from plant nibblers to predators

It is believed that about 70 million years ago a group of small tree-dwelling creatures colonized Australia. They were all marsupials—mammals whose young are born at an early stage of development and complete

their growth while attached to teats in the mother's pouch (*marsupium* in Latin). Marsupials are thus different from the more common and familiar placental mammals, whose young develop to a more advanced stage in the womb.

With the melting of polar icecaps, rising seas submerged Australia's land links with other continents and the Australian marsupial species became stranded.

Then, although evolving in isolation, these mammals, while retaining their pouches, developed along lines similar to those of placental mammals in other parts of the world. Dogs, moles, flying squirrels, and many other placentals all have marsupial counterparts in Australia. Other Australian marsupials fill the same environmental niches as placentals elsewhere, but do not resemble them.

The possums, extremely agile tree-dwellers

Feather-tail glider Narrow strips running from the hind paws to the forepaws enable this marsupial to glide downward for short distances as it moves from branch to branch seeking food

A tail for gripping The dormouse possum hangs by its tail as it reaches for a branch

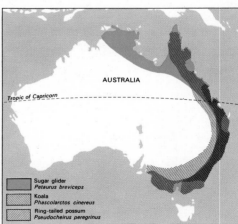

Riding piggyback After leaving the pouch, the koala infant rides on its mother's back

Ring-tailed possum While feeding, it uses its prehensile tail for balance and as an anchor

Marsupials of eastern Australia Sugar gliders and ring-tailed possums are common species of Australian mammals, but koalas are much rarer

Australian possums, members of the Phalangeridae family, are agile, tree-dwelling marsupials. They are an entirely different family from the American opossums. Some possums and other phalangers have a fold of skin called a patagium on each side of their body connecting the back and front legs, enabling them to glide from tree to tree like the flying squirrels of the northern hemisphere. Sugar

gliders are a fairly common member of this group. They measure 16 inches from head to tail, and can make downward glides of 50 yards. They feed on insects and nectar.

Leadbeater's possum looks like a sugar glider except that it has no patagia. It was once thought to be extinct, but since 1961 a few individuals have been seen in the mountain forests of Victoria.

Ring-tailed possums, of which there are about five species, have tapering, curling tails that are used to grasp branches while climbing. Unlike other phalangers, ring-tailed possums, as well as the greater glider and the koala, hold their first two fingers against the other three when grasping. These possums are named for their long, prehensile tail, which is usually curled into a ring.

Food and refuge in eucalyptus trees

The koala is the largest of the phalangers and the only one without a tail. It feeds on the leaves and shoots of about 20 species of eucalyptus. Female koalas give birth to a single offspring, less than an inch long. After six months the baby emerges from the mother's pouch and clambers onto her back. It remains dependent for the first year.

Flesh-eating marsupials of the Dasyuridae family fill a role similar to that of the weasels, civets, and dogs of other continents. They are active mainly at night, preying on small mammals, birds, reptiles, and insects.

A very rare dasyurid is the large, doglike Tasmanian wolf, or thylacine. Thylacines prey on kangaroos and wallabies, and also on small mammals and birds. Another dasyurid, the squat, strongly built Tasmanian devil, is still plentiful in the forest and underbrush of Tasmania.

Among the smaller dasyurids are the marsupial "mice," including several species of *Antechinus*—swift, agile predators that feed mostly on insects but also kill mice. In some species of *Antechinus* the males survive for only one breeding season; females may live longer. Males born in September are sexually mature by the following August. After mating, they all die.

Perhaps the least typical of the dasyurids is the banded anteater, or numbat. It feeds by day and exists solely on termites, consuming 10,000 to 20,000 a day. Termites also provide the numbat with a home: it lives in logs that they have eaten hollow.

One group of marsupials, the wombats, shows adaptations similar to those of burrowing rodents of other continents—such as teeth that grow continuously throughout life. It further resembles rodents in having only one pair of upper and lower incisors.

Bandicoots are so named because they look like large rodents of the Indian genus *Bandicota*. Bandicoots live on insects and grubs, and on roots which they dig up with their snouts and strong foreclaws.

Grazers and browsers

Kangaroos and wallabies live both in open country and in forest. The swamp wallaby, a solitary animal, browses in the denser parts of the forest, while the more gregarious whiptail wallaby grazes on luxuriant grassy patches in open forests. The pademelon wallabies live in the thick scrub and undergrowth of wet forests.

The two species of gray kangaroos live in forest, grazing at night in grassy clearings. The paler form inhabits open forests in eastern Australia, while the darker species lives in the more densely forested areas of South and Western Australia.

The gray kangaroo is the largest living marsupial. It continues to grow throughout its lifetime. The animal's strongly muscled hindquarters and powerful tail help it make tremendous leaps—as much as 30 feet in one bound. Most gray kangaroos can go without water for long periods.

Tasmanian devils These sturdy animals emerge from hiding at night to hunt small mammals and scavenge for carrion. When the Tasmanian wolf was plentiful, they often fed on its leavings

Protected pouch Young wombats are protected from dirt and debris when the mother is digging, because her pouch faces backward. Wombats dig wide, deep burrows. An adult wombat may be more than four feet long

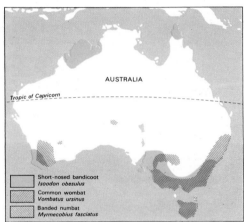
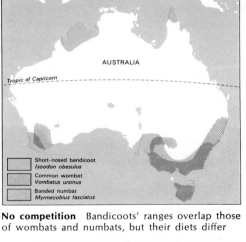

AUSTRALIA

Tropic of Capricorn

- Short-nosed bandicoot *Isoodon obesulus*
- Common wombat *Vombatus ursinus*
- Banded numbat *Myrmecobius fasciatus*

No competition Bandicoots' ranges overlap those of wombats and numbats, but their diets differ

Forager of the forest floor The short-nosed bandicoot has strong foreclaws for digging

Nocturnal hunter Mice, birds, and insects are the food of the native cat *Dasyurus viverrinus*

The numbat Scratching aside leaf litter and fallen logs, the numbat searches for termites to eat

Animals high and low in Australian forests

The superb lyrebird makes its home in the eucalyptus forest. During mating time the male builds platforms on which to perform a spectacular dance concert

Australia has two main temperate forest regions: wet low-lying areas with fairly dense forest and luxuriant ground cover, and drier mountain areas with less dense vegetation.

Both areas are described as sclerophyll, or hard-leaved, forest, as the numerous species of eucalyptus, or gum trees, have thick-skinned leaves that prevent loss of water by evaporation. These gum trees provide a rich feeding ground for insects and birds. One group of birds—the honey eaters—feeds on the nectar of the eucalyptus blossom, a particularly reliable food source because dif-ferent species of eucalyptus blossom at different times of the year, and about 500 species are found in Australia.

Typical of the honey eaters is the yellow-fronted honey eater. Like other members of its family, it has a distinctive tongue used for licking up nectar. The tip is split into four parts with delicately frayed edges, which enable it to be used like a brush.

Lyrebird and kookaburra: exotic birds of the eucalyptus forest

Hardworking mother The female superb lyrebird builds a large domed nest of sticks and moss, with an inner wall of bark fiber lined with feathers

A bird that is unique to the forests of eastern Australia is the lyrebird. There are only two species: the superb lyrebird and its small relative, Prince Albert's lyrebird.

The superb lyrebird is probably best known for the male's elegant tail plumage. But equally spectacular is the courtship display of the male to assert its territorial rights and attract a mate. It builds a mound from debris on the forest floor as a platform for display. Then it extends its tail feathers, showing the silvery underside of the plumes, and breaks into resonant song, "dancing" in time with its own melody. A male lyrebird will defend a territory perhaps half a mile long, and build as many as a dozen display platforms, performing on each in turn.

The males and females of both species are skillful vocal mimics, but this ability is more marked in the males. There are few sounds they cannot reproduce; they can imitate the calls of other birds and animals with uncanny accuracy.

The kookaburra, a member of the king-fisher family, feeds on any small animals it can kill. Its raucous call, often heard in cackling chorus, has earned this bird the nickname laughing jackass. The kookaburra is frequently found near towns. It establishes its home by burrowing into the nests of termites.

The broad-billed dollar bird is a relative of the kingfishers. Birds of this species, also called rollers because of their ability to somersault in flight, feed on insects caught on the wing.

Male superb lyrebird displaying The lyrebird of the Australian eucalyptus forest derives its name from the shape of the male's tail. As the 16 tail feathers sweep forward in an elegant display, the two curved ones at the side momentarily resemble the form of a lyre

Boobook This owl preys on insects and occasionally mice and birds. Its common name sounds like its cry

Kookaburra Lizards, small snakes, and insects are the staple foods of the omnivorous kookaburra

Frogmouth Named for its large mouth, it feeds mainly on the ground, making short flights to capture mice and frogs

Native rodents and bats

Australia's only native placental mammals are rodents and bats. The most numerous are the rats, which have colonized Australia in relatively recent times. The bush rat inhabits hardwood forest and is extremely plentiful. Another species, the eastern swamp rat, is found in swampy, grassy clearings in the eucalyptus forest.

The mosaic-tailed rats live mainly in trees. Their tails, which are partly prehensile, have an irregular mosaic of scales that provide extra grip on the branches. Most rats have evenly ringed tails.

The fruit-eating bats range in size from large fruit bats or flying foxes, weighing about two pounds, to small blossom bats weighing only a half ounce. Fruit bats hang from branches in swamps by day, flying at dusk to feed on fruiting trees.

Horseshoe bats These insect-eaters spend the day in dark caves, with their wings folded

Eastern swamp rat Distinguished by its hairless tail, this rat is at home on land or in water

Haunts and hunting methods of invertebrates

Invertebrates are well represented in the eucalyptus forests. Some species are peculiar to Australia, including several scorpions, spiders, and flatworms. The large brown scorpion *Hormurus caudicula* makes its home under damp logs. It has a painful sting, but the venom is strong enough to kill only other invertebrates.

Land planarians, a type of flatworm, live in wet leaf litter, and at night crawl out on tree trunks. The most widespread, *Geoplana*

caerulea, has a bright yellow streak down the middle of its back and a cobalt blue underside. A coat of glistening mucus acts as a lubricant when the animal is crawling, helps reduce water loss, and serves as a trap for small insects. When an insect becomes stuck in the mucus, the flatworm pours juices over the victim which digest it. Then the worm absorbs the prey through its mouth.

One of Australia's most deadly animals is the funnel-web spider, whose bite is fatal

even to man. This spider is so named because it makes its lair by spinning a tube of silk in a hole or crevice. The 1½-inch-long female lurks in the mouth of the lair, ready to strike. The male is also poisonous.

When funnel-web spiders mate, the male must somehow prevent the female from attacking him with her poisonous fangs. If the male remains with the female too long, even a moment after mating, he is very likely to be devoured by her.

Tree-dwelling frogs and blue-tongued lizards

Frogs and toads are the only amphibians in Australia. There are two main groups, ground-dwellers and tree-dwellers. The most colorful ground-dweller is the yellow-and-black-striped corroboree frog, found in sphagnum moss bogs in the Australian Alps. These frogs were so named because their stripes were thought to resemble the painted bodies of aborigines at their tribal gatherings, or corroborees.

The most widespread of the tree-dwellers, White's tree frog, is an expert climber but

spends much of its time on the ground foraging for insects. It also swallows snails whole, disgorging the shells later.

The blue-tongued skink is viviparous—that is, it does not lay eggs like most reptiles, but gives birth to living young, usually 10 to 15. When threatened, it puts out its brilliant blue tongue and puffs up its body.

Australia has fewer nonvenomous snakes than other continents. One of the most common of these is a race of diamond python called the carpet python.

Feet of a climber White's tree frog can climb up tree branches and perch among the leaves. Its disk-tipped digits enable it to stick to vertical surfaces

Carpet python Sleeping birds, mice, and bats are the preferred prey of the carpet python, which is easily recognizable by the pattern on its back. Like all pythons, it is not poisonous

Blue-tongued skink This lizard, which can grow up to two feet long, is feeding on a snail

Flightless birds and ancient survivors

New Zealand's isolated islands are a natural laboratory for a large-scale experiment in evolution, nurturing such unique animals as the flightless kiwis

More than 60 million years ago, when many of the types of mammals common today arose and spread across the earth, New Zealand was already formed into islands, isolated from the other land masses by wide stretches of water. For millions of years, the seals around the coasts and two species of bats were New Zealand's only mammals.

But although New Zealand lacks some groups of animals, it has a wealth of native species, especially birds.

In the absence of ground predators, many birds in the dense forests became flightless. The most spectacular of New Zealand's flightless birds, the huge moas, were hunted to extinction by the Maori. The largest species, which stood more than ten feet high, probably died out over 200 years ago.

One theory places the moa in the same group as the African ostrich, the Australian emu, and the South American rhea. Some authorities see the similarity between these flightless birds of different continents as evidence that the southern continents were once linked in a great land mass.

Slow-growing reptile from the age of dinosaurs

Sharing a nest Tuataras often nest in petrels' burrows. Occasionally a tuatara will eat a seabird's chick, but otherwise it eats insects

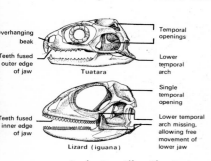

Ancient reptile The tuatara, now found only on the fringes of New Zealand, differs from lizards, particularly in its skull and jaw structure

Frog without a tadpole stage This is one of the three rare frogs that are New Zealand's only native amphibians. They hatch as tiny frogs with tails

Giant weta This fearsome cricket—about four inches long—can inflict a painful wound by kicking with its spiky hind legs

New Zealand provides a great range of habitats—forests, rivers, lakes, swamps, grasslands, and mountains—with a wide variety of climates. But the years of European occupation, and with it the introduction of foreign animals and plants, have upset the original balance of nature and caused immense changes. Unable to adapt to altered conditions or to change their habitat, some species have not survived and others, once common, are now rare.

The tuatara, an animal found only in New Zealand, is the sole survivor of a group of reptiles, the Rhynchocephalia, which otherwise have been extinct for 100 million years.

Superficially, the tuatara looks like a lizard; it grows to about two feet long, with a crest of spines down its head and back.

Like lizards, it can grow a new tail if necessary. It has a rudimentary "third eye," called a pineal eye, on top of its head. Tuataras lay their eggs in a depression, which is then covered over. The eggs remain buried and unattended until they hatch 15 months later. Tuataras grow slowly—a rate of a half inch in eight years has been recorded—and they have a long life-span; one is known to have lived for 77 years.

New Zealand's true lizards are the geckos and the skinks. Geckos hunt insects, mostly in the foliage of trees and shrubs. Skinks feed on vegetables, fruit, and earthworms, and live on the ground, under stones and logs.

The three species of native New Zealand frogs are both primitive and rare. They lay their eggs in moist places under rocks or logs. Since they are adapted to living on mountain ridges, far from water where tadpoles could develop, minute frogs emerge straight from the eggs, bypassing the free-swimming tadpole stage of other frogs.

Arthropods—animals with segmented bodies and jointed limbs—are represented by wood lice, millipedes, spiders, and insects. In addition there are four species of *Peripatus,* which live under rotten wood and in moist soil. These belong to a group of animals called the Onychophora, which have segmented, soft, flexible bodies and are intermediate between arthropods and annelid worms, such as earthworms. Their ancestry goes back 400 million years. The New Zealand species may be three inches long and have up to 25 pairs of legs.

Kakapo This large parrot, up to 26 inches, climbs trees and makes long glides to earth. It has well- proportioned wings, but its breast muscles are not strong enough to sustain true flight

Rediscovered bird The takahe was thought to be extinct for 50 years, until it was spotted in 1948

The kiwi, takahe, and kakapo—New Zealand's flightless birds

Many of New Zealand's native bird species have dwindled in numbers as forests were cut over. Also, introduced species almost invariably predominated over native birds in areas put under cultivation. Many native species still survive in the bush, lakes, and swamps, but roughly 12 native species are now extinct.

Some New Zealand birds probably became ground foragers in the absence of land mammals to prey on them and no other species competing with them for food. These birds evolved heavier bodies and smaller wings than other birds. Over the centuries they became flightless.

The kiwi is one of the most familiar flight- less birds. It gets its name from its call. There are three species, all robust birds hav- ing powerful legs and a long slender bill with nostrils at its tip. The feathers are loose, shaggy, and hairlike, the reduced wings are almost invisible, and there is no tail. Kiwis forage at night, plunging their bills deep into the earth to seize worms and insect larvae, which they detect by smell—a faculty rare among birds. Another flightless bird, the takahe, was believed extinct until a colony was discovered in Fiordland in the South Island. It nests in a kind of bower between tussocks in alpine valleys and in winter moves to the beech forest.

The kakapo is another rare, flightless bird that survives only in Fiordland. It lives in mossy beech forest from sea level to about 4000 feet. The kakapo feeds on the fruit of mountain shrubs and the leaves and roots of grassland plants. It chews blades of tussock grass, leaving balls of fibrous matter hanging from the plant.

Rare birds in the mountain forests

The kea, an inquisitive, fearless parrot, is found only in the mountain forests and grassland of the South Island. Its food nor- mally consists of leaves, buds, and fruit, but the kea will eat carrion—the only instance of a parrot with flesh-eating tendencies.

The tui is a melodious songster with a range of notes that extends beyond human hearing. It is one of several New Zealand honey eaters and feeds on nectar, fruits, and insects.

Two species of predatory birds present in New Zealand are the rare New Zealand fal- con, or karearea, and the harrier, or kahu, found throughout the southwest Pacific.

Kea
Nestor notabilis
Kakapo
Strigops habroptilus
Takahe
Notornis mantelli

NORTH ISLAND
TASMAN SEA
SOUTH ISLAND
NEW ZEALAND
PACIFIC OCEAN

Mountain birds Kakapos and takahes live only in isolated val- leys. Keas are more widespread

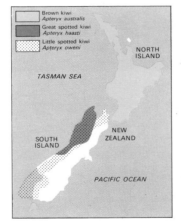

Brown kiwi
Apteryx australis
Great spotted kiwi
Apteryx haasti
Little spotted kiwi
Apteryx oweni

NORTH ISLAND
TASMAN SEA
SOUTH ISLAND
NEW ZEALAND
PACIFIC OCEAN

Forest parrot The kaka, an active, noisy bird with a harsh call, lives in the forest

Birds of the woodland Kiwis are becoming adapted to life in open country, since much of their original forest habi- tat has been destroyed. Fe- male kiwis lay enormous eggs, each amounting to as much as one seventh of the bird's weight. Because of their nocturnal habits, kiwis are sel- dom seen

The kea This parrot usually eats plant food, but it will feed on carrion such as dead sheep

Pukeko Related to the takahe, the pukeko, found in swampy areas, has not lost its ability to fly

Tui The tui is also known as the parson bird be- cause of the tufts of white feathers at its throat

THE GRASSLANDS

Vast areas of grassland lie in the interiors of the continents. Man has taken much of the temperate grasslands for farming, but great herds of wild animals still roam the savannas of tropical Africa

The grasslands of the world separate forest from desert. They form transitional zones where dry and moist climates shade into each other, where rainfall is often erratic and drought an ever-present threat.

Many factors determine the character of a region of grassland, and of the animals it will support—from the herds that feed on the grass to the flesh-eaters that prey on the herds. One such factor is soil composition, but the most important is climate—rainfall and temperature. Both temperate and tropical (savanna) grasslands are considered here. The animals of the plains, large and small, plant-eaters and flesh-eaters, ultimately depend on the grasses for their food.

Grass is one of the most reliable food sources. After being cropped by animals, it grows quickly by putting out horizontal stems. Many species are stimulated to new growth by being trampled flat by grazing animals, and they put out additional roots from the nodes, which are the joints dividing the hollow grass stems into sections. Grasses tolerate the dry climate better than trees, and savanna grasses quickly renew themselves after fires.

Temperate grasslands

Grasslands occupy the interiors of continents in the temperate zones, where summers are hot, winters are cold, and rainfall is low throughout the year. In such regions, a rolling carpet of grass covers the surface; only on the shores of lakes and along river-banks is there enough moisture to allow even the hardier species of trees to grow. These roughly are the conditions that prevail in the steppes of Eurasia, the North American prairies, the South American pampas, the South African veld, and the Australian downlands.

The largest area of temperate grasslands is the Eurasian steppe, a great plain stretching for more than 2000 miles from Hungary through southern Russia to China. To the north it merges with the deciduous or coniferous forest; to the south it is bordered by the Black Sea, the Caspian Sea, and the deserts of central Asia.

In earlier centuries the North American prairie stretched from Canada's prairie provinces almost to the Gulf of Mexico, and eastward to the land south of the Great Lakes. In the humid low prairies to the east the grass sometimes grew 12 feet high, swallowing up animals and men. Now, in the tall-grass areas that remain, the grass is five to eight feet high. Farther west, in the drier middle prairies, "mid-grasses" grow to four feet high. The high prairies in the lee of the Rockies are still drier, supporting clumps of short, wiry grass that seldom grow higher than a few inches.

The pampas of Argentina cover 200,000 square miles of plain south of the rain forest, sloping gradually from the foothills of the Andes to the Atlantic. The western pampas are mainly desert, but the wetter eastern pampas near the coast are a region of tall, coarse, tufted grass. The pampas merge with the swampy savanna of the Gran Chaco in the north, and fade into desert in Patagonia, in the south.

The veld in southern Africa, being close to the sea, does not suffer from great extremes of temperature, but the climate gets drier from east to west and the grassland passes gradually into desert.

Australia's temperate grasslands occupy most of the Murray-Darling river basin, sloping down from the eastern mountains to the central plain. In the east, where more rain falls, the grasslands are dotted with eucalyptus trees. In the west the grass is scant, giving way in places to mulga scrub—dwarf acacias like those that grow in the drier parts of India.

Tropical grasslands—savannas

The tropical grasslands are in areas where temperatures are relatively high all year round and rain falls only in the summer. Here, the dominant vegetation is tall, coarse grass, sometimes more than ten feet high. The flat-topped trees that dot the region are so widely spaced that they do not compete with one another for water during the dry winters. The savannas of Africa, India, and northern Australia, and the llanos and campos of South America, are characterized by this type of vegetation.

More than a third of Africa's 11 million square miles is savanna—wide plains of tall grass with clumps of cactuslike euphorbias or solitary acacias and baobab trees. The savannas lie north and south of the equatorial rain forest and are linked in East Africa by the high-altitude grasslands of Kenya and Uganda.

The grasslands of India are man-made. The dry, open woodlands that once covered the peninsula have been cut over and converted to short-grass savanna dotted with small trees.

To the north of the equatorial forest in South America lie the llanos of Venezuela and eastern Colombia, watered by the Orinoco and its tributaries. South of the forest are the campos of the Brazilian highlands—savanna with stretches of woodland growing along the slopes.

Tropical grassland An alert cheetah watches for prey from the boughs of an acacia. The extensive savanna of Africa is dotted with these drought-resistant trees

Plants of the dry plains

Grasses can withstand drought, recover from fire, and regrow after cropping by animals; they need all of these qualities to survive in the dry continental heartlands

All the grasslands have a short rainy season. The savannas, lying in subtropical zones, have hot, dry weather—except in summer when the tropical rain belt, which shifts north and south with the sun, brings torrential rain. The temperate grasslands lie either in the heart of the continents or in the lee of mountain ranges, and the winds carry rain to them only in spring and early summer.

Grass, shrubs, and trees flourish during this brief annual watering; but the moisture in the soil quickly evaporates in the dry season, and growth comes to a standstill.

In the temperate grasslands the rate of evaporation is lower in winter because of the cold; but in the tropics the level of a lake may drop six feet during the dry season.

Temperature, another controlling influence, varies throughout the grasslands. The steppes and prairies are extremely hot in summer, but the winter is cold and frosts preclude plant growth. In the tropics temperatures never fall below 64° F. (18° C.).

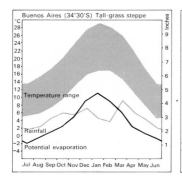

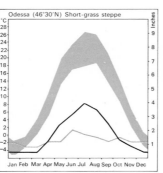

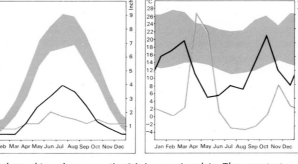

Grassland climates In the grasslands, potential evaporation outstrips rainfall in the course of a year because of the dry conditions and clear skies that prevail. Of the three examples, the savanna of Kenya shows the least variation in temperature (given here in centigrade). The greatest extremes occur at Odessa. Savanna scrub near the equator has a longer wet season than the pampas

Response to rain The dry season bakes the Kenya highlands, and exposed soil crumbles (top). Temperatures drop with the coming of the rains, and grass quickly covers the hills (bottom)

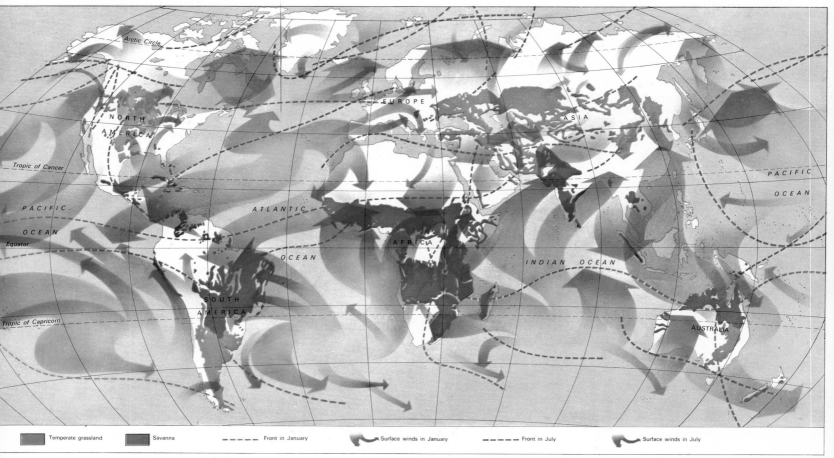

| Temperate grassland | Savanna | Front in January | Surface winds in January | Front in July | Surface winds in July |

The world's grasslands The seasonal rainfall of the grasslands is related to their location. The temperate grasslands of the northern hemisphere lie far inland, away from the moderating influence of moist sea winds. Southern hemisphere grasslands, though closer to the sea, lie in the path of dry winds for most of the year. The savannas lie in the dry high-pressure zone, but the equatorial rain belt shifts, bringing rain for a few months each year

Tussocks on the pampas The Argentine pampas stretch from the Atlantic to the foothills of the Andes, broken only by low hills. The soil is hard, and the rain, falling mainly in heavy showers over a short period, seldom penetrates beyond the top layer. Tussocks of feather grass cover most of the eastern pampas, patches of scrub and forest dot the damper hollows. In the arid west, grass is rare, and thorny shrubs and small trees are the main cover

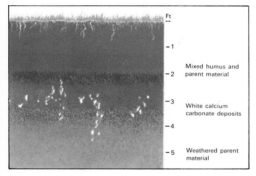

The making of black soil The most widespread type of soil in temperate grasslands is called chernozem—Russian for "black earth." The blackness of the top layer comes from humus

Basic food of the plains

The plant communities of the grasslands include many drought-resistant shrubs and trees—acacias in Africa, mesquite in North America, and saltbush in Australia are typical examples. But the grasses are dominant, and form the basic food on which nearly all animal life in the region ultimately depends.

Grasses thrive in a wide variety of soils and climates, from the rich black earth of the prairies, steppes, and pampas, to the poorer soil of the African savannas. Grasses not only survive better than most trees in dry, drought-prone climates, but also recover quicker from fire, which is always a potential danger in the dry season. Savanna fires often ravage vast areas of grass and scrub. The shrubs may take years to regrow.

The plant that keeps growing

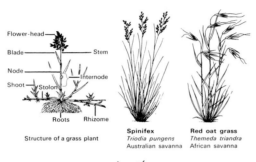

Structure of a grass plant

Spinifex
Triodia pungens
Australian savanna

Red oat grass
Themeda triandra
African savanna

Blue grama grass
Bouteloua gracilis
North American prairies

Dallis grass
Paspalum dilatatum
South American pampas

Crested wheat grass
Agropyron cristatum
Russian steppes

After being cropped by animals, grass grows quickly by producing horizontal stems—either stolons or rhizomes. After being trampled flat, many species survive by putting out growth from the nodes—joints that divide the hollow stem into sections called internodes. In the dry season grass withstands the lack of moisture in the upper layers of the soil by means of fibrous roots, which may reach as deep as 15 feet. Grasses tolerate flooding better than woody plants, and savanna grasses renew themselves after fires, some by putting up new shoots and others by having a large crop of seeds that lie dormant until the wet season returns

A sea of flowers Flowers bloom after rain in a dry area in Australia. Many plants die down after flowering and conserve nutrients in their roots

Destruction and regeneration on the dry savanna

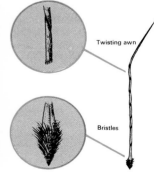

Storks feed on fleeing lizards when fires break out on the African savanna in the dry season. The red oat grass survives because its seeds are buried in the soil. The bristly seeds are forced into the soil as their moisture-absorbing awns twist in response to changes in humidity. When the plant cover is removed and the roots die, the soil becomes vulnerable to erosion by wind and rain. These gullies resulted from overgrazing by hippos

Adaptations to grassland life

The world's largest plant-eaters and swiftest predators are found in the grasslands, where, because hiding places are so scarce and concealment is difficult, size and speed are the best defense

The mammals of the plains have become adapted to life in the open country, where grass is the dominant vegetation. Since grass is spread in a thin layer over a firm surface, it is best exploited by large, fast-moving animals such as antelopes, zebras, and buffalo. Their size and speed also equip these animals to escape from predators. The small grass-eaters, which are unable to run swiftly, shelter in burrows.

Teeth, lips, and stomachs designed to cope with the tough grass

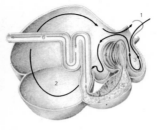

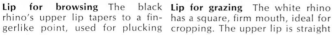

1 Oesophagus conveys food from mouth
2 Rumen, where bacteria break down cellulose
3 Reticulum conveys food to omasum
4 Omasum filters food and extracts water
5 Abomasum breaks down proteins by enzyme action
6 Small intestine continues digestion

■ First digestion   ▨ Second digestion

Ruminant's stomach Ruminants have four-chambered stomachs. Vegetable food is first broken down in the rumen, brought back to the mouth as the cud, then chewed and swallowed again. It passes through two intermediate chambers; then digestion begins in the abomasum

Lip for browsing The black rhino's upper lip tapers to a fingerlike point, used for plucking

Lip for grazing The white rhino has a square, firm mouth, ideal for cropping. The upper lip is straight

Chewing hard food such as grass wears down teeth. The cheek teeth of many herbivores grow continuously, so they maintain the same height despite constant wear. The grinding surface consists of ridges of dentine and enamel which wear at different rates. Thus the grinding surface remains ridged. Teeth made of a uniform material would soon become smooth and inefficient.

Vertebrates cannot themselves manufacture the enzymes that break down cellulose, which forms the cell walls of plants. In grazers these enzymes are produced by bacteria and protozoa, small organisms that live in the gut. The bacteria are able to act on the food more easily because large grass-eaters, such as antelopes and cattle, chew the cud. They first swallow the grass and store it in fermentation chambers in the stomach, where the enzymes begin to break down the plant tissue. Later, the animals regurgitate it and chew it into smaller pieces, providing the enzymes with a greater surface area to work on.

Numbers and keen eyesight promote survival

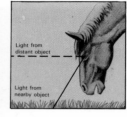

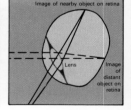

A grazer's eyes

Horses' eyes enable them to keep distant and nearby objects in focus at the same time—to watch out for predators as they graze. Eyes set high and wide apart in the front give horses almost all-round vision

Protection in a herd Many large grazers gain protection by feeding in herds. A signal from one animal will send the whole herd galloping off, like these bison, and the confusion may prevent predators from singling out a victim. Bison have a keen sense of smell and hearing

Long-distance sight is more important to the animals of the grasslands than to those of other biomes, or life zones, since the plains often provide an uninterrupted view. A predator can usually spot its plant-eating prey in the open, although herbivores are well-camouflaged. Herbivores in turn must be able to spot a predator before it comes too close if they are to make the best use of their running power.

The eyes of grazers are usually set well above the snout. The animals can often see over the top of the grass while they feed. As a further adaptation, herbivores generally feed standing on four legs, ready to flee.

Small animals overcome the difficulty of seeing over the grass by hopping up and down or standing on their haunches. The South African meerkat, a species of mongoose, stands on its hind legs to spot the small rodents and snakes it preys on. Hares have developed strong hind legs which enable them to leap and to run rapidly.

Many of the larger herbivores feed in herds, which gives them increased protection, since each animal in the herd is alert to danger. European and North American bison feed in this manner. Both species have poor eyesight but keen senses of smell and hearing, and can detect the approach of a predator while it is still some distance away. The bison has been hunted almost to extinction on both continents, but it is now under protection. Herds are growing, and the animal's survival seems assured.

Small animals such as ground squirrels seek protection from predators and shelter from the climate by burrowing. They are more sensitive to heat and cold than bigger animals because their body surface is large in relation to volume. Burrowing also offers protection against variations in moisture.

Sprinter of the plains The cheetah can hit 70 miles per hour over short distances. It will walk openly toward a herd of grazing gazelles until they bolt, then streak after its intended victim. The cheetah lacks stamina, however, and gives up the chase if it fails to bring down its quarry in 500 yards

Two runners An animal's speed depends partly on the length of its stride, and runners like the horse have evolved long legs. The cheetah's legs and body are shorter, but its more flexible back and limb joints help give it a long stride. A cheetah could outrun a horse over a short distance

Swift-footed hunters and grass-eaters

Some grassland species, such as the elephant, are relatively safe from predators because they are so large that few animals will attack them. And some, like the squirrel, are small enough to hide away in their burrows. But many species owe their survival to their speed, which enables them to flee.

The speed of a running animal is determined by the distance it can extend its legs and the rate at which it strides. In the horse, the powerful muscles that move each long leg are bunched at the top of the limb, so that a small muscle movement can move the slender lower part of the leg over a considerable distance. The bones of the horse's foot have become elongated and the number of toes reduced to one, because one thick bone is stronger than several thin ones. The functional toe bears a tough, protective hoof.

The fastest sprinter in the world is the cheetah. It has shorter legs than the horse, but its supple spine and limbs give it a long and rapid stride. The cheetah, however, soon becomes tired, whereas the horse can maintain a speed of 30 miles per hour for at least four miles.

African springhaas This burrowing rodent can make two-foot leaps with its strong hind legs

Speedy emu The emu is typical of flightless grassland birds. It has long, powerful legs and can run at 35 miles per hour. Up to six feet tall, it is the world's second largest bird

The feet of grassland runners and forest-dwellers

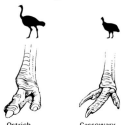

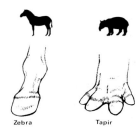

Ostrich   Cassowary   Mara   Pacarana   Zebra   Tapir

Fewer toes The ostrich, fastest of the flightless birds, has only two toes. The cassowary, a forest-dweller, has three

On tiptoe The South American mara moves fast on tiptoe; its forest-dwelling relative, the pacarana, has flatter feet, thicker legs

One-toed hoof The zebra has a one-toed hoof for running, while the forest-dwelling tapir's feet are unmodified

The leaper Kangaroos move in a series of bounds on strong hind legs. The long, thick tail helps balance the weight of the foreparts

Large running birds

Flightless birds are found in three major grassland areas—the rhea inhabits the pampas of South America; the ostrich, the African plains; and the emu is found in Australia.

The ostrich is the fastest of the running birds. Like the swift mammals, such as the horse, it has evolved long legs and a reduced number of toes. It often feeds with herds of large herbivorous mammals. Its height and keen eyesight help it spot danger.

Rhea South America   Emu Australia

Ostrich Africa

Birds that look alike The flightless rhea, emu, and ostrich evolved on the flat grasslands of different continents, possibly from large flying birds that needed to make a long run before taking off. They resemble one another because they have evolved in similar environments

Feeding on plants without competing

Many species of vegetarian animals feed on the African grasslands. Most herbivores have evolved as specialist feeders, permitting them to coexist without severe competition

More than 40 species of large mammals feed on the plants of the African grasslands. In addition to these are the widespread smaller antelopes and other herbivores which are now more common in arid regions of the north. In any one habitat—for example, the bushy grasslands of Kenya or the wooded savanna of Tanzania—as many as 16 species of large herbivores are found together.

The population density of these large grass-eaters on the African grasslands is also high. Nairobi Park in Kenya supports nearly 100 of these animals per square mile.

This concentration of animals does not lead to severe competition between species for food, because each has its own preferences, even when several different species graze upon the same plant. Red oat grass, for instance, is eaten by the zebra, the wildebeest, and the topi, but each feeds upon it at a different stage of the grass's growth. This limited competition, the result of evolution, permits a great variety of animals to fit into an environment. Every species has its niche, from the smallest insect to the elephant.

Herbivores are adapted so that they take advantage of different levels of the vegetation, or they have developed preferences for the main plants of different habitats. Some feed by day, others by night. Some animals can remain in the arid plains during the dry season, while many others must migrate to water. Different combinations of all these factors in different species allow many species to share a habitat.

Variations of food and habitat

Browsing animals of different heights can share the same tree. The long-necked giraffe can browse on 18-foot-high branches; the eland feeds on shrubs and the lower leaves and twigs of trees; and the tiny dik-dik (only 12 to 16 inches high at the shoulder) eats the lowest growth. Grass-eaters also have different preferences. Buffalo eat coarse woodland grasses, wildebeests and zebras the grasses of the plains, and impalas the fine grass of wooded savanna. Warthogs graze, and also feed on the underground parts of plants, which they grub from the earth with their snouts and teeth.

The African savanna contains a great variety of habitats. Open grassland grades into parkland studded with tall acacia trees, or shrubby acacias and thorn scrub. In some places there is dense bush, and trees may grow along the edges of rivers.

Some animals stay only in one habitat—the sitatunga keeps to marshy areas, and the lesser kudu to dense cover—but most prefer areas where different kinds of vegetation meet. These areas offer wider choice of food, shade, and avenues of escape.

The lives of all African animals are dominated by the wet and dry seasons. When food is abundant after the rains, herbivores disperse widely; but in the dry season, many must move to areas near rivers and lakes, to find drinking water and better pasture. Not all species congregate in the same area. In the Rift Valley of Tanzania, migrant zebras and wildebeests congregate some 40 miles apart.

On plains that are flooded annually, the waters retreat at the beginning of the dry season, gradually exposing different types of grasses which attract various animal species in succession. As the floods recede from the flats around lakes in Tanzania, elephants and hippos move into the marshes and shallows to feed on semifloating grasses. Their heavy trampling helps to stimulate fresh growth, the young shoots of which are food for buffalo. The grazing buffalo leave short

The tree-eater With its long neck, the giraffe can reach up to tender leaves inaccessible to other animals. Giraffes leave a browse line in the trees at the limit of their reach

Eland The eland, a versatile feeder, grazes and browses with equal ease. Farmers encourage its presence in some places because it helps reduce shrub growth and promote grazing areas for sheep

Dik-dik browsing The dik-dik, one of the smallest antelopes, eats the lowest twigs and leaves

Marginal zone Zebras and impalas graze in wooded savanna at the edge of riverside forest. Such mixed zones, where habitats blend, offer a variety of food and escape routes

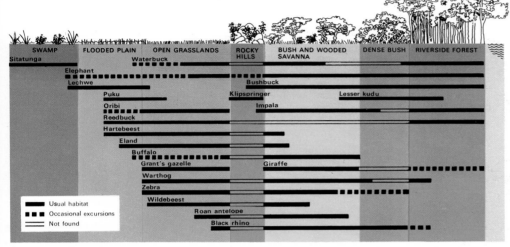

Sharing the savanna Herbivores divide available food by exploiting separate areas or by feeding on different levels of vegetation. In the dry season some stay on the plains, others migrate

Biomass in lb. per 10 sq. miles

No of animals per 10 sq. miles

Nairobi National Park biomass The biomass is the total weight of animals supported by a given area

grass in their wake, and it makes suitable pasture for antelopes. Many of these lakes are alkaline, and as the waters recede still farther, grasses which tolerate alkaline conditions appear and provide grazing for zebras.

Grazing pressure is intense between June and October, and the pastures may appear overgrazed. But when the November rains flood the lakes the grasses grow again. Toward the end of the dry season fires often sweep through the parched grass.

The animal community

The many species of herbivores that live on the African savanna are not a haphazard collection of animals but an interrelated community. Different species with varying food preferences and feeding habits have evolved in close proximity to each other.

As a consequence, the carrying capacity of natural grasslands is extremely high. Food supplies and animal populations vary from one area to another, and the two are best related in terms of biomass—the total weight of animals living in a particular area. This gives a more useful picture for comparison than counting the animals present, since an 8000-pound elephant eats 20 times more food than a 130-pound impala. The almost 100 animals per square mile in Nairobi National Park represent a biomass of 70,000 pounds. Other such areas may support a biomass of 100,000 pounds per square mile.

The total animal community includes large carnivores and a multitude of insects and birds. All these are part of a living system which rests on the balance between the plant community and the animal community.

Lakeside pasture Elephants feed on grass in retreating floodwaters at the start of the dry season

Impalas grazing Impalas do not need to drink; they get water by eating dew-moistened grass

End of the great migration Zebras, greater kudus, and elands drink together at a water hole. During the dry season large mammals like these migrate to grasslands near water

97

The great herds

The browsers and grazers of the savanna live in huge herds sometimes numbering in the thousands. The very size of the herd offers protection against predators

Many of the animals that feed on the grasslands live in herds. One of the biggest advantages of this mode of life is that the chances for detecting the approach of a predator increase with the size of the herd. One or several animals can spread the alarm for the whole herd to flee.

Herds of more than 100 elephants are common, and a buffalo herd may number 500 to 600; but the greatest herds of all are the congregations of 10,000 or more wildebeests and zebras which live on the plains of East Africa.

One of the few undisturbed areas that can still support these immense herds is the 15,000-square-mile Serengeti Plain, lying between Lake Victoria and the Rift Valley in Tanzania. Zebras, gazelles, and wildebeests form the dominant herds of the Serengeti. In a 1963 census 330,000 wildebeests were counted in this area. Wildebeests make regular migrations in huge herds.

Mating, birth, and death on the wildebeest's trek

Wildebeest herd Wildebeest, or "wild ox," is the Afrikaans name for the brindled gnu. Adult males are 4½ feet high at the shoulder. Over 300,000 wildebeests inhabit the Serengeti Plain

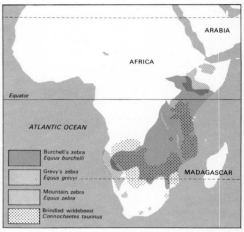

Zebras and wildebeests The South African wildebeest, or white-tailed gnu, is now rare

The wildebeest is the Serengeti Plain's chief herbivore in terms of biomass; and it is the chief prey of large carnivores such as lions and hyenas.

During the rainy season wildebeest herds are widely dispersed over the eastern Serengeti. At the onset of the dry season the easternmost sections quickly dry out. The wildebeests concentrate on the remaining green parts, gradually forming huge herds, which finally move off westward in search of fresh areas for grazing.

The migration is scarcely under way before the annual rut begins. Like many male antelopes, bull wildebeests establish territories which they defend against rivals and within which they try to assemble herds of females. But the bulls in a migrant herd can connect and maintain their breeding herds only during pauses in the trek. As soon as the mass movement resumes, the female herds merge.

The herds spend the dry season in the western part of the Serengeti. At the end of this season they begin moving back toward the east, in anticipation of the fresh pasture that grows after the rains.

The start of calving usually coincides with the start of the rains and reaches a climax at a time when the wildebeests are improving in condition.

How breeding and migration are keyed to the rains on the Serengeti

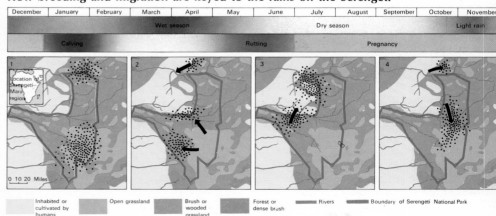

The great trek A herd of wildebeests moves in summer along ancient trails to the river lands

1 During the rainy season wildebeest herds, widely spread on the Serengeti and in the Mara area farther north, graze on a flush of grass. 2 As the dry season advances, the herds join and move west.

The animals mate during the migration. 3 The herds spend the dry season in wooded grassland near rivers. 4 As the rainy season nears, the herds split and return to open grassland for calving

Burchell's zebras All zebras reinforce family ties by mutual grooming. Burchell's zebra has several races, distinguished by their stripe pattern. One race has shadow stripes between the main bands

Grevy's zebra This species forms mixed herds with Burchell's zebra in areas where their ranges overlap

Zebras maintain family ties in herds of thousands

Zebras occupy the same habitat as wildebeests and migrate with them. To some extent the two groups compete, since both graze on the Serengeti's red oat grass.

Burchell's zebra is the common zebra of East Africa, though two other species overlap its range—Grevy's zebra in the north and the mountain zebra in the south. Grevy's and Burchell's zebras may form mixed herds.

All species of zebras have dark bands arranged over part or all of a lighter-colored body, and an erect mane. Burchell's zebra has the greatest variation in width and number of stripes.

Zebras move in large herds which are loose gatherings of family units drawn together by the availability of pasture. A family consists of a stallion and about six mares with their foals. Family groups are stable. If the stallion is killed, the group does not disperse but the mares and foals are adopted by another male.

Young stallions are tolerated by their sire and remain with the family until they are three years old, when they leave and join bachelor herds. Young females, however, are sought by all males, and though the sire fights strongly for their possession, they are usually enticed away from the family before they are two years old.

Zebras give birth all year round, but the majority of foals are dropped during the rainy season. Adult zebras weigh 700 pounds and stand four feet at the shoulder.

Zebras mingle with many other animals of the savanna, including wildebeests, elands, and ostriches. This is partly an adaptation for mutual defense. For instance, the keen eyes of the ostrich supplement the zebras' sense of smell, giving intensified awareness of the approach of predators. When alarmed, the zebra emits a yelping bark.

Gazelle herds that graze on the Serengeti Plain

Thomson's gazelle A white disk on the rump and a dark side stripe are the marks of this gazelle

Grant's gazelles These gazelles are larger than Thomson's gazelle, up to 35 inches high at the shoulder. The horns are larger, the rump patch is T-shaped, and the side stripe is paler or absent

Two species of gazelles also form large herds. One of them, Thomson's gazelle, is the most numerous species in East Africa, totaling 500,000 to 800,000 head on the Serengeti Plain. The other, Grant's gazelle, is less numerous, with 100,000 head.

Thomson's gazelle is a grazer. It prefers short-grass savanna and needs access to surface water, so it follows the migrations of the wildebeests and other grazers. Grant's gazelle, a larger animal, is a grazer and browser and can live without surface water, so it can spend the dry season on the plains.

The two gazelles have many similarities in behavior and appearance, and mixed herds are commonplace. They differ most markedly in their territorial and threat behavior.

Grant's gazelles have large territories, half a mile in diameter. Thomson's gazelles' territories are 200 to 300 yards in diameter. In settling territorial disputes, Grant's gazelles go no further than striking threatening postures. Thomson's gazelles fight, though usually without injury.

When danger threatens, both gazelle species make abrupt, stiff-legged bounds and their white rump hairs flare out in warning. Jackals take many fawns, and adults are run down by cheetahs and hunting dogs. When a gazelle is pursued, it sometimes runs back into the herd. This confuses the predator, which loses sight of the intended victim among the many other animals, and often gives up the chase.

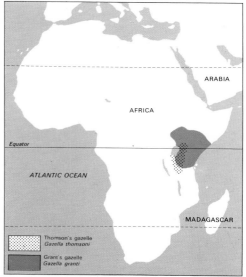

Grassland gazelles Thomson's gazelles live mainly on the Serengeti Plain

Antelopes

Antelopes live in all regions of Africa, from forest to desert, but are most common in the savanna, where many species occupy a mosaic of habitats without conflict

Antelopes are members of the family of grass-eating animals called Bovidae, which includes cattle, sheep, and goats. The Bovidae, one of the most successful groups of mammals, are ruminants, or mammals that chew the cud.

All antelopes have horns, including the females of some species. Horns vary from short spikes to huge, spiraling curves.

Antelopes probably originated in Africa and spread into Eurasia, although modern Asian species, such as the nilgai, evolved there. Africa now has 72 species of antelopes. The waterbuck, greater kudu, duiker, suni, and Grant's gazelle are among them.

Not all antelopes live in the savanna. Duikers, for example, are typically animals of the forest. Unlike antelopes of the open plains, which usually band together in herds, forest-dwelling antelopes are often solitary creatures, since they can take cover among the trees and undergrowth.

Among giants and midgets, a sharing of food

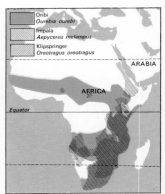

Impala bucks fighting   At maturity young male impalas challenge herd leaders, and eventually gain harems

African antelopes   Lower map shows distribution of spiral-horned Bovinae; upper, the smaller Antilopinae

Many species of antelopes are able to live on the African savanna, because each has developed adaptations and food preferences that have reduced competition.

Some antelopes have become so efficient at exploiting a particular niche in the environment that their habitats do not overlap. For example, the lechwe lives in flooded grassland; the eland in arid open grassland; the nyala in bush savanna; the sitatunga in marshes. The sitatunga is perhaps the most specialized, for it has long, splayed hooves that enable the animal to move freely over the swampy surface.

The range of sizes that exists even within a single tribe is illustrated by the spiral-horned antelopes. The largest, the giant eland, is ten times heavier than the 180-

Biggest and smallest

The grassland antelopes range in size from the giant eland to the tiny suni. In both cases the size is a result of adaptation to the environment

pound bushbuck; yet their common ancestry is obvious in their strong spiral horns and in the faint white vertical stripes on the sides of their deep bodies.

Another group of large antelopes includes the roan antelope, the sable antelope, and the oryxes. Roan and sable antelopes both graze in woodlands, but the species do not intermingle where their ranges overlap. Both like to be near water. The oryxes, on the other hand, live in conditions of extreme aridity, obtaining moisture from roots.

Africa's smallest antelopes include the klipspringer, two species of oribis, seven species of dik-diks, and the suni. These are shy creatures which live in cover and rarely form herds of any size.

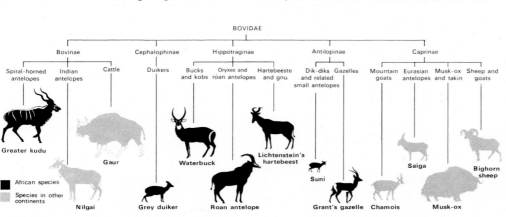

Family tree   Antelopes are members of the family of grass-eating animals called Bovidae, which includes cattle, sheep, and goats. The 72 African species represent four of the five subfamilies

Dweller in farmland The greater kudu survives in settled parts of Africa where most other antelopes have become rare

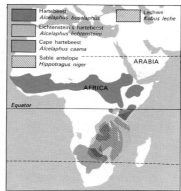

Hartebeests and their relatives Hartebeests belong to a widespread tribe of large antelopes. They are gregarious, herding animals, and will often post a sentinel on a hilltop to warn the herd of danger

The klipspringer This antelope lives on rocky hills. Its cylindrical hooves make it surefooted

Sable antelopes These are among the largest African antelopes, weighing 600 to 700 pounds. The bulls' sweeping horns measure about five feet

Lechwes Lechwes live in large herds on floodplains, where they feed belly-deep on reeds and inundated grasses, moving with the rise and fall of water. They have little competition for food

Jackson's hartebeest A female is shown with her young. All hartebeests have a "rocking-horse" gait which makes them appear awkward, but when alarmed they can gallop swiftly

Horns for fighting and display

There are records of sable antelopes impaling leopards on their horns and of oryxes spitting lions; but antelopes' horns are mainly used in combat between males of the same species, and not against predators.

During evolution, the horns of antelopes have become more and more elaborate. The simplest type are the short, spiky horns of the duikers and dik-diks. As larger horns evolved, an increasing element of ritual entered into their use. Long, sharp horns are dangerous weapons, so fighting behavior and horn shape have both become modified.

The horns of many species have a backward curve. Some may have a thickened base, which shields the skull. The elaborately curved and spiraled horns of some species become securely interlocked when the males fight, so that they cannot inflict much damage on each other.

In other species, males with large horns intimidate rivals without actually fighting. Two rivals confront each other in defiant attitudes, standing stiff-legged, with necks arched and heads held high so that the horns are displayed to their best advantage.

The males of many antelope species hold territories against other males, and mark them by defecating or leaving glandular secretions. Competition is fierce, and only a prime male can hold a territory. There it mates with any receptive females that enter.

101

The giraffe and the gerenuk

The evolution of the giraffe, tallest of living land mammals, has been dominated by one simple fact: high in the trees is an abundant supply of green food

Weirdly shaped trees dot the arid savanna of Africa. Some look like outsize umbrellas, others like hourglasses; still others, no more than four feet high, may stretch into the distance for mile after mile.

These strange shapes are the work of giraffes, whose immense height enables them to escape competing with other herbivores for ground-level vegetation.

The umbrella-shaped trees are those which have branched out above the reach of the tallest giraffe, but have been stripped of foliage below. The hourglass shape is left after giraffes have eaten away branches at about their own head level; and the "dwarf" trees are those whose top shoots were ripped off by giraffes when the trees were young and never re-grew.

Male giraffes, the tallest of living land animals, can tower 18 feet high, and females 15 feet. This height, allied with keen eyesight, gives them the longest range of vision of any ground-living animals.

About 10 million years ago, the giraffe family was represented in Eurasia as well as Africa, but today it has only two species, both in Africa—the giraffe, found in dry savanna, and the okapi, which lives in dense forest.

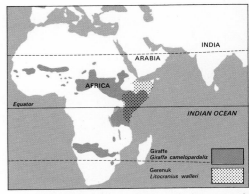

Woodland ranges The giraffe and the gerenuk both live in wooded savanna, but the gerenuk prefers thicker cover and has a smaller range

Timid giants that fight with their heads

Time of danger Because of its long neck and legs, a giraffe must spread its forelegs wide apart before lowering its neck to drink. This awkward position makes it vulnerable to the lion, its only predator, which chooses drinking time as the best moment to attack. Here, adults watch while the young drink

Feeding technique Giraffes pluck leaves from trees by curling their tongues around them. A giraffe can extend its tongue as far as 18 inches

Giraffes are inoffensive and timid toward other animals. They live in rather loose social groups and, though they may gather in herds of 20 or more, lone bulls and groups of two or three giraffes of mixed sexes are more common.

Giraffes will eat from a variety of trees, though acacia leaves form their staple diet. They have four-chambered stomachs, and regurgitate semidigested food. They chew each wad of cud about 40 times.

In spring, when many trees are not yet in leaf, giraffes often spend more than 80 percent of their daylight hours in browsing. In summer, when trees are in full leaf, browsing on foliage may take up only half a giraffe's day.

Mating can occur at any time of the year. Calves are born after a gestation period of about 16 months.

A giraffe's long neck, like that of man and most other mammals, is made up of only seven vertebrae. The individual bones are elongated, attached to one another with ball-and-socket joints which make the neck flexible. When the animal walks, its head and neck move forward and backward, shifting forward the center of gravity and so helping to move its ton of weight along. It can gallop at 35 miles per hour, its neck oscillating in rhythm with its stride. Partly because rising from a lying position is a problem for such a huge animal, a giraffe usually sleeps standing up.

A generous deposit of bone over the top of the male giraffe's skull gives protection in fighting—the heavy, hard head makes a hammerlike weapon when swung by the long neck. Both males and females have short, skin-covered horns.

Problems of a long neck

The spectacular height of the giraffe raises some awkward physiological problems. A massive heart—24 inches long and weighing about 25 pounds—is necessary to pump blood to the head, which soars to ten feet above it. The heart pumps with a force two or three times that of a healthy man, though by the time the blood reaches the giraffe's brain, its pressure has been much reduced by gravity.

When a giraffe lowers its neck to drink, its head dips seven feet below the heart. This could cause a dangerous rush of blood to the brain; but a complex arrangement of blood vessels at the point where the arteries enter the brain, together with valves in the large veins, are built-in defenses against these drastic blood-pressure changes.

Remnants of a widespread species

There are eight races of giraffes in Africa with distinct ranges that are now greatly reduced. The Nigerian giraffe once occupied a great belt of savanna across West Africa, but its range is now fragmented. The other races are the reticulated, Baringo, and Masai giraffes of East Africa; the Kordofan and Nubian giraffes of central Africa and the upper Nile; and the Thornicroft's, Angolan, and Cape giraffes of southern Africa.

The Baringo giraffe is sometimes called the black giraffe, because adult bulls have large, very dark spots which tend to split up into starlike shapes. The female has much more irregular spots, reddish in color. Old bulls usually have several horns.

Reticulated giraffes are a warm reddish brown, with clearly defined, widely separated white lines forming regularly shaped figures all over their bodies, giving them the appearance of being caught in a wide white net. The reticulated is the most northerly of the three East African races of giraffes. It lives in Kenya and Somalia. The Masai giraffe, of Tanzania, is marked with leaf-shaped blotches. The Cape race is a large, dark-colored giraffe, with fewer bony protuberances on its head than the other races. The large, almost black spots of the old bulls are regularly shaped, and stand out clearly on a pale tawny ground. The Nubian race of central Africa is almost the reverse in coloring: it has large, regular, tawny spots on a dark background.

Long-necked antelope

The gerenuk, a member of the gazelle group of antelopes, is another animal that feeds on high foliage. Also known as the giraffe-necked gazelle, it has evolved both a long neck and the habit of standing on its hind legs and resting its forefeet on the bush or tree on which it browses. It measures some 40 inches at shoulder height, with a head, neck, and body length of about 54 inches. The male gerenuk has big horns for its size.

Neck fighting Physical contact is important in relationships between male giraffes. Homosexual mounting is common and males are frequently seen "necking" together, one gently rubbing its head and neck against the head, neck, and body of another. Necking can lead to sparring, but this is usually nothing more than a graceful swinging of necks, more like a dance than a fight. In serious fighting the head is used like a weighted club, swung down to gain momentum for the upswing. Sometimes the necks become entwined and the giraffes must resort to pushing each other

The birth and early struggles of a giraffe

Forelegs first, a giraffe calf emerges in the first stages of birth. After the calf has dropped to the ground—some eight feet—the mother nuzzles it into making its first weak movements. The calf topples forward when it attempts to rise, but can stand on its own within a half hour after its birth

Gerenuks Grasping a branch with its forefeet, a gerenuk reaches above its companion to browse. They are partial to the top leaves of acacias

103

Rhinos, buffalo, and warthogs

Two differing species of rhinos live in Africa; the black rhino is a solitary browser, while the less aggressive white rhino feeds on grass and lives in small herds

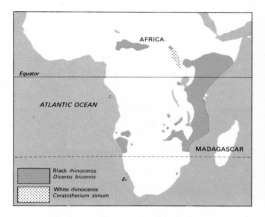

Ranges of African rhinos The black rhino is much more widespread than the white

White rhinos White rhinos are gregarious, forming herds of up to 12 animals, including several adult males as well as females and youngsters. Fighting breaks out occasionally between males

Black and white rhinos: short-sighted giants that graze and browse

The rhinoceros group emerged about 60 million years ago. One extinct member of the family, the Mongolian *Baluchitherium*, was a gigantic herbivore 18 feet tall and 28 feet long—the largest land animal known to have existed. The two African species—the white and the black rhinos—are highly evolved creatures whose drastically reduced range is largely the result of indiscriminate slaughter by man. For centuries, rhino horn has been supposed to have aphrodisiac qualities, and both white and black rhinos have been ruthlessly hunted for their horns.

The black rhino stands up to 5½ feet at the shoulder and can weigh 1½ tons; because of its enormous size it is virtually immune from predators. Its massive horns consist of closely packed fibers rather than true bone-cored horn. The front horns of some animals may measure as much as four feet in length.

One of the reasons why the black rhino thrives, when left alone by man, is that it can eat coarser vegetation than most other herbivores. Its upper lip comes to a small, fingerlike point which enables the animal to pluck twigs, buds, and leaves. Its powers of smell and hearing are acute, but its vision is poor; it probably cannot see stationary objects much beyond 25 yards.

This poor vision probably accounts in part for the black rhino's nervous, wary nature. What appears to be a charge may be no more than an exploratory approach. But such an approach may easily develop into a real attack. The rhino can charge at about 25 miles per hour and change direction with

Adaptations for feeding The white rhino (right) is a grazer and has a longer neck than the browsing black rhino—an adaptation for ground-feeding

surprising agility. Because of its unpredictable nature, it is highly dangerous.

Black and white rhinos are both, in fact, slate gray under the dust that usually covers them, but otherwise the two species differ unmistakably. A grazing animal, the white rhino has a square upper lip with no trace of a point. Its name probably derives from the Afrikaans *wyd renoster*, which means "wide rhino," referring to the broad upper lip. The white rhino is larger than the black species, weighing up to 3½ tons. It has a longer head with larger ears, and carries it lower than does the black rhino.

White rhinos are more placid and sociable than their browsing relatives, and herds of up to a dozen are common. Calves of both species are extremely attached to their mothers and show distress if they become separated. Adult males sometimes attack unprotected calves. Both species of rhinos are promiscuous, rarely forming even semipermanent pairs.

Black rhinos The black rhino is less sociable and more aggressive than the white. It is usually solitary. The male maintains its home range against intruders

Tusked pig of the grasslands

The warthog gets its name from a pair of thick outgrowths from the skin beneath each eye. The males have a second, smaller pair growing on the snout, just above the tusks. These growths may help protect the warthog's eyes when it is grubbing for food; they also exaggerate the size of the head and give mature animals a more fearsome appearance. Male warthogs have large upper tusks, 15 to 25 inches long, which curve sharply outward and upward. The short, sharp lower tusks are used for slashing.

Warthogs live singly, in pairs, or sometimes in family groups. They occupy a well-defined home range and shelter at night in burrows, which they usually take over from other animals and enlarge. They feed by day on grasses, sedges, and tubers. Warthogs like to take mudbaths, and sometimes lie on their backs with all four feet in the air.

Keeping cool in the mud Buffalo frequently wallow in mud to reduce their body temperature. Wallowing probably protects their hide from insects. Crocodiles sometimes attack the calves

Grass-eaters that will charge an attacking lion

Buffalo are Africa's only wild representatives of the Bovini tribe, which consists of cattle-like animals. They are gregarious and often run in herds of 100 or more. Up to 1000 may gather around water holes in dry periods.

Herds are made up of males and females of all ages, but adult cows outnumber bulls by about three to one. Adult bulls form a hierarchy dominated by an animal in its prime, perhaps 10 to 12 years old, weighing 1800 pounds, and standing more than five feet at the shoulder. Bulls engage in usually harmless pushing contests, which end with one bull wandering off either to live alone or to join a bachelor group. These bulls are more exposed to attack by predators, and thus they may inadvertently protect the breeding herds from lions and other carnivorous predators.

The oldest bulls, 13 years old or more, lead celibate lives. By this age the animals' horns have worn down and their coats have become thin.

Crocodiles occasionally take calves wallowing in shallow water, but the buffalo's chief enemy is the lion. Buffalo are not always afraid of lions; irritable old bulls sometimes even charge them. In fact, many lions, especially young ones, are killed while attempting to pull down buffalo.

Buffalo are grazers. They prefer well-watered areas with soft grass, and reed beds in which they can shelter from the heat.

Mating takes place throughout the year with a sharp peak of conceptions toward the end of the wet season, when food is plentiful. Calves conceived at this time are born more than 11 months later, at the beginning of the rains.

In West Africa and the Congo Basin there is a forest-dwelling dwarf race of buffalo known as the bush cow, which weighs around 450 pounds and stands about 43 inches at the shoulder.

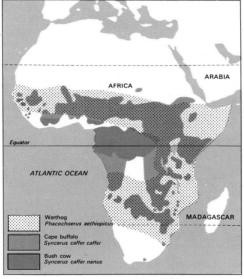

Buffalo races The bush cow is a forest-dwelling dwarf race in West Africa and the Congo Basin

Protected forehead Massive horn bosses, completely covering the forehead of adult male buffalo, protect them in pushing contests. Oxpecker birds are busy picking ticks from this animal's head

Warthog mother and young Warthogs usually have three or four offspring. Family groups live in well-defined home ranges, sleeping in burrows at night

Warthogs pair up for one breeding season and, where the rainfall is high, breed at any time of the year. In drier areas, breeding is seasonal; the young are born just before the beginning of the rains, which bring a plentiful supply of food.

These animals are extremely prolific. A census recently carried out in the area of Rhodesia's Zambesi Valley showed that about 70 percent of the female warthogs were pregnant. The warthog's fertility is based on the shape of the sex organs. The penis ends in a spiral, which fits into a spiral canal through the female's cervix, so sperm enters the uterus directly.

This high rate of fertility is balanced by a high mortality rate. Many of the young drown in the rainy season. Others fall victim to lions, leopards, and jackals. On the average, only one in four survives the first year, but these mature rapidly.

Lions prey heavily on warthogs, especially in the wet season when the tall vegetation makes stalking easier. Where the ground has been softened by heavy rains, lions often dig warthogs out of their burrows.

The lion – lazy killer of the grasslands

The lion, predator supreme of the savanna, spends most of its life resting. It hunts only when it is hungry; even then it may steal another animal's kill instead

Most cats are solitary creatures, but lions live in groups, or prides, made up of from 2 to 30 individuals. The prides are not harems, because they often contain two or more adult males; nor are they exclusively family groups, although lionesses in the group are usually related. A fairly typical pride might consist of two adult males, one very old female, and two younger females, one with three cubs and the other with two.

Lions do not fit easily into community life. Because they are competitive and aggressive animals, relationships within a pride are often tense, and sudden flare-ups occur from time to time. Nevertheless, living in prides has clear advantages, such as the communal rearing of cubs. Sometimes members of a pride appear to hunt together, one lion driving a victim down wind of its partner, in effect setting up an ambush.

Each pride has its own territory, which can vary from 15 to 50 square miles. The male lion plays an important role in the defense of the territory. A full-grown male can weigh 450 pounds, half as much again as a female. While a group of hyenas will sometimes drive unprotected lionesses from a kill, they seldom come close if a male lion is in the vicinity.

The size of a territory depends on the population density of prey. A typical ratio is three or four lions to every 1000 herbivores. Lions prey mainly on antelopes, zebras, pigs, and an occasional giraffe. They will also eat carrion. Open, sandy country is the lion's preferred habitat, with some trees for concealment and shade.

The year's prey of six lions

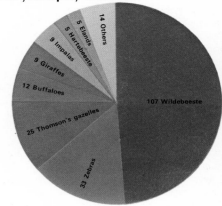

107 Wildebeeste
33 Zebras
25 Thomson's gazelles
12 Buffaloes
9 Giraffes
9 Impalas
5 Hartebeeste
5 Elands
14 Others

Medium-size antelopes, such as wildebeests, are the favorite prey of lions. Wildebeests made up 49 percent of the 219 animals killed in one year by a pride consisting of one male, two females, and three cubs in open country in East Africa

Burst of speed before a kill   A hungry lioness springs in a 35-mile-per-hour charge which carries her into a herd of panic-stricken zebras

Lion with prey   In larger prides lionesses do most of the hunting, but the males eat first

Food for a family   A kill usually provides food for a whole pride. Lions cannot produce vitamin A. They obtain it from their prey, especially from the liver, where the vitamin is stored

Lions, which are fairly common in African grasslands south of the Sahara, are hard to see even in the daytime because their tawny coats blend into the background.

From an evolutionary point of view, lions are the most advanced animals in the Carnivora order. Their teeth are the most highly adapted of all carnivores for biting. The four carnassial teeth, a pair in each jaw, work together like the blades of a pair of scissors. The male lion has a thick tuft of hair at the tip of his tail covering a naillike growth, the purpose of which is unknown. It may be of use in swatting flies.

Lions breed at any time of the year. The female leaves the pride to give birth in a secluded spot, and three or four cubs, weighing about three pounds each, are born after 100 days' gestation. The first ten weeks of their lives, before they are introduced to the pride, are critical. When the lioness leaves them to go hunting, they often fall victim to predators such as hyenas. Fewer than half the cubs live to maturity.

Social relationships in the pride become temporarily more harmonious after young cubs are introduced. Even adult males tend to become more tolerant in their behavior, and two mothers with cubs sometimes share the task of suckling them. The presence of cubs limits the movements of a pride; but as the young grow older the group makes longer journeys, and thus the cubs soon gain knowledge of their home range.

Cubs do not become competent hunters until they are at least 18 months old. At this point, also, their mother is likely to breed again and begin to lose interest in them. More importantly, the older members of the pride become less tolerant of them, sometimes robbing them of their kills and driving young males from the pride.

When the lion turns scavenger

Hunting—carried out at dawn and dusk and also during the night—usually involves protracted stalking followed by a sudden charge. The lion lacks the stamina for a long chase.

Lions kill by leaping at the forequarters of the victim, pulling it to the ground, and biting its throat so that it suffocates. Sometimes a lion will leap onto an antelope's hindquarters, breaking the animal's back with its weight. Many herbivores are swifter than the lion, however, and four out of five hunts end in failure.

Lions generally hunt only when they are fairly hungry, and after a kill they gorge themselves. A hungry lion can eat up to 75 pounds of meat—perhaps one fifth of its own weight—at a time. Meals are followed by a long sleep. In fact, the lion spends most of its life either resting or asleep.

Hyenas often lurk in the background until lions have fed, then scavenge on the carcass. Sometimes the roles are reversed and lions drive hyenas away from their own kills. On the Serengeti Plain as many as a quarter of the carcasses on which lions feed are those of animals that were killed by hyenas.

Games that teach Cubs romp with a male lion, learning to develop their inborn capabilities. In games cubs learn the rudiments of stalking and attacking and how to use their forepaws

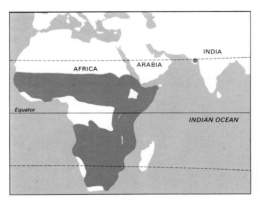

Last refuge The lion, which once ranged from Africa to India, now survives only south of the Sahara and in the isolated Gir Forest of India

Spots that changed The spots on the cub's coat, less obvious on the mother's, may be vestiges of camouflage worn by forest-dwelling ancestors

Affection in the pride The whole pride, even the adult males, seems to treat young cubs with affection

Hunters and scavengers

Fleet-footed hunters are followed by hosts of scavengers that squabble over scraps and pick the bones of carcasses clean

The herds of wildebeests, zebras, and other herbivores that graze on the African savanna support a varied range of flesh-eaters. Some of these live entirely by killing, but hunt only one or two species. The cheetah, for example, specializes in the smaller antelopes, such as impalas and Thomson's gazelles. The cheetah is so swift a runner it manages to

kill one out of every two gazelles it pursues.

Another group of flesh-eaters—hyenas, jackals, vultures, and marabou storks—are typically scavengers.

Hyenas hunt as well as scavenge. In the Ngorongoro Crater, in Tanzania, they are more numerous than the lions, cheetahs, leopards, and hunting dogs combined, and play a greater part in controlling the population of the prey species than any other carnivore. Hyenas hunt in big packs, sometimes numbering as many as 30 animals.

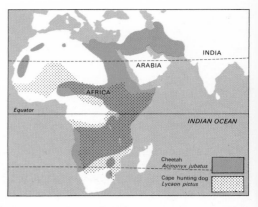

Cheetahs and Cape hunting dogs Cheetahs, now rare in most of their ranges, live in open plains and wooded savannas. Hunting dogs, found from sea level to above the tree line in East Africa, move when the food supply is exhausted

The cheetah, fastest short-distance sprinter in the world

Sprinting to kill A swift cheetah singles out a gazelle, knocks it down with a sweep of the forepaw, and grabs its throat in a suffocating grip

Dinner time Hungry cheetahs in a family party quickly tear a newly killed animal apart. Any delay would allow lions and hyenas to rob them of their meal. Small antelopes such as impalas and Thomson's gazelles are the cheetah's main prey. They often escape, for cheetahs lack stamina for long chases

Long, wiry legs, powerful muscles, a supple spine, and nonretractable claws that grip like the spikes in an athlete's shoe help make the cheetah the fastest sprinter in the animal world. From a standing start it can reach 45 miles per hour in two seconds. Its top speed is 70 miles per hour.

Cheetahs are sometimes seen alone, but they move about more frequently in twos or in small family groups. Females give birth to a litter of two to five cubs after three months' gestation, but only about 50 percent of these survive the first six months.

Cheetahs live almost entirely on small antelopes, such as Thomson's gazelles and

impalas. The cheetah hunts during the day, especially in the early morning and late afternoon. It moves very little during the rest of the day, and will spend hours resting on a termite mound or in a low tree.

When a hunt begins, the cheetah follows one of two basic systems. The first is to walk slowly and openly across the plain toward its prey, perhaps a herd of Thomson's gazelles. The gazelles do not panic, but watch the cheetah with alert attention. When it has come within 80 yards of the herd, the female gazelles begin to move away, but territory-holding males allow it to come to within 50 yards before they turn to run. The

cheetah then chooses a particular gazelle, usually one that is moving somewhat apart from the herd, and bounds after it in a tremendous burst of speed. It can maintain its sprinting speed for only 500 yards at the most. The cheetah is built for speed rather than stamina; if it does not overtake its prey quickly, it must give up the chase.

The second hunting technique is to stalk the prey. The cheetah creeps up quietly on grazing gazelles, freezing into a motionless crouch whenever one of the animals looks up. When it has come within 30 yards of its intended victim, it waits until the animal's back is turned before launching a final sprint.

Cape hunting dogs closing for a kill After a chase, the pack closes in on a weakening wildebeest. The dogs tear at its flesh until it falls

Cape hunting dogs run down prey by teamwork and persistence

Cape hunting dogs are social animals. They usually live in packs of six to ten individuals. The pack lives in the open, moving within a home range of 10 to 60 square miles. But when pups are born, the dogs make a temporary den in a warthog or aardvark burrow until the young can run with the pack. Hunting dogs prey mostly on gazelles and young wildebeests. They usually hunt at dawn or just before dusk, and invariably approach a herd quite openly. When the herd panics and runs, the dogs select a single quarry and start after it in a relentless chase across the plains which may not end for five miles.

Food-sharing is vital in the communal life of a pack. The dogs take turns hunting, so that some can remain to guard the pups. When they make a kill, the dogs gorge themselves, bolting chunks of meat before hyenas can assemble and drive them away.

After returning to the rest of the pack, the hunters vomit some of the meat, which is then eaten by those guarding the litter. The guards in turn disgorge meat for the pups. Food is disgorged in response to ritual begging, in which one dog pushes its muzzle against the side of the mouth of another, wagging its tail, whimpering, and lowering its body submissively.

Hyenas and jackals successfully combine scavenging with hunting

Three species of hyenas occur in Africa: the striped, the brown, and the spotted. Hyenas are scavengers by day. A group of spotted hyenas will often drive hunting dogs, cheetahs, or lionesses from their kills and take over the feast for themselves.

In some areas the hyenas themselves become hunters, running down prey at night in packs of up to 30. In the Ngorongoro Crater spotted hyenas kill about 80 percent of the animals they eat—mainly wildebeests, zebras, and Thomson's gazelles. Their kills are also a major source of food for lions.

The savanna has three species of jackals: the golden, the side-striped, and the black-backed. All of them live singly, in pairs, or in small family groups, but they often gather in great numbers to scavenge. Jackals also hunt small antelopes such as dik-diks. In East Africa they are the chief predator of Thomson's gazelles, taking large numbers of newborn calves. Jackals themselves are frequently killed by leopards.

Scavengers at a carcass A spotted hyena and jackals contest the remains of a kill. Packs of up to 30 spotted hyenas run down prey and fill the air with laughterlike noises as they feed

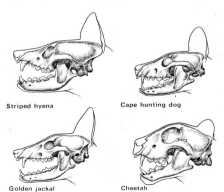

Striped hyena

Cape hunting dog

Golden jackal

Cheetah

Jaws for tearing and crushing The jaws of the hyena and cheetah, both in the cat super-family Feloidea, are more powerful than those of the jackal and Cape hunting dog, of the dog family

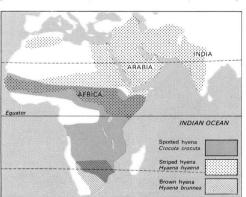

Hyenas In parts of East Africa spotted hyenas outnumber all the other carnivores combined

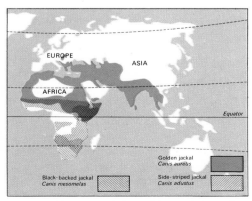

Jackals The range of the golden jackal overlaps that of the two other species in East Africa

The elephant

The elephant, heaviest of land mammals, devastates savanna vegetation. But when its grinding teeth wear out, it faces a slow death from starvation

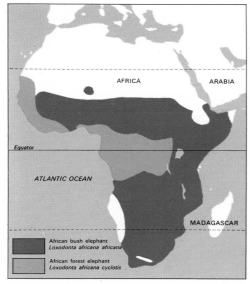

Elephant ranges The natural range of the bush elephant once extended throughout most of the African savanna south of the Sahara, but is now much reduced. The forest elephant is smaller and has rounded ears and thinner tusks

Continuous growth Elephants grow taller and longer all their lives. This sequence of females culminates in a 40-year-old cow standing almost nine feet. A year-old calf can stand between her legs

Nose like an extra limb One of the elephant's most valuable assets is its trunk, an extended nose that can be used as a sensitive, free-moving limb to perform a variety of tasks. With it the elephant tears down high, succulent tree branches, sucks up water to squirt into its mouth or spray over its back to cool itself in hot weather, and picks up fruit or clumps of grass from the ground

Elephants eat a wide variety of plant food, ranging from grasses to tree bark and foliage. They tear down branches and uproot trees with their trunks, and strip other trees of their bark, leaving them to wither and die. In this way they help convert forest to open woodland, paving the way for grass fires, which can ultimately convert a region to treeless savanna.

Not all their work is destructive. In some ways elephants enrich the country and make survival easier for other animals. They provide extra food for browsers by leaving toppled trees and broken branches behind them; they make water available in times of drought by digging wells in dry riverbeds; and they open up salt licks in sodium-rich soil with their feet and trunks.

Elephants prefer wooded country. In the past they migrated from forest areas they had despoiled, giving the vegetation a chance to recover. Today they are largely confined to national parks and reserves. Their movements are restricted and they are forced to circle the same wasted areas over and over again.

Retarded growth in poor conditions

After the seventh year male elephants grow more quickly than females. A 50-year-old bull may weigh 6½ tons and a cow of the same age 4 tons. Few males live longer than 50, but females sometimes survive to 60.

Females usually reach sexual maturity at about ten years, males a year or two later. Bulls sometimes chase cows and fight each other for supremacy. Cows remain in heat for one or two days. A single calf is born after a gestation period of 660 days. Under normal conditions a cow will come into heat again in two years, and will continue to suckle the calf during the next pregnancy.

Today, however, many herds live in such poor conditions, with overcrowding and insufficient food and shade, that fertility is often retarded. In some areas cows do not become fertile until the age of 18, and more than eight years, instead of the usual four, may elapse between successful pregnancies.

The elephant, like many other large mammals in hot climates, has had to find ways to get rid of excessive heat. This is one reason why elephants and rhinos wallow in water with such vigor, and regularly plaster themselves with cool mud. The African elephant has another method of controlling body temperature. Its large ears, sometimes measuring six feet long and five feet across, contain a complex set of blood vessels, and as the ears are fanned backward and forward the blood in them cools as much as nine degrees.

The bones of the elephant's legs are aligned vertically to form straight, pillarlike supports and to minimize the strain on the joints. The springy, resilient pads on the feet serve as weight absorbers, spreading under the enormous load.

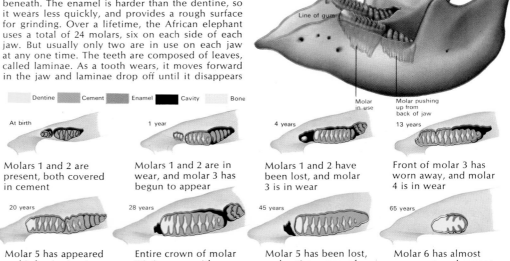

Wasteful feeders

At birth an elephant calf weighs about 250 pounds. A big bull may weigh up to 6½ tons. To support its huge frame, an elephant eats about 5 percent of its weight in food every day, and drinks about 40 gallons of water, sucking up two gallons at a time.

Where there are few trees, grass can form up to 90 percent of the elephant's food, but in wooded areas it relies mainly on branches and leaves. It likes to chew the sap out of roots, which it digs out of sandy soil. The animal sniffs out a buried root with the keen scent organs in its trunk, digs it clear with its front feet, and pries it up with its tusks.

Much of the food emerges almost unchanged in the droppings. The elephant passes a large volume of food quickly through the gut so that only the most nutritious parts are digested. In this way, it can extract adequate nourishment from woody, indigestible food.

A succession of molars

Elephants are rough feeders, destroying much more vegetation than they eat. They pull up tufts of grass by the roots, swallow earth from salt licks, and chew hard, dusty bark—all of which causes severe wear on the teeth. Their huge grinding molars are lost piece by piece as they wear down, and are replaced six times in a lifetime.

When the last of its teeth have gone, an elephant can no longer chew food and may face starvation and death. Old bulls often spend their last years near rivers, where the vegetation is easier to swallow.

Top cow leads the herd Elephants form small family herds of 4 to 16 individuals, consisting of mothers, their young, and immature animals of both sexes. Herds are led by the oldest and biggest cow. These herds last until the leader dies. Then the younger females move off to form their own herds. The males remain with the family group only until maturity, when they join bachelor herds

New teeth to replace the old

The elephant's teeth are so strong that it can chew the branches and roots of trees. At birth, the crowns of the teeth are covered in cement, but this soon wears down, exposing the dentine and enamel beneath. The enamel is harder than the dentine, so it wears less quickly, and provides a rough surface for grinding. Over a lifetime, the African elephant uses a total of 24 molars, six on each side of each jaw. But usually only two are in use on each jaw at any one time. The teeth are composed of leaves, called laminae. As a tooth wears, it moves forward in the jaw and laminae drop off until it disappears

Line of gum

Molar in use

Molar pushing up from back of jaw

| Dentine | Cement | Enamel | Cavity | Bone |

At birth — Molars 1 and 2 are present, both covered in cement

1 year — Molars 1 and 2 are in wear, and molar 3 has begun to appear

4 years — Molars 1 and 2 have been lost, and molar 3 is in wear

13 years — Front of molar 3 has worn away, and molar 4 is in wear

20 years — Molar 5 has appeared and is beginning to replace molar 4

28 years — Entire crown of molar 5 is in wear, with molar 6 appearing

45 years — Molar 5 has been lost, and entire crown of molar 6 is in wear

65 years — Molar 6 has almost worn out, and cannot be replaced

Locked in combat Two large bulls fight over a cow in heat. Such conflicts are soon over, since the stronger animal has little difficulty in proving its superiority. The main weapons the elephant uses are its trunk and tusks. The tusks, actually enlarged incisor teeth, can reach a length of ten feet

Monkeys

African grassland monkeys live in groups; these include many males in areas where food is plentiful. In harsher regions each group can support only one adult male

Dominant males   Other adult males   Adult females   Juveniles   Infants

Baboons on the move When a baboon troop moves, nursing females and their infants travel in the center, protected by dominant males. This central group is surrounded by subordinate males and juveniles of both sexes, but the dominant males determine the direction the group takes

Eight species of monkeys have invaded the African grasslands—probably from the African tropical forests, for monkeys evolved in forest. There are four species of baboons living on the savanna—the yellow baboon, the olive baboon, the Guinea baboon, and the chacma. All are closely related but each occupies a separate area of the grasslands. A fifth species, the hamadryas baboon, lives in arid, rocky country.

Patas monkeys live in arid country bordering the Sahara, and in long-grass savanna. Vervets keep close to the forest fringes, and geladas live in temperate grasslands high in the Ethiopian mountains.

All the savanna baboons and vervets live in large troops which include many adult males. But the basic groups of the hamadryas baboon, the gelada, and the patas monkey contain only one adult male. These one-male groups may be an adaptation to a rather harsh, arid environment. Since one male can fertilize any number of females, other males are eliminated from the group.

The troops formed by savanna baboons vary considerably in size. The average is 27 in the arid country of South-West Africa, 46 in Rhodesia, and 80 in Amboseli National Park, Kenya.

The troop has a home range with a clump of tall trees as a base. The baboons sleep in the trees at night and forage during the day for seeds, fruit, flowers, bulbs, and grasses. In the dry season, baboons dig down as far as 15 inches for roots and tubers. If there is a plague of insects the baboons will eat them, but usually they eat insects only when vegetable food is scarce. Some troops kill an occasional hare, young bird, or infant gazelle.

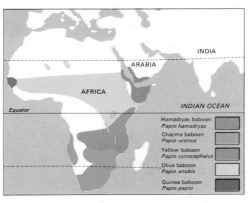

Baboon lands Baboons are the most widespread group of monkeys in Africa. Some authorities consider them races of one species, *Papio hamadryas*

Hamadryas baboon
Papio hamadryas

Chacma baboon
Papio ursinus

Yellow baboon
Papio cynocephalus

Olive baboon
Papio anubis

Guinea baboon
Papio papio

Chacma baboon All baboon young cling to their mother's belly for the first five weeks of life, then ride on her back

Within a baboon troop, all adult males are dominant over all females. A female with an infant acquires temporary rank, but there appears to be no permanent rank order among females. Males, however, have a strict rank order. But often two males will act together to overcome another who is dominant over either of them individually.

When there is a straight hierarchy, the dominant male of the troop has a virtual monopoly over females in heat, and so fathers about 80 percent of the next generation. Other males are at liberty to mate with females that are immature or not in heat.

The dominant male is the most aggressive animal, both to other members of the troop —even females—and to intruders. Females with infants come to it for protection. Young males are extremely pugnacious as they attempt to work their way up the hierarchy. They do not achieve dominance over the females until their fifth year.

Hamadryas baboons have a different pattern of behavior. The full troop is separated into groups, each with a single male and up to six females. These groups, plus a bachelor band of surplus males, forage separately by day and return to cliffs where they all sleep.

Olive baboons Like other savanna baboons, olive baboons sleep in trees at the center of the troop's home range. They leave this core area by day to forage

The females follow the male, which has lifelong associations with all its mates. In other species the males follow the females and the consort pair lasts only while the female is in heat. The hamadryas males prevent other males from herding their females, but they are not sexually jealous.

At three or four years, the male begins to herd by "borrowing" a juvenile from its mother. Two years later, he begins to adopt and herd orphans of both sexes. Finally a female becomes permanently adopted. When the female is sexually mature they mate and become sexual as well as social partners. On meeting a strange female, the hamadryas male will try to herd it, but will not immediately try to mate with it. When the male dies or loses its females in a fight, the females follow another male—perhaps one of the bachelors.

Females that compete for status

Like hamadryas baboons, geladas live in one-male groups which collect together in huge troops. However, their relationships, within both the troop and the group, are different.

Female geladas have a distinct rank order. Each one herds its immediate inferior and tries hard to keep the male away from it. Thus the least dominant females are least likely to bear offspring. Female baboons have more equal chances of reproducing.

Patas monkeys live in groups consisting of one male and as many as ten females with their offspring. Groups have home ranges of about 20 square miles, and very rarely meet. A group may travel half a mile a day, foraging for insects, birds' eggs, and fruit.

The females have a rank order, and the dominant one determines the group's movements. The male is essentially a sentinel, investigating disturbances and, when there is danger, creating a noisy diversion while the others silently run away. The dissociation of the male from the troop, and the troop's lack of contact with other troops, are unique among primates.

Vervet monkeys are members of the genus *Cercopithecus*, which has many forest species. They live near the edges of forest, where fruit and insects are more abundant than in open country. They have the loosest social organization of the savanna monkeys, and live in small troops of 6 to 20 of all ages, with slightly more females than males. Males are dominant over females, but do not have a strongly expressed rank order.

Tail gives support The patas monkey props itself up to peer over grass. The patas is highly adapted for life on the ground, with long forearms and shanks, shortened digits, and a slim, tapered body like that of a greyhound. All these features make for speed and agility. The male weighs about 27 pounds, the female only 11 to 15 pounds

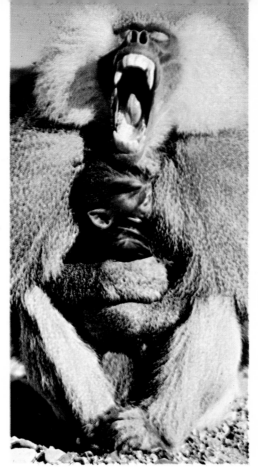

Adult and infant An adult male hamadryas protects a threatened infant, displaying the long canine teeth that are characteristic of all baboons

Tree-dwelling monkey Vervets forage on the grasslands during the day, but seldom move more than a few hundred yards from the trees where they sleep. The troop keeps in touch with barks

Male submission A young male hamadryas baboon submits to the dominant male by "presenting" its rump, imitating the female's sexual submission. This reduces aggression in the dominant male

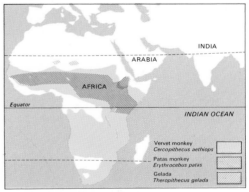

"Herding" the females The male hamadryas threatens and sometimes bites its females when they do not follow closely. They quickly learn to obey

Grassland monkeys Geladas live in temperate grasslands on the Ethiopian plateau. Vervet and patas monkeys both live in the savanna, but vervets prefer wooded savanna and habitats near the forest

Baboonlike geladas Geladas are sometimes called gelada baboons, but they are not closely related to baboons. The two groups have come to resemble each other through adaptation to like habitats

113

Plant-eating birds

The African savanna is the home not only of a vast array of mammals but also of a multitude of birds. The seed-eaters may breed in colonies of millions

Most numerous of all savanna birds are the true weaverbirds of the Ploceidae family. The name weaverbird comes from the birds' method of making their nests with intricately woven vegetable fibers. On the savanna they depend on the grasses for food and nesting material. They have thick bills for husking seeds, and muscular gizzards in which the seeds are ground by small stones before passing farther down the alimentary canal.

The most common and destructive of the weavers is the red-billed dioch *Quelea quelea*, sometimes known simply as the quelea. Since the adults eat only seeds, the estimated 100 billion queleas rival the locusts as one of the scourges of Africa. They ruin vast crops of millet, rice, wheat, and corn.

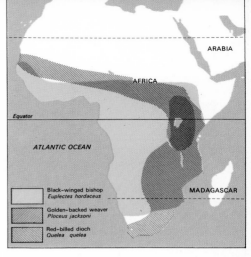

Weavers' ranges These weavers belong to one of the most populous bird families in Africa. Most species are seed-eaters, and they often damage crops

Weavers like the quelea make long flights to find food and avoid rain

Golden-backed weaver Like most of the weavers of the savanna, the golden-backed weaver is polygamous. The cocks build several nests

Guardian male The red bishop, another weaver, is strongly territorial. Each male defends a territory housing the nests of up to six females

Construction of a weaver's nest Using beak and feet to thread, weave, and knot, a weaver constructs a firm vertical ring of grass on supporting vegetation (left). A nesting chamber is built on the ring (center), its size determined by how far the bird can reach from within the ring. Finally the roof is built down over the front. The bird leaves an entrance hole in the underside

Birds, like all animals, must have enough food to live and rear their families, and must be able to escape from predators. To meet these conditions, different kinds of weaverbirds have evolved various solutions.

The queleas may travel up to 1000 miles, in dense flocks, to find small areas with abundant food and water. Once they find such an area they may ravage the entire ground vegetation.

Millions of queleas may appear in an area after the rainy reason has ended and the first flush of grass has appeared. They congregate in huge breeding colonies, covering up to four square miles. These sites are usually new each year, which protects them from predators.

The male weaverbird starts building the nest and the female accepts it, laying the eggs within 24 hours. There may be as many as 400 nests in a single acacia tree or thorny bush. So successful is their nesting and breeding that 87 percent of all eggs laid produce fledglings—a high percentage for perching birds.

Because sheer numbers make a heavy demand on the food supply, both parents cooperate in searching for food.

Communal nests and foster parents

Other species of weavers do not congregate in such large numbers as the quelea, although the sociable weaverbirds of southwestern Africa cooperate to build large communal structures with nesting chambers for as many as 300 pairs.

Golden-backed weavers nest in loose colonies, with the nests suspended from the tips of palm fronds, often over water. The black-winged bishops, by contrast, place their nests low down in strands of vegetation.

Another family of birds that exploit the seed crop are the weaver finches of the Estrildidae family, which includes mannikins and waxbills. A group of parasitic weavers, called whydahs, lay their eggs in the nests of some species of estrildids, leaving their young to be reared by the host bird. A specific choice of a nest is necessary because the host will feed only nestlings that show the same mouth markings and down-pattern as its own young. Consequently, a young whydah must closely resemble the young of its host. The queen whydah, for example, lays its eggs only in the nest of the violet-eared waxbill; the young are almost identical.

Male kori bustard Strutting with swollen throat to attract a mate, the bustard displays white wing and tail feathers

Vulturine guinea fowl This bird usually runs when it is disturbed. Its bare head helps it to dash unhindered through scrub

Parasites and hosts

Queen whydah
Vidua regia

Violet-eared waxbill
Estrilda granatina

Cocks

Hens

Young

The young queen whydah is almost identical to the young violet-eared waxbill, whose nest it shares, but the adults differ greatly

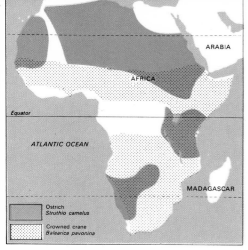

Birds of grassland and desert The ostrich and the crowned crane are grassland-dwellers, but range into the desert as well, the ostrich in the Sahara, the crane in southwestern Africa

Running from danger

The savanna is the home of the ostrich, the world's largest living bird. Males stand about eight feet tall; females are somewhat smaller and duller in color. Five subspecies of ostrich live in Africa.

Both sexes have bare thighs and sparsely covered heads and necks. The lack of feathers helps them to radiate excess heat, for such a large bird has a small surface area to expel heat. The ostrich offsets dehydration, which it can tolerate better than most birds, by drinking large quantities of water. It also obtains moisture from its food —mainly berries and succulents, supplemented by occasional reptiles and insects.

Ostriches are polygamous; each male mates with three or four females. The cocks have conspicuous mating displays in which the white plumes on the wing ends are spread and closed rhythmically. The usually silent cocks emit deep booming calls during this period.

All hens belonging to a cock lay their eggs in a common nest, a hollow scooped out of the ground by the cock. The nest will contain 15 to 20 eggs, each weighing about three pounds. Although these are the largest eggs laid by any bird, their size represents only 1.4 percent of the body weight of the ostrich. Both sexes incubate the eggs, though the male incubates at night, when his conspicuous plumage is less of a handicap. When danger threatens a clutch, the adults may try to lead predators away from the nest with a "broken-wing" display.

The chicks hatch after 40 days. As soon as they dry out, the young, standing about 12 inches high, are able to run. They are fully grown at 18 months, but do not breed for another 3½ to 4 years.

Adult ostriches can run for long periods at up to 40 miles per hour. Like many of the swifter hooved mammals of the grasslands, ostriches have only two toes on each foot, with one toe much enlarged by a strong nail. Their powerful legs enable them to take great strides and their toes provide excellent traction on the firm ground.

The bustards of the Otididae family also have powerful legs adapted for running, but —unlike ostriches—these birds can fly. Sixteen species occur in Africa, ranging from the little brown bustard *Heterotetrax humilis*, which is the same size as a domestic chicken, to the 3½-foot-tall kori bustard. These birds usually feed on insects, but they will occasionally eat vegetable matter as well.

Descent to the nest This handsome bird, the crowned crane, gets its name from the tuft of bristlelike feathers on its head. Cranes are shy, wary birds, particularly when nesting. They are usually seen only when they emerge to search for food—grain, insects, worms, and frogs

Alert ostriches A mirage is barely visible in the background of this photograph. Ostriches survive on the savanna because they can outrun most enemies and because of their watchfulness. Their great height and keen sight give them a commanding view. Grazers like zebras and antelopes use these timid birds as an alarm system by feeding close to them. Ostriches in turn depend on the mammals' keener sense of smell for warning of approaching or concealed predators

115

Hunting and scavenging birds

Many birds of prey and scavenging birds soar high above the open savanna. Their keen eyes scan the ground for prey and carrion

The savanna is home to more species of predatory birds than any other region. They hunt alongside the flesh-eating mammals, and help keep up a ceaseless pressure on the smaller prey. Many of these birds are specialists and do not compete for food. Some kill and feed on different animals, and others eat only certain parts of a carcass, leaving the rest for other birds.

Vultures, more than any other animal, feed on carrion, and they are well equipped for this. Far up in the sky, these keen-eyed birds can survey many square miles of territory. They can also watch for other vultures planing down from the sky to feast. Most have bare heads and necks. A thick covering of feathers would be unhygienic when the vultures are delving deep down into the carcasses.

With long, broad wings, they can soar easily on warm air currents rising from the ground. In strong air currents, they gain height rapidly. Even in still air, vultures with outstretched wings drop only two or three feet per second. Deeply slotted, or "fingered," wings enable the birds to fly slowly without stalling and to maneuver down toward carrion in tight circles.

When a lion, leopard, or other hunter makes a kill and rips open a carcass, as many as six kinds of vultures may gather to feed on the remains. Competition between the species is minimized because they feed on different parts of the carcass. The first arrivals are Ruppell's griffon vulture and the white-backed vulture. With long bills and necks and rasplike tongues, they feed mainly on the soft muscles and intestines. The more powerful lappet-faced vulture and the white-headed vulture use their strong bills to feed on the tough skin and tendons. Two vultures with feathered necks and narrow bills, the Egyptian vulture and the hooded vulture, pick up any scraps that may be strewn around the carcass.

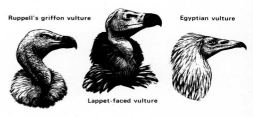

Necks and bills A bare neck and long bill enable Ruppell's griffon vulture to delve into a carcass. The lappet-faced vulture can tear skin with its bill, while the Egyptian vulture, which feeds on scraps, has a feathered neck and a narrow bill

Scavengers at a feast Vultures soaring above the savanna are usually the first animals to spot carrion. They are not always the first to eat, however, because their descent attracts more aggressive scavengers, such as hyenas. Different species of vultures feed on different parts of the carcasses

Egyptian vulture This vulture cracks ostrich eggs by forcefully dropping stones on them until they shatter. The stones weigh as much as two pounds

Using a stone as an anvil If an egg is small enough, the Egyptian vulture picks it up in its bill and hurls it on a stone until the shell cracks

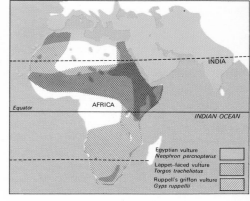

Wide-ranging vultures Most of the species of vultures that scavenge on the African grasslands also range widely into desert and scrub country

Secretary bird and young Secretary birds spend most of their time on the ground. Male and fe-

male work together to build a huge, platformlike nest in a thorn tree, often used more than once

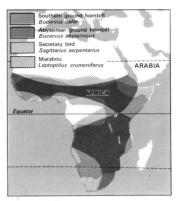

Hunting birds The secretary bird has a smaller counterpart, the dark chanting goshawk

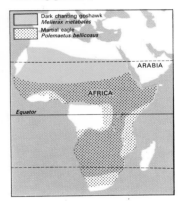

Scavengers and snake killers

Maribou storks compete with vultures for carrion. They also hunt live prey, gathering in flocks at the edge of a grass fire to snatch up rodents and reptiles fleeing from the heat. These storks breed during the dry season. Only 10 to 20 percent of the population nests each year, and on the average

only one chick is produced by each pair. This low birthrate is compensated for by the storks' long life—individuals have been known to live up to 20 years.

Secretary birds, named for their crest of quill-like feathers, and ground hornbills hunt small mammals, insects, and reptiles on foot. They pound snakes to death with their feet, protecting themselves from the fangs with outstretched wings.

A variety of additional hunting techniques are used by other predatory birds. The martial eagle soars high and swoops on its prey, which may be as large as a duiker. The pygmy falcon, only 7½ inches long, the lesser kestrel, and the African hobby all catch insects in flight. Bee-eaters move in flocks, eating various insects and breeding in colonies on sandy cliffs or riverbanks. The carmine bee-eater is one of the most colorful.

Shrikes store their food in a kind of open-air larder; they impale small prey such as lizards on thorns after killing them.

Taking a drink The tawny eagle feeds chiefly on frogs and carrion. It does not soar

Ground hornbill This savanna predator—the size of a turkey—holds a lizard in its bill. It hunts birds, reptiles, and small mammals on the ground

Scavenging storks Marabou storks get most of their food from carrion. They often join vultures at a kill and are capable of sustained, soaring flight

Insect-eaters Carmine bee-eaters breed in colonies. They take many kinds of insects on the wing, often seeking them around grass fires

117

Insects and insect-eaters

Millions of insects help to mold, develop, and maintain the African savanna. All plant and animal life is dependent upon their presence

The countless millions of insects in the African plains help to create the landscape and to control the animal populations. The insect orders with the greatest influence are those of the locusts and grasshoppers, the termites, and the ants. By comparison, arachnids, such as spiders and scorpions, and other invertebrates, such as snails, have a negligible effect on the environment.

In temperate lands, earthworms turn over nutrients in the soils and clear away plant debris. Termites and fire fill these functions in the savanna. Fire turns dry grass, leaves, and wood into mineral ash, water vapor, and carbon dioxide. Termites shift and decompose plant material. They feed on cellulose substances, such as wood. Micro-organisms in the termites' digestive systems and fungi in their nests break down this tough cellulose into food for the termites and for other insects, plants, and animals. Termites in effect bring cellulose back into circulation.

Without fire and the insect hordes—perhaps as many as 100,000 species live south of the Sahara—the energy cycles that support plant and animal life would collapse.

Kissing bugs and sweat bees live off large animals

"Kiss" of death A kissing bug sucks the body fluids from a caterpillar, holding it with its legs. Some kissing bugs feed on mammals

Army of destruction Caterpillars of the *Spodoptera exempta* moth, known as army worms, swarm across the grasslands by the millions, eating ravenously

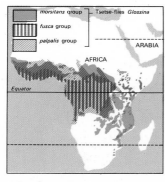

The fly belt Three groups of tsetse flies form the genus *Glossina*. The *morsitans* live mostly in savanna, the *fusca* in rain forest, and the *palpalis* in trees beside permanent water

Tsetse fly emerging The blood-sucking tsetse fly transmits parasites which cause sleeping sickness in man and similar diseases in domestic stock. Here a young adult tsetse fly struggles out from the puparial shell

Only a few insect species, out of the thousands living in the African grasslands, interact directly with vertebrates. Mosquitoes and tsetse flies, for instance, suck blood; other species feed on carrion and dung.

Army worms and locusts indirectly relate to the larger animals in that they devastate their pasture. Army worms are not worms at all; they are the caterpillars of various species of moths. Like locusts, they swarm in countless numbers across the plains, eating grasses and cereals. Swarming does not occur every year and is probably the result of a particular climatic balance which causes the eggs to hatch in such numbers that birds and other predators can make little impression on them.

Kissing bugs, also known as assassin bugs, are related to aphids and bedbugs. They insert their powerful triple-jointed beaks into the bodies of other insects, sucking out their vital fluids. Two species of kissing bugs, *Triatoma rubrofasciata* in Africa and *Triatoma megista* in South America, prey upon mammals.

Other insects dependent upon animals are sweat bees of the genus *Trigona* and the closely related genus *Melipona*. Both genera build nests in hollow trees and line them with wax and vegetable gum. At night, the entrance is sealed with the same substance. During the day, it is left open and guarded by workers. In addition to visiting flowers, these bees eagerly lick up the sweat and the exudations from the eyes and nostrils of mammals. Their honey is strongly flavored as a result.

A tiny scavenger

The dung beetles belong to the widely distributed Scarabaeidae family, which includes the Egyptian sacred scarab. Using their forelegs, dung beetles mold the dung of herbivores into a ball several times their own size. Their feet have diminished in size and the lower sections of their legs have become enlarged, flattened, and serrated, forming combined scoops and rakes.

Moving backward, the dung beetle pushes the ball away and digs a hole to contain it. The beetle then clambers in after it and sand trickles down, burying both. It remains there until it has eaten the entire ball.

Using a moist fecal ball, the breeding female dung beetle lays a single egg inside it and then buries it in the soil. The larva feeds inside the ball, leaving the crust intact until it emerges as an adult.

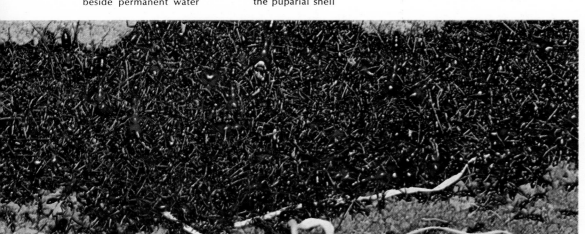

Ant march Driver ants seek food in columns composed of scouts, soldiers, and carrying parties

Termite colonies

Termites have a social organization similar to that of bees and ants: a queen lays eggs, workers attend the eggs and collect food, and soldiers guard the nest.

After hatching, all young termites spend some time as workers. Later, many develop as winged males or females, and fly away to mate and found colonies. Others become permanent nurses, workers, or soldiers, and remain in the nest. The soldiers of some species develop bulbous heads from which they squirt sticky fibers that enmesh enemies.

To found a new colony, a pair of winged termites first lose their wings, then seek out a crevice, where they mate and hide. As the colony grows, the workers ensure balanced production of the various castes by feeding the young on appropriate foods, acting in response to chemical stimuli received during mutual grooming and stroking of antennae.

Giant egg producer The sausage-shaped mass is the queen termite. She may live for 50 years, producing an egg every two seconds at certain periods. Small worker termites swarm over her, grooming her and carrying away the eggs. Red-headed soldier termites stand guard. When a pair of termites mate to found a colony, the female lays eggs that hatch workers. These build the nest and feed her

Termites' nests transform the savanna landscape

These huge mounds are nests built by termites of the genus *Macrotermes*. The shape depends on the species and the nature of the soil particles they cement together with saliva. The mounds are highly fertile and can support forest vegetation. Thousands of plants were found on a mound 48 feet across

A *Macrotermes* termite mound contains a heating unit and air conditioning. Fungus breaks down wood pulp stored above the foundation, making food for the termites and giving off heat. Termites block or open ducts in the outer ridges to keep a constant temperature in the queen's chamber (circled)

Invaders and destroyers of termite fortresses

Termites and other insects are a major source of food for many small invertebrates. Shrews and pangolins hunt insects on the ground, bush-babies search the savanna trees, while bats flutter after flying insects. Broken termite nests form valuable salt licks for herbivores, because they contain large quantities of mineral salts, a by-product of decomposed plant material that has been broken down by the termite inhabitants.

The driver ant is one of the species that wage constant war on termites. When a driver ant column approaches a termite's nest, a few scouts go forward to seek out the entrance. Then soldier ants make a frontal assault. Soldier termites, which fiercely defend the entrance, often repel the intruders. But if the ants are victorious, they enter the nest, paralyze the termites with poisonous bites, and pass them outside to parties waiting to carry off the prey. It is not uncommon to see long columns of driver ants of the genus *Dorylus*, each ant with a captured termite in its jaws.

Termites have no defense against larger predators, such as the aardvark, which eats little else. *Aardvark* means "earth pig" in Afrikaans. It is a powerful animal, about 4½ feet long, and in one night can rip a large termite nest apart with its strong-clawed forefeet. The aardwolf also digs out termites. This animal is related to the scavenging hyena, but because its jaws are weak and its teeth small, it can only eat insects.

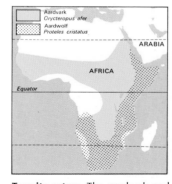

Termite-eaters The aardvark and aardwolf are insect-eaters with a preference for termites

Aardwolf The aardwolf, unlike the other three members of the Hyaenidae family—the three species of hyenas—is not carnivorous. Its jaws are weak and its diet consists entirely of insects

Aardvark The thick, bristly hide of the aardvark is impervious to the bites of soldier termites

Hidden world in the grass

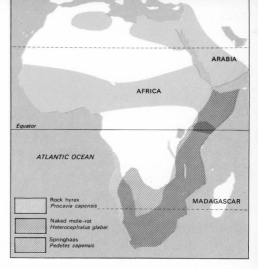

The tooth and foot structures of the hyrax, a small mammal weighing about seven pounds, indicate that it is the closest living relative of the six-ton African elephant

The world of lions and antelopes is reflected on a reduced scale by the smaller animals of the savanna. The tall grass conceals a world of little-known predators and plant-eaters, which far outnumber their larger neighbors on the grasslands.

The predators are cats, mongooses, civets, and weasels. These live mainly on rodents, of which there are about 200 species. Reptiles, too, play an important role in the life of the savanna. Large lizards, such as Bosc's monitor, and numerous species of snakes, both venomous and nonvenomous, also prey on the rats and mice. The silver fox is another predator on rodents.

The rodents enjoy a rich supply of food. Stems, leaves, roots, and seeds form the grass-eaters' diets, while other species eat large quantities of invertebrates.

Varied savanna The savanna provides a range of habitats—sandy soil for the mole-rat, grass cover for the springhaas, rocky hillside for the rock hyrax

Plant-eaters so small they are rarely seen

Rock hyraxes Hyraxes spend most of their time in their homes among the rocks, venturing out only to feed. They always graze together. Herd vigilance is their best protection against predators

Hinged shell Bell's hinged tortoise, unlike most other tortoises, has a hinge on the rear part of its shell. When threatened, it withdraws its hind legs and tail and closes the back of the shell. Forelegs are also withdrawn, protecting the head

Front view

Mole-rat Large feet, fringed with fine hair, help the naked mole-rat scoop out burrows in sandy soil

On the alert The Cape striped mouse is always ready to leap away from danger

The smallest plant-eating mammals of the grasslands are the rats, gerbils, and mice. Some subspecies of pygmy mice are the smallest living rodents; when fully grown a pygmy mouse may weigh less than one fifth of an ounce.

The striped grass mice are daytime foragers and so prefer areas with thick grass cover. They react quickly to the slightest disturbance, leaping straight up in the air before scampering away. Another mouse is the multimammate mouse, which has up to a dozen pair of teats and gives birth to a litter of 12 or more.

The Nile grass rat inhabits the thick grass of the floodplains and burrows extensively in the soil. In the dry season, when the soil is rock-hard, it lives in the deep fissures that appear in the ground. These fissures protect it from the fires that frequently scour the parched grass. Its habit of nocturnal feeding helps to shield it from predators, particularly after the grass cover has been burned away.

The next largest group of rodents are the mole-rats. Typical of these is the root rat of eastern Africa, which lives under the soil in burrows. Root rats have small eyes and ears, large feet, huge incisor teeth used for tunneling, and furry lips that close behind the teeth to protect the mouth from debris. They defecate under their nests and the droppings ferment, giving off heat which helps to keep the animals warm in colder weather.

The springhaas leaps from its lair

The springhaas, which looks like a small kangaroo, is in fact a rodent. It is about the size of a rabbit and comes out at night to feed on bulbs and roots, digging them up with the curved claws of its front feet. It spends the day in a burrow, and blocks most of the entrances with earth, leaving only one open. At dusk it may emerge with a spring into the air, thus eluding lurking predators.

The rock hyrax, or dassie, weighing about seven pounds, is too large to be consumed by mongooses or small cats, but is a favorite prey of the leopard and the rock python. Rock hyraxes leave their droppings in heaps around the entrances to their homes and spray nearby rocks with urine. When the urine coating dries, it turns a dazzling white in the sun, providing a conspicuous signal to other hyraxes that the territory has been occupied.

Serval Long grass and reeds provide cover for the serval during the day. At night it hunts in open country for lizards, rats, birds, and hares

Caracal lynx Small antelopes are a favorite prey of the caracal lynx, which is easily distinguished from other grassland cats by its tasseled ears

Puff adder Its venom kills small animals almost instantly. The venom also breaks down animal tissue to provide digestible food

Small relatives of the large carnivores hunt through the grass

All major African families of carnivores include small forms that live on the numerous prey in the tall grass. The dog family is represented by the bat-eared fox and the silver or Cape fox; the cat family by the serval, caracal lynx, and wildcat. Other small flesh-eaters of the region are the striped weasel, the African civet, the genet, and the mongoose.

The silver fox, like all foxes, is an opportunist, eating almost anything. Its diet consists of rodents, insects, and sometimes plant food.

The conspicuous markings of the striped weasel—a white crown and nape and white stripes running along a black back—resemble those of two other animals of the African grasslands, the zorilla or striped polecat and the honey badger. All three spray their enemies with a foul-smelling fluid, ejected from their anal glands, and the similar colorings serve as a warning to other animals.

Banded mongooses are gregarious animals that live in groups of about 30 to 40. They move around in compact parties during the day, chattering to keep in contact as they scratch for insects, snails, and mice.

An even more agile hunter with similar habits is the dwarf mongoose. This species is noted for the way it marks its territory and its young with a scent from its cheek glands, so each family acquires a distinctive odor of its own.

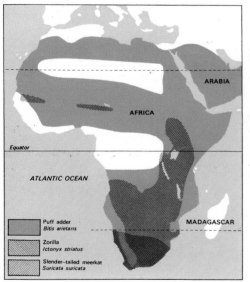

Puff adder
Bitis arietans

Zorilla
Ictonyx striatus

Slender-tailed meerkat
Suricata suricata

Contrasting ranges The zorilla and puff adder are found widely throughout the savanna, but the meerkat is confined to the dry southern grasslands

A cautious killer avoids a deadly sting

The gray meerkat, a species of mongoose, is such an aggressive creature that it will attack without any preliminary threat or display, a rare occurrence in the animal world. It will usually kill with a neck bite, but with a scorpion, as seen above, it first bites off the stinger. Meerkats, also called suricates, are sociable animals; colonies of them dig shallow burrows and sleep there at night

Zorilla Its striking skunklike coloration reminds enemies of the animal's foul smell

Backs to the sun Slender-tailed meerkats often emerge from their burrows early in the morning to warm themselves in the sun. They stand on their hind toes, using their strong tails for support

121

American prairie grazers and birds

Buffalo and pronghorns have virtually disappeared from the American plains; now the ground-hugging birds have all but lost their former prairie habitat

For centuries, the North American grasslands were the home of buffalo and pronghorns, which, constantly wandering and grazing, helped maintain the unbroken seas of grass. Buffalo, for example, have a habit of rubbing against trees and killing them.

The virgin prairie and its characteristic life began to disappear as settlers spread west across North America. Large sections of the country were converted to farmland and pasture, and the animals of the prairies were gradually confined to narrower or more remote ranges. Indians had always hunted buffalo, but it was the white settlers and commercial buffalo hunters who almost destroyed the species.

The treeless stretches provide little shelter for perching birds, but many migrating flocks rest there for a few days.

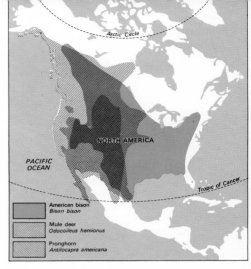

Former buffalo range Buffalo were once widely distributed over North America, but their numbers have dwindled; the majority are found in Canada

Once, a sea of buffalo moved upon a sea of grass

Buffalo in combat Two bulls fight for dominance over a herd. These massive animals, six feet high, fight with quick, upward jabs of the horns

Buffalo, or bison, are the giants of the North American plains. A fully grown bull stands six feet tall at the shoulder, measures up to nine feet from muzzle to tail, and weighs up to 2000 pounds.

These animals roamed the plains from the Mississippi to the Rocky Mountains. Before

Confined to reserves The few remaining buffalo herds must now graze in small dry reserves

1800 there were buffalo as far east as New York and Pennsylvania. It is estimated that at one time there were 60 million buffalo. In the nineteenth century, however, they were hunted almost to the point of extermination. Today about 40,000 remain in the United States and Canada, all protected and most in nature preserves.

Buffalo usually walk or trot in a leisurely manner, but can gallop at 30 miles per hour. Herds are constantly on the move, plodding slowly forward, seeking grazing grass. Before their large-scale slaughter, buffalo herds tended to move south as winter approached. In spring, when the snow melted and fresh grass appeared, they would move back to their northern grazing areas. These movements could not be called migrations, since they took place only sporadically, depending on weather conditions and the availability of food and water. Nor did the buffalo use the same trails year after year. The so-called buffalo trails were the result of herds making short local forays, many of their paths joining and intersecting one another, so that after a long period of time, a human observer could piece together a long, straight-

line "trail" by connecting the shorter paths.

Male buffalo sometimes engage in battles to determine leadership of the herd and dominance during the mating season. Two rival bulls walk slowly toward each other, shaking their heads and bellowing threats. The weaker animal often backs down, but occasionally the bulls savage each other with their horns.

In the herd, subordinate animals usually avoid the dominant bull. Leaders maintain their dominant position by swinging their heads with their menacing horns, or simply by giving a challenger a warning look. They are the first in the herd to feed, drink at water holes, rub against posts, or use a freshly made wallowing hole.

Breeding bulls spend the winter in bachelor groups. They return to the main herd in July and August, when mating begins.

Calves are born after nine months' gestation. The cow sometimes leaves the herd to give birth to her single calf, rejoining the rest as soon as the calf is strong enough to keep up. Buffalo travel with their mothers for about four years after birth, and the herd guards the young from predators.

North America's fastest mammal

The pronghorn, like the buffalo, was hunted almost to extinction in the nineteenth century. Now protected, its numbers are increasing. The only member of its family, and confined to North America, the animal is named for its back-curving horns.

The pronghorn is the fastest wild mammal in North America. It has a top speed of 40 miles per hour, and can maintain 30 miles per hour over several miles. Such speed and endurance—with their survival value against such formidable predators as wolves and coyotes—are associated with a heart twice the size of that of a sheep with the same body weight, a wide windpipe, and large lungs. Also, the species' hearing and sense of smell are acute.

When grazing, the animals frequently raise their heads to look around. As soon as one spots a predator the hairs on its rump stand erect, revealing two brilliant white disks of hair underneath. This signal sets the whole herd galloping off.

Small herds of pronghorns range over the dry western plains in summer, eating grass, sagebrush, and other plants. In late summer the bucks fight for possession of does. The winners round up harems of 7 to 15 females for the three-week mating season. Later, pronghorns form herds of 100 or more, and move south for the winter. In April or May, females leave the herd to give birth in an area with good ground cover.

Lying in safety A pronghorn kid is hidden in the grass. Its mother stands guard a distance away

A horn that sheds A pronghorn's horn is unique because it resembles those of cattle and those of deer. Like a ruminant, it keeps the solid core of bone all year. Around the bone grow hairs that are solidly massed into a sheath. This part is shed annually after the breeding season

Sheath of fused hair
Soft hair
Bony core
Skull

Alert pronghorns These cautious grazers lift their heads to look for predators. Two centuries ago their population was estimated at 40 million. Today there are only about 350,000

Prairie chickens spend most of their time on the ground

Display before mating In the mating season male sage grouse spread their feathers and strut around in front of the females. The cocks often fight and the winner mates with most of the females

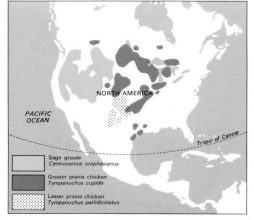

NORTH AMERICA
PACIFIC OCEAN
Tropic of Cancer

Sage grouse
Centrocercus urophasianus

Greater prairie chicken
Tympanuchus cupido

Lesser prairie chicken
Tympanuchus pallidicinctus

Vanishing species Prairie chickens once had a wide range but now they face extinction

Greater prairie chicken To attract a mate, this male inflates its throat sacs and displays feathers

There is no North American equivalent of the flightless ostrich of Africa or rhea of South America. But there are prairie birds that spend most of their time on the ground, and fly off only at the last second when disturbed. These are the prairie chickens, members of the grouse family.

Throughout the summer the birds are inconspicuous and live separately. In winter large flocks gather to feed on berries, seeds, and other plant matter. From February to May the cocks contend for females.

The males strut before the apparently unconcerned females, inflating air sacs on each side of the throat. Yellow fringes over the eyes expand, neck tufts stand erect, the tail fans out, and the wings droop. Meanwhile each male keeps up a loud booming call.

The displays and fighting establish which cock is master of the flock. The dominant bird mates with most of the hens, and in May each hen lays 7 to 17 olive-spotted eggs in a shallow, grass-lined nest on the ground. The eggs, chicks, and adult birds are preyed on by foxes, weasels, badgers, raccoons, and a variety of snakes.

The dwindling populations of greater and lesser prairie chickens live mainly on what were formerly the long-grass prairies of the Midwest. The sage grouse lives in semidesert conditions on the western sagebrush plains.

During the peak north-south seasonal migrations, many varieties of migrant birds often stop over on the old prairie land, where they feed on seeds and insects.

Burrowers and hunters

Beneath the prairie certain small animals build a world of tunnels and burrows, where they find refuge from the heat, cold, and predators of the land above

In the prairie lands, where the temperature varies from parching heat to below-zero cold, and where sudden storms ravage the land in all seasons, some small mammals find protection from these extremes of climate by living in burrows. But burrowing does not completely protect the animals from predators. Birds of prey pluck them from burrow entrances; weasels, snakes, and ferrets pursue them into burrows; and coyotes and badgers dig them out. Prairie dogs and pocket gophers are typical plains burrowers.

All of these plant-eaters support dozens of flesh-eaters. The coyote is one of the most successful plains carnivores. The puma, however, is gradually disappearing from the plains as the numbers of its main prey, the deer, decline.

Owls and hawks patrol the prairies. The golden eagle comes down from the mountains to hunt.

Snakes are common and are both hunters and hunted, particularly by the birds of prey. The rattlesnake is one of the most numerous and widely distributed species.

Prairie dogs, gophers, and other rodents burrow beneath the prairie

Greeting behavior Prairie dogs often visit neighboring burrows where they rush to greet each other

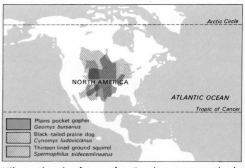

Patterned coat Unlike other ground squirrels, the thirteen-lined ground squirrel has a distinctive pattern on its coat, from which it derives its common name. It carries food in its cheek pouches and stores it in underground chambers. In summer it feeds on leaves, nuts, and small animals

Hibernation in the north On the more northerly prairies, ground squirrels hibernate all winter, until the mating season in spring

The "towns" of the black-tailed prairie dog may have populations of 1000 or more individuals. Each burrow, marked by a mound at its entrance that gives some protection against flooding, houses a basic family unit called a coterie. This family group usually consists of a male, three females, and about six young. Prairie dogs are so sociable that even when two males that are strangers to each other meet, they go through the same formal greeting ceremony common among coterie members.

The youngest prairie dogs lead a sheltered life, nursed by any adult female they come across, groomed and nuzzled by all the males. As the pups mature, the adults emigrate from the coterie territory, perhaps to escape from the pups' constant demands for care. But, in time, the adults gradually reclaim their original coterie territory, and large numbers of yearling males are killed off in the process.

If threatened, a prairie dog will utter the sharp, doglike bark that gives it its name. These stout-bodied rodents, about 13 inches long, are preyed on by many of the plains carnivores.

Another group of plains rodents are the pocket gophers, named for their large cheek pouches, or pockets, in which they carry roots and tubers to be stored in their burrows. The plains pocket gopher prefers the sandy soil of the more easterly regions. The northern pocket gopher lives in the western grasslands and mountains.

Pocket gophers dig two-level tunnel systems, with foraging tunnels near the surface and living quarters deeper down. The eastern mole, which lives in the easternmost prairies, digs a similar home, except that it leaves a ridge of disturbed soil on the surface above its foraging tunnel.

The prairie vole digs extensive tunnels through the topsoil and beats down pathways in the vegetation around its colony. It is not as sociable as the prairie dog.

Spotted skunks build nests of dry vegetation in burrows or under piles of rocks. Up to eight individuals may share a nest during the day, coming out at night to feed on insects, mice, eggs, and carrion.

Solitary burrower The valley pocket gopher lives alone in an elaborately constructed burrow and most of its life is spent underground

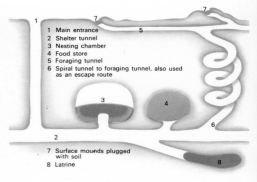

1 Main entrance
2 Shelter tunnel
3 Nesting chamber
4 Food store
5 Foraging tunnel
6 Spiral tunnel to foraging tunnel, also used as an escape route
7 Surface mounds plugged with soil
8 Latrine

Gopher burrow plan The deeper tunnels are for shelter, nesting, food storage, and waste disposal. The surface openings are plugged from within

The hunters and their food

The plant-eaters of the prairies support dozens of species of flesh-eaters, among the most successful of which are coyotes. These hardy, adaptable members of the dog family have moved into the central grasslands from the west in the past 100 years. They have thrived while wolves, once major predators on the prairies, have been pushed farther and farther west into more mountainous and barren areas.

The coyote, usually brown flecked with black and gray, looks like a medium-size wolf. The two can easily be distinguished, however, because the coyote's tail droops between its legs when it runs, whereas the wolf holds its tail horizontally. The coyote can run as fast as 38 miles per hour. They usually hunt singly or in relays, rather than in packs. Mating appears to be for life. When coyotes breed with domestic dogs, the puppies often grow up to be indistinguishable from coyotes in the wild.

The largest member of the cat family on the prairies is the puma, or mountain lion. Its favorite food is deer, and as the number of deer has declined, so has the number of pumas. The puma has been hunted throughout its range because it attacks domestic livestock and game. A good climber, the animal will seek refuge in a tree when it is pursued.

Several kinds of owls, hawks, falcons, and eagles prey on the prairie animals. Some of these birds, such as the snowy owl and Harlan's hawk, breed in the Arctic and only winter in the grasslands. Others are also found elsewhere in the world. These include the burrowing owl, which usually occupies an abandoned prairie dog burrow, and lives in both North and South America.

One of the biggest and most fearsome of the birds of prey, the golden eagle, swoops down over the western valleys and prairies from its home in the mountains in search of food—mainly small mammals.

The ferruginous hawk, a predominant bird of the prairies, preys almost exclusively on small mammals and reptiles.

A wide variety of snakes are adapted to life on the prairies. There are plenty of small mammal holes where they can nest and hibernate, and prey is abundant. Rattlesnakes, which are very common throughout the prairies, feed on various small mammals. They sometimes live in prairie dog burrows and catch either the young prairie dogs or burrowing owls.

The prairie falcon This bird nests in mountain areas but hunts throughout the grasslands for small rodents, reptiles, insects, and other birds. It is so maneuverable in flight that it can catch birds on the wing or snatch a ground squirrel as the rodent peeps from a burrow entrance

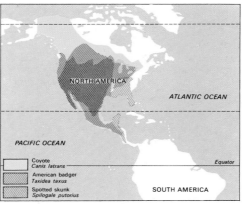

Coyotes on the advance Unlike many other prairie animals, coyotes have not decreased with the onslaught of civilization. In fact, these animals have extended their range and habitat

Spotted skunk Like other skunks, it is usually docile, but it will quickly raise its tail to warn off any opponents. If this warning is ignored, it will eject a foul-smelling liquid

The hog-nosed snake Its hard snout enables this snake to burrow beneath the soil. When frightened, it rolls over on its back and feigns death

Lone howler that accepts help Coyotes usually live alone, although they do form relays in hunting rabbits and rodents. Coyotes are known as resourceful hunters; they have been observed waiting at gopher holes while a badger digs out a gopher, then grabbing the badger's victim

Small plant-eaters

The steppe winter is so severe that most plant-eaters hibernate. They must spend the summer storing food for the rigors that lie ahead

Central Eurasia is too far from the sea for oceanic winds to moderate its climate. There is icy cold in winter, searing heat in summer, and a year-round lack of moisture. In winter cold air flows from the center to the oceans, leaving snow in its wake. In summer hot air rises in the center and is replaced by moist, cooler air which brings rain to the Eurasian coasts. There, forests flourish, but the central areas are desert. Between the forest and the desert lie the steppes—vast plains receiving 10 to 30 inches of rain a year. In most parts the rainfall supports only grass and a few tuber-rooted plants; in moister areas there are shrubs and clumps of trees.

The extremes of temperature mean that steppe animals must be able to avoid the heat and cold. Consequently, small burrowing rodents are common. Many feed on grass, the most abundant food source. Ground squirrels, characteristic of both Eurasian and North American grasslands, include susliks and marmots. All of these rodents are a basic source of food for the predators of the steppes.

Collecting and storing food in underground tunnels

Wary grazer A bobak marmot pauses in feeding to look for danger. The first mammal to emerge from hibernation, it is prey to wolves and eagles

European susliks A suslik spends the entire summer browsing on vegetation and often ravages cornfields. It crams its cheek pouches with seeds, which it stores in one of several burrows. Susliks' winter quarters have a sloping tunnel to the surface that is sealed in winter

The mole-rat of the genus *Spalax* digs a network of tunnels in which it lives and feeds, and which it rarely leaves. It harvests dandelion and chickory roots and stores these in food chambers for the winter. The animal uses its head to push earth away, almost like a drill, burrowing with amazing speed. It also digs and then seals off a succession of latrines as they are filled. The mole-rat is a solitary animal, intolerant even of its own kind. After mating the female will drive the male away if he does not leave quickly enough to suit her.

The common hamster prefers damper conditions than the mole-rat. It too is a burrower, and digs out a large central chamber with other rooms leading off. The hamster is a tidy animal. It organizes its food stores meticulously, making separate compartments for different kinds of food. It uses its teeth to carry large food items, and stores small ones in its cheek pouches. In the fall the hamster blocks up all the entrances to its burrow, rolls itself up in a ball, and goes into a light sleep.

Marmots are larger than susliks, which are called ground squirrels in North America, with flatter skulls and less well developed cheek pouches. Both animals live in large colonies, are active by day, and dig deep burrows where they hibernate for half the year. Susliks may also estivate—become torpid in summer—in times of drought.

Susliks and marmots are the favorite prey of wolves, eagles, and large hawks. They do not move far from their burrows, and when they feed on the surface, they post sentinels, whose warning calls send the whole colony underground.

Mammals that are too small to migrate far enough to escape extremes of heat or cold

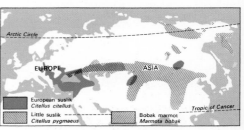

Burrowing rodents The marmot lives farther north than the suslik and hibernates half the year

Common hamster This nocturnal forager nests in shallow burrows during the day. This hamster of the eastern European wooded steppes becomes inactive in winter, but wakes periodically to feed

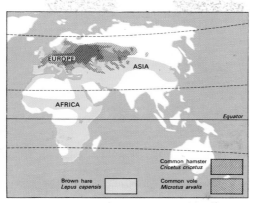

Wide-ranging hare The brown hare, found throughout the Eurasian and African grasslands, is the only small animal living on the steppes that does not burrow

Common hamster
Cricetus cricetus

Brown hare
Lepus capensis

Common vole
Microtus arvalis

Safety through speed Aided by its acute senses of hearing and smell, the brown hare relies on speed and vigilance to escape from its predators. It conceals its young among grassland tussocks

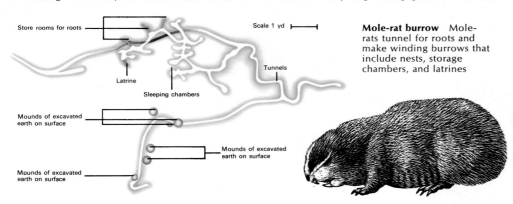

Store rooms for roots

Scale 1 yd

Latrine

Tunnels

Sleeping chambers

Mounds of excavated earth on surface

Mounds of excavated earth on surface

Mounds of excavated earth on surface

Mole-rat burrow Mole-rats tunnel for roots and make winding burrows that include nests, storage chambers, and latrines

retreat underground, where most hibernate.

The steppes are by no means uniform. Rainfall varies considerably, affecting the growth of food plants. The zone includes not only grasslands but also scrub and semi-desert. The different steppe animals are adapted for the habitats in which they live.

The great jerboa, a rodent with long hind legs, is adapted to dry, open country, where it uses its speed—traveling at up to 35 miles per hour in three-foot bounds—to escape predators. The Daurian pika of Siberia and Mongolia lives near water. A relative of hares and rabbits, it carries out a form of haymaking in summer. It collects the leaves of plants, such as iris, cinquefoil, and wormwood, and dries them in the sun for winter fodder and bedding. The pika is one of the few steppe herbivores that remain active in winter, when it is the prey of eagles, wolves, and corsac foxes.

Overpopulation can sometimes lead to un-usual stresses in animals. One steppe bur-rower, the common vole, has a breeding cycle in which population reaches a peak every four or five years. Some time after the peak there follows an equally spectacular crash, which seems to be due neither to starvation nor to predators but to the effect of over-crowding on hormone production. The re-sulting hormone imbalance may be a direct cause of death among the animals generally, or it may prevent the mothers from making enough milk, so that the young starve.

The sagebrush vole, also called the steppe lemming, suffers from similar population ex-plosions. Females are sexually mature at six weeks, males a little earlier. Breeding lasts from April to early October, and during this period a female may produce six litters of three to seven young. When population peaks occur, large numbers of sagebrush voles move massed together in the manner of lemmings (see page 29).

Birds of the wooded steppes

At the beginning of spring, steppe black grouse, like black grouse in other areas, establish courtship arenas, or leks. There the males strut, with wings and tails dis-played as a challenge to other males and as an enticement to hens. After mating, the cock continues to display. The hen typically lays a single egg next morning, and, in inter-vals during incubation, may return to the arena in search of another mate. Males in the center of the lek secure the most matings. In the breeding season the male is a hand-some bird, with red wattles over his eyes, lyre-shaped outer tail feathers, and prom-inent white wing bars.

Like other black grouse, steppe black grouse—the subspecies *Tetrao tetrix virid-iana*—prefer wooded areas. They live in the eastern Ukraine and north of the Caspian Sea and the Aral Sea, where clumps of birch and shrubs dot the steppes.

Arena of challenge and courtship In an elaborate display used to challenge cocks and entice hens, male steppe black grouse fan out their tails and wings as they hop, strut, and utter burbling calls

127

Grazers and predators

Mass migrations to escape extremes of temperature and find food set the rhythm of life for the animal herds of the steppes and their predators

The spread of agriculture in this century has reduced the ranges of many animals in the Eurasian steppes. As their ranges disappear, the numbers of animals decline. Larger species have suffered the most. There is still sufficient virgin grassland, however, to support herds of hooved animals, such as the saiga antelope.

Saigas are nomadic animals which, according to fossil evidence, roamed throughout Eurasia as much as 20,000 years ago. Each winter they migrate south in herds of thousands to escape the bitter cold and feed on pastures free of deep snow. In a dry summer they move hundreds of miles away from their usual feeding ground to find better pasture.

Saigas mate after the winter migration. Males mark and defend a territory, using their horns to challenge other males for possession of females. Successful males maintain harems of 5 to 15 females. But many males, weakened by fighting and mating, succumb to the winter cold. Only 5 to 10 percent survive to make the return journey north in spring. Even so, about a million saigas now live under protection in the wild, and are increasing at a yearly rate of 7000 head.

As horses spread into the Old World, new forms evolved

Female saiga Unlike the male, the female saiga has no horns. Its highly developed snout may serve either to warm cold inhaled air or to filter out dust. The female matures earlier than the male and mates when seven months old. The steppe winter takes a heavy toll of both the young and old, but the saiga's early maturity, coupled with a high frequency of twins, maintains the population

Open grassland is the natural home of horses. Przewalski's horse, the only truly wild relative of domestic horses, is probably the most primitive living member of the horse family. It is smaller than domestic horses, and has a heavier head, an erect mane, and a long tail, which often almost touches the ground. It is now rare in the wild, but long ago it roamed the eastern steppes in great numbers. Herds were small, usually consisting of one stallion and 6 to 12 mares and foals. In captivity, Przewalski's horse lives to about 30 years of age.

Przewalski's horse lives closer than any other horse species to the ancient land bridge across the Bering Strait between America and Eurasia. It appears that horses, after crossing this bridge from America, gradually evolved into new forms as adaptations to the new environments they encountered as they spread into the Old World. These changes involved the fusion of some of their smaller chromosomes—the cells through which genetic information is transmitted to the next generation. As a result, those horse species that live farthest away from the land bridge have the lowest number of chromosomes. Przewalski's horse remained on the steppes, after crossing the Bering Strait, so it underwent the fewest adaptations and therefore has more chromosomes than any other horse species.

Przewalski's horse This rare animal is probably the most primitive member of the horse family

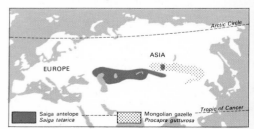

Ancient antelope The saiga has wandered Eurasian steppes for perhaps a million years. In the eastern part it is replaced by the Mongolian gazelle, whose golden brown coat turns white in winter

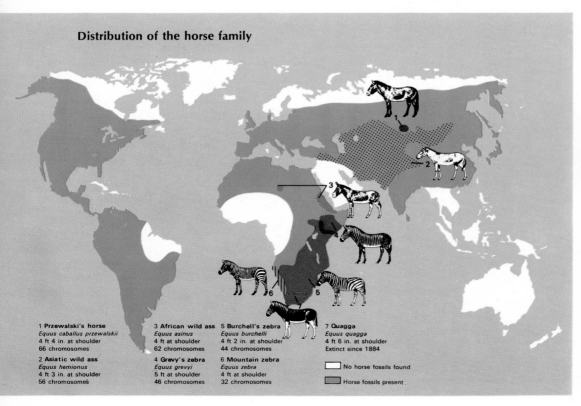

Distribution of the horse family

1 **Przewalski's horse**
Equus caballus przewalskii
4 ft 4 in. at shoulder
66 chromosomes

2 **Asiatic wild ass**
Equus hemionus
4 ft 3 in. at shoulder
56 chromosomes

3 **African wild ass**
Equus asinus
4 ft at shoulder
62 chromosomes

4 **Grevy's zebra**
Equus grevyi
5 ft at shoulder
46 chromosomes

5 **Burchell's zebra**
Equus burchelli
4 ft 2 in. at shoulder
44 chromosomes

6 **Mountain zebra**
Equus zebra
4 ft at shoulder
32 chromosomes

7 **Quagga**
Equus quagga
4 ft 6 in. at shoulder
Extinct since 1884

No horse fossils found

Horse fossils present

Saiga antelope
Saiga tatarica

Mongolian gazelle
Procapra gutturosa

Hunters in the great grasslands

Adult horses and saigas have little to fear from most of the predators of the steppes. Only the wolf is large enough to attack them, and this animal is becoming increasingly rare on the steppes, as elsewhere.

Given sufficient warning, both horses and saigas can outrun wolves. The only adults vulnerable to these predators are females giving birth. At this time, the large grazers gather in groups on flat open ground where any approaching danger can be seen from a great distance.

Wolves, like the smaller carnivores of the steppes, depend on rodents and hares for their basic diet. Wolves live in many different habitats, but the corsac fox is native to the steppes and semideserts of central Eurasia alone. It has exceptionally large eyes and ears, and a keen sense of smell. The corsac's soft, thick fur varies in color from reddish yellow in summer to near white in winter, which helps the animal to blend into the snowy landscape.

The great expanses of the steppes make an ideal hunting ground for the larger predatory birds. The tawny eagle, or steppe eagle, for instance, flies in great arcs, surveying miles of steppe in each sweep. Ground squirrels are its major food, but it is alert to the movements of bustards, snakes, and hares, which also form part of its diet.

There are several subspecies, or races, of the tawny eagle living throughout Africa and Asia. One race winters in Mesopotamia and Africa. Males and females pair off when they return in the spring, and build an untidy nest of twigs, lined with wool, feathers, and feces, either on the ground or in a low tree. The young hatch in June, make their first flight in August, and migrate south with their parents in October.

Steppe harrier's courtship

The steppe harrier is another migratory bird. It spends the winters in southern Asia or Africa and returns to the steppes in summer. Males and females pair—apparently for life—during the spring flight northward, though their elaborate courtship display does not begin until they reach their nesting grounds in the steppes.

During the courtship flight the male and female harrier fly together in great spirals, breaking off occasionally to bank and glide downward. Later, during the mating flight, the male displays to the female, who watches from the ground. He stops his circling movements and glides slowly down toward his mate, hovering before her with outspread wings. Suddenly he dives straight at her, soaring up just in time to avoid a collision. During these maneuvers the male displays to the female his light-colored breast, even turning toward the sun so as to appear brighter.

The steppe harrier, which feeds on voles, black grouse, and larks, patrols a regular route over its hunting ground. On seeing potential prey, it plummets groundward, using its tail and wings as diving brakes and rudders, and seizes the victim in its sharp, curved talons.

Viper of the steppes

Among the reptiles on the steppes is the steppe viper, which is closely related to the common viper, or adder, of Europe. It prefers areas, such as valleys, where there is good vegetation cover. This little viper is mainly active at night, when it preys on voles, hamsters, and shrews. Like all vipers, it is an aggressive and dangerous predator. Although usually found in dry habitats, the steppe viper is sometimes seen in marshland.

Corsac fox and Russian polecat

Corsac foxes lead a nocturnal, nomadic existence, sleeping by day in marmot holes. They occasionally hunt in packs, and will eat anything they can overcome, from insects to hares and susliks. They will feed on carrion as well.

The steppe or Russian polecat is a hunter of rodents and reptiles, and will also attack domestic animals. It ranges from Poland to the Pacific. It is possibly the species from which the domesticated ferret was derived.

The polecat sometimes takes over marmot burrows after killing the original inhabitants. It then enlarges the hole, and drives further tunnels into nearby marmot burrow systems. Like the skunk, the polecat defends itself when threatened by emitting a foul-smelling fluid from its anal glands.

Pallas's cat also takes a toll of steppe rodents and birds. Unlike most cats, but like many steppe animals, Pallas's cats live in burrows, caves, and rocky clefts. This species also lives in wooded country and in semidesert regions.

Snake-eater The short-toed eagle kills snakes by crushing their heads. As cultivation advances, its numbers have decreased on the steppes and it has retreated into desert and woodland

Marbled polecat It warns off predators by erecting its body hairs and curling its tail. Then it releases a foul-smelling liquid from its anal glands. It lives under logs, and in rotting trees or old burrows

Tawny eagle An opportunist, this species will eat any flesh, including carrion. Two races live on the steppes—one between the Black and Caspian seas and the other in Mongolia and China

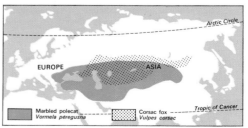

Small predators The corsac fox lives in a semi-desert area east of the Urals, where its light coat blends with the landscape. Polecats, like corsac foxes, are nocturnal hunters

129

Animals of the Far Eastern plains

The man-made grasslands of the Indian peninsula have become the home of a unique group of animals—forest-dwellers adapted to life on the plains

In arid parts of India, man's activities have created a short-grass savanna, seasonally swept by the monsoon rains. Thousands of years of cultivation and grazing by domestic animals have destroyed the original open woodland. In neighboring countries—Burma, Thailand, and Cambodia—there are semiarid natural grasslands, but except for the rare Cambodian kouprey, a wild ox that appears to be a true savanna native, no grassland mammals have evolved there.

The western Indian plains have been colonized by adaptable species from the deserts of the Middle East and North Africa, such as gerbils and gazelles. The only animals unique to the Indian plains are those descended from Indian woodland species that have become adapted to open country—the bonnet macaque monkey, the nilgai, and its closest relative, the four-horned antelope. Another plains animal, the blackbuck, is one of the most beautiful antelopes.

Grass-eaters descended from desert- and forest-dwellers

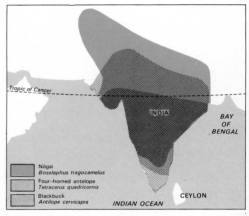

Antelopes of India The blackbuck inhabits open country, the nilgai lives in sheltered areas, and the four-horned antelope lives in the tall grass and the open woodland. Their populations are reduced

Blackbucks These are easily recognizable by the males' long, spiraling horns. They can outrun most predators, and often bound with a stiff-legged gait called spronking, all four feet landing together

A herd of nilgai The dominant bull has a darker coat and a swollen neck, which indicate superiority

Extra pair of horns The male four-horned antelope is the only wild mammal with two pairs of horns

Blackbucks have two rutting seasons, when most mating takes place—one in the middle of the dry summer, about April, and the other at the end of the wet season, from August to October. Dominant bucks establish territories of about 20 acres for herds of up to 50 animals, including females, infants, and subordinate adult bucks. Territories are held against other bucks by a system of threat displays, which rarely lead to fighting. At the end of the rut, territorial defense is abandoned and several herds join together. Fawns are born six months later.

The nilgai, a horselike antelope, inhabits

Threat postures
Blackbucks and nilgais use these threat postures in the rutting season in defense of their territories. Both display their ears. The blackbuck also bobs its head and exposes its white rump patch. The nilgai bull displays its white throat patch

Blackbuck

Nilgai

areas with trees, which provide shelter during the hottest part of the day. Like the blackbuck, it gets most of the water it needs from the leaves and grass it eats. In early winter the bulls establish large breeding territories of about 200 acres, marking the boundaries with dung piles.

The Indian plains support a wide range of smaller plant-eating animals. The black-naped hare and the Indian gerbil are common in open country. The hare keeps to the surface but the gerbil spends the day in a burrow, emerging at dusk to feed on seeds, succulent plants, insects, and young birds.

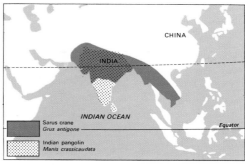

Giant crane The sarus crane, standing nearly six feet tall, seldom strays far from water. During the breeding season and occasionally outside it, both sexes display their broad wings in a courtship "dance." Mates pair for life and take turns in incubating the eggs and feeding the young

Pangolin and its varied habitat The sarus crane keeps mainly to marshland, but the Indian pangolin is found in most types of country

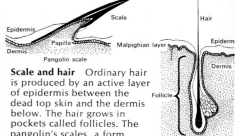

Scale and hair Ordinary hair is produced by an active layer of epidermis between the dead top skin and the dermis below. The hair grows in pockets called follicles. The pangolin's scales, a form of hair, grow from fleshy protuberances

Pangolin—the only mammal with scales The Indian pangolin has a long, tapering body with overlapping scales, except on the snout and underparts. It moves slowly, tail dragging. When threatened, it curls up tightly, protected by the scales

Cheetah and other predators have vanished from the Indian plains

Many of the large predators that once prowled the Indian plains have either been hunted to extinction or forced into remote habitats. The Asiatic race of lion, *Panthera leo persica,* is confined to the Gir Forest in northwest India, where about 300 individuals still survive. This lion, essentially a hunter of large, hooved animals such as nilgai and deer, is a little smaller than the African lion. Its mane is shorter, and its tail tuft thicker.

In the past the chief predator on the blackbuck and gazelle was the cheetah, but this animal is now extinct in India. Another hunter, the wolf, has almost vanished from the plains but is still found in the deserts. In India wolves hunt singly or in pairs.

The most numerous predators of the Indian plains are small carnivores that take rodents, reptiles, birds, and insects. The ratel, or honey badger, is practically omnivorous. It will eat snakes, carrion, and plants, and is particularly fond of honey. Its large forefeet, armed with strong claws, make it an expert burrower.

Shrews, hedgehogs, pangolins, and bats feed on insects. The long-eared hedgehog, found in the drier areas of the northwest, shelters in a burrow during the heat of the day. The Indian pangolin sleeps in a moist burrow about ten feet below the surface. It breaks open ant and termite nests and catches the insects on its long, sticky tongue.

The golden jackal and the striped hyena have entered the Indian savanna from the nearby deserts of the Middle East. Both are scavengers, though the jackal also preys on small animals.

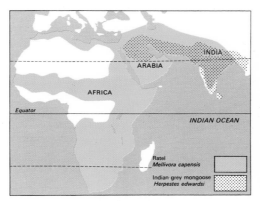

Mongoose and ratel The ratel inhabits a broad and varied range that extends even into some desert areas. The Indian gray mongoose is found in both the grasslands and the deserts

"Skunk" of Africa and Asia The ratel's coat may warn enemies of its ultimate weapon—noxious spray from its anal glands. A shaggy coat and thick layer of sub-skin fat protect this honey lover from bees

Cobra The raised head and spread hood of the Indian cobra warn that it may be about to strike

Snake killer The mongoose can overcome a large cobra, seizing it by the head as the snake rears to strike. If bitten, the mongoose often survives, having a partial immunity to the venom

Plant-eating mammals and birds

There are few hiding places on the windy, treeless pampas. Herbivores must seek protection from predators by burrowing or living in herds. Some are fast runners

The treeless pampas of Argentina suffer from droughts and extreme temperatures and are swept in all seasons by the pampero, a violent southwest wind. In these conditions, many small animals live underground, and most species of birds are migrant visitors, leaving when food is scarce.

The tropical grasslands of South America—the campos of Brazil and the llanos of Venezuela and Colombia—are broken up by forests, providing more shelter for animals living or feeding in the open. Some typical burrowing rodents of the South American grasslands are the viscacha, the mara, or Patagonian hare, and the tuco-tuco. Wild guinea-pigs are also common.

The rhea, or South American ostrich, lives in flocks on the pampas, sometimes joining a herd of cattle to feed.

Rodents that live in centuries-old tunnels

Alert maras Maras keep a constant vigilance, and, if disturbed, run off with a bounding gait

Pampas deer These deer wander in pairs or small herds. When startled, they bound off with lifted tails. The white underside may be a danger signal

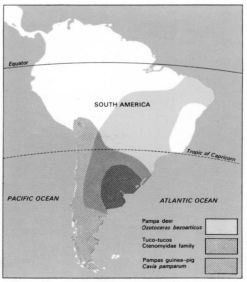

Rare and common pampas-dwellers The dwindling pampas deer have a large range, but tuco-tucos and guinea-pigs have both large populations and ranges

One of the most energetic burrowers of the South American grasslands is the viscacha, a large rodent related to the chinchillas of the high Andes. Viscachas live in a group of tunnels, known collectively as a viscachera. Some viscacheras have been used for centuries. The soil brought up by the burrowing animals forms mounds at the tunnel mouths, sometimes several feet high. The ground is always cleared around the viscachera, so approaching predators can be easily seen.

Viscachas are very sociable, even with viscachas from nearby colonies. Mating takes place in March and April, and the young are born in September, fully furred, with their eyes open.

The mara, also known as the Patagonian cavy or Patagonian hare, is common in the pampas and on the more barren Patagonian plateau. These nervous animals often take over an abandoned viscacha tunnel. If none is available, they dig a short, shallow burrow. They live in groups of about 12 and feed during the day, except in areas where predators are numerous.

The tuco-tuco, widely distributed in southern South America, is a typical pampas-dweller. It gets its name from the noise it makes in its tunnel—a *tuc-tuc-tuc-tuc*, which starts very slowly and then gets faster and faster. Each animal digs its own tunnel.

Wild guinea-pigs, or cuis, are found in grassy areas. One species, *Cavia pamparum*, lives mainly on the pampas. They feed at dawn and dusk in groups of several hundred individuals. When startled, they quickly hide among tufts of grass or run off along their well-trodden paths.

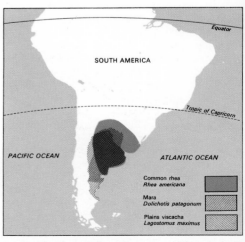

Pampas-dwellers with small ranges Although these three animals have relatively small ranges, their populations are quite large

Tuco-tuco Ctenomys talarum

Plains viscacha Lagostomus maximus

Pampas guinea-pig Cavia pamparum

Rodents of the open grasslands Tuco-tucos and viscachas shelter in tunnels during the day, while guinea-pigs live on the surface, nesting in the tussocks. Tuco-tucos regulate the microclimate by making openings that catch prevailing wind when hot, and plugging these holes when cold

A flock of rheas Foraging for leaves, roots, seeds, and insects, rheas roam the pampas in flocks of 3 to 30, though old males usually live alone.

When its nest is threatened, a rhea tries to lure the predator away by running off, trailing its outspread wings as if it were wounded

The running rhea and other birds of the pampas

The rhea is a long-legged, flightless bird well suited to life on the open grassland. It is tall enough to look over high grass, and its gray color and slender neck allow it to blend with the gray haze of the background. Before man introduced the horse, the rhea was the fastest runner on the pampas.

At the start of the breeding season, the cocks fight for the females, twisting one another's necks, and biting and kicking. The victorious cock displays in front of six or more hens, running to and fro and extending its wings for them.

After mating, the cock makes a nest in a natural depression in the ground. In it several hens lay 13 to 30 eggs. As many as 120 eggs have been found in one nest. All the hatching is done by the cock.

The spotted tinamou and the rufous tinamou live almost entirely on the ground, and fly only if disturbed. They are solitary birds, but several of them are often found in the same area. Up to 12 dark purple eggs are hatched by one parent, probably the male, although a female may take over.

Nearly 200 species of flying birds, includ-

ing ducks, geese, ibises, herons, flamingoes, and plovers, may be seen on the pampas, but most are migratory. The brightly colored burrowing parrot travels north from its breeding grounds in the Patagonian desert to winter on the pampas. Another bird, Wilson's phalarope, breeds on the North American prairies, but migrates in the fall all the way to the pampas in order to avoid the cold northern winter.

Many birds from wooded areas feed on the savannas of South America, but few species can be considered typical of the region.

Spotted tinamou About the size of a small quail, the female courts the male and the male incubates the eggs

Spurred wings The crested screamer, so named for its screams when alarmed, has two curved spurs on the front of each wing. It lives in marshy areas of the pampas

Marsh-dweller The red-headed blackbird, widespread throughout South America, forages in marshy land for roots, leaves, seeds, and grubs

133

Predators of the plains

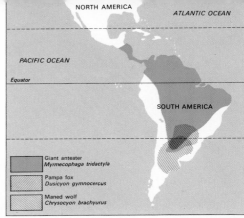

The survival of many of the predators that inhabit the Brazilian campos and the Argentine pampas depends on their ability to eat practically everything

Maned wolves and pampas foxes are typical predators of the South American grasslands. Small mammals are their preferred diet, but they will also eat reptiles, birds, and insects.

South America has six species of skunks, which root in the ground for insects with their broad, bare noses. A closely related animal, the huron, or lesser grison, has adapted to open country by standing on its hind legs to scan the plain for prey. Armadillos, anteaters, and burrowing birds eat insects.

The larger predators The maned wolf and pampas fox live in the grassland, while the giant anteater is found throughout the grassland and tropical forest

Wolf, fox, and anteater patrol the pampas for prey

Maned wolves Unlike other wolves that hunt in packs, these animals hunt alone for small mammals

The slow pampas fox Small mammals are the normal diet of the pampas fox, but it is omnivorous. When danger approaches, it will sometimes freeze. This may be due to the fact that it cannot run fast

The maned wolf, with its long legs, is well adapted to plains life, yet is found mainly in areas where there are trees for shelter.

This shy, nocturnal, usually solitary animal has a sometimes prominent mane on the back of its neck. It eats small mammals such as cuis (wild guinea-pigs), rabbits, and young viscachas, as well as birds, insects, reptiles, and fruit. This wolf sometimes utters an eerie cry at dusk. Pups, usually two, are born in winter.

Like the maned wolf, the pampas fox, or Azara's fox, will eat practically anything. It sometimes takes over a tunnel system inhabited by viscachas, apparently living alongside them. But in spring, when the young viscachas leave the safety of their dwelling, the fox turns upon this easy, close-at-hand food supply.

The giant anteater is inappropriately named. It prefers termites. Only if these are unavailable will it eat ants. It rips open the termite nests with the powerful claws on its forefeet and picks up insects, eggs, and cocoons on its long, sticky tongue.

Giant anteaters do not seem to have permanent bases, but spend their time wandering with their noses close to the ground in constant search of food. When they want to sleep, they find a secluded spot and curl up with the head between the forelegs, the head and body covered by the enormous bushy tail. From the tip of its long, tubular snout to the end of its tail, a giant anteater may measure seven feet. The young are born in spring, usually singly, and are carried around on their mothers' backs.

Anteater's claws Turned inward as the animal walks, these are used to tear open termite nests

Giant anteater Inhabiting swampy areas of the grasslands, the giant anteater is a strong swimmer and can ford wide rivers. On land it walks with its long, tubular snout close to the ground, and runs off at a clumsy gallop when in danger. If cornered, it will fight with its powerful forelegs

The armored burrowers

Armadillos, the only mammals with shells, usually dig their own holes, but they sometimes take over abandoned viscacha burrows. Most of the 21 species of armadillos are widespread and abundant.

Though armadillos are protected by their shells, which are made of plates of bone covered by horny scales, they also escape from canine predators and birds of prey by rapidly burrowing into the ground.

Hairy armadillos are very common on the pampas. Other animals often use the holes they dig. The smallest species, the five-inch-long fairy armadillo, which is now rare, has a shell that is almost completely separated from its body.

Quads nearly every time The nine-banded armadillo, common in South America, is unique in that the female almost always bears identical quadruplets. The fertilized egg divides into four parts

Hairy armadillo When disturbed, this armadillo burrows into the loose soil. Other animals may use the burrow after it is abandoned

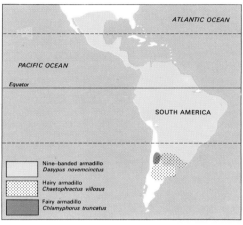

Abundant armadillos Even though they destroy large numbers of insects and snakes, armadillos are so abundant that they are treated as pests

Fairy armadillo Spending most of its life underground, the five-inch fairy armadillo is the smallest of 21 species of armadillos found in the grasslands

Body length 5–7 in.

Burmeister's fairy armadillo *Burmeisteria retusa*

12–27 in.

Naked-tailed armadillo *Cabassous centralis*

16 in.

Pichi *Zaedyus pichiy*

17 in.

Three-banded armadillo *Tolypeutes tricinctus*

Patterns of armor Widely separated small plates cover the tails of the naked-tailed and Burmeister's fairy armadillos. Like many others, the pichi has hair projecting from its armor, and the three-banded armadillo has an overhanging shell with movable bands, enabling it to roll into a tight ball

Burrowing birds and other predators of the pampas

Soil piled up around the mouths of viscacha tunnels is easily spotted on the flat pampas. These long-lasting earthworks attract other animals, including burrowing birds such as the small burrowing owl. Several of these birds can often be seen sitting side by side on the viscacha mounds, where they keep a sharp lookout for the small rodents, insects, and reptiles on which they feed. The viscachas seem to be quite undisturbed by their presence.

The miner *Geositta cunicularia* and the small swallow *Atticora cyanoleuca* make their burrows in the viscacha mounds and feed on the abounding insect life.

Other predatory birds live on the savannas of Brazil and Venezuela—where trees provide perches—rather than on the open pampas. The ovenbird, however, has become common on the pampas, building its mud nests on houses and poles erected by man.

Another pampas predator, the escuerzo, is a large poisonous anuran which lies concealed in the grass, camouflaged by its color and pattern, waiting for prey.

Ungrateful boarder The burrowing owl will co-habit with many burrowing animals and will sometimes eat the food and young of its host

Ovenbird Its common name is derived from its clay nest, which is large and shaped like a kiln

Poisonous toad The escuerzo lies in wait for prey, such as other toads, birds, and rodents

Kangaroos

While hooved grazing mammals evolved in other continents, a remarkable array of big-footed hopping marsupials—the kangaroo family—was emerging in Australia

Isolated for millions of years on an island continent, Australia's marsupials, or pouched mammals, developed along lines of their own. All mammals are descended from egg-laying reptiles, and one direction of evolution was that, instead of laying eggs, certain mammals gave birth to immature young that were carried in the mother's pouch. This was the direction taken by marsupials. Among the marsupials are the kangaroo family, hopping animals with long hind feet. This highly successful family of some 50 species ranges in size from the red kangaroo, about 4½ feet tall in its usual squatting posture, to the rat-kangaroos, which are only about one foot high. The kangaroos occupy the niche that is filled by ruminants in other lands.

While hooved animals gained speed and mobility by evolving long, slender legs and hooved toes, the kangaroos achieved the same result by developing much longer hind legs than other marsupials, and by adopting a bounding gait.

At the same time they evolved long, muscular tails, which are as useful to them as extra limbs. A kangaroo's tail acts as a counterweight to the body, stabilizing the animal as it hops along. It is a prop when the kangaroo is at rest or grazing, and it becomes a lever on which the animal rears its body when fighting.

The red kangaroo is perhaps the best known of the larger kangaroos. The males are usually red-brown and the females, or does, blue-gray.

Female red kangaroos mate again soon after giving birth. Implantation in the womb of the blastocyst, a hollow sphere of cells derived from the fertilized egg, is delayed for about 200 days while the newborn infant

Speed by leaps Large kangaroos reach about 30 miles per hour in a series of 12-foot leaps. A single slow hop takes them four to six feet

Fighting style In typical kangaroo fashion, these gray kangaroos hold with their forefeet and administer powerful kicks with their hind feet

Dry-country kangaroo A red kangaroo, which lives on Australia's arid inland plains, rests on its hind legs, propping itself on its long, muscular tail. When danger threatens, red kangaroos scatter in all directions, with the bucks showing little inclination to protect either the does or the young

completes its development in the pouch. The blastocyst comes to full term at about 235 days and the new offspring is usually born within a day after the first infant leaves the pouch. The female then mates again, so it has two dependent young—one on foot and one in the pouch—when it is again pregnant with an unimplanted blastocyst. If the young in the pouch is lost, the blastocyst comes to term 31 days later and replaces it.

Red kangaroos occur in semiarid areas. The four-foot-tall gray kangaroos are found in better-watered regions. The two species of gray kangaroos live mostly in open forest.

The wallaroos

Wallaroos belong to three different species. The eastern wallaroo and the euros form one species. The others are the black wallaroo and the antilopine kangaroo. Most of them are about four feet tall and more sturdily built than either the red or gray kangaroos. Because they usually live in dry regions with little vegetation, wallaroos are adapted to drought conditions and can survive without drinking water for 14 days or more. They have the ability to form concentrated urine and so reduce water loss. Wallaroos avoid the worst heat of the day by sheltering under rock ledges or in caves.

Gray kangaroos Less well adapted to arid conditions than red kangaroos, they must drink about three times more often. They rest in the day and feed in the cooler hours

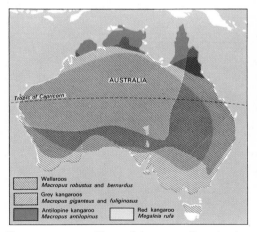

Kangaroo ranges The red kangaroo lives in the highlands, the gray in lower-lying prairies

Wallaroos
Macropus robustus and bernardus

Grey kangaroos
Macropus giganteus and fuliginosus

Antilopine kangaroo
Macropus antilopinus

Red kangaroo
Megaleia rufa

Siesta time These red kangaroos are resting during the hottest part of the day. One has a young kangaroo in its pouch. The young live in the pouch for nine months, but they do venture out after three

Kangaroo birth Kangaroos are only partly formed at birth, and spend a further period of development in the mother's pouch. Still protected by embryonic membranes, the baby appears at the urinogenital opening. Fully emerged, the infant, less than an inch long, crawls upward toward the pouch. Once inside, it finds one of the mother's four teats and attaches itself. About eight weeks later, the young kangaroo has well-formed hind legs and a tail

137

Australia's unique mammals

The animals of Australia include such creatures as the spiny anteater, a mammal that lays an egg and then incubates it in a temporary pouch

Mammals fall into three groups, according to how they produce their young. Australia is the only continent with all three. It has monotremes—the platypus and the spiny anteater—whose young hatch from eggs; it has marsupials, whose young continue to develop in the mother's pouch after birth; and it has placentals, whose young are nourished in the womb by a placenta, and are well developed at birth.

Examples of marsupials are the kangaroos, wallabies, wombats, and marsupial mice. These are all grass- or insect-eating animals. The native cats are dasyurids, or carnivorous marsupials.

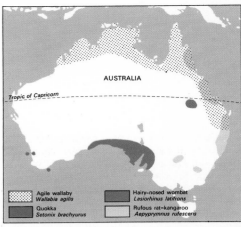

"Little kangaroos" The ranges of the rufous rat-kangaroo and quokka have been reduced by man's effects on their habitat

Some small kangaroos are dying out on the mainland

Wary forager Eyes and ears alert for danger, a rufous rat-kangaroo searches for roots and leaves

The large members of the kangaroo family, the kangaroos and the wallaroos, are still fairly common. However, some of the smaller members—the rat-kangaroos and others—have declined considerably in numbers in this century.

The short-nosed rat-kangaroo is now uncommon on the mainland, although it is still plentiful on offshore islands. These animals dig large communal burrows with their strong foreclaws. Their hind feet are longer than their heads. The rat-kangaroo feeds on roots and underground fungi. Hare wallabies, once numerous, are now very rare. These marsupials have a bounding gait and, like hares, rest by day in "forms" among tussocks. One species gives a whistling call when pursued. A hare wallaby, chased by dogs, was observed to turn back in its tracks and jump over a man.

Some half a dozen species of rock wallabies fill the role usually occupied by mountain sheep and goats in other countries. The brush-tailed rock wallaby, still common in parts of central Australia, lives on the outcrops of rocks on the open plains; it is a surefooted and skillful climber.

The nail-tail wallabies derive their name from a small naillike spur at the end of the tail, the function of which is unknown. Active at night, they feed mostly on roots, grasses, and herbaceous plants. These wallabies are also known as organ-grinders, from their habit of extending their arms sideways and rotating them while they hop along.

Agile wallaby A young agile wallaby is resting, supported by its tail. The powerful and heavily clawed middle toes of its hind legs are used in fighting. The agile wallaby has a large population and a wide range in the tropical open woodland. It is a nocturnal animal and lives in small groups

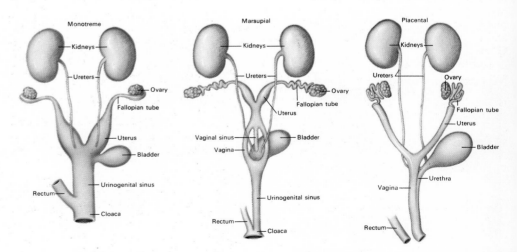

Three ways mammals give birth to young Monotremes hatch from eggs; marsupials start off as eggs that then are born as very immature young; a newborn placental is comparatively well developed, due to being richly nourished by the mother's placenta as it grows in the uterus. In monotremes, eggs are passed through the urinogenital sinus and out an aperture called the cloaca. Marsupials' embryos pass down through the vaginal sinus and then continue out like a monotreme's egg

Wombats and other marsupials

The hairy-nosed wombat is found in the open plains of Queensland and South Australia. These wombats live in extensive communal burrows, emerging at night to feed on grasses, roots, and bark. They have fine, silky hair, and considerably longer ears than the forest-dwelling common wombat.

The smallest of all marsupials is the Kimberley marsupial mouse, named for its mouselike appearance. This tiny animal measures just over two inches from head to base of tail. This voracious insect-eater and its related species fill the niche occupied by shrews elsewhere in the world. They are found in the Northern Territory and in parts of Queensland and New South Wales, mainly in the open grass savanna.

In the more arid parts of the Australian plains, one of the insect-eating marsupials is the fat-tailed marsupial mouse. This mouse-size nocturnal animal shelters in burrows or nests on the ground. It eats mostly insects, but will occasionally take mice and lizards. The female has a better-developed pouch than most other marsupial mice.

Another group of insect-eating marsupials, the jerboa marsupial mice, bear some resemblance to the hopping desert rodents called jerboas. Unlike jerboas, however, they do not hop on their hind legs but run on all fours in a galloping rhythm. They live in open savanna woodland and semidesert grassland, and are nocturnal.

Among the largest dasyurids—flesh-eating marsupials—are the native cats. Most species are forest-dwellers, but the northern native cat is plentiful in the open savanna woodland of the Northern Territory and Queensland. Like most dasyurids, it feeds at night, on insects as well as small vertebrates, such as lizards, rodents, and birds.

Stored fat The swollen tail of the fat-tailed marsupial mouse may be a reserve of food and water

Tail for carrying The brush-tailed rat-kangaroo loops its tail around bundles of grass, used in its nest

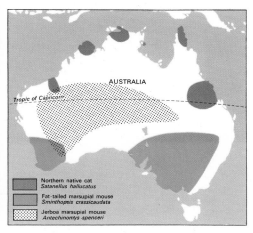

Northern native cat
Satanellus hallucatus

Fat-tailed marsupial mouse
Sminthopsis crassicaudata

Jerboa marsupial mouse
Antechinomys spenceri

Geographic races The northern native cat has six isolated ranges and has developed four races

Drinking quokka When thirsty, the quokka will readily enter the water to drink. Found in the scrub and dense tussock grasslands, this marsupial rests during the day and emerges at night to feed

The mammal that develops a pouch to carry its egg

The egg-laying mammals, or monotremes, may have had as ancestors a different group of mammallike reptiles than the other mammals. The only living monotremes are the platypus and the spiny anteaters, or echidnas, and they are confined to Australia and New Guinea.

During the breeding season, the female spiny anteater develops a temporary pouch in which a single egg is hatched and its young is fed. It is believed that the female's ability to turn the end of its cloaca (see the drawing on facing page) inside-out makes it possible for the egg to be laid directly from the cloaca into the pouch. When the female curls up, the cloaca touches the lip of the pouch.

Suckling monotremes Monotremes have no teats. The young of spiny anteaters are fed within the pouch, where milk ducts open at skin pores. They obtain the milk by sucking from these pores

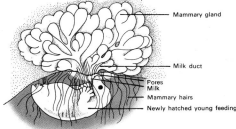

Mammary gland

Milk duct

Pores
Milk

Mammary hairs

Newly hatched young feeding

Spiny anteater Well protected from enemies by its short, sharp spines, this animal can use its strong claws to burrow quickly, so that only its spiny back is visible. Its claws are also helpful in digging ants and termites out of their nests. Then it licks up these insects with its long tongue, which is covered with sticky saliva. Like all adult monotremes, the spiny anteater has no teeth

Animals of the outback

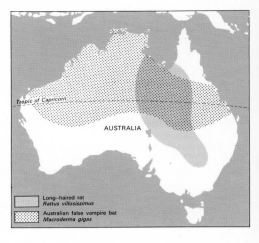

Self-defense in the Australian grasslands takes many forms—none stranger, perhaps, than the ferocious attitude adopted by the frilled lizard to scare away predators

The wildlife of Australia is not easily related to precise life zones, for the distribution of types of vegetation is highly complex. The grasslands run the length of eastern Australia, temperate grassland merging into trop-ical savanna in the northern part of the country. Both these types of grassland in turn merge with desert, scrub, and savanna woodland.

This complexity of vegetation patterns is reflected in the distributions of the animals occupying these regions. Many species of reptiles, for example, range over widely different zones across the length and breadth of the Australian continent.

Native placentals False vampire bats roost in caves. Long-haired rats inhabit burrows and cracks

Bats and rodents shelter in crevices and burrows by day

Australian hopping mouse Usually this mouse moves slowly on all fours, but when alarmed it will leap rapidly on its powerful hind legs

Bats and rodents are the only placentals—mammals whose young are fed before birth through a placenta attaching them to the mother's womb—among Australia's native land mammals. Few species of bats are restricted to the grasslands.

Distributed across the whole of the northern part of the continent in tropical regions from Western Australia to Queensland is the Australian false vampire bat, or ghost bat, which usually roosts during the day in caves or crevices in rocks, often in groups numbering in the thousands.

The false vampire bat, which has a two-foot wingspan, feeds mainly on small mammals—including smaller bats—and reptiles. Like other carnivorous mammals, it has long canine teeth. This name for the bat reflects the erroneous belief that it sucks blood. Its lower jaw juts out, giving its face a bulldog appearance. It is called the ghost bat because

Night flier The wing membrane of the yellow-bellied sheath-tailed bat encompasses its body, leaving only its head and part of its tail free. The tail protrudes through to the upper surface

its wings, belly, feet, and thin, leaflike ears are pale in color.

Several species of native rodents live in the Australian grasslands. One of them, the long-haired rat, which inhabits the savannas of western Queensland and the Northern Territory, is the only native rodent whose numbers can reach plague proportions. When this happens, the long-haired rats do considerable damage to vegetation; grass roots are destroyed and trees are stunted. The

stressful effects of overcrowding, the practice of cannibalism, and predators eventually reduce the population to its original level.

The stick-nest rat of the Nullarbor Plain has fluffy hair, a blunt nose, and large ears. It looks like a small rabbit with a rat's tail. These rats form communities and pile up sticks to make large nests which provide protection against predators. The nests may be four feet across, and are often built around a small bush or against a rock.

Termite nests that face north, away from the hot sun

The compass or meridional termite, which lives on the plains around Darwin, in northern Australia, builds huge, slab-sided nests that rise like great tombstones above the flat country. These nests may be 12 feet high and 10 feet long, but are rarely more than 3 feet thick.

The nests usually point north-south, so that their broad sides face east and west. This may be an adaptation to the force of the prevailing wind, but it also means that the sides get maximum exposure to the sun

at the coolest parts of the day. At midday, when the sun's heat is at its fiercest, the galleries and chambers inside receive some protection. The nests, known as termitaria, are built with soil cemented together by a mixture of saliva and glandular secretions.

Most termites tunnel for food, and seldom visit the surface. Termites of one Australian genus, however, the *Drepanotermes*, regularly forage in the open for plant debris, which they carry back to the nest. But they venture out only at night or on cloudy days.

Protected nest Compass termites build nests which point north–south. The thin outer walls get maximum exposure to the sun at sunrise and sunset, the coolest parts of the day. At noon, when the sun's heat is greatest, the nest receives minimum exposure

Giant lizards with defensive displays

Expert climbers Clinging claws, an extendible neck, and a mouthful of teeth equip common goannas for hunting in trees—and elsewhere

Ferocious show When frightened, the frilled lizard expands the frill around its neck, enlarging the apparent size of its head as a deterrent to predators

Monitor lizards, of the Varanidae family, have long, heavy bodies, long heads and necks, squat legs, and forked tongues. Some Australian species grow to six feet in length. Most are predators, on anything from insects and birds' eggs to mammals. All monitor lizards lay leathery-shelled eggs, varying in number from 7 to 35, usually depositing them in a hole in the ground.

Australia's smaller lizards are often extremely fierce in appearance, but their threatening displays apparently function primarily in frightening off attackers. The bearded dragon lizard, for example, has a "beard," or pouch below the jaw. When threatened it distends this pouch and flattens out its body until it becomes almost circular. Its mouth appears enormous. The bearded dragon feeds on insects, small vertebrates, and plant material, and may grow to two feet in length.

The frilled lizard assumes an even more dramatic appearance to deter predators. If cornered, it expands around its neck a frill which is normally folded back against the body. In the middle is the mouth, wide open and hissing.

The widely distributed grass skink grows to about four inches long. Another common skink is the shingle-back, which may reach 18 inches. This strong-jawed, slow-moving lizard will eat anything that is available, either animal or plant food. It gets its name from the rough scales on its back.

Bearded dragon Its name is derived from its appearance when facing danger. The head appears to double in size and the stretched mouth and extended throat emphasize the neck's spiked scales

Shingle-back skink This lizard gets its name from the rough scales on its back

Birds of the arid plains

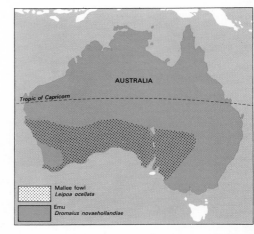

The lives of birds on the dry Australian plains are geared to the availability of water. For example, the first drops of rain set off courtship among the budgerigars

Australia has 650 species of birds, a small number for a continent of almost 3 million square miles. It offers fewer kinds of habitat than other continents and some types of birds are absent—there are no woodpeckers, for example. On the other hand, early bird colonists have had a long time to evolve in their own way. Australia has been cut off from other continents for at least 60 million years. Today there are many species there which are found nowhere else.

The emu is the Australian counterpart of the ostrich of the African grasslands. Though the two species are not closely related, they show similarities because they have become adapted to similar habitats. Both have exchanged flight for large body size and speed.

Tenacious emus Victims of a past extermination campaign, emus are now protected

The emu and the mallee, two of Australia's most curious birds

The male emu, which is slightly smaller than the female, incubates the eggs, and in doing so may lose up to 20 pounds in weight. The clutch of 9 to 12 deep green eggs is laid in a sheltered nest with a good view of the surrounding country. If the incubating bird is disturbed, it slinks off with its neck outstretched parallel to the ground so as not to draw attention to itself.

The chicks are camouflaged in brown and yellow stripes. Even so, some fall prey to dingoes (wild carnivorous dogs) and eagles. The chicks stay with the cock for 18 months.

About 50 of the world's 315 species of parrots are found in Australia. Parrots are basically forest birds—equipped with powerful bills which can crack hard fruit cases, strip bark, and act as a third limb in climb-ing—but in Australia they have spread into the grassland. The parakeets, or rosellas, are particularly adapted to life in the open. They feed on the ground, exploiting the vast annual crop of buds and seeds.

The best-known, and smallest, parakeet is the budgerigar, green in its wild state and found almost everywhere in Australia, nesting in holes and roaming the plains in large

Flightless emus Because emus are flightless, they are restricted to Australia and almost certainly evolved there. The male incubates the eggs and rears the chicks for the first few days. The chicks have alternating stripes of white and gray

The cock that builds an incubator

After a brief courtship, the cock mallee fowl spends the year building and tending its unique nest. As rain comes, it digs a pit, and puts in wet leaves, twigs, and grass. Then it covers the pit with sand

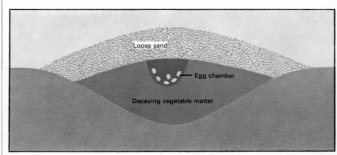

When the rotting vegetation gives off enough heat, the male scoops out a hole. The hen lays one egg a week for the next six months. The temperature is critical. The male judges it with its tongue, and removes or replaces sand to maintain a constant temperature

Chicks are hatched at weekly intervals, and are left to fend for themselves. They can run within hours and can fly within 24 hours

Safety in confusion Budgerigars whirl around a water hole, making it difficult for any birds of prey, which often lurk nearby, to select a single victim

flocks. These intensely sociable birds will accept humans as substitute companions, which accounts for their popularity as pets.

Another highly gregarious parrot found on the plains is the galah, a cockatoo which digs for bulbs and roots.

In a land where seasonal or even yearlong droughts are commonplace, water holes are especially important. Great flocks of birds must visit the water holes each day to drink, and predators inevitably find these profitable sites for ambush. Birds of prey such as falcons and kites, and dingoes, await the arrival of this supply of airborne food.

Consequently, birds such as budgerigars, cockatoos, and flock pigeons have evolved protective behavior. Many approach water holes in great whirling flocks, confusing predators by sheer numbers. Others drink at dusk and dawn, or drop to earth some distance off and approach the water on foot.

The congregations at water holes also present opportunities for social activities such as mutual preening and for pairing.

There is a close relationship between mating and the availability of water. After the rains, breeding birds can take advantage of a brief abundance of plant and insect food. But rainfall in the Australian plains is infrequent and irregular. Birds must be prepared to breed at short notice—to build nests, lay eggs, and rear the chicks before food is again in short supply.

It may be that, in this environment, the very sight of rain is the stimulus that promotes breeding. Wood swallows and budgerigars begin courtship within hours of rainfall, and the zebra finch lays its eggs one week after the arrival of the rains. Nest building, too, must be rapid. Several species have made dry-country adaptations to hasten the process. Such adaptations can be seen operating within a single species. In moister climates, only the female zebra finch builds the nest; but in the desert, the male joins in and the nest is built more quickly. The gray-crowned babbler takes the process a stage further; nest building is a communal task for the whole colony. Some small birds in arid regions are able to mate at an early age—budgerigars can do so at only eight weeks.

Mulga parrots Water sources are important to the mulga parrots, which range widely over the drier areas of southern Australia. They are ground-feed-ing parakeets, with the characteristic parrot beak —the lower part completely fits into the larger upper part when the bill is closed

Wedge-tailed eagle This species feeds on rabbits, young marsupials, and birds. It lives in both open country and woodland

143

DESERTS

Deserts are inhospitable environments for animals. The scorching heat of the day may give way to bitter cold at night, and water is in short supply all year round

More than 14 percent of the world's land surface, an area as big as South America, is occupied by desert. Every continent has at least one desert. The largest single desert is the Sahara, covering an area the size of the United States. It in turn is part of the Great Palearctic Desert, the largest belt of desert in the world, stretching from the Atlantic almost continuously across northern Africa and Asia Minor to northern India and the Gobi Desert in Mongolia. Other areas that could be classified as desert or semidesert stretch over large parts of southern Africa, North America, South America, and most of Australia. The Australian desert is, on the whole, the least arid of these regions.

Rainfall is the main factor in classifying a desert. Any region that receives less than ten inches of rain a year is defined as a desert. The tundra across Alaska, Canada, northern Europe, and Siberia, which fits this description, is often termed a cold desert. To further clarify a "true" desert, the definition has been extended to cover any area where evaporation exceeds precipitation. (The opposite occurs in the tundra.)

Deserts are as different in appearance as the climates and geological factors that produced them. A desert is sometimes a rocky plateau, sometimes a pebbly plain. In some places shallow temporary lakes form after rainfall and then quickly evaporate, leaving a surface layer of glistening white salt. In other places there may be mile after mile of shifting sand dunes, some as high as 700 feet. Elsewhere there are steep, rocky slopes.

Three types of deserts

Mountain deserts are formed where mountain ranges drain the moisture from winds before they can pass over the land. These mountain deserts have distinct seasons and a wide range of annual temperature. The Sahara and the Kalahari deserts in Africa are *inland deserts*. They are the source, not the recipient, of continental air masses. Here there are no distinct seasons, but the daily temperature range is very great. A third type of desert lies on the western coasts of continents. Temperatures on these *western coast deserts* are much lower than on inland and mountain deserts because of cold air currents that cool the land. These are sometimes called foggy deserts. Although fog is common, it is not accompanied by rain.

In the middle of rocky deserts the wind, carrying the loose, abrasive sand, has molded and polished the rocks and hills into a variety of strange shapes and patterns.

In spite of temperature extremes and lack of water, many deserts support a relatively rich variety of plant life. Along the Mediterranean coast of Africa, for example, spring rains transform the desert landscape with a vivid outburst of flowers and plants.

Rainstorms in other deserts may be violent and localized, delivering a year's supply of water to a small area in a matter of minutes. The typical plants are well adapted to utilize every drop. Seeds that may have been dormant in the parched earth for years grow, mature, and reproduce in just a few short weeks after rain.

How animals survive

For many animals the desert is an inhospitable environment. They must somehow live and reproduce in a land with little groundwater and an unreliable rainfall, and be able to survive the heat of midday. (An air temperature of 134° F. (56.6° C.) has been recorded at Death Valley, California.) Cold nights often follow the hot days, since heat dissipates rapidly into the cloudless sky.

Some animals protect themselves from these extremes of temperature by living in burrows. Below the surface the microclimate provides them with a more favorable and relatively constant temperature. Dusk and dawn, when temperatures are more moderate and humidity rises, are the best times for animals. Then the desert comes alive. Small mammals, reptiles, and other animals emerge from their burrows and hiding places to seek food.

Water conservation is the main problem for all desert animals. Gazelles form concentrated urine, which has a low water content and thus cuts down on water loss. They must still drink water, however, so they travel from one oasis or water hole to the next. Some other animals never drink water at all, but get moisture from seeds and succulent cacti.

Even in the extremely arid regions, such as the central Sahara, dried vegetation carried on the wind from the land bordering the desert supports a small insect population. Lizards, spiders, and scorpions prey on the insects.

A comparatively slight alteration in conditions can turn a desert into a fertile region. Man has had some dramatic successes in making desert lands fertile, as in the southwestern United States, by introducing enough irrigation to support sufficient plant growth, which binds the soil, prevents erosion, and, above all, reduces moisture loss—for the greatest necessity of all life in the world is water.

Arizona desert Even in this forbidding, sunbaked land in Monument Valley, there is animal life, as evidenced by tracks in the sand

145

The arid lands

The scanty, irregular rainfall of desert regions can support plants, even though some lie dormant for years before they receive enough moisture to flower

The deserts are the driest zones on earth. The little rain they receive is often seasonal and unevenly distributed. The dry, clear air provides poor insulation for the desert surface, so temperatures soar during the day, causing further drying, and drop at night. Winds, which increase the aridity, blow unobstructed by any thick vegetation. The winds erode the rock into sand and blow up sandstorms, which accelerate the erosion by their abrasive effect.

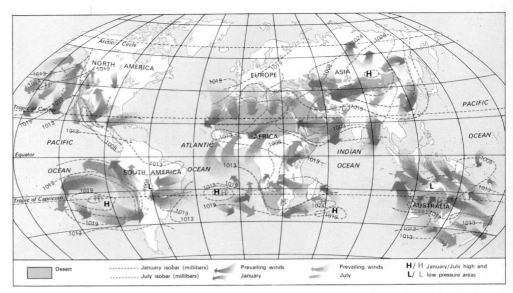

The world's deserts Lying inland, the Sahara and Gobi deserts are out of reach of rain-bearing winds. The deserts of Chile and Peru are in coastal regions where cold currents bring fog and mist, but no rain. Mountain ranges of North America drain the moisture from winds blowing east off the Pacific

Molded by the wind One seventh of the Sahara is shifting sands, called ergs, within which the dunes may be 700 feet high. There are two types of dunes— crescent-shaped where sand is scarce and wind direction constant; and sword-shaped where winds are variable. A single erg can be as large as France

Stony waste Pebbles and gravel cover the surface of many deserts, as at the left. Most such areas were once river basins that have been dry for a long time. Clumps of vegetation are scattered about

Polished rock Rocky deserts occur where wind strips the soil and exposes the underlying rock. The erosion-polished rock in the Mount Olga region of central Australia tends to reflect the light

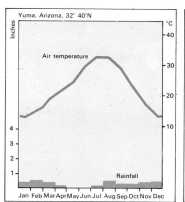
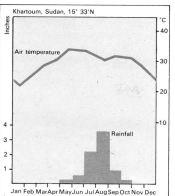
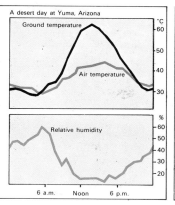
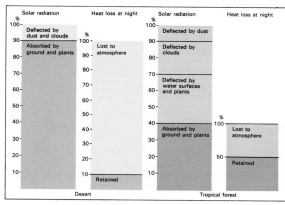

Differing desert climates Variations in temperature (given here in centigrade) and rainfall distinguish one desert from another. Arizona's desert has a great annual temperature range with spotty rainfall throughout the year. Around Khartoum, a semiarid region, the annual temperature range is small and rain falls in one season. Desert ground temperatures rise rapidly because of the lack of clouds and plant cover, but at night most of the heat is lost to the air. Tropical forests, by contrast, receive less heat, but lose less at night. Humidity increases at night, providing moisture for desert life

Where plants get their moisture from the night air

Desert conditions severely limit plant growth. Most of the rain falls in thunderstorms, and rapidly evaporates or runs off the parched surface of the land, usually causing gully erosion. Plant growth is further affected by scorching heat during the day, followed at night by cold that can cause frost damage.

In periods of extreme drought some plants survive on moisture from the air. At night the temperature drops, and though the moisture content of the air remains the same, the relative humidity rises, causing dew to condense on plants and other surfaces. These plants, by absorbing moisture from the night air, make water available to insects, snails, and other small plant-eaters.

The cloudless desert skies cause high evaporation and high ground temperatures during the day. Deserts receive about 90 percent of available solar radiation, compared with 40 percent in the more humid equatorial regions, where much radiation is absorbed by clouds, dust, water, and vegetation. But at night deserts lose 90 percent of their accumulated heat, compared with 50 percent in more humid areas.

The soil provides desert animals with the best insulation against these extremes of temperature. While the surface temperature during the day may reach 183° F. (84° C.), as at Wadi Halfa in the Sudan, conditions are much more bearable only a short distance below the surface. In the Sahara, at a depth of 20 inches, there is hardly any variation between day and night temperatures, and the relatively high humidity of the air surrounding the loose grains of sand at this depth is crucially important to burrowing animals.

Brief drenching A downpour creates a flash flood, drenching these creosote bushes. They are one of the most common plants of American deserts

Plants that survive by evading or resisting drought

Water is vital for all plants. Those that survive in the desert can be classified as either drought-evading or drought-resisting.

The drought-evading plants, called ephemerals, may lie dormant for years as seeds, then spring to life after rain and complete their life cycles within weeks. The African *Boerhaavia repens* can produce seeds just eight to ten days after sprouting. These plants bear large, gaudy flowers, develop no deep roots or water-storage organs, and provide for the future only by producing a huge seed crop.

Trees such as acacia or mesquite may have roots that reach down 100 feet or more to subterranean water.

Typical drought-resisting succulent plants have very small or even no leaves, thick waterproof skins, and leaf pores that can be tightly shut—all of which reduce water loss by evaporation—and often elaborate methods of water storage. Water may be stored in tuberous roots, fleshy stems, or leaves. The best-known plants of the desert are probably the cacti and euphorbias. Their fleshy tissues can hold vast amounts of liquid, and their shallow, widespread roots absorb surface moisture. Other desert plants can withstand water loss, but become dormant during periods of drought.

Most successful desert plants have evolved some means of defense against browsing animals. Shrubs and cacti have thorns, and the creosote bush has distasteful, pungent juice.

Trapping the dew The welwitschia plant of South-West Africa has two curling leaves, split into longitudinal flaps. Dew condenses on them at night, providing moisture for the shallow roots

Colorful cactus Bright red blossoms of the mound cactus give splashes of color to the sere wilderness of the Mojave Desert in California. These cacti and other such succulents grow in semi-deserts. They have thick skins protecting their fleshy stems, where water is stored. Also, their leaves are spikes, cutting water loss

Giant water tank Pleats on the stems of the saguaro cactus open in moist weather and close in dry. Saguaros are the tallest cacti, reaching 50 feet

147

Adaptations to desert life

Arid lands baked by a searing sun provide a home for a surprisingly large variety of animal species, all capable of withstanding severe drought and heat

Water, the main requirement of life, is in short supply in the deserts, and animals that live in these regions have had to evolve ways of conserving water in their bodies by avoiding, tolerating, or controlling the heat.

When the ancestors of present-day land animals first crawled or flopped out of the sea, they became adapted to fluctuating temperatures on land, and some evolved waterproof skins that reduced moisture loss.

Animals that have made their home in the desert have become further adapted. Some desert-dwellers have developed burrowing habits that enable them to escape the extreme temperatures of the surface. Others have hard, impermeable outer coverings that minimize water loss from the body. Still others have become adapted by developing body systems that can function efficiently solely on the water contained in the food they eat, so that they hardly ever—in some cases never—need to drink.

Escaping from heat and conserving vital moisture

Avoiding heat A gecko of the Kalahari Desert stands on tiptoe to avoid the scorching sand

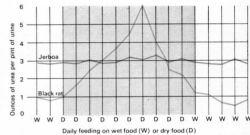

Conserving water Specialized kidneys enable the jerboa to endure a waterless diet. The graph shows an experiment in which wet and dry diets were fed to a jerboa and a black rat. The jerboa excretes concentrated urine no matter what its water intake, while the rat suffers kidney failure

Land animals may lose body moisture in three ways: by evaporation through the body surface; by exhaling moisture during respiration; and by expelling moisture during excretion. Animals that live in deserts have ways of coping with all three forms of water loss.

Some, like scorpions and reptiles, evolved almost impermeable outer coverings that fit them for desert life by reducing moisture loss. Others, such as the camel, have developed a greater tolerance to heat than mammals in more humid climates; their body temperature fluctuates more, reducing the amount of moisture that would otherwise be lost through sweating and panting.

Many of the smaller desert mammals cool exhaled air in their noses before it leaves the nostrils, so that moisture condenses and is not lost as water vapor.

Proteins form a large part of the chemical makeup of all animals, and as cells constantly die and are replaced, the proteins of the dead cells are broken into their component amino acids. These, and excess amino acids resulting from digestion of food, are further broken down, releasing ammonia. This chemical is poisonous, and animals protect themselves from it by combining it with other substances to form either urea or uric acid, both harmless.

Urea, which must be excreted in solution, is formed by mammals and some reptiles. Birds, most reptiles, and insects reduce water loss by excreting a crystalline nitrogenous compound once thought to consist of uric acid, although recent investigations on birds show the substance to be a more complex crystal than simple uric acid. The kidneys of desert mammals concentrate urine so that it contains less water for a given quantity of urea than the urine of nondesert species.

Desert animals must not only reduce their water loss but must also be able to live without taking much water in. Many survive on the moisture that is contained in their plant or animal food.

All animals produce metabolic water in their bodies when atoms of hydrogen combine with atoms of oxygen. Desert animals can subsist almost entirely on this metabolic water, and some can even produce it on a diet of dry seeds. Nondesert animals, on the other hand, would die if deprived of an exterior supply of water.

Some arthropods, a group which includes insects and spiders, can absorb moisture from the air through their outer coverings.

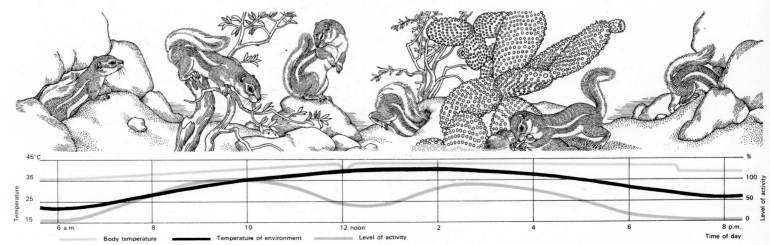

Tolerance of furnacelike temperatures The antelope ground squirrel of the Mojave Desert in California is one of the few mammals adapted to intense activity during the peak temperatures of a desert day (given here in centigrade). Normally, its body temperature is even slightly above the environment's temperature. But its temperature does have a critical point; when this is reached the animal either burrows or lies in the shade

Protected against sand The American chuckwalla has fringed ears, which keep out the sand

Deep burrower *Scorpio maurus* escapes African heat by digging burrows with its enlarged claws

See-through eyelids Transparent lids protect the whip-tailed lizard's eyes when burrowing

Sand swimmer The Australian skink has flipper-like legs that enable it to "swim" through sand

Adaptations for burrowing and living in sand

The most common ways in which desert animals escape the full heat of the sun are by burrowing and by taking shelter in a crevice. In a burrow or crevice an animal is provided with a microclimate that is more humid than the surface when the surface is very dry, cooler when the surface is hot, and warmer when it is cold.

Many desert animals have physical adaptations that help them to burrow under the desert surface. The enlarged claws of desert scorpions are ideal for this purpose. One scorpion, *Scorpio maurus,* has been known to burrow to a depth of almost three feet. Lizards have wedge-shaped heads that cleave the sand; and several species of beetles have become so flattened and platelike that they can burrow into the sand by moving their bodies from side to side.

Burrowing to escape the extremes of the desert's surface is mainly confined to small animals, but all desert animals, large or small, show both behavioral and physical adaptations to their environment. Many avoid the extreme heat of the day and become active only at night. Others, such as "sand-swimming" lizards and snakes, can dive headfirst into sand as though it were water. These reptiles usually have nostrils that are turned upward, protecting them from sand. The eyes of some lizards have large, overhanging, eyebrowlike shields.

Many sand-swimming lizards are legless, or have very short legs. Other lizards have fringed feet that enable them to move rapidly over sand and to burrow quickly beneath it.

Rapid burrower Digging with its nose and feet, the American fringe-toed lizard quickly buries itself

Sinking into the sand The Asian sand viper undulates from side to side and gradually disappears into a trench. Only its eyes and nostrils remain above the surface. Thus covered, the snake is protected from the burning sun. Because it is practically invisible, it usually catches prey unaware. Many desert reptiles show similar adaptations. Some have thicker and wider bodies, and burrow with sideways and vertical movements, instead of plowing forward into the sand. Some lizards have fringed ears and upturned nostrils to keep out sand

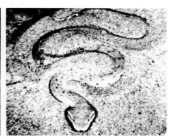

Convergent evolution: why unrelated animals look alike

Extraordinary resemblances have developed between unrelated animals in widely separated desert areas. This phenomenon, known as convergent evolution, has occurred because the problems of living in the desert, whether in Arizona, Africa, Asia, or Australia, are often the same. American kangaroo rats and African jerboas all evade predators by jumping swiftly on elongated hind legs. Jackrabbits in North America, other desert hares of Africa and Asia, and the quokka, an Australian marsupial—all nocturnal desert animals—have developed large ears. Because these dissipate body heat, they are an advantage to desert animals.

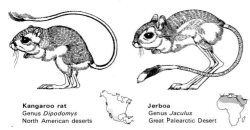

Kangaroo rat
Genus *Dipodomys*
North American deserts

Jerboa
Genus *Jaculus*
Great Palearctic Desert

Desert hoppers The American kangaroo rat, with its large hind legs and a hopping gait, closely resembles the African jerboa

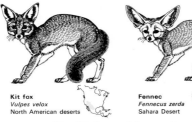

Kit fox
Vulpes velox
North American deserts

Fennec
Fennecus zerda
Sahara Desert

Large ears The kit fox and fennec have evolved large ears that catch sound efficiently and aid in dissipating heat from their bodies

Sidewinder rattlesnake
Crotalus cerastes
North American deserts

Horned viper
Cerastes cerastes
Great Palearctic Desert

Similar snakes Except for its rattle, the sidewinder rattlesnake resembles the horned viper. Both twist across the sand with a similar motion

Camels

The camel's ability to survive in the desert has been exploited by man for so long that few truly wild camels survive, all of them of the Bactrian species

The camel family, which includes the llama, alpaca, vicuna, and guanaco, originated over 10 million years ago in North America. Those forebears that crossed the Bering Strait land bridge to Asia and Africa have evolved into the twin-humped Bactrian camel and the domesticated single-humped Arabian camel, or dromedary.

Apart from domestic beasts run wild, the Arabian camel is now completely under domestication. However, there are still genuinely wild Bactrian camels in the Gobi Desert of Mongolia. Their short brown hair and slender build contrast sharply with the long-haired and stocky domestic breed of Bactrian.

Both the Bactrian and the Arabian species have been essential to man's desert travel since prehistoric times. The tall, slender Arabian camels are used for riding and load-carrying in the hot deserts of the Middle East and North Africa. The long, dark winter coat and short, sturdy legs of the Bactrian camel make it more suitable for work in the mountains and cold deserts of central Asia.

From the ground to the top of the hump, the Bactrian measures about seven feet, and the Arabian about eight feet.

Camels are well adapted to arid conditions, though the popular, long-held belief that they store water either in stomach sacs or in the hump is unfounded. The hump is actually a food store of fat. Since the insulating fat is concentrated in one place, the rest of the body acts as a radiator which dispels heat.

Camels use water with great economy. A camel loses little water in urine—less than a quart a day—and does not begin to sweat until its temperature reaches about 104° F.

A camel's gait Camels reach their top speed—about ten miles per hour—by pacing (advancing both legs on one side while the legs on the other side take the weight). Because of this gait, they can gallop for only a few yards at a time. Laden camels average 2½ miles per hour over 18 hours

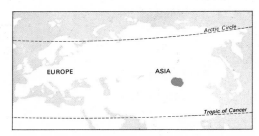

Wild camels of Asia The only truly wild camels are the slim-legged, two-humped Bactrian camels of the Gobi Desert. Other wild herds of both species are descended from escaped domestic stock

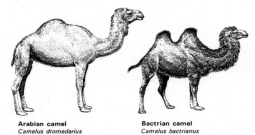

Arabian camel
Camelus dromedarius

Bactrian camel
Camelus bactrianus

Beasts of burden The longer-legged, lighter-built Arabian camel can travel faster and farther; but the Bactrian camel can carry heavier loads for a short distance and is better suited to cold climates

Desert adaptations Long eyelashes and muscular, closable nostrils protect camels from blowing sand. Their feet have two toes, linked by pads that distribute weight evenly, making sand travel easier

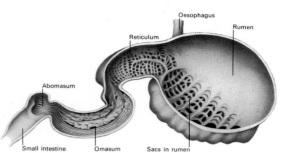

Arabian camels Camels can drink almost 30 gallons of water at a time, but they become thin and their humps sag if they are without water for a week. Eating salty plants helps them retain water

Chambered stomach A camel's stomach has four chambers. The rumen, reticulum, and omasum break down plant food, while the fourth chamber, the abomasum, completes digestion of protein

(40° C.). By this time, the day is usually far advanced, and the camel can dissipate its accumulated body heat gradually during the cooler hours of the night.

In most mammals extreme dehydration in hot, dry air causes "explosive heat death." Water is drawn from the blood to replace water lost in perspiration, and the blood thickens until it cannot circulate quickly enough to carry away internal metabolic heat to the skin. The body temperature soars and death follows. In extreme dehydration a man will lose about 12 percent of his body weight in fluids.

Camels, however, can lose 30 percent of their body weight without apparent distress. The animal's fluid is lost mainly by its fleshy tissues, with little effect on its blood. A dehydrated, emaciated camel can drink almost 30 gallons without danger of water intoxication. If a man tried to replace lost water at the same rate he would die. But the camel's egg-shaped red blood corpuscles can quickly expand into spheres to absorb the sudden intake of water without rupturing. The cam-

el's normal body weight is quickly regained as moisture is restored to the tissues.

The camel will usually drink only to balance weight loss. During the winter, when juicy vegetation is available, it may not drink at all. In summer it can subsist entirely on dry plants.

Bactrian camels rut in January and February, and Arabian camels have a rutting season at the time of the rains. The males become bad-tempered and fight, giving slashing bites with their long canine teeth. Gestation takes about a year for the Arabian camel, and 13 months or more for the Bactrian camel. The young camel is hardy from birth and can follow its mother by the end of its first day, although it is suckled for three or four months.

The wild Bactrian camels in the Gobi Desert live in herds of one or two males and three to five females. They sleep in open spaces and feed during the day on whatever vegetation is available. In spring they migrate to the northern part of their range, returning south in autumn.

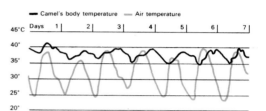

Varying body temperature This graph shows how the body temperature of a camel deprived of water rose and fell with the air temperature. At night the camel's temperature dropped several degrees, helping to delay heating up the next day

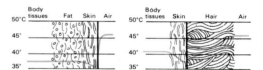

Heat exchange Heat easily penetrates a man's bare skin (left), but fat impedes the loss of body heat. Sweating, a heat-dissipating mechanism, lowers man's body temperature. The camel (right) has a higher body temperature than man, but no fat to prevent the loss of heat

Bactrian camels Facing the sun with tucked-under legs, Gobi Desert dwellers expose minimum body surface. Camels rarely sweat, reducing moisture loss

Antelopes and asses

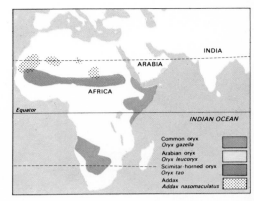

Large mammals in the deserts obtain most of their water from plants; oryxes, gazelles, and wild asses roam for miles in a constant search for vegetation

All of the larger mammals that live in the Old World deserts face the problems caused by a lack of groundwater and a scanty and unpredictable rainfall. Wild asses, like camels, survive in the deserts of Asia and Africa by being able to go without water for long periods and to absorb water copiously when they do drink. The oryx, a species of antelope, gets water from plants more often than from water holes. Gazelles, particularly the dorcas gazelle, vary in their ability to go without water.

All of these Old World antelopes and asses are hardy, long-distance travelers, and can range far afield to find water or shade.

Ranges of oryxes The common oryx of Africa is called gemsbok in the south and beisa in the east

Long-horned antelopes of the barren desert lands

Large antelopes that never drink Addax antelopes are not as fast as oryxes, to which they are related, but they can live in more arid regions. The small herds live in the remote reaches of the Sahara. They obtain moisture only from plants. Their widely splayed hooves enable them to cross sand without difficulty; but, due to their slowness, they face extinction by hunters, who track them in vehicles and light aircraft

Battle wounds The Arabian oryx bull in the lead shows multiple slashes on its shoulder. Missing a horn, this bull is vulnerable when fighting rivals

Common oryx bulls When fighting among themselves, their horns usually become safely locked

The oryxes have long, spear-sharp horns that reach almost four feet in some species. They will often turn on wild dogs and cheetahs rather than flee. One report describes a lion impaled on an oryx's horns, neither able to get free. Oryxes charge with the head down, thrusting the horns from side to side with scythelike movements and snorting through the nostrils. Bull oryxes have extremely thick skin on their necks and shoulders, so that the wounds given each other in dominance fights are seldom fatal. The female, which has horns but does not fight, has thin skin.

In their stony desert habitat oryxes rarely drink. They obtain moisture from plants. In the hottest weather many migrate to the edge of the desert to find shade, and it is often there, at the time of the rains, that the young are born. Oryxes are found throughout the deserts and grasslands of Africa.

The Arabian oryx, smallest of the desert species, stands about three feet high at the shoulder. It has been hunted almost to extinction in recent years.

Some gazelles and wild asses survive without water

Leaping springboks This common name comes from the springboks' habit of leaping into the air—sometimes ten feet high—when playing or startled. A fold of skin, covered with lighter hair, extends over the back and is raised when danger is spotted. Although they can obtain moisture from certain plants, springboks will drink if water is available. Large free-ranging herds, once found across southern Africa, are now restricted to the Kalahari Desert

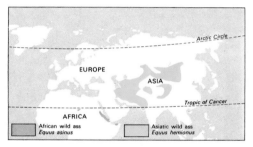

Where asses run wild The two species of wild asses have dwindled in numbers and face extinction. One Asiatic race became extinct this century

Typical of the Old World desert gazelles is the dorcas gazelle, which lives in stony, flat desert. This small animal, standing only two feet high at the shoulder, is alert and can run as fast as 50 miles per hour. It is usually found in small herds of from five to ten.

In desert regions of the Mediterranean basin, dorcas gazelles can get along with only the moisture from succulent roots and plants. Yet the same species in the Sudan cannot survive in the hot season for more than five days without drinking. It appears that in the Sudan dorcas gazelles are less well adapted to a low water intake than camels. Their survival depends on their ability to travel great distances to water.

The African and Asian deserts and the Asian steppes are inhabited by wild asses, which resemble camels in their ability to tolerate a considerable degree of dehydration and to withstand a water loss amounting to 30 percent of their body weight. They can also make up water loss quickly. Within a few minutes, a wild ass can drink water amounting to more than a quarter of its body weight.

The Asiatic wild ass has several races, including the onager, which is the "wild ass" of the Bible. The African wild ass has two races, the Nubian and Somali wild asses, but the Nubian race has been much interbred with domestic asses.

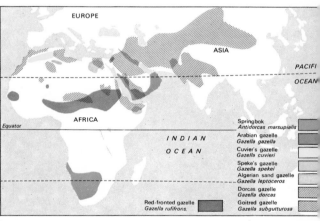

Desert gazelles Across the northern half of Africa and into Asia, there are several species of gazelles. The springbok lives in arid areas of southern Africa

Female dorcas gazelle One of the smallest of the gazelles, the dorcas (left) stands less than two feet at the shoulder. Young are born from April to June and within a week can run up to 50 miles per hour

Indian wild asses Part of the Asiatic species, they once had a broad range, but the majority are now confined to the sparsely covered desert plains of northwestern India. They sometimes band together to form herds of up to 100 individuals, but these herds disperse before the females give birth

153

Small mammals

Many small desert plant-eaters never drink, yet their moist tissues and body fluids supply predators with water

Most small desert mammals would become fatally dehydrated if they spent a high noon on the sun-fired desert surface. Evolution has led them to live in burrows during the day; and several species of desert animals become dormant during the hottest months.

A common adaptation in many small desert mammals, particularly those that burrow, is an enlargement of the bone surrounding the ear, known as the auditory bulla. It is believed that this enlargement greatly increases hearing sensitivity and enables desert animals to detect the approach of predator or prey quickly.

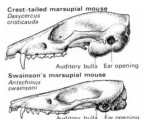

Hearing in soil The skull of the desert marsupial mouse (top), compared with related species, shows an enlarged bulla, which may resonate with vibrations in the soil, warning of predators

One hour on the open desert may mean death from dehydration

Among the most successful desert animals are several groups of small rodents. The jerboas of Asia and North Africa, the kangaroo rats of North America, and the desert mice of Australia can all live with little or no water and have the same quick reactions to danger.

Most animals of these species have developed long hind legs and a bounding, kangaroolike gait. These adaptations give the animals both speed and agility, and, in addition, reduce the area of their bodies that comes in contact with the hot sand. The short forelegs are used for burrowing—an essential activity, since even one midday hour on the desert surface could mean death from dehydration.

Most remarkably, these desert rodents can live without ever drinking water. Their diet consists entirely of dry plant material. When this material is broken down by the body

Kangaroo rats Using their tail for balance these North American rodents hop on long hind legs

Gerbil and young African gerbils are able to extract water from a seemingly dry diet

metabolism it yields metabolic water—all the animals need to live on.

In addition, the rodents' urine is highly concentrated, and almost all water in the feces is reabsorbed by the large intestine.

The animals have no sweat glands, so little water is lost by evaporation. Within a burrow, evaporation is further reduced because the rodents' exhaled breath increases the humidity of the air in the den.

Small cats and foxes are the largest predators of the desert interior

An occasional lion may stray into the fringe of the Sahara to hunt gazelles, but most desert predators are not much bigger than domestic cats.

The desert cats of Arabia and the Sahara—the sand cat and the caracal lynx—like Pallas's cat of Eurasia, prey upon gerbils and jerboas. Small desert foxes, such as the kit fox of North America and the Sahara's fennec fox, also hunt rodents. Foxes in particular depend upon water from the body fluids of their prey. The diet of the fennec fox includes not only rodents, but also insects, birds, lizards, and plants. The coyote, often found in the desert, is similarly omnivorous. Unlike other members of the dog family, the coyote hunts alone or in relays.

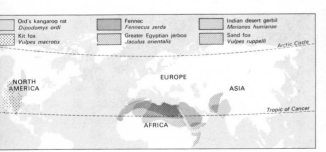

Ord's kangaroo rat *Dipodomys ordi*
Kit fox *Vulpes macrotis*
Fennec *Fennecus zerda*
Greater Egyptian jerboa *Jaculus orientalis*
Indian desert gerbil *Meriones hurrianae*
Sand fox *Vulpes ruppelli*

NORTH AMERICA
EUROPE
ASIA
AFRICA
Arctic Circle
Tropic of Cancer

Desert predators and prey Rodents such as the kangaroo rat, jerboa, and gerbil have adapted to a diet that completely lacks drinking water. Desert predators—kit fox, fennec, and sand fox—obtain their water from the body fluids of these rodents

Sand fox This desert predator is rarely seen near water, for it lives in the most arid areas

The need for moist food

Even though many desert rodents can live without drinking water, birth of their young tends to coincide with a rainy season. A brief growth of juicy grass provides the mothers with the moisture necessary for milk production.

In dry riverbeds enough moisture may remain to support succulent—but extremely salty—plants. These in turn provide moist food for such animals as the North African sand rat. The excess salt is passed off in urine that is four times saltier than seawater.

In American deserts some species of pack rats eat the juicy fruit of cholla cactus. Another cholla fruit-eater, the Mojave Desert ground squirrel, becomes dormant during the hottest summer months.

Other small animals find moisture by eating invertebrates. The grasshopper mice of western North America, the long-eared hedgehog of the Sahara, and the mulgara, a marsupial that inhabits the most arid central parts of Australia, all eat insects as well as small rodents.

Grant's desert golden mole This golden mole escapes heat in the Namib Desert of southwestern Africa by "swimming" beneath the sand. Blind and lacking external ears, it preys on lizards and insects

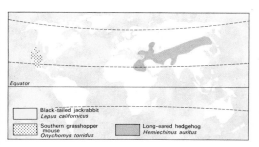

Moisture seekers Long-eared hedgehogs and grasshopper mice get moisture from eating insects and tiny rodents. Jackrabbits seek dew-wet plants

Long-eared hedgehog This animal exists for weeks at a time without eating. It walks and runs with its body held off the ground

Flesh-eater The grasshopper mouse eats lizards and insects

Hares' large ears are for sharp hearing and losing heat

For many desert creatures—large and small, predator and prey—the cool nights are the time of greatest activity. For these nocturnal animals, the sense of hearing is the most vital sense of all.

The ears of desert hares are considerably larger than those of hares in other environments. The favorite prey of a large number of carnivores, hares seldom burrow, thus lacking a form of defensive behavior used effectively by other small desert mammals. Instead, hares such as the American black-tailed jackrabbit and the Saharan brown hare must rely on their acute hearing and 45-mile-per-hour speed to escape from their predators.

Hares do not ordinarily become active until after nightfall. By day, they rest in shallow depressions, or in the shade beneath a bush. But even there, the desert heat can be fierce, and the hare's body temperature must not rise too high. Apparently, some of the hare's body heat is dispersed to the atmosphere through its large ears. These are usually held erect, and are richly supplied with blood vessels that bring "overheated blood" to the skin surfaces for cooling.

Always on the surface The jackrabbit does not burrow—an unusual way of life for a nondrinking animal

Birds of the deserts

Many species of birds can tolerate the desert heat, but most of them must stay well within flying range of surface water for drinking purposes

Apart from being generally paler in color, most desert bird species are hard to distinguish from their relatives in humid climates. The most numerous desert birds are insect-eaters, though seed-eating and carnivorous birds are present.

Carnivorous and insect-eating birds can obtain considerable moisture from their food. But, like the seed-eaters, they seldom stray more than a day's flight from a surface water supply. Small birds, especially, lose water by evaporation more rapidly than mammals of comparable size. Most water is lost by panting; birds have no sweat glands. Because birds have higher body temperatures —usually 104 to 108° F. (40 to 42° C.)— than mammals, they breathe out warmer air, which contains more moisture.

One bird with exceptional adaptations to desert living is the mourning dove. Few other desert birds can match its ability to withstand heat, to endure dehydration, and to fly long distances without drinking.

Most birds of the deserts are diurnal, that is, active by day. To escape the midday heat, they will make use of any shade that is handy. Owls and nightjars are active at night and shelter by day in clefts in rocks.

Birds do not lose much water in waste products expelled from their bodies. Their urine is a complex crystalline form that contains little water.

For some desert birds, salt water serves instead of fresh—a capacity rarely found in

Widespread falcon The bird-eating lanner falcon, though mainly a desert bird, ranges over all but the wettest parts of the African continent

California roadrunner This snake killer allows the snake to strike at its outspread wing feathers before dispatching its prey with its bill

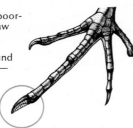

Grooming claw The poorwill has a comblike claw on its middle toe. This is used to clean and straighten bristles around the bird's wide mouth— which help to catch insects—or to scratch the feathers on its head

Desert quail Gambel's quail of America nests under clumps of the spike-studded prickly pear. The female incubates up to 20 chicks and will adopt orphaned chicks in the vicinity. The male guards the tunnel to the spiky nest, but nevertheless tough-skinned lizards slip past to take eggs

Collecting water for the young Although spotted sandgrouse may nest miles from water, they and their chicks need water daily. Thus the males, while drinking, saturate their wing feathers to carry water back to their chicks. Although they fly well, sandgrouse never perch, and hunt by walking

land birds. One is Pallas's sandgrouse, which feeds on salty, succulent plants. Another is the ostrich, which drinks salty water. Like seabirds, it has a large nasal gland that excretes excess salt. The ostrich is also able to tolerate dehydration and increased body temperature.

The scarcity of shade and the hot, dry climate affect the breeding habits of most desert birds. Their eggs, particularly those of the smaller species, can be cooked by the fierce heat of direct sunlight. Some birds, such as Africa's sooty falcon and two-banded courser, breed under the harshest conditions; but many species, such as the red-billed dioch, do not reproduce in dry years.

Birds nest wherever shelter can be found on the desert. Larks nest mainly under shrubs and bushes; wheatears in small caves or holes; and Gambel's quail under prickly pear cacti.

Some California and Arizona desert birds live in holes in saguaro cacti excavated by two species of woodpeckers, the Gila woodpecker and the gilded flicker. The woodpecker tunnels about eight inches into the cactus, excavating a round chamber at the end, which the bird then gives a waterproof lining of saguaro sap. When the woodpecker abandons its home, such birds as the elf owl, screech owl, and American sparrowhawk move in.

A bird that hibernates

Another squatter in these woodpecker nests is the poorwill *Phalaenoptilus nuttallii*, which becomes dormant for long periods. In winter this bird sleeps so deeply that it can be handled without being awakened; its temperature drops to 55° F. (13° C.), and its heartbeat is too faint to hear. When ornithologists were first told of a hibernating bird by Arizona Indians over a century ago, the scientists thought this was just one more delightful legend. Bird hibernation was unheard of. It was not until the 1950s that the legend was proved true.

The lanner falcon, widespread in Africa, is one of the swiftest members of the falcon family. Spiny-tailed lizards are its main desert prey, although it frequently preys on smaller birds as well. The loggerhead shrike of the American desert impales lizards on the sharp thorns of cactus. The bird then commences to remove the lizard's thick, inedible skin before eating its prey.

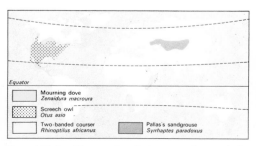
Desert birds The two-banded courser lives only in deserts, while the mourning dove, screech owl, and Pallas's sandgrouse have wider ranges

Merging with the landscape The stone curlew (adult, top), living in the desert and less arid zones, hatches well-camouflaged young (bottom)

Continuous breeding Many desert birds do not reproduce in dry years, but the two-banded courser breeds thoughout the year, even in severest drought

American mourning dove This dove can endure a high body temperature and considerable dehydration. These desert adaptations, plus the ability to fly long distances, allow it to live far from water

Birds that take over old nests Flycatchers (left) and screech owls (right), as well as elf owls and sparrowhawks, occupy deserted woodpecker nests.

In the southwestern United States woodpeckers excavate nests in 30-to-50-foot-high saguaro cacti, plants that provide food for many bird species

157

Lizards and tortoises

Desert reptiles face the same problems as desert mammals and birds; they too have developed ways of surviving with little water under a fierce sun

Life in the desert is not easy for any animal; but reptiles, particularly lizards and snakes, have physical advantages which make desert living easier for them. Water loss through their skins is reduced to a minimum; urinary wastes carry away very little water; and many lizards have glands opening into the nose, through which excess salts taken in with their food are expelled.

Even so, the desert sun can bake a reptile to death. Many lizards and tortoises avoid extreme heat by burrowing; others shelter in clefts in rocks. The desert iguana of Colorado and Mexico digs itself a burrow under creosote bushes.

Horned toad Actually a lizard that just resembles a toad, its ferocious appearance comes from spiky scales

Defended by scales, poison, and fearsome appearance

Desert lizards feed mainly on insects and spiders, though some species, such as the chuckwalla of North America and the spiny-tailed lizards of the African and Asian deserts, are plant-eaters.

The desert monitor of the Old World, which may reach a length of five feet, is speedy and rapacious, eating any animal that it is strong enough to overcome. It can survive in unusually high temperatures.

The slower-moving but equally carnivorous Gila monster kills its prey with its strong jaws and its venom. Like most lizards, the Gila monster and the desert monitor track prey by flicking their tongues over the spoor. An organ in the roof of the mouth, called Jacobson's organ, detects chemicals picked up by the tongue.

Many lizards, particularly the slow-moving ones, have a form and coloring that enable them to blend into the background until they are literally invisible. Faster-moving lizards can achieve the same effect by their speed and agility. They skim over surfaces so quickly that they seem almost to disappear into thin air.

Spiny-scaled lizards

The American "horned toad," actually a horned lizard, and the Australian mountain devil have spiny scales that give them a fierce appearance. Both live only on insects, however.

The mountain devil can absorb water from damp sand. The water does not enter the body directly through the skin, but moves by capillary action along open channels in the outer layer of the skin until it reaches the mouth.

Armadillo lizard's defense This African lizard has armorlike plates on its head and back with a bony layer that makes them rock-hard. When attacked, the armadillo lizard protects its soft underbelly by turning on its back and rolling into a ball, grasping its spiny tail in its mouth

Venomous lizard The Gila monster of North America (left) is one of only two poisonous lizards in the world

Inflated for protection The chuckwalla (above) escapes danger by hiding in rock crevices where, by inflating its body, it cannot be removed

Gecko, skink, and Gila monster: cold-blooded?

In the Sudan, both the diurnal African five-lined skink and a nocturnal gecko, *Trentola annularis,* become paralyzed and die if exposed to temperatures of more than 104° F. (40° C.) for 24 hours. The less active gecko can survive long waterless periods far better than the skink. The gecko has a flattened body, with the hard scales mostly on its underparts. This makes it particularly vulnerable to predators. The gecko spontaneously contracts the muscles in its tail when it is seized by a predator. This causes the tail to fall off and permits the gecko to escape. A new tail grows within a short time, but it is never as perfectly formed as the one the gecko was born with.

Skinks are the most common group of lizards in the world. Many species have such an elongated body and tail that they are sometimes mistaken for snakes. Their limbs tend to be short. The five-lined skink of North America is hatched with five distinct stripes on its body and a blue tail. The stripes fade and the blue of the tail vanishes as the skink matures.

The blue-tongued skink of the Australian and Tasmanian deserts grows to two feet long. This skink can withstand a wide range of temperature. The sand skink of the Sahara, on the other hand, requires a constantly high temperature.

Broad-tailed lizards such as the Gila monster accumulate fat in their tails, possibly as reserves of food and metabolic water that enable the lizard to survive periods of extreme drought. These lizards also shelter in burrows. Gila monsters eat mainly ants and reptile eggs, which they dig out of their incubation holes in the sand.

The internal temperature of warm-blooded mammals and birds is regulated, partly by sweating or panting, so that it remains within a relatively narrow range providing optimum conditions for cell metabolism and all related body activities. But the temperature of cold-blooded reptiles and fish is controlled by, and varies with, their surroundings. This makes a lizard or a tortoise sluggish in cold weather, because the body cells lack the warmth to operate effectively. The technical term describing a variable body temperature is "poikilothermic." "Cold-blooded" is a familiar but misleading term, because the temperature of such a creature may be higher than that of a mammal or a bird in very hot weather.

Mountain devil Inhabiting sandy areas of Australia, its diet consists of black ants, of which it consumes as many as 1500 in a single meal

Western rock skinks Like many other lizards, these shelter in crevices during peak desert temperatures

Coping with the desert's temperature changes

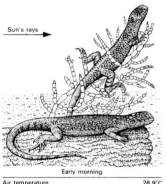 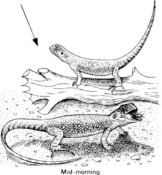 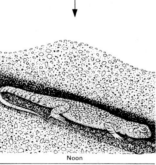  

Early morning		Mid-morning		Noon		Mid-afternoon		Late afternoon	
Air temperature	28.9°C	Air temperature	28.8°C	Air temperature	43.4°C	Air temperature	35.2°C	Air temperature	33.1°C
Ground surface temperature	38.9°C	Ground surface temperature	42.0°C	Ground surface temperature	56.4°C	Ground surface temperature	46.5°C	Ground surface temperature	35.8°C
Tunnel temperature		Tunnel temperature	37.5°C	Tunnel temperature	43.5°C	Tunnel temperature	43.2°C	Tunnel temperature	43.5°C
Body temperature	32.2°C	Body temperature	36.7°C	Body temperature	39.2°C	Body temperature	39.0°C	Body temperature	33.1°C

A lizard's behavior varies through the day. It is most active in midmorning, least in the noon heat. In early morning and late afternoon it basks in the sun. To avoid high surface temperatures, it "stilts," raising its tail and body off the ground. When stilting, it becomes paler, absorbing less heat

How desert tortoises keep cool and obtain water

Desert-dwelling tortoises escape from the heat of the sun by burrowing, venturing out at night to browse on cacti and other vegetation. Some, such as Horsfield's tortoise of the Asian deserts, also hibernate to escape the worst of the desert winter.

During the morning and evening, when the air is cool, most tortoises warm their bodies by basking in the sun. The Greek tortoise, widespread in the Mediterranean region and Asia Minor, basks until the temperature reaches almost lethal limits before it retires to the shade. The grooved tortoise, which lives on the southern edge of the Sahara, cools its head, neck, and forelegs with its own saliva when its body temperature exceeds 105° F. (40.5° C.).

Serrated tortoise This Kalahari Desert dweller is one of three species of star-patterned tortoises found in southern Africa

Water-storing tortoise The American desert tortoise stores water in its enlarged bladder. Most desert tortoises get moisture from plant food

Snakes

Of all the ways that animals track prey, one of the strangest is that of the pit viper, which is sensitive to the body heat given off by its intended victim

Desert strangler On the ergs of Africa and Asia, sand boas (like pythons) kill animals in the coils of their powerful body, crushing and choking them. The sand boa's victim here is a weaverbird

Snakes of the deserts seek holes and crevices in which to escape the most extreme heat. Their almost impermeable skin, and the production of highly concentrated urine, help reduce water loss. But perhaps the most important factor in their survival is their eating habits: since snakes are carnivorous, their diet is rich in moisture.

All three groups of venomous snakes are represented in deserts: those with fangs at the back of their jaws; those with fixed front fangs; and the vipers, which have long fangs hinged backward against the roof of the mouth. Nonpoisonous snakes found in deserts include members of the Colubridae family, which swallow prey alive. Other nonpoisonous snakes, such as the sand boa of India, strangle prey by coiling their powerful bodies around the victim.

Snakes can swallow large prey because their upper jaw is attached only loosely to the skull, and the lower jaw is split into two halves joined by elastic ligaments so they can be moved separately. The skin of the neck can be stretched to a remarkable extent to accommodate large prey, and the entrance to the windpipe can protrude from the throat into the mouth, so that the snake's breathing is not obstructed.

Snakes' sight and hearing are poor at best; but snakes have other faculties that serve them admirably in hunting prey. A constantly flicking forked tongue conveys information from the ground, and carries molecules from the air or ground to a sensing region in the roof of the mouth, Jacobson's organ. Snakes use their tongues and keen sense organs to find mates, to seek out other snakes and form big, coiled groups

Many-horned adder Snakes of the *Bitis* genus are short and thick-bodied. They have enormous venom glands and fangs up to 1½ inches long

Periscope eyes The sidewinder rattlesnake, found in North American deserts, has elevated eyes that remain above the sand when the snake burrows

Immune to venom This California king snake is swallowing a lizard, but its usual diet is pit vipers, to whose venom it is immune

Snake senses and weapons

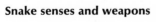

1 All snakes are deaf to airborne sounds, yet they can sense ground vibrations. Often their senses of smell and vision are poor; but all snakes and some lizards have a specialized sense receptor called Jacobson's organ, consisting of two sacs that open to the mouth's roof. The flicking tongue transfers molecules to these sacs, and information is transmitted to the brain

2 Vipers' fangs are highly effective, for they operate like hypodermic needles. The fangs are located in the front of the jaw, folded back in a sheath until used

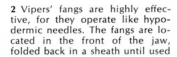

Venom gland.

3 A thrusting motion of the viper's head with the jaws open allows the fangs to fall forward. Vipers follow their prey after striking, aided by Jacobson's organ, until the venom takes effect. Some poisonous snakes, like Africa's boomslang, have fangs in the back of their jaws and must grip victims to chew poison into them

4 The rattlesnake's rattle is made of interlocking pieces of skin that remain attached to the end of the tail when the rest of the skin is shed. Snake skin lacks elasticity and wears out, so it is shed

The wide gape of a killer A desert rodent vanishes into the mouth of a diamondback rattlesnake. Jaws loosely linked to the skull, and elastic skin on the neck, enable snakes to swallow large prey

when the time comes to hibernate, and to scent predators.

A rattlesnake exposed to the smell of a king snake, which preys on other snakes, reacts with a defensive, head-down posture. But if the rattlesnake's tongue is removed, the response does not occur, even when the king snake is in full view. Jacobson's organ is highly developed in snakes and lizards, and is also present in the tuatara (see page 88), turtles, amphibians, and some mammals, including monotremes, marsupials, and elephant shrews.

Many vipers have sensitive indentations, or pits, between the nostrils and eyes. The pit vipers of the Americas, one of the sub-families of vipers, include the rattlesnake genus *Crotalus*.

The pit is lined with membranous skin, and a large nerve leads from it to the brain. The pit has sometimes been compared to a "sixth sense." Warm-blooded animals, the pit viper's prey, radiate infrared energy. This infrared energy strikes a membrane in the viper's pit, where it is converted to heat. The membrane heats up a cavity behind it, and there sensitive cells respond to the heat. The pit viper can sense its prey in complete darkness, at a distance of up to 18 inches. The viper's poison usually does not kill immediately; but the snake tracks down the dying animal with its keen senses.

The venom of snakes differs in its effects; that of the Elapidae family (cobras) affects the nervous system and induces paralysis, while the venom of vipers—the Viperidae family—affects the blood and causes collapse and heart failure. Most poisonous desert snakes belong to the two viper sub-families—true vipers in Africa and Asia and pit vipers in America.

Some male and female snakes come together only for mating. In the case of boas and pythons, courtship begins with the male scratching the female's back. Vipers, cobras, and rattlesnakes have a different approach: sometimes a pair may perform a sinuous dance before mating.

How the vipers and the rattlesnakes move their bodies by waves of muscular contraction

Rattlesnakes have a fang and jaw structure similar to that of other vipers. The bones of the jaw can be swung up and forward as the head elongates, moving the fangs with them. The fangs are hollow teeth at the front of the mouth which have become modified and have a canal running down the center that carries the venom. Vipers need not bite their victims at all, only strike them, since the tips of the fangs are beveled at the edges and the venom runs down the canal in each fang. The fangs of a true viper are almost as long as its head. The venom of the diamondback rattlesnake can kill a man in as little as one hour.

The rattle of rattlesnakes, like the hissing of other vipers, is thought to be a warning to potential predators. The saw-scaled viper of the Asian and African deserts gives a similar warning signal by vibrating its scales and rubbing them together, producing a noise like violently boiling water. One of the more curious evolutionary incidents is the mimicking by certain nonpoisonous snakes of the angry warning sounds and threatening gestures of venomous species that live nearby. This reptilian fakery actually does deter predators from attacking.

Poisonous snake has a harmless twin

The nonpoisonous king snake seems to have benefited from its close resemblance to the highly poisonous Sonoran coral snake, which has the same colors but in different sequence. (The coral snake has a red background, with a narrow band of yellow on either side of a much wider black band; the king snake also has a red background, with a black band on either side of a yellow band, all bands approximately equal in size.) In the process of evolution of behavioral tendencies, some predators on snakes doubtless tended to avoid a black-yellow-red pattern while others were oblivious to it. The latter were killed trying to prey on a coral snake, so the coral snake increased in relative numbers. King snakes were thus beneficiaries of this evolutionary situation, since their red-black-yellow color scheme was less often preyed upon.

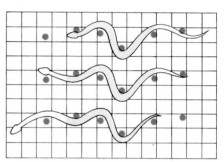

A snake moves in waves of muscular contractions (green), which flow from head to tail. The snake's sides push against irregularities (reddish spots) on the ground

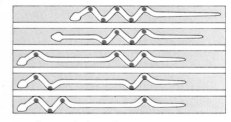

A snake travels through a narrow opening by pushing its sides against the walls. If the walls are too smooth to provide traction, the snake remains stationary

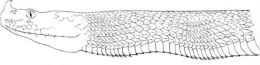

In many thickset snakes, the "power wave" is restricted to the underside, where broad scales provide traction by catching against the ground. Hence, the snake moves in a straight line

A sidewinder rattlesnake "sidewinds" across the sand (left). It travels at an angle to the parallel tracks it leaves. The contractions lift successive parts of the snake off the ground

Scorpions, spiders, and crustaceans

Being small increases an animal's risk of dehydration under the burning desert sun; but some small animals have made adjustments to compensate

The constant shortage of water in the desert is especially hard on small animals. This is because small animals have more surface area in relation to body volume than large animals and so have a proportionately greater area through which to lose moisture. However, insects and many arachnids—such as spiders and scorpions—can resist water loss by evaporation because their outer coverings, or exoskeletons, are relatively impervious to water vapor. This protection is given by a very thin layer of wax secreted on the surface of the exoskeleton.

Two crustaceans are fairly widely distributed on the deserts of the world: *Triops*, a shrimplike crustacean whose life cycle revolves around the infrequent desert rains; and desert wood lice, which are confined to oases and dry riverbeds.

Scorpions, the oldest arthropods, have been found in fossils dating back 400 million years. Venomous species in the southwestern United States inflict a sting that can kill children or old people; but only a handful of the some 700 species of scorpions are dangerous to man.

The camel spider, another common desert arachnid, lacks venom, but is equipped with pincers which, considering their power in relation to their size, are probably the strongest biting jaws on any animal.

Scorpions wait in their lairs for unsuspecting insect prey

Carried on its mother's back Fertilized scorpion eggs develop inside the mother and the young are born alive, enveloped in a membrane from which they escape by lacerating it with their stingers. Until their first molt, about a week later, the weak young are carried on the mother's back

Scorpions, like many desert animals, are active by night and spend the day in shelter. Some species live in shallow scrapes under rocks and stones; others, where conditions are more extreme, dig deep burrows. In Arizona some species often dig three feet down into sandy wastes and dried riverbanks. Scorpions dig with their claws or legs. Some of the most efficient excavators, such as the North African *Scorpio maurus*, have enlarged claws.

Scorpions, which are strictly carnivorous, seldom seek their prey, but wait in their lairs for insects entering to hide. When hungry, however, they emerge at night with their claws extended ready to catch insects. The sting at the end of the scorpion's tail contains venom, which kills the prey.

Baby scorpions climb up on their mother's back immediately after they are born, and remain there about a week; then they become independent. A scorpion becomes sexually mature about a year after birth.

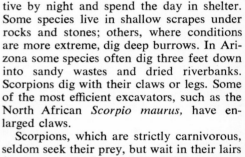

Scorpions' wide range Scorpions occupy many warm regions of the world, besides actual deserts. They range in length from ½ inch to 8 inches

Camel spider This desert hunter has a varied diet, and preys on small birds and lizards as well as spiders, scorpions, and insects

A tail that stings The scorpion's sting kills or paralyzes its prey, according to the type of venom it has. The venom of one, *Parabuthus transvaalicus*, is strong enough to kill a man

Mating dance The male scorpion maneuvers the female by her claws until she picks up a package of sperm

Death of a fly A crab spider seizes a fly inside a flower. Crab spiders lie in wait for prey; some of them can change color to match plants or the ground, thus becoming virtually invisible

Acute eyesight The large eyes of this wolf spider betray exceptionally good sight, an aid in hunting

Unequal mates A male wolf spider must identify himself to the larger female before mating

Colorful warning The color of this red velvet mite warns predators that it is distasteful

Long-legged night hunters

Scorpions are common in grasslands and forests as well as in deserts, but another group of arachnids, the camel spiders, or sun spiders, is found mainly in arid lands. These long-legged animals differ from true spiders, a separate group, in lacking venom, and they crush insect prey between their pincers. The long legs of camel spiders—some species, such as *Galeodes arabs,* can span six inches—enable them to move so fast that they sometimes resemble large balls of thistledown blown across the sand.

Most camel spiders hunt at night, to satisfy appetites so great that they sometimes gorge themselves almost to a standstill. Like scorpions, they spend the day in burrows or under stones.

As with scorpions, mating involves the transfer of a spermatophore, an encased cluster of sperm, from the male to the female. The male scorpion deposits the spermatophore on the ground and performs a dance with the female that induces her to pick it up. The male camel spider, however, takes the case in its jaws and inserts it directly into the female. In this respect camel spiders resemble true spiders, and their mating habits may represent an evolutionary stage between those of scorpions and spiders.

Spiders do not produce spermatophores; instead, the male weaves a small pad of silk on which a drop of sperm is deposited. The male then draws up the sperm into special organs at the end of his claws, called pedipalps. After some form of courtship, which varies from species to species, the male inserts the palpal organ into the female.

While the layer of wax covering most arachnids helps them to conserve body moisture, it also keeps in carbon dioxide and keeps out oxygen. However, arachnids have developed various breathing mechanisms which overcome this handicap. The most striking of these are the book lungs of the scorpions, so called because their folds resemble the leaves of a book.

Life-span of Triops is governed by the rare desert rains

The infrequent rains of the deserts bring a brief active life to shrimplike crustaceans of the genus *Triops.*

The life of *Triops* seems to be a race against time. Their drought-resistant eggs lie dormant, sometimes for years, beneath the surface of dried-up hollows that collect water during the rains. When these hollows fill again with the rare and unpredictable desert rain, water filters through to the eggs. The development of *Triops* is resumed, but they must mature and lay eggs before the pools dry up, so their active life-span often lasts no longer than two weeks. Other crustaceans that lay drought-resistant eggs include ostracods, fairy shrimps, clam shrimps, and water fleas.

Desert wood lice, also members of the class Crustacea, are not adapted to desert life to the same extent as *Triops.* They are confined to oases and dry riverbeds, where they dig communal burrows that protect them from the daytime heat. They emerge at dusk to feed in the cooler evening.

Rain brings life Filter-feeding crustaceans of the genus *Triops* hatch to active life when a water pool forms. The eggs from which they have hatched were laid after the previous rain, and remained dormant until this rain

Avoiding hot sand

Desert wood lice such as *Hemilepistus reaumuri* of the Sahara (above) have longer legs than wood lice of more humid climates (below), and they run on "tiptoe" across the hot sands. Some desert species also have high, arched backs that reduce the amount of surface exposed to the sun's rays

163

Insects

Locusts, after living for generations in scattered groups, form destructive swarms that migrate thousands of miles, stripping the land of vegetation

Insects are better suited to living in deserts than most other invertebrates, because they have evolved ways of preventing excessive water loss from their bodies. In the north-west Sahara alone, no fewer than 26 of the 32 known orders of insects are represented.

Some desert species have evolved ways of obtaining water from dry material, such as wood.

Desert locusts differ in shape, color, and behavior depending on whether they are solitary or swarming. Solitary hoppers (the young of locusts) are green. But if they mature in an overcrowded area they change to the swarming form and become black and orange. The two forms of the desert locust were once thought to be two different species.

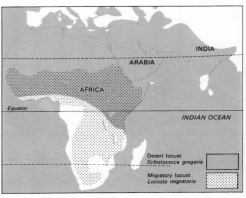

Where locusts swarm Much of Africa is subject to invasion by desert locusts, and also suffered migratory locust plague from 1928 to 1941. Desert locusts can travel 1000 to 3000 miles

Vast clouds of swarming locusts may cover 2000 square miles

Flightless young Locust hoppers, hatched after 35 to 50 days, move along the ground in dense bands

Migratory locusts As soon as locusts reach maturity, they mate, staying together for several hours

Signs of swarming Desert locusts differ in shape, color, and behavior, depending on whether they are solitary or swarming. Prominently spotted wings indicate these desert locusts are swarming. This variety is produced when overcrowding triggers hormone changes in solitary locusts

Laying eggs A migratory locust lays 20 to 100 eggs in sandy soil that is dry on top and damp beneath. A frothy liquid binds the eggs together

True locusts are types of grasshoppers; they have the same structure as other grasshoppers, and differ from them mainly in behavior. True locusts swarm in certain conditions, but other grasshoppers never do.

Species such as the desert locust usually live as solitary individuals, and in this state they cause little damage. But from time to time a food shortage forces the insects to gather together into the few areas with green vegetation. This overcrowding triggers changes in hormone production, and produces a generation of swarming locusts.

When the hoppers mature into adults, they form enormous swarms, sometimes covering 2000 square miles. These are carried on the wind to low-pressure areas where the rainfall is sufficient to provide moist soil and green vegetation—the conditions most suitable for breeding.

Many species of bugs live among the sparse desert vegetation. The coccid of South America covers itself with a waxy coating called a cyst. Inside, it can suspend activity and survive drought for many years.

Most wasps and ants are burrowers. Some wasps dig holes and galleries in sandy soil and place paralyzed insects beside their eggs to serve as food for the larvae when they emerge from the eggs.

Burrowing ants and insulated beetles are protected from the sun

One drought-resistant ant, *Acantholepis frauenfeldi*, burrows deep to get water from the moist layers of sand below the surface. The California harvester ant lives in a deep nest and forages only for brief periods during the cooler parts of the day.

Many small moths of the American deserts spend their pupal stages underground. A few, such as the bagworms of the Psychidae family, pupate in cases they spin around themselves, hanging from twigs or branches.

Robber flies and black beetles

Among the numerous species of desert flies are the robber flies of the Asilidae family, which have elongated mouth parts for piercing the skin of the insects they feed on. Horseflies of the Tabanidae family suck the blood of camels and horses, and one species of botfly, belonging to the Oestridae family, lays its eggs in the nostrils of camels. The mature larvae are later sneezed onto the sand, where they pupate. Worm-lions, the larvae of rhagionid flies, live in sand pits like those of ant-lions.

Beetles of the Tenebrionidae family are the insects best equipped for desert life. Among them are the black darkling beetles, which get all their water from dry food.

Most of the Tenebrionidae do not have flying wings. Other beetles have hard forewings, or elytra, but in the Tenebrionidae these are fused together to form a case over the beetle's back. An air space between the elytra and the body helps to insulate the insect from the heat of the sun and reduce water loss. In the Tenebrionidae all the breathing holes, or spiracles, open into this air space, and the amount of moisture lost during respiration is thus reduced. Members of the Tenebrionidae family eat plant material, carrion, and feces. Most of them are active only at dusk and at night.

Blister beetles of the Meloidae family are plant-eaters. They secrete an oily fluid which raises blisters on the skins of predators. The adults are vividly marked in various color combinations—black and green, brown and red, or red and blue—which offer further protection by serving to warn away predators. Dung beetles roll pellets of animal droppings, storing them for food.

Moth falls victim A robber fly holds insects with its bristly legs, piercing them with a sharp proboscis

Transporting food Dung beetles roll mammals' dung into pellets, which they store underground

Living on dry food The darkling ground beetle of the genus *Eustatus* eats dry vegetation and dung

Ant-lion larvae use pincer jaws to trap and drag prey

The larva of the ant-lion, so called because it feeds mainly on ants, traps its prey with long, curved jaws

To capture prey, the larva buries itself in sand. It opens its jaws and waits for an insect to come

The larva tugs a grasshopper into the sand. Liquid from its jaws paralyzes the victim and breaks down its tissue. The larva then sucks the body dry

The adult ant-lion emerges after a one-to-three-year larval stage, depending on abundance of prey. Adults live only long enough to mate and lay eggs

Trapping insects in a pit In certain ant-lion species, the larva digs a steep funnel in loose sand, then lies at the bottom. When an insect

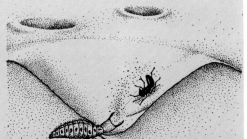

slides into the pit, the larva flings up sand, preventing the victim's escape. After eating, the larva flips the husk out of the pit

Paralyzing a victim *Sphecius speciosus* paralyzes a cicada with a sting and stores it beside its larva. The helpless cicada is eaten later by the larva

TROPICAL FORESTS

In some parts of the tropical forests, constant high temperatures, high humidity, and abundant, well-distributed rainfall are the raw materials which provide the background for a fantastic variety of plant and animal life

The moist tropics, which cover about 10 percent of the earth's surface, provide the most favorable environment in the world for plant and animal life. Here the climate varies less than in any other life zone on land. The temperature remains high and constant throughout the year. Abundant, well-distributed rainfall means that the atmosphere never becomes dry and unfavorable for growth. Plants can grow and reproduce fruit all year round, and because of this constant, dependable supply of food, animals can specialize in feeding on one particular kind of seed or fruit.

Tree species in certain sections of the tropical forests may number in the hundreds. The wide variety of plants, trees, and shrubs makes for a many-layered forest, with clearly defined boundaries between canopy, shrub, and ground layers. In an immature forest, the tallest trees are scattered and sunlight can reach the lower layers. In mature forest, sunlight is blocked out by the closely woven canopy of taller trees. The undergrowth is reduced to scattered, shade-tolerant shrubs.

Animal niches in the forest

The great variety of tree and plant species within a small area, combined with the sharp contrasts between top, middle, and bottom layers, increases the variety of niches, or places for animals to live. As a result, there are more animal species in tropical forests than in temperate forests, although individuals of any one species may be few and somewhat scattered.

The high temperature in the tropical forests is particularly favorable to insects and other invertebrate animals that have little internal control over the temperature and moisture content of their bodies. In colder environments these animals are forced to become less active when the temperature drops.

Because of the consistently high temperature, the metabolism, or chemical machinery, of tropical forest animals can operate at a high rate. This is reflected in the large size of many animal species. Butterflies and moths are huge. Stick insects and katydids, dragonflies, spiders, and centipedes grow to a much greater size than related species found in the temperate zones. Among the cold-blooded vertebrates are large frogs and toads, enormous snakes, and lizards that resemble miniature dinosaurs.

The high metabolic rate of many invertebrates,

especially insects, allows them to complete their life cycles in a much shorter time than similar species in temperate regions. They produce many generations each year. This increases the chances of genetic variation, and may cause certain species to evolve more rapidly than they would in more temperate zones.

The crash of a rotten tree

Since many forest creatures are nocturnal, it is possible to walk in some mature tropical forests during the day, between the columns of the 125-foot trees, and hear nothing except the occasional chattering of parrots overhead and the distant crashing of monkeys as they move through the treetops farther off.

Sometimes the daytime silence is broken by the crash of a rotten tree falling, perhaps bringing down some of its weaker neighbors. The rotten wood of the fallen tree provides food and homes for invertebrates and fungi. But the most far-reaching effect of a fallen tree is the clearing it makes in the dense forest. The close-knit canopy is pierced, and sunlight can now reach the ground. A rich growth of shrubs and herbs begins to take root, creating a lush new habitat for animals of the lower forest niches.

A similar effect may occur as the result of primitive agricultural methods still followed in some places. All the trees in a small area are often cut down and the ground cover burned. The ashes are used to fertilize the land. A crop is grown for two or three years, until the soil is exhausted. Then the cultivators move on to new ground. In the abandoned clearings herbs, shrubs, and trees spring up.

Mountain tropical forests

In mountainous regions, tropical forests are characterized by extremely high humidity. Such regions are frequently shrouded in mist and cloud, and usually have a high annual rainfall. Day temperatures are high, but at night the temperature drops and the air is damp and chilly. In central Africa, these regions are the home of mountain gorillas. They wander about in family groups, feeding on vegetation so juicy that they never need to drink water.

The cloud forest is the poetic but accurate name for the lower mountain rain forest. Here, the lower temperatures condense water out of the air, which is filled with a constant mist. All the contours of the vegetation are softened by dripping mosses, ferns, spongy lichens, and orchids, which flourish in the cool, moist air.

Alone in a forest An infant spider monkey calls for its mother from its perch on a branch in the dense tropical forest of Barro Colorado Island in the Panama Canal Zone

167

The rain forests

The canopy of a mature tropical rain forest towers 120 feet above the shady floor. The tight-woven foliage is pierced at intervals by taller trees

The tropical rain forests are among the wettest places on earth. Rainfall reaches an average of 160 inches a year in the lowlands near the equator. This drenching rainfall is distributed throughout the year in the narrow equatorial belt, where the forest growth is at its richest.

Farther away from the equatorial belt, there are usually one or two wet seasons a year, alternating with dry spells. The height, complexity, and density of the forest diminish as it nears the savanna. Even in this zone, though, there are fringes of richer forest along the riverbanks.

As the vegetation pushes up toward the sunlight, it forms a series of distinct layers, each a miniature life zone where animals can live and feed. There are sometimes as many as five such layers in mature tropical forest.

The top layer consists of scattered trees, called emergents, which tower above a closed canopy layer formed by the crowns of tall trees. Below this canopy is the third or middle layer, formed by smaller trees whose crowns do not meet. The fourth layer is composed of woody and herbaceous shrubs. Finally there is the ground layer of nonwoody herbs and tree seedlings. Little light reaches this layer. The rain forest canopy averages 120 feet in height, the shrubs 6 to 15 feet, and the herb layer about 2 feet.

Close-knit roof of foliage The treetops in the lowland tropical forest on the Rio Negro in Brazil form a closed canopy, admitting little light to the forest floor. Brilliant flowers can be seen in parts of the canopy. Because the tropical forest is constantly warm, some vegetation is always in bloom

The five layers of the tropical forest Emergent trees; continuous canopy; middle layer of smaller trees with long, narrow crowns; sparser layer of dwarf trees, palms, and shrubs; ground layer of nonwoody herbs

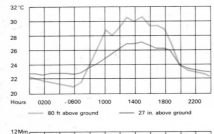

Forest temperatures The undergrowth receives less light and so has a smaller temperature range than the canopy, which heats up during the day and loses heat at night. At 80 feet above the ground the daily temperature range is almost 10 degrees centigrade (18 degrees Fahrenheit)—more than twice that at 2 feet

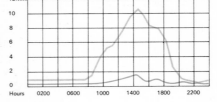

Forest humidity During the wet season the air within the undergrowth is saturated with moisture. Around the canopy, the humidity is higher at night when the temperature falls, and lower during the day. This graph measures the humidity in millimeters of barometric pressure—the lower the reading, the higher the humidity

Where seasons are based on rainfall Rainfall varies more than temperature in the tropics, so wet and dry seasons replace the seasonal temperature cycle of middle latitudes. In equatorial places such as Singapore, precipitation is evenly distributed through the year. But between 4° and 10° N and S, in areas such as Guyana, there are two wet periods; while areas between 10° and 23° N and S, such as Queensland, have only one

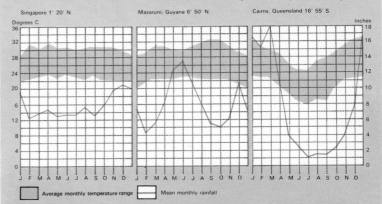

There are three main tropical forest zones. The largest runs from southern Mexico to southern Brazil; the most limited in variety of plant species is in west and central Africa; the tallest and richest in plant species is the Indo-Malaysian forest, which runs from southern India and Ceylon through Southeast Asia to Queensland in Australia. The three zones have few species of wild plants in common.

Near the equator, seasonal temperature variations are less clear-cut than farther north or south. Temperature is related more to altitude, and average temperatures are usually very high. The lowland equatorial belt, for example, has a mean annual temperature of about 77° F. (25° C.). The daily temperature range is narrow, since the sky is often cloudy during the day and water vapor in the air prevents loss of heat by radiation at night. This makes the forest an ideal habitat for cold-blooded creatures, since they can function without having to adapt to temperature changes.

The high humidity of the tropical forest means that there is less evaporation than there would be if the air were drier. This suits many small invertebrate animals that need moisture, because even their exoskeleton, or hard outer shell, does not protect them completely against evaporation. Leeches are examples of these invertebrates.

Trees flourish in this humid climate, and the high humidity also means that forest fires are rare. But the forest soil is not suited to extensive cultivation. The humus breaks down rapidly and the frequent heavy rains wash away the mineral and organic salts that are needed by plants.

Subalpine vegetation This high-altitude zone found above the tropical rain forest of the Congo-Uganda border consists of moisture-adapted plants.

Because this forest is more open than the cloud forest below, sunlight penetrates to the floor, promoting a richer growth of shrubs and herbs

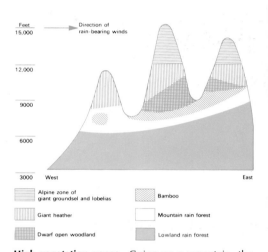

High vegetation zones Going up a mountain, the tall lowland rain forest merges into cloud forest. Then come bamboos, dwarf woodland, giant heather, and finally subalpine grass and herbs

Cloud forest At altitudes above 6000 feet the temperature is low enough so that moisture condenses from the air. Due to constant mist, trees are covered by mosses and lichens

Wind patterns of the tropical forest This zone receives a high rainfall from the moist, unstable equatorial maritime winds. There is little variation in the temperature—either daily or annually. Thunderstorms develop frequently, but pressure fronts are weak and strong winds rare

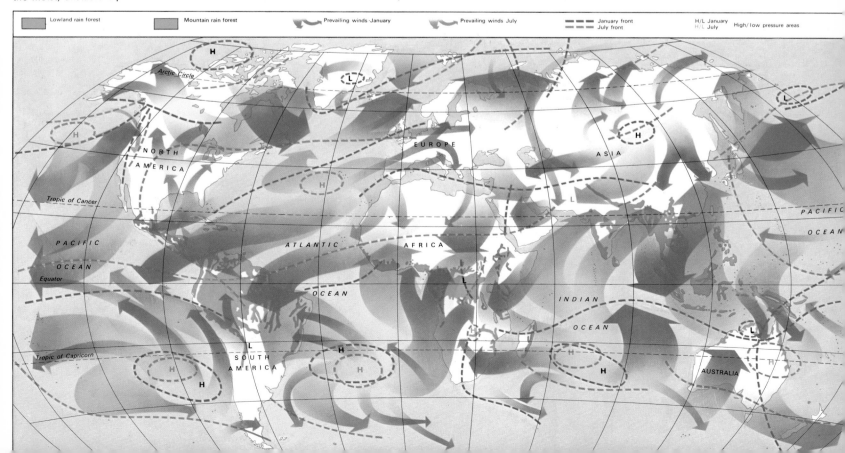

Plants in hot, moist climates

There are no clearly marked seasons in the tropical forests. Year-round warmth, humidity, and rainfall mean that plants can grow, flower, or fruit at any time

In the moist tropical rain forest as a whole, there are no marked seasonal changes, although individual plant species have their own rhythms of growth and decay. Some plants flower as many as six times annually, others only once in 40 years. Animals can always find plant food, though any one kind may be in intermittent supply.

Flowering and fruiting seasons vary widely over the year from area to area. In Malaya, for instance, 30 percent of the trees are deciduous and may be bare for any period from 24 hours to three or four weeks, but the different species shed their leaves at different times of the year.

Trees with aerial roots and flowering trunks

Rain forest trees have many characteristics not found among trees of the temperate forests. Many species, for instance, have roots that form triangular-shaped buttresses at their bases, providing a firm anchor for the tall, usually rather slender trunks. Some tree species, which soar straight up without branches for over a hundred feet, have such smooth and cylindrical trunks that they have been called technologically perfect—that is, man could hardly improve on them.

Evergreen species have dark green, often leathery leaves which taper sharply to a "drip tip." Flowers sometimes erupt from the trunks and larger branches of many smaller trees, instead of from the twig ends. The flowers can easily be reached by butterflies and other animals.

A striking feature of some trees in swampy areas is their breathing roots, or pneumatophores. These roots, branching off from horizontal roots, rise above the surface and help the tree to breathe in soil which contains little oxygen. As silt or peat accumulates and the land level rises, new root systems are sent out and the older roots below are gradually covered over, and die off.

Afara
*Terminalia
superba*
West Africa

Rain forest trees A mature 125-foot tree (right) branches only near the crown. Many trees are hung with lianas and may have stilt roots (left)

Trunk that sprouts flowers The Malayan custard apple is cauliflorous—it produces flowers that grow straight out of the branches and trunk

Pale blossoms in the gloom of the lower forest layers

Shrub layer In some parts of the tropical forests small palms dominate the shrub layer, while in other parts true shrubs and small trees predominate

Herb layer Ginger grows in the Malayan swamps. Like most other herbs growing on the dimly lit floor, ginger has dull-colored flowers

Decaying agent Fungi, abundant saprophytes in the forest, feed on the dead and rotting vegetation on the forest floor and so hasten decay

The shrub layer, 6 to 15 feet high, consists mainly of woody species and young trees, with some herbaceous plants. Shrubs which are rounded and branch just above the ground are known as true shrubs, while those resembling miniature trees are called dwarf or pygmy trees.

The herb layer, up to six feet high, grows most richly around streams, in clearings, and in other places where light penetrates. In deeper, poorly lit parts of the forest, herbs are scattered or in clumps.

The herbs consist of ferns and their moss-like relatives, the selaginellas; gingers and their relatives; and aroids, plants of the genus *Arum*. Common features among herbs are white or light green spots or stripes on the leaves. Some leaves have a metallic blue sheen, but the flowers are seldom colorful. Among the brightest colored are flowers of saprophytes, which grow on leafless stalks just above the ground.

There is less ground litter in the tropical forests than in temperate forests because decay is rapid and plants do not all shed their leaves at once.

Cloud forest epiphytes These get sunlight by growing on branches. The dangling roots pick up moisture from the air and support moss

Passion flower One of the big climbers, this flower is pollinated by birds that drink its nectar. Its delicate ovaries, which contain the seeds, are protected from the birds by overhanging petals

Plants that depend on others

Plants that grow on other plants are common throughout the rain forests. There are climbers, stranglers, parasites, and epiphytes, which use other plants for support but are not parasitic.

The large climbers, especially the lianas, or bush ropes, hang in huge loops between the crowns of the trees. Lianas thrive in clearings and on riverbanks. Most of the smaller climbers spend their lives in the shade. They are particularly abundant where the sun can penetrate.

Epiphytes need a relatively large amount of sunlight, and obtain it by growing on taller plants, nourished by humus lodged in cracks. Many have developed mechanisms for storing water. Some epiphytic orchids have spongy tissue in their roots. The staghorn fern accumulates water-holding humus in its leaves. Other epiphytes have dangling roots which absorb moisture from the humid air. Some have tightly overlapping leaves that point upward and form a tank that holds water. These water-holding epiphytes provide a place where algae, lichens, mosses, and ferns can grow. Many epiphytes are also the nesting places for ants, mosquito larvae, and other small aquatic creatures that go through a larvae stage.

Stranglers grow from seeds lodged in the forks of large trees. They send roots down to the soil, which twine around the host and eventually kill it, leaving the strangler standing as a hollow tree when the host rots away. The most abundant stranglers in Africa, southern Asia, and Australia are the strangler figs. They often grow to enormous size, as big as the biggest trees.

Apart from fungi and bacteria, which usually feed on dead vegetation rather than living plants, there are two types of parasites in tropical forests—root parasites, which grow on the ground, and semiparasites, which, like epiphytes, grow on trees. The most spectacular root parasite is the Malayan *Rafflesia*, which produces huge, brilliantly colored flowers. This parasite penetrates the roots of lianas to feed on their sap. Semiparasites belong to the mistletoe family. They take only part of their food from their hosts, making the rest themselves by the process of photosynthesis.

Insect trap The pitcher plant lures insects into its water-filled pitcher by a combination of color and scent. From the insects, it obtains nitrogen

Epiphytic orchids Needing sunlight, these orchids use branches to gain altitude. Long-tongued moths, attracted by flower tubes, are dusted with pollen

Strangler figs Using another plant for support, strangler figs eventually kill the host. Then they become independent trees that may be larger than the host

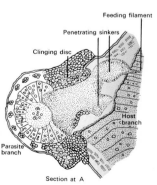

Parasite coils round host plant

Feeding filament

Penetrating sinkers

Clinging disc

Host branch

Parasite branch

Section at A

Treetop mistletoe Forming disks that cling to its host, this parasite then penetrates the bark, making way for filaments to enter and absorb nourishment

Climbing lianas Characteristic of tropical forests, they can be as thick as a man's thigh. Their long ropelike stems loop among the trees, binding them together

171

Living in warm, humid forests

The tropical forests provide abundant plant food all year round, but much of it is high in the trees. Nonflying animals must be agile climbers to reach it

All the varied habitats provided by the tropical forests are alike in one way—they are not subject to the dramatic changes of climate of other land habitats. Because there are always some trees and shrubs bearing fruit, foliage, or flowers during the course of the year, plant-eating animals can rely on a single food source.

Since most of the food produced by trees is found high in the lush forest canopy, nonflying animals have to climb to reach it and so tend to be small and agile. Some animals are adapted for leaping between branches and clinging to twigs and trunks. They may have suction pads and opposable digits on the hands and feet—that is, thumbs and big toes that bend in opposite directions to the other digits—and prehensile, or grasping, tails which can encircle a branch, giving the animal greater control over its environment.

Tree snakes cling to branches by looping their bodies over them. They can do this easily because they are more slender than other species of snakes that live on the ground.

Effects of a round-the-year abundance of food

Red-billed toucan Its bill is similar in size to that of the great hornbill, yet the bird itself is smaller. The bill, looking almost too heavy for the bird, is made of light, honeycombed cellular fibers

Great hornbill This hornbill feeds almost exclusively on fruit, pushing through foliage with its bill to obtain it. It lives up to an altitude of 5000 feet in the heavy rain forest of Southeast Asia

With food available all year in a relatively constant climate, many tropical forest animals have developed body structures and habits which enable them to make the maximum use of a restricted diet.

Some animals rely largely or even exclusively on flowers or fruit as a food source.

Hummingbirds, hawkmoths, some sunbirds, and long-nosed bats are not only physically equipped to eat nectar, but have also developed the technique of hovering in front of flowers when feeding. They hover by beating their wings rapidly backward and forward.

Hornbills and toucans are unrelated birds; yet because they are both adapted to eating fruit in their widely separated habitats, they have developed similar-looking bills. These heavy birds can use their long, strong bills to reach fruit on thin branches that would not support their weight and to push through tangled growth in search of fruit.

Another group of fruit-eaters, the fruit bats, have evolved palates containing ridges against which the tongue can crush fruit.

There is no grass on the tropical forest floor. The forest relatives of open-country grass-eaters have become browsers, feeding on the leaves of the trees and the herbs in the lower layers.

The hawkmoth Different groups of animals have developed similar characteristics because they have adapted to the same circumstances—such as comparable diets. Hawkmoths and hummingbirds have both adopted the technique of hovering in front of a flower as they are feeding on its nectar

Hummingbird These remarkable birds can fly backward for a short time, and while feeding they hover for long periods by rapidly beating their wings

Breeding throughout the year in an equable climate

The lack of seasonal variation in climate means that many tropical forest animals have no exact breeding time.

Their counterparts in other biomes tend to have breeding seasons geared rather precisely to the rainy season and the resulting abundance of food.

For example, the angwantibo, a small primate, has been observed to breed throughout most of the year in the tropical forest of Gabon where food is available all year round. The related Senegal bush-baby of the African savanna breeds only at the beginning of the wet season, the one time of year when there is abundant food in the grasslands.

The high humidity of the forest allows some amphibians, such as frogs, to lay eggs on land instead of in pools, and consequently to eliminate the larval stages which are gone through by frogs in drier climates.

Most tree-living animals in the tropical forests have keen eyesight. It seems probable that many of the reptiles and birds have keen color vision. Males in particular are adorned with bright colors and distinctive frills of skin or feathers. Behavior patterns, such as moving the body to display vivid markings or a dramatic crest, help these highly colored animals to attract mates and to warn off rivals or predators.

Moving through the forest

Because of the thick undergrowth, large mammals in the tropical forest tend to be compact in shape compared with related animals in other zones. They usually lack large horns or antlers, which would impede their freedom of movement.

The dense forest also provides a refuge for small plant-eating animals, such as miniature antelopes, which run through the undergrowth and use their well-worn paths almost like tunnels.

Wingless animals which live in trees have evolved gliding techniques, diving from trees to escape predators or find food. Some lizards have flaps of skin on their sides, stretched between their front and hind limbs, which help them to glide smoothly from branch to branch.

Animals such as monkeys have grasping hands or prehensile tails, which help them to climb. More climbing animals have evolved in tropical forests than in temperate because food is always available in the tropical canopy. Many trees in temperate regions are seasonally bare.

The development of the opposable thumb and big toe in primates enables the hands and feet to grasp branches with a pincerlike grip as the animals move through the canopy.

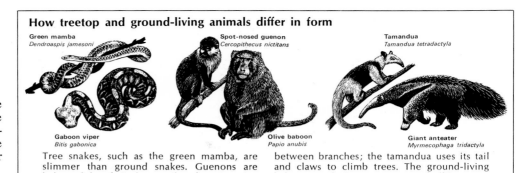

How treetop and ground-living animals differ in form

Green mamba
Dendroaspis jamesoni
Gaboon viper
Bitis gabonica
Spot-nosed guenon
Cercopithecus nictitans
Olive baboon
Papio anubis
Tamandua
Tamandua tetradactyla
Giant anteater
Myrmecophaga tridactyla

Tree snakes, such as the green mamba, are slimmer than ground snakes. Guenons are balanced by their long tails when jumping between branches; the tamandua uses its tail and claws to climb trees. The ground-living baboons and giant anteater are bulkier

Iguana's foot The five long digits have tiny rough scales and end in sharp, curved claws. Many lizards have velvety hairs between the digits. All of these features aid the animals in climbing trees

South America
Red-rumped agouti
Dasyprocta aguti
Asia
Lesser Malay chevrotain
Tragulus javanicus
Africa
Maxwell's duiker
Cephalophus maxwelli

Animals of the undergrowth These forest browsers from different continents and groups have developed small, compact shapes that allow them to move freely through the dense undergrowth

Feet for clinging The pygmy anteater grips a branch with its large claws and prehensile tail. Its hind feet have jointed soles that enable the claws to bend beneath them and grasp firmly

Tail for grasping South American porcupines of the genus *Coendou* use their prehensile tails to help them move from branch to branch. These animals rarely descend to the ground

Keen sight gives judgment in leaping between branches

For tree-living animals, vision is the most important of the senses, particularly for accurate judgment of distances when jumping or swinging from branch to branch.

Most reptiles have eyes set on the sides of their heads, but reptiles of the tropical forests tend to have a narrow snout, and eyes closer to the front of the head, which allows the visual fields of the eyes to overlap, producing binocular vision, as in man.

The sense of smell in primates is poorly developed compared with their senses of sight and hearing. Forest-dwelling marsupials are similarly adapted. The cuscus, an arboreal tropical forest marsupial, has a short snout and eyes set at the front of its head. Ground-living marsupials of open country tend to have long snouts and eyes on the sides of the head.

On the dim forest floor, where the dense growth prevents any long-range view, the sense of sight becomes less important than the sense of hearing. Animals such as the okapi of the Congo forest have evolved long ears which quickly pick up the slightest sound. Since okapis themselves make little vocal noise, it seems clear that the long ears are for defense and not for communication.

Binocular vision The East Indian long-nosed tree snake has a narrow, elongated snout, so the visual fields of its eyes overlap, giving binocular vision. This is an important asset for judging distances between branches

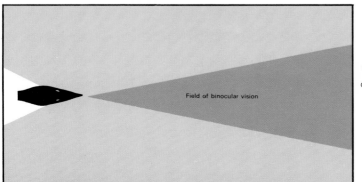

Field of binocular vision

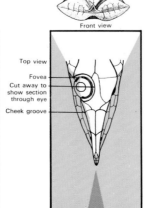

Front view
Top view
Fovea
Cut away to show section through eye
Cheek groove

Mating call A leaf frog of the genus *Hyperolius* calls its mate with its balloonlike throat sac inflated. As recognition by sight is difficult in the forest, many frogs find mates by distinctive calls

173

Lower primates

The tarsiers and lorises of the tropics, and possibly the tree-shrews, too, are lower primates—primitive members of the group to which man belongs

Primates are essentially tree-dwellers. Some, such as baboons and man, have taken to living on the ground, but still possess the same characteristics as their tree-living relatives. All primates have mobile fingers and toes for grasping, and highly developed senses of touch and sight.

There are two suborders of primates—the anthropoids, which include monkeys, apes, and man, and the prosimians, or lower primates, which include lemurs, lorises, tarsiers, and possibly tree-shrews. Some authorities suggest that tree-shrews belong to the insectivore order, or even to an order of their own.

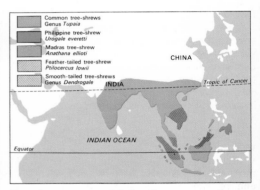

Prosimians A suborder of primates, they are below monkeys and apes in the evolutionary scale

Tree-climbers that have changed little in 70 million years

Aggressive tree-shrews When two male common tree-shrews are introduced to each other in captivity, they often fight to the death. Normally they are solitary animals, and the males mark their territory with feces and urine and with scent from a gland in the chest. The young—usually twins—are born after 50 days' gestation. The male lives in a separate nest until the young are weaned

Tree-shrews, or animals closely resembling them, have lived on earth for at least 70 million years. In that time, these small mammals have changed little. The living species are forest-dwellers like their distant ancestors and, like them, they are mostly six to ten inches long, with a tail of equal length, and have long snouts and small ears.

In appearance and habits tree-shrews most closely resemble squirrels. The reason some scientists believe the tree-shrew may belong to the primate order, even though it bears no obvious physical resemblance to primates, is that it possesses a relatively large brain case, two main arteries closely resembling comparable arteries in man, and, in the male, a permanent scrotum for the testes. Tree-shrews also resemble primates in their tree-dwelling habits, and in their lack of a specialized body structure geared to one type of activity, such as swimming, flying, gliding, or digging.

There are marked differences of behavior among the species. Some tree-shrews are solitary and aggressive, but others, such as the mountain tree-shrew, are sociable. These rare animals, which live in the high mountains of northern Borneo, gather in groups of 8 to 12. Sociability continues even during the mating season: the several males in each group tolerate one another, and females in heat accept two or three males in succession.

All tree-shrews are active by day. In this they contrast sharply with more typical low primates. Nearly all of the many tree-shrew species have brown or olive coats.

The long-footed tree-shrew lives in polygamous family groups consisting of a dominant adult male and several females. The females form groups, sharing food, combing one another's fur with their long incisor teeth, and sleeping together. When a female is pregnant she builds a nest. The other females combine to repel the male while she gives birth.

Common tree-shrews live singly or in pairs. The female builds the nest and suckles the young only once every 48 hours, feeding them until three fifths of their body weight is milk. Between feeds the female leaves the

Tree-shrew ranges Of the five genera of tree-shrews, the most widespread is *Tupaia*. This genus contains 12 species. The Madras tree-shrew ranges beyond the forest into scrub

Feather-tailed tree-shrew Unlike most tree-shrews, it is nocturnal, and is rarely seen in the wild

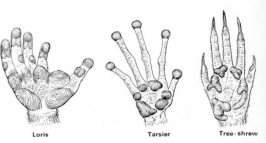

Paws and hands The hands of the loris have reduced index fingers that increase the hands' span and strengthen their grip on prey and branches. The tarsier has long fingers with tips expanding into disks, giving a larger gripping surface. The tree-shrew's forepaws are long, supple, and clawed

young and sleeps with the male in a separate nest. The young, usually two, are born blind and hairless. They are weaned after 40 days.

Loris and tarsier cling with ease

The prosimians, represented in Asian forests by the loris and the tarsier, all show much clearer primate characteristics than are present in the tree-shrews. Their hands are more adapted to grasping, and usually have nails instead of claws. Prosimians have forward-facing eyes that give them binocular vision and help them judge distance when they leap from tree to tree.

Lorises, which are related to the pottos and bush-babies of Africa, move slowly and silently. They stalk insects and small vertebrates until they are almost on top of them, then seize them with both hands. They move easily even on the undersides of branches, hanging upside-down, gripping with their powerful hands and feet.

All species of lorises can grip branches with their hands and feet for long periods without tiring. In other mammals, contracted muscles usually squeeze the blood vessels and restrict the flow of blood. But in the loris the blood vessels remain open, and the blood carries away the chemicals that build up in the muscles and normally cause fatigue.

The tarsier is a little over five inches long, with a ten-inch tail. Tarsiers live mainly in the forest's shrub layer, and are well adapted for clinging and jumping. The tips of the fingers and toes, expanded into suckerlike disks, give a firm grip, and the long tail can be whipped across the back to act as a brake when the tarsier is leaping.

Tarsiers, like lorises, creep up on their prey. After watching the intended victim for a time, they crouch, focus their huge eyes, and leap at the animal, seizing it with both hands. If it is a lizard, the tarsier skins it, then sits upright on its haunches to eat. The tarsier has the curious habit of constantly furling and unfurling its thin, almost hairless ears.

Female tarsiers give birth after a gestation of six months. The young are furred at birth, their eyes are open, and they are able to cling to a branch or to the mother's fur almost as soon as they are born.

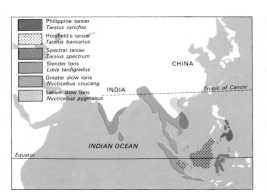

Survival in isolation Tarsiers have survived because they live on islands where they face little competition from more advanced species

Tarsier—a mighty leaper Only about four to six inches long, the tarsier can leap six feet from branch to branch. Before it lands, its tail whips up over the back, acting as a brake. The disks on its fingers and toes will grip any surface. Its forward-facing eyes help it to judge distances

Sleeping upright Even when fast asleep, the tarsier clings to a vertical stalk with the help of disks on its fingers and toes. Its tail gives extra grip when pressed against the stalk. This is the tarsier's normal sleeping position, since it is not known to build a nest

Slender lorises They weigh only about seven ounces and have two breeding seasons a year with a long gestation

Careful climber The slow loris spends its entire life in the trees. It sleeps during the day curled up in a branch or hollow, but at night it hunts for insects and small mammals and forages for fruit. Gripping tenaciously with its hands and feet, the slow loris moves carefully from branch to branch

175

Monkeys

Most monkeys of the Asian forests live in close-knit social groups in which rank is all-important—but struggles for dominance often disturb the usual order

There are two major groups of monkeys in the Asian tropical forests: macaques and langurs. The aggressive and quarrelsome macaques, which will eat almost anything, live mainly on the ground or in the middle layers of the forest. Most macaques have long, nonprehensile tails, cheek pouches for storing food, and well-developed thumbs. They are gregarious, forming bands of from 10 to 30 individuals. Each band defends its hunting ground, and if another band approaches it is usually driven away. The leader, an older male, scouts ahead of the foraging party, and may climb a tree to get a better view. He then communicates to the group by means of cries whether it is safe to go on. Macaques foraging in large bands may cause considerable damage to crops.

Langurs are leaf-eaters; most of them are less aggressive than macaques. They often live in the upper layers of the trees. When the ranges of langurs and macaques overlap, langurs usually live in the very tops of the trees, above the macaques. Langurs live in large bands. They resemble macaques in possessing a nonprehensile tail, but are thinner. Unlike macaques, langurs have no cheek pouches.

Noisy, aggressive macaques are numerous and widespread

The strongly built macaque monkeys of the oriental forest tend to live in large social groups containing all ages and both sexes.

The habits of this group are typified by the best-known species, the rhesus monkey. The rhesus is an intelligent animal, curious about everything in its environment. It can be taught to distinguish colors and shapes and to work with simple tools. This species was familiar to generations of city-dwellers as the organ-grinder's red-jacketed beggar.

Rhesus monkeys congregate in troops of from 10 to 30 individuals. The center of each troop's home range is usually occupied by a coalition of two or more dominant males. When a female is sexually receptive, she mates with a dominant male. They form a consort pair, traveling and feeding together and grooming each other.

Troops have overlapping home ranges, and the troops themselves are ordered by rank, a subordinate troop giving way to an approaching dominant troop.

Replacing the rhesus in southern India is the bonnet monkey, a small species—up to 20 inches long, with a 27-inch tail—with a red face and a circular cap of long hairs. Troops of bonnet monkeys tend to be larger than those of the rhesus, with equal numbers of males and females. There is a central coalition of up to six dominant males. Bonnet monkeys are more promiscuous than rhesus monkeys, and do not form pairs.

In Southeast Asia and Indonesia, the common species of macaque is the crab-eating monkey. Like the bonnet monkey, it has a short body and a very long tail.

Crab-eating monkeys live in troops of up to 70, several females to every male. They generally remain in the trees, and fights between neighboring troops are rare. They are common near rivers and along the coasts. They eat fruit, nuts, leaves, insects, and perhaps even a few crabs.

The pigtail monkey of Burma, Malaysia, Sumatra, and Borneo has a short tail—only five to eight inches long. Pigtail monkeys live mainly in the lower branches or on the ground, in troops of 30 to 50.

About six species of Celebes apes live on the Indonesian island of Celebes. They are thickset animals that resemble baboons in shape. Despite their name they are monkeys because, unlike the tailless apes, they do have tails, although they are only an inch long.

Bonnet monkey This species lives in troops of 25 to 30, dominated by up to six of the stronger males, to which subordinates make submissive gestures. They live in trees and on the ground

Tropical macaques The ranges of different species of the genus *Macaca* do not tend to overlap, one species being replaced by another in a different area. The rhesus monkey has the widest range

Rare macaque The lion-tailed macaque lives in the mountain forests in southwest India. Instead of leaping from one tree to another, this macaque climbs down one tree and up the next

Leaf-eating langurs

Langurs are more agile than macaques, and most species spend the largest part of their lives in trees. They eat only leaves, and have specialized, three-part stomachs, with a chamber where finely chewed leaves are digested with the aid of bacteria. Langurs do not have cheek pouches for storing food, unlike omnivorous monkeys such as macaques and baboons.

Entellus langurs, or hanumans, unlike most other langurs, spend much of the day on the ground. They live in troops of 15 to 30 individuals. The ranges of neighboring troops may overlap, but each troop has its own central area where its favorite sleeping trees grow. Troops show no marked antagonism when they meet.

A sexually receptive female langur presents herself to the male—he does not court her. She has a single offspring, which spends its early life clinging to its mother's belly. The mother allows other females to handle the infant at any time.

In dry areas of India entellus langurs show exceptional behavior. Troops of females and young of both sexes are led by single adult males. The other males form all-male troops, sometimes banding together to oust the dominant male from a mixed-sex troop. The males then fight among themselves. The winner takes over the troop, and kills or tries to kill the infants. This behavior is in marked contrast to the friendly interest in the young that is normally shown by the male entellus langurs and indeed by all monkeys.

Young proboscis monkey This leaf-eating species lives in swampy forests, climbing tall trees at night. Each troop roams within its home range, which usually covers about half a square mile

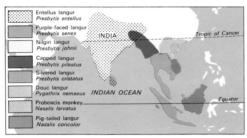

Entellus langur *Presbytis entellus*	
Purple-faced langur *Presbytis senex*	
Nilgiri langur *Presbytis johnii*	
Capped langur *Presbytis pileatus*	
Silvered langur *Presbytis cristatus*	
Douc langur *Pygathrix nemaeus*	
Proboscis monkey *Nasalis larvatus*	
Pig-tailed langur *Nasalis concolor*	

Ranges of langurs About 20 species of langurs live in Southeast Asia, India, and China. Some, like the silvered langurs, share their ranges with macaques, but the langurs give way in any encounter

Male proboscis monkey The nose of this langur monkey becomes huge and pendulous with age. It erects and straightens out when the male makes his loud and honking alarm call

Infant 1: from birth to 3-5 months, when coat changes from brown to grey	Infant 2: from end of colour change at 3-5 months to weaning at 12-15 months	Juvenile: 15 months to 3 years in females, 4 years in males	Sub-adult: from 3 years to maturity at 4 years in females; from 4 years to maturity at 6–7 years in males	Adult: from birth of first infant at about 4 years in females; from full muscular development at 6-7 years in males
Sounds				
				Whoop
				Grinding of teeth ♂
			Belch ♂	
		Grunt		
	Bark			
	Alarm bark			
Alarm chirp				
Scream				
Squeal				
Whine				
				♂ = male only
Gestures Grimacing				
Mounting				
Embracing				
Slapping ground				
Presenting				
Staring				
Threat bob				
Biting air and grimacing				
Soliciting by oestrus female				
Moving tongue in and out				
Dominance fighting				

Indications of maturity and status The gestures and noises made by langurs change with age. This chart demonstrates both sexual differences and the dominance of adults over infants

Entellus langurs Troops of these langurs spend much of the day on the ground and sleep in trees at night. Within each troop there is a rank order, but the order is not so pronounced as it is among macaques. When quarrels develop within the troop, the dominant male does not intervene. However, he will chase and bite a subordinate male and then "dismiss" it by placing a hand on its shoulder

Gibbons and the orang-utan

Some of man's closest relatives live in the oriental tropical forest: the gibbons and the orang-utan. These agile apes are somewhat awkward on the ground

There are only four types of apes—the gorilla, the chimpanzee, the orang-utan, and the gibbons. They are all restricted to the tropical forest. The apes are the primates which most closely resemble man. They share certain of man's characteristics: a highly developed brain, the ability to walk upright, and the absence of a tail.

The orang-utan and the gibbons, which live in Southeast Asia, are the best adapted of all apes for life in the trees. Gibbons are extremely agile and active, swinging rapidly through the branches by their long arms and making great leaps from tree to tree. They are the only apes that regularly stand and walk erect when on the ground. Orang-utans are more deliberate in their movements, although they too swing by their arms from branch to branch. Their flexible toes give them superior climbing ability. Most authorities believe that the orang-utan's ancestors branched off from the main line of ape evolution before the gorilla and the chimpanzee, but after the gibbons. Others regard it as merely a giant relative of the gibbons.

Orang-utans are losing the battle for survival

Male orang-utans are about 4½ feet tall when standing upright. The females are about eight inches shorter, and only half as heavy as the males, which can weigh up to 220 pounds. Both sexes have permanently curved fingers and toes on their long hands and feet. When orangs stand erect their arms reach down to their ankles.

The single species of orang-utan—the name is Malay for "man of the woods"—is becoming increasingly rare in its native Borneo and Sumatra. Even though these apes are supposedly protected, they are exported to foreign zoos and circuses. As a result, specimens for laboratory experiments are in short supply, and relatively little is known about the species. But tests indicate that the orang-utan nearly equals the chimpanzee, both in intelligence and in learning ability.

Orang-utans are less agile in the trees than gibbons. Occasionally they walk upright along a branch—gripping it with their feet and holding on to the branch above with their hands. They feed mainly on fruit, especially that of the durian tree, but also on leaves, seeds, bark, and birds' eggs.

Seeking food Orang-utans cling with their feet and one hand, and reach for fruit with the other

Infant

Adult female

Adult male

Facial development The features of an orang-utan, particularly when young, sometimes look remarkably human. Adult males develop huge muscular cheek flaps that make their faces look very broad. Both sexes have throat pouches; in the males these become heavy dewlaps. Orang-utans have small eyes and ears and a low-slung jaw

Resting in a tree Orang-utans spend most of their time in trees. At night, they sleep in crude nests of sticks and vines in tree forks, sometimes with a canopy added for protection against rain

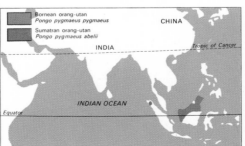

Bornean orang-utan
Pongo pygmaeus pygmaeus   CHINA

Sumatran orang-utan
Pongo pygmaeus abelii

INDIA   Tropic of Cancer

INDIAN OCEAN

Equator

Orang-utans Found only in lowland forests and mountainous regions of Sumatra and Borneo, this species is rapidly declining in numbers

Swinging through the trees Gibbons are the only primates that regularly travel by a method known as brachiation—swinging hand over hand with the legs drawn up out of the way. Other apes, especially when young, will also occasionally use this method, but none do it as frequently or as ably as the gibbons. When gibbons do descend to the ground, they walk upright with their arms outstretched at shoulder height for balance

Noisy acrobats that announce changes in the weather

Gibbons, the smallest of the apes, range in height from 15 inches to 36 inches. They are slender, swift-moving animals, with arms that almost reach the ground. Extremely vocal, they begin hooting and shrieking as soon as they awake in the morning. The cries become louder when the weather changes.

Gibbons move rapidly through the trees

Specialized hands The hands of orang-utans and gibbons are adapted for hanging and swinging. The gibbon has longer, more mobile thumbs, used for grasping, while the orang-utan has reduced thumbs that are not very much used

Orang-utan   Gibbon

with their hand-over-hand motion, called brachiation.

A gibbon walking through the forest is a startling sight. It walks erect, holding its long arms outstretched in front of its body at shoulder height. Sometimes the arms are raised directly above the head. These posi-

tions apparently help the gibbon to maintain its balance.

The lar, or common gibbon, is the most widespread species. Like most gibbons, the lar is territorial and lives in family groups: a male and a female with up to four young. There is no special mating season, and only one offspring is born at a time. The baby is almost hairless. To keep it warm, the mother draws up her legs and holds it between her thighs and belly.

Members of a family often groom one another, which reinforces the bond between them. But adults of the same sex appear to be strongly antagonistic to each other.

Lar gibbons live in the middle layer of the trees. They frequently go up to the canopy to feed on fruit. While feeding, the family moves toward the edge of its territory. If one family intrudes into the territory of another, the members of each group will hoot at each other, but this appears to establish their respective locations rather than to provoke or challenge the neighboring family. The male at such times lets out his conflict hoots and the female her "great-call," a series of whoops rising to a shrieking crescendo.

Forest acrobat Hooked fingers enable gibbons to hang easily and to grasp branches after a leap through the air, covering up to 50 feet at a time

Color variation The agile gibbon lives in central and southern Sumatra and northwest Malaya. In Sumatra 60 percent are black, the rest are yellow-brown; in Malaya over 90 percent are black

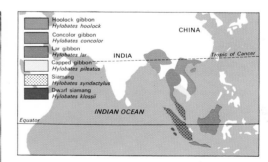

Hoolock gibbon *Hylobates hoolock*	
Concolor gibbon *Hylobates concolor*	
Lar gibbon *Hylobates lar*	
Capped gibbon *Hylobates pileatus*	
Siamang *Hylobates syndactylus*	
Dwarf siamang *Hylobates klossii*	

Ranges of gibbons Lars are the most widespread of the six species of gibbons that live in the oriental tropical forests

Boom-maker Siamangs make their calls with the aid of a large throat sac. Air is inhaled with a resonant "boom" and then released through the mouth with a harsh shriek as the sac deflates. The two sounds alternate rapidly. Siamangs sit when they call

179

Small mammals that live on plants

Mammals that climb, leap, fly, and glide can go after food in the treetops; there are more gliders in the tropical forests of Asia than anywhere else

In the moist tropical forests, where seasonal variation is less severe than in any other life zone save the sea, abundant vegetable food is available all year round. Evergreen trees provide a constant supply of leafy food, and there are always plenty of trees in flower or in fruit.

A host of small mammals flourishes on this abundance of food. Fruit-eating mammals are particularly characteristic of the tropical forest. To eat fruit on a tree a small mammal must be able to climb into the forest canopy, as do giant squirrels, flying squirrels, and colugos, or to fly up into it, as do the fruit-eating bats.

While such animals live in great numbers in the upper layers of the forest, a varied population of small mammals—most of them rodents—scurries about the forest floor, eating the shrubs and herbs, grubbing for roots, and foraging for the fruits and seeds that drop from the canopy. The black rat and the burrowing brown rat, which have spread all over the world, probably originated in Asian tropical forests.

Colugos, fruit-eating bats, and flying squirrels

The two species of colugos—sometimes wrongly called flying lemurs—are both about 16 inches long, with long tails, and covered with woolly fur.

The colugos, most highly adapted of all mammals for gliding, have a large gliding membrane that stretches the length of their bodies on both sides. The two species of colugos were finally put into a separate order of mammals (the Dermoptera, or skin-winged) by naturalists, since they do not conform closely enough to either lemurs or insectivores, the two groups they most nearly resemble. Voluminous double folds of skin join the front and hind limbs and tail, stretching taut when the colugo glides. The folds give the colugo the appearance of being wrapped in a woolly blanket when it rests, hanging with its head facing upward as it clings to the underside of a branch.

Bats are the only mammals that truly fly. Unlike gliding mammals, they propel themselves through the air by flapping their wings, which are formed by thin folds of skin that are actually extensions of the skin on the belly and back, stretched out, when the bat flies, by the fine-boned, elongated fingers of its forelimbs.

Fruit-eating bats are of necessity tropical animals, since they can live only in regions where some type of fruit is constantly ripening. They feed almost exclusively on fruit, chewing the food to extract the juices and then spitting out the squeezed pulp. The principal fruit bats belong to the family called flying foxes. They are the world's largest bats.

Carrying the young A female Malayan colugo hangs from a branch, sheltering her offspring within her gliding wings. When the mother glides, the young colugo travels with her, clinging to her belly

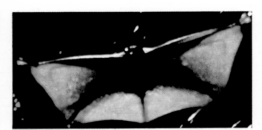

Colugo gliding The colugo stretches out its limbs, spreading the folds of skin that enable it to glide. Highly adapted for gliding, the tree-feeding colugo is also a skillful climber

The world's largest bat The kalong, a flying fox that lives in the forests of Indonesia, is the largest of all bats, with a wingspan that may exceed five feet. It lives almost entirely on fruit

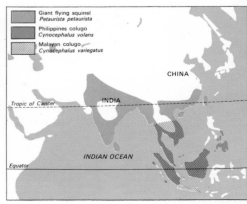

Hillside flying squirrels Giant flying squirrels usually inhabit densely forested hillsides, more than 2900 feet above sea level. They live singly or in small family groups and feed in the night

The numerous species of flying squirrels in the oriental tropical forest belong to the same family as those in the coniferous forest and, like them, do not fly but glide.

Brightly colored squirrels

Unlike all other squirrels, flying squirrels are nocturnal, and sleep by day in hollow trees or in nests made of sticks and twigs. They are skilled gliders, and even appear to make use of updrafts in valleys to give them a lift. They eat fruit, nuts, leaves, and an occasional insect.

The flying squirrels range in size from the dwarf flying squirrels of the genus *Petinomys,* some of which are only five inches long, up to the giant flying squirrels of the genus *Petaurista,* which may be as much as 23 inches long. The giant flying squirrels have bushy tails which are as long or longer than their bodies, and they are handsomely colored in patterns of yellow-gray, chestnut, black, and white.

A variety of bright colors is found among the giant squirrels of the genus *Ratufa,* and the numerous small tropical forest squirrels of the genus *Callosciurus,* which are among the most brilliantly colored of all mammals.

Most mammals are color-blind or have very poor color vision, and it is perhaps significant that they are usually drably colored in shades of gray or brown. The fact that these squirrels are more brightly colored suggests that they may be able to perceive some colors.

Rats and porcupines

Bandicoot rats, which are widespread in southern Asia, resemble the common brown and black rats, found throughout the world, but are larger, up to 14 inches long. They dig extensive burrows that contain chambers for nesting and storing food, such as grain, nuts, and roots. Each burrow is apparently occupied by a single individual. Like the common rats, bandicoots are a pest to man, damaging crops.

The Malayan short-tailed porcupine is a powerful burrower which throws up great quantities of earth while working its way below the surface. It is about two feet long, fairly large for a rodent, and weighs about 60 pounds. Like all porcupines, it is covered with long, sharp quills.

Brush-tailed porcupines of the genus *Atherurus* live in Africa and Asia. They are smaller than the short-tailed porcupines and have tufts of coarse hair at the tips of their tails. The tail breaks off easily and is often lost. These porcupines, like the short-tailed porcupines, are nocturnal. Asiatic brush-tailed porcupines spend the day in deep burrows, as many as ten individuals living in one burrow.

Unlike the short-tailed porcupines, most brush-tailed species climb into the trees in search of food. But both groups eat the same type of food: fruit, roots, tubers, and many kinds of tree bark.

Warning rattle The Indian porcupine, like others of its genus, has a cluster of open, hollow quills among the sharp ones on its tail (right). If threatened, the porcupine turns its rump toward the predator, stamps its feet, erects its quills and shakes them, making a noise similar to that of an agitated rattlesnake. A persistent attacker then gets a salvo of quills

Tree mouse The Malayan pencil-tailed tree mouse is one of eight species of a genus of tree-living mice native to Southeast Asia. It is an aggressive small animal with soft, dense fur

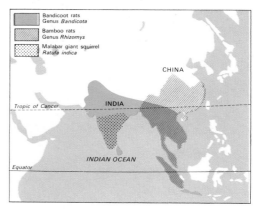

Asian tropical rats Bamboo rats spend most of their lives underground, in burrows dug beneath dense stands of bamboo. They feed on the bamboo roots, but may also seek food above ground

Asiatic squirrels These striped palm squirrels are found only in India and Ceylon, where they are numerous. They forage on the ground during the day, eating seeds, buds, and insects

Rhinos, the tapir, and the elephant

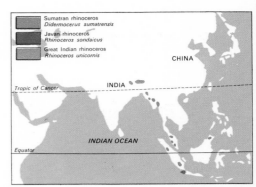

With their bulk and their thick, almost hairless hides, rhinos seem akin to elephants; yet their closest relatives are the timid, piglike tapirs

Elephants and rhinoceroses were once believed to be related. They were both called pachyderms, from two Greek words meaning "thick skin," but mainly they were classed together because they are both big,

sparsely haired animals. In fact, their relationship is distant and they belong to different orders.

African and Indian elephants are the remnants of a large order of mammals called Proboscidea—animals with an elongated nose and the upper lip fused into the trunk. Rhinos belong to the same order as horses and tapirs. Elephants and rhinos are the world's two largest land mammals.

Close to extinction Asian rhinos are closer to extinction than the African species. Fewer than 800 Indian rhinos remain; there are perhaps 100 to 170 Sumatran rhinos left; and probably fewer than 30 Javan rhinos. Their ranges have also diminished

End of a line—the disappearing rhinos of Asia

Rhinos and tapirs, together with the horse family, are the only living members of the Perissodactyla ("uneven-toed") order. The name comes from the fact that in all its members the main axis of the foot passes through the middle toe. This central toe bears the body weight, as the big toe does in man.

In horses the other toes remain only as vestigial bones, but in rhinos and tapirs, which are more closely related to each other than to horses, some of these toes still function. Members of the other order of running herbivores, the Artiodactyla ("even-toed"), which includes antelopes and cattle, have two central weight-bearing toes on each foot instead of one.

Asian rhinos have been hunted almost to extinction on account of their horns—dense, fibrous structures which some people believe have aphrodisiac and medicinal qualities. The horn is ground and used in powder form. The Javan rhino, a forest species, ranged from Sikkim to Java until about 100 years

Protective mud bath A Sumatran rhino lies half asleep in its mud wallow. Rhinos spend a great deal of time like this, constantly renewing their coat of mud, which helps keep them cool and prevents insects from laying eggs in their skin. Insects are visible on its back and neck

Female Javan rhino The female Javan rhino's horn is sometimes vestigial, reduced to a bump. The males have a single short horn

The small Sumatran rhino Standing just 4½ feet high at the shoulder, this rhino is the smallest in the world. Its skin folds are less conspicuous and young animals are covered with hair

Indian rhino The single-horned great Indian rhino, 14 feet long, 6 feet high, and weighing two tons, is the largest of the Asian species. It is only marginally a forest-dweller, since it usually grazes in reed beds and swamps. A distinguishing feature is its extremely thick hide, covered with studlike granules, which falls in stiff, heavy folds and resembles a suit of armor

A change of coat that may mirror evolution

The young Malayan tapir goes through a series of changes in coat pattern and coloration before it assumes its adult coat. At birth the Malayan tapir and the South American tapirs are almost iden-

tically marked—a hint that millions of years ago they may have had a common ancestor. The adult markings differ, because each species has evolved in its own environment

Adult tapir A fully grown Malayan tapir stands about three feet high and can weigh 400 pounds. It browses at night in dense forest stands and, like the rhino, leaves its droppings in special areas

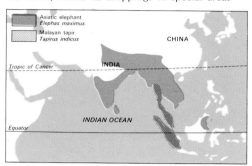

The range of Asiatic elephants This species' herds are believed made up of just one family. A dominant bull heads the herd, but any extensive treks in search of food are initiated by an old female

ago. Now there are probably fewer than 30 left. Their low birth rate makes it unlikely that the species can survive.

The great Indian rhino, a solitary animal of uncertain temper, lives in swamps at the edge of the forest. During the mating season, between February and April, female Indian rhinos seek out males. The young are born after a gestation of about 16 months. Rhinos must drink water every day, and in dense forest they burrow through the undergrowth, making long, tunnellike trails from grazing area to riverbank.

Ancestors of the tapirs were once widely distributed throughout the northern hemi-

sphere, at a time when a land bridge joined Asia and North America in the region of the Bering Strait. Gradually, through the ages, they migrated south into the tropics of the New and Old Worlds, and today tapirs are found only in South America and Southeast Asia. Although the present-day descendants of the ancient tapirs are isolated from each other on opposite sides of the globe, there are few differences between the species. All tapirs are rounded in back and tapering in front, which is an ideal shape for running through the undergrowth. Tapirs are timid, browsing animals with a fondness for water plants. They seldom move far from water.

The Asiatic or Indian elephant is smaller than the African

Solitary male This bull elephant, crossing a stream in the Thai jungle, lives alone and will join a herd only when seeking a mate

The Asiatic or Indian elephant shares a common ancestor with the African elephant, but there are marked differences both in physique and in preferred habitat.

The African elephant is heavier, with much larger ears and tusks, and in many areas prefers the savanna. The smaller Asiatic species has a more rounded shape, and is essentially a creature of the forest. Indian elephants, like African, are gregarious, living in herds that are led by an old female. They rest during the heat of the day, feeding in the morning and evening.

Baby elephants are born with a coat of brown hairs. This coat becomes less obvious as the elephant matures, but all elephants have hair on their bodies throughout their lives. The woolly mammoth, an extinct species of elephant, was covered with long, coarse hair that grew over a woolly coat, like that of the present-day musk-ox.

A bathing bull Elephants bathe frequently. They usually stand in relatively shallow depths, sucking

up water into their trunks and squirting it over themselves to cool off. They eat plants from lake beds

African elephant

Asiatic elephant

Differences between African and Asiatic elephants The African elephant is larger than the Asiatic. Other differences are the Asiatic elephant's smaller ears, its high, domed forehead with a cleft, and

its sloping back. African elephants generally have fewer nails on their feet; they also have two "fingers" at the tip of the trunk, whereas Asiatic elephants have only one

183

Cattle, deer, and pigs

The dense thickets and grassy clearings of the tropical forests shelter a variety of large mammals: shy deer, aggressive buffalo, and herds of foraging pigs

All of the large plant-eating mammals of the tropical forests except elephants, rhinoceroses, and pigs are ruminants—chewers of cud. They feed in forest glades during the early morning and evening, then retire to chew the cud in the shelter of the trees, where they are less apt to be attacked by predators.

In the forests of India and Burma live some of the largest cattle in the world. Among them are the huge gaur and the water buffalo. The Asian tropical forests are also the home of the smallest wild cattle in the world.

In spite of its size, the gaur, reaching a height of six feet at the shoulder and sometimes weighing over a ton, is shy and timid. If it is startled it will gallop away at considerable speed. The gaur has a conspicuous hump, beginning at the shoulders and continuing halfway down the spine. It is a handsome animal, dark reddish brown, with white stockings, and huge, curving horns up to 44 inches long.

Gaurs usually live in small herds of about six animals. They spend most of the day in the forest, on hillsides, emerging at dawn and late in the evening to graze in grassy clearings farther up the hill.

The gayal is known only as a domestic animal, in the Chittagong Hills of Pakistan and northern Burma. It is probably related to the gaur, since it too is dark brown and has white stockings and a hump. But the gayal is smaller, and its horns grow sideways and are only slightly curved.

The banteng, slighter in build than the gaur and the gayal, prefers lightly forested areas with open grassy clearings. It lives in herds of from 10 to 30 animals, although solitary bulls are often seen. The herd feeds almost constantly all through the night. The banteng moves to the higher ground of the hill forest when the heavy monsoon rains begin.

The water buffalo, found as a domestic animal not only in Asia but also in parts of Europe, is becoming rare in the wild.

Some experts think the "wild" herds are actually feral, that is, not truly wild but descendants of escaped domestic animals that have acquired some of the characteristics of wild animals.

The water buffalo has two close relatives, the anoa, found in Celebes, just over three feet high and the smallest of all the wild cattle, and the tamarau, found on Mindoro Island in the Philippines. Both species tend to live near water.

Solitary gaur bull Old gaur bulls usually live away from herds formed by the females and younger adult males. But in the mating season they join the herds and establish territories, driving away the other adult bulls. When the rutting season ends, the old bulls leave, and the cows and younger males form a herd again. Bulls utter a high-pitched piping or whistling call in this season

Water buffalo Their herds live near water in swamps and marshes, grazing in the evening, night, and morning. They shelter from heat in long grass, or in mud and water, with just their nostrils showing

Anoa   Tamarau   Water buffalo

Forest cattle The natural ranges of all these cattle are greatly reduced, but the banteng and water buffalo have been domesticated in many places, while the anoa and tamarau are becoming rare

Gaur *Bos gaurus*
Banteng *Bos banteng*
Water buffalo *Bubalus bubalis*
Anoa *Anoa depressicornis*
Tamarau *Anoa mindorensis*

CHINA
Tropic of Cancer
INDIA
INDIAN OCEAN
Equator

Cattle of southern Asian forests The world's smallest cattle are found here: the anoa, a native of Celebes, stands about 3¼ feet at the shoulder, and the tamarau, found on the Philippines' Mindoro Island, is only slightly larger. The water buffalo stands up to six feet at the shoulder

A rival departs A male sambar guards a female while a rival stag retreats back into the forest. Sambars live in small herds of about six animals, from India and Ceylon to the Malay Peninsula

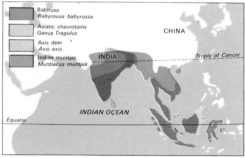

Sociable axis deer Also known as chitals, these animals are slender and white-spotted. They are the most gregarious of all deer of eastern Asia. Although a herd usually numbers 10 to 30, occasion- ally axis deer form huge herds, particularly near rivers and streams. Some stags retreat from the herd when they shed their antlers, but they return as soon as a new set has grown, in about two months

Eastern deer The Indian muntjac inhabits dense forests, while the axis deer lives near rivers. Asiatic chevrotains also live near water, and graze and browse in the forest at night

Sambar and swamp deer

The deer that browse in the Asian forests, though hunted by man and other predators, are still numerous. The biggest of them is the sambar. It weighs 500 to 700 pounds, larger than the red deer of Europe, which it resembles in shape. Its antlers, with fewer points than those of red deer, spread up to 50 inches. Sambars live in small herds of about six.

Swamp deer, or barasinghs, widespread in the wetter forests and also in open coun- try, live alone for three months of the year. At this time males grow complex antlers, with up to 20 points, and the females give birth. When the mating season begins the deer again form in herds.

Primitive ruminant The chevrotain, which weighs six to ten pounds, looks like a small antelope, but it belongs to a separate family, the Tragulidae

Indian muntjac This deer's antlers are carried on hair-covered outgrowths from the skull. Living alone or in pairs in the rain forest, it utters a bark- like call in the mating season or when alarmed

Cloven-hooved animals that eat flesh

Pigs, unlike most cloven-hooved animals, are not ruminants; nor are they strictly herbivo- rous. Although they eat much vegetable food, they will feed on anything edible, in- cluding carrion and insect larvae, which they dig up with their snouts.

The wild boar, found throughout much of Europe, southern Asia, and northern Africa, forages in groups of 6 to 50. During the night the group may travel a considerable distance to get to a favorite food source. Wild boars, like all wild pigs, are good runners and swimmers.

Unique upper tusks The long upper tusks of the babirusa do not protrude from between the lips as in other pigs, but grow through the skin below the eyes. The lower tusks project upward out of the mouth. Since both pairs curve backward toward the skull, they cannot be used as weapons

185

The tiger

The tiger, largest of the cats, can easily bring down a fully grown deer with a blow of the forepaw, then kill it with a suffocating bite on the throat

Teeth for cutting A tiger swallows meat in chunks, rather than chewing it. The two large canines in each jaw are used for seizing prey, and the other sharp teeth for shearing skin, meat, and gristle

Tigers are usually solitary animals, except when breeding or when a female is rearing cubs. But they are not completely unsociable. When a tiger makes a very large kill, several animals from the same district may gather together to feed on it.

Male tigers defend territories of 25 to 250 square miles against other males. These territories often cover the home ranges of several females. Both males and females mark the boundaries of their territories by spraying the vegetation with a mixture of urine and scent. The resident male tiger usually has a preferred central area in its home territory where it spends most of its time and to which it returns after a kill.

Both sexes sometimes announce their whereabouts with a startlingly loud roar, which can be heard two miles away. Females roar to call cubs to a kill or to attract a male during mating periods.

The tiger spends the day sleeping or resting in the forest, sometimes lying in a pool of water to keep cool. At dusk it emerges to hunt, and may travel more than 20 miles in

a night's search. It detects its prey—perhaps a deer or a buffalo—by sight or hearing rather than scent, then steals up to within 30 to 80 feet of it before making a sudden rush from behind. The tiger kills by knocking down the animal with a blow of the forepaw or by pulling it down with the claws. It suffocates large animals with a throat bite, but kills small prey by biting through the back of the neck. The throat grip, which pins the victim to the ground, makes the tiger less vulnerable to being gored or kicked by its prey.

Sometimes a tiger will crouch near a water hole or a trail and wait for an animal to come within striking distance. Tigers need thick vegetation for concealment, since they lack the stamina to chase prey in the open.

Hooved mammals, such as deer and pigs, form the bulk of the tiger's diet; but it will also eat birds, fish, and even crocodiles. Tigers kill about 1000 persons a year in India. They sometimes become man-eaters after raiding domestic cattle herds. But as long as wild prey is available, tigers appear

Markings that camouflage The tiger's black-striped, tawny coat breaks up the outline of its body, enabling it to merge into the background of broken light and shadow. With its ability to move inconspicuously and quietly, a tiger can creep up behind its prey and capture it in a single bound. Muscular and broad-shouldered, males weigh up to 400 pounds and measure nine feet from nose to tail tip. Females, 6 to 12 inches shorter, weigh about 300 pounds. The immense strength of both sexes enables them to bring down and overcome large animals such as buffalo and nilgais

A deadly grip Charging from behind, a tiger brings down a buffalo and holds it with its claws and teeth. Then it transfers its grip to the throat. The animal usually suffocates in less than ten minutes

to avoid encountering humans. A tiger eats 40 to 50 pounds of meat in a meal lasting about two hours, then hides the remains of the kill among rocks or under vegetation for future meals.

Vulnerable cubs

A typical tiger litter consists of two or three cubs, born after three months' gestation. Six months later, however, usually only one or two of these cubs remain alive.

After six weeks of suckling, the cubs begin accompanying their mother on hunts. At six months the cubs are allowed to kill small prey that the mother has brought down. A one-year-old cub can bring down a deer, but many cubs die when they go after prey that is too strong for them. They are vulnerable to predators for hours at a time when the mother goes off hunting.

Tigers of all subspecies have recently been threatened with extinction. More and more of their habitat is being invaded by man and hunters have taken an enormous toll. There are now only a few thousand tigers left in the wild.

Hiding a carcass Before feeding, a tiger drags the carcass to a secluded spot in a thicket or among rocks. It hides the excess meat for future meals and will return to feed until only the bones remain

Ears signal the mood By turning the ears forward, tigers expose white spots (left). Some zoologists think this is a signal of aggression. For defense (right), the ears are flattened and teeth exposed

Reduced range Tigers once ranged from Turkey to China, but today the main populations are confined to India and Southeast Asia. Only small numbers inhabit the other remaining areas

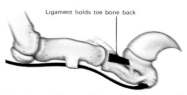

Retracted claws Tigers, like most cats, walk with their claws retracted and sheathed in folds of skin. This sheath keeps them from becoming blunt and scraping against the ground

Extended claws When seizing prey or climbing trees, a muscle in the leg contracts, the tendons attached to it pull the last toe bones forward, and the claws emerge from the protective sheath

Cats of the Orient

The leopard, stealthiest of the big cats, silently stalks its prey in thick cover, or—climbing a tree—waits for a victim to pass below, then springs

The leopard is smaller than either the lion or the tiger. An adult male measures just under five feet and weighs about 100 pounds. But the leopard is just as skillful a predator as its larger relatives.

It is the wariest and most secretive of the big cats, rarely seen even by its victims. It spends much of its time resting in the trees, concealed by foliage. From this perch it can spot approaching prey without being seen.

Of all the big cats, the leopard is the most agile. It can run, jump, swim, and climb trees with equal facility. Its long tail acts as a counterweight and helps to steady it.

Leopards live throughout much of Asia and Africa, not only in dense tropical forest but also in more open wooded country. In Asia, the ranges of tigers and leopards often overlap. Large hooved mammals form the main part of the tiger's diet, but the leopard eats monkeys, rodents, and birds as well as smaller hooved mammals.

Leopards hunt mainly at night. They usu-

ally detect game by sight, then creep silently up on it, or drop down on it from a tree.

The sleek yellow coat of the leopard is closely dotted with black spots. On the head and limbs the spots are scattered at random, but those on the sides form clusters, called rosettes. The animals keep their coats glossy by frequent grooming with the tongue.

Leopards, like most other cats, are solitary except in the mating season, when they form pairs. About three cubs are born after a three-month pregnancy. When they are big enough they accompany the mother on hunting expeditions.

The leopard, wariest and most agile of the big cats

Stalking its prey Within striking distance, this leopard crawls close to its prey. It is camouflaged by its yellow coat covered with black spots

Preparing for a meal A leopard drags the carcass of an axis deer into a thicket, where it can feed undisturbed. Before eating, it disembowels the car- cass. It eats the heart and liver first, then the haunches. Then the leopard may haul the remains into a tree to keep it from scavengers

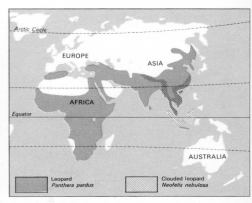

Widespread leopard Species range widely from West Africa to Sumatra. The clouded leopard, how- ever, is confined to jungles and scrubland

Hunter at rest The leopard is as agile in trees as on the ground. It not only rests in the trees, but will hunt by springing from a branch

The smaller cats, like the tiger and the leopard, are solitary

All the smaller cats of the Asian forests are solitary. The males do not help to care for their young, which are born in underground lairs or in hollow trees.

The smaller cats are expert hunters. Most of them climb trees and prey on mammals, ranging in size from monkeys to mice, as well as birds, reptiles, and insects.

The jungle cat kills birds, including pheasants and partridges. It ranges from the Middle East to Southeast Asia, living in the drier and more open parts of the forest, and in patches of grassland. It weighs 17 to 20 pounds, as does the fishing cat, which is usually found near water in swampy forests. The fishing cat preys on small mammals, and is said to scoop up fish with its paws, which have slightly webbed toes.

The clouded leopard, measuring three feet from head to rump and weighing about 45 pounds, is intermediate in size between the leopard and the smaller cats. Its tail, 2½ feet long, helps it balance when climbing. The clouded leopard hunts at night for birds and small mammals. It is prized in the fur trade for its beautiful coat.

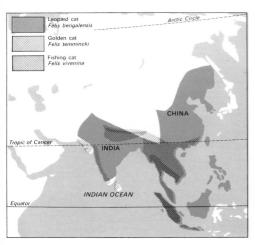

The smaller cats The leopard cat is one of the most widespread of the smaller cats. The golden cat also has an extensive range but is rarely seen

Fishing cat This small cat is said to crouch on rocks and riverbanks to scoop fish out of the water

Golden cat One of the few members of the genus *Felis* without a patterned coat, it does have two black stripes on its cheeks and a line over its eyes

Leopard cat This hunter's head and body length is less than two feet. It resembles a small leopard

Coat patterns of forest cats

The black panther is a dark leopard and not a separate species. In certain lights dark spots can be seen

The clouded leopard has a yellow-gray coat. In older animals, the gray blotches tend to fade, leaving only the outlines

The fishing cat of the swampy forest has spots on its body that are arranged in rows, but those on the limbs are less distinct

The jungle cat lives in thickets, reeds, and low-lying forest. It has dark rings near its tail tip and tufts of hair on its ears

The marbled cat is slightly larger than a domestic cat. Large blotches outlined in black give a marble pattern to its coat

189

Predators on small animals

**The myriads of plant-eating animals
that live among the trees of the
Asian tropical forests are in turn preyed
on by small, nocturnal carnivores**

The flesh-eaters that prey on plant-eaters in the Asian tropical forests range from agile civets and wild dogs to slower-moving bears and moles. Insect-eating bats hunt in the treetops; scaly-coated pangolins roam the forest floor and climb the trees, preying on ants and termites.

Most members of the civet family, the Viverridae, can climb, and they hunt small animals in and among the trees. They are the most typical small and medium-size predators in the Old World tropical forests. Civets are long-bodied, short-legged animals, with long tails, pointed snouts, and rounded ears. Their fur is generally sleek, soft, and spotted or blotched. In some species the tail is ringed or banded. Civets have scent glands at the base of the tail. When attacked, they discharge a pungent fluid from these glands. The odor is unpleasant, and the civet's bold markings may serve as a warning to its predators. The strong-smelling secretion is also used as a recognition device between individuals of the same species. Some species are kept in captivity and milked of the secretion, which is used in making perfume.

There are a few weasels in the Asian tropical forests, notably the yellow-throated marten and the ferret-badger.

Bears typical of this region include the sun bear, smallest bear in the world, and the nocturnal sloth bear. The sloth bear is famous for its ability to fall asleep quickly under any circumstances, accompanied by loud snoring.

The moon rat, like the sun bear and the sloth bear, is an insectivore. Its long, mobile nose and narrow body allow the animal to squeeze into the crevices where its insect prey hides.

Civets, weasels, and wild dogs prey on the plant-eaters

Catlike hunter The spotted linsang, like its close relative the banded linsang, is armed with claws that are sheathed like the claws of cats. Linsangs, good tree climbers, are generally active at night and hunt by springing out of a tree. They often catch their prey unaware

Nocturnal rasse The rasse seldom resorts to trees. It is omnivorous, and stalks at night

Shaggy binturong The binturong, unlike other members of the civet family, has long, coarse hair. It eats fruits and plants, and sometimes carrion

Civets live alone or in pairs. They rest in dens in the ground or in hollow trees during the day and emerge at night to hunt.

The rasse, or lesser oriental civet, hunts mainly on the ground, but it can climb trees. Like other civets, it may be found on the outskirts of towns and villages, where it preys on rats and mice. Rasses are solitary animals; they meet only to mate, and the female rears the young alone. The banded linsang and the spotted linsang, which live in trees, are civets that have much softer fur than the rasse.

The spotted civet has long, loose fur with black and white spots on a gray or tawny background. A crest of hairs which becomes erect when the animal is excited distinguishes it from the rasse. Spotted civets inhabit Southeast Asia, preying on small mammals, birds, frogs, snakes, and insects.

Toddy cat and binturong

Like most small forest predators, spotted civets eat practically anything, as do palm civets. Some species of palm civets have a taste for the juice of the toddy palm, which has earned them the alternative name of toddy cats. Spotted civets are often found near houses, where they prey upon vermin.

The largest member of the civet family, the binturong, is nearly three feet long. Unlike other civets, it has long, shaggy black hair, and it uses its tail as a fifth limb when climbing trees. The binturong eats mainly fruit and other vegetation.

The role filled by civets is similar to that occupied by the weasel family in more northerly regions, but the weasels do have a few representatives in the Asian tropical forests. The yellow-throated marten lives and hunts in the trees, preying on birds and small mammals, such as squirrels. Like all martens, it is solitary, and active both night and day. Martens sometimes travel up to nine miles in a night, although this is probably rare in the tropical forest, where there is an abundance of food even for carnivores. The young of martens become solitary as soon as they are fully grown, at around three months.

The ferret-badger has black-and-white face markings, which give it a masklike appearance. Although it can climb, it hunts mainly on the ground, feeding on small animals and fruits. It is active at dusk and during the night. The mother apparently nurses her young (usually one to three per litter) until they are nearly full-grown. Since it destroys insect pests, this ferret is allowed to enter houses in some places.

Tireless dogs that trail prey

The dhole, or Indian wild dog, looks like a large fox, with red fur and a blunt snout, but its closest relative is the African hunting dog. It hunts in packs of up to 30, which attack any creature from wild pigs to buffalo, although the most common prey are deer. Smaller packs may be made up of single families, but the large packs are probably combined family groups, since several females often raise their young together. The pack will drive off even tigers and leopards and steal their kill. Dholes have great stamina and trail the scent of their prey for miles. They are usually silent hunters. Even the largest groups make no sound as they run through the forest after the prey. Dholes do not bark but have a howling call; and they yap loudly just before a kill.

The insectivores—animals highly adapted for eating insects

The sun bear, which ranges from Burma to Indonesia, is the smallest of all bears, only three to four feet long. It has short, dark fur with a white patch on the chest, and a relatively large head and shoulders. It has a peculiar pigeon-toed walk. The sun bear is an agile tree-climber and appears to be extremely intelligent. One bear opened a locked cupboard containing a sugar bowl by using its claw to turn the key. The sun bear feeds mainly on plants, although it also eats ants and breaks open bees' nests for honey. To collect ants, the bear tears open a nest and inserts its paw. The ants swarm onto the paw, which the bear then licks clean. It sleeps by day in a crude nest of branches.

The sloth bear is nocturnal, and it spends the day asleep in thick brush or among rocks. It is five to six feet long and has a clearly defined V-shaped band on its chest, lighter in color than the rest of its coat. It feeds on ants and termites. It digs a hole in the insects' nest, inserts its snout, and sucks them up. It can close its nostrils at will, thus allowing it to blow dust off termites' nests without getting the dust up its nose. It has a gap in its front teeth and a hollowed palate, which are further adaptations for sucking up termites.

Moon rats, or gymnures, live alone in hollow logs or crevices. They are not true rats (which are rodents), but insectivores. They hunt at night, mainly for insects, but they

Termite-eating bear The lips and tongue of the sloth bear are adapted for sucking up termites, which form a major part of its diet. It first digs out the nest, then blows off the dirt, and finally noisily sucks up the termites. Sloth bears asleep in the brush can be heard snoring loudly

may swim after frogs and fish. The largest species is the Malayan moon rat.

Upon and beneath the forest floor live small insect-eaters, such as musk shrews and the eastern moles. Musk shrews, which are five or six inches long from the end of their long snouts to the tip of their short tails, are named after their strong musky smell. They are often found near human habitations. Besides insects, they will eat meat, bread, and whatever else they can scavenge from their surroundings.

Musk shrews are nocturnal. They make shrill chattering sounds as they run about at night hunting food. In some species both parents collect material for the nest, caring for the young until they are nearly grown. The moles burrow for worms and grubs, with claws highly adapted for digging. They have no external ears and are virtually blind.

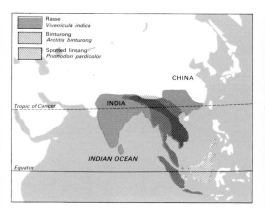

Small predators The Viverridae, a large family of carnivores, are typical small predators of the Southeast Asian forests. The rasse has the largest range

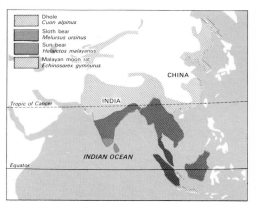

Bears, dogs, and moon rats The ranges of the sun bear and the sloth bear do not overlap. The dhole, a wild dog, ranges extensively

The chattering musk shrews Among these species are some of the smallest mammals in the world. The Chinese call them money shrews because their chattering sounds like the jingling of falling coins. The major part of their diet is comprised of invertebrates and other small animals

A multitude of birds

Birds of the rain forest keep to their own level, almost as though there were sheets of glass separating one layer of the forest from another

The layered structure of the vegetation in the tropical rain forest is mirrored in the stratification of its birdlife. Above the canopy live a few rapid-flying species which feed on insects and other birds. In or below the canopy, where the main mass of birds live, swift flight for any distance is impossible. Some of the small birds live in the canopy, but most of them live beneath it,

feeding on insects and fruit. The forest floor is the feeding ground for many large birds. Most of them rarely fly, since much of their food falls to the ground from above.

The brilliantly colored Indian jungle fowl feeds on fruits, buds, insects, and seeds. It prefers the mountainous tropical forest, and is rarely seen below 3000 feet. The cock has a ringing call, and resembles game cocks in its aggressive behavior. Grain-eating birds, abundant in the drier tropics, are rare in the rain forest, since the absence of grass there results in a shortage of seed suitable for these birds to eat.

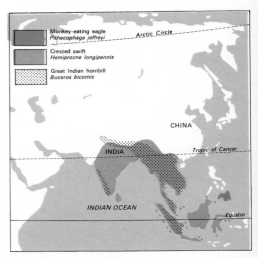

Birds above the canopy These three species seek their food above the roof of the tropical forest. Crested swifts catch insects in flight and hornbills drop into the treetops for fruit and small animals

Falconet, swift, and hornbill fly above the canopy; "bird armies" feed below

Rare monkey-eating eagle Found only on Mindanao in the Philippines, this eagle preys mainly on monkeys. It spots them while soaring high above the trees

Typical of the birds that fly above the treetops in the Southeast Asian forests is the falconet, which lives in the branches projecting above the canopy. This fast-flying bird is little bigger than a sparrow, but it looks like a falcon and is just as aggressive. It hunts large insects and small birds. A much larger bird that often hunts above the forest is the black eagle. It preys on bats, lizards, and small rats.

Insects above the canopy are the prey of the fast-flying swifts. The smallest of these are the swiftlets, which nest in caves in huge colonies. The birds maneuver by a system of echo-location, like bats. One of the most abundant Bornean species, the brown-rumped swiftlet, feeds up to 900 feet above the forest. The spine-tailed swifts of the

genus *Chaetura* are much larger than the swiftlets, and fly at speeds up to 60 miles per hour. Their tail spines are really stiff feathers that the birds use as props when clinging to the hollow trunks in which they make their nests.

The three species of crested swifts are brightly colored and bear distinctive crests. They lay single eggs in nests so tiny that the chicks leave the nests when still very small and sit on branches, where they are fed by their parents. True swifts remain in the nest until they are ready to fly.

Among the largest birds in the canopy are hornbills, which feed on fruit and small animals in the treetops. The most spectacular are the rhinoceros hornbill, which has an upswept, solid casque, or helmet-shaped

growth, on top of its beak, and the great Indian hornbill.

The great mass of forest birds live between the canopy and the ground, feeding on insects and fruit. It is at this level that "bird armies" are found. A typical bird army may consist of 40 insect-eating individuals of about ten species, moving steadily through the forest after insects. Each species usually keeps to one height and feeds in its own way.

The long-tailed munia is ranked as a pest in the uplands of Borneo. Large flocks of these birds, which belong to the same family as grass finches, appear occasionally and devastate rice crops. Otherwise they are rarely seen and nothing is known of their breeding habits. In the Himalayan mountain forests, parakeets have become pests.

Silver pheasant This species has been found in mountain forests at altitudes as high as 9000 feet

A stitched-up nest The Indian tailorbird builds a nest from leaves. Piercing the edges of one or more leaves, it stitches them with fibers to form a tube

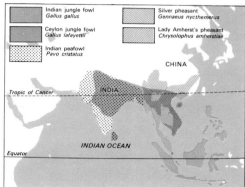

Indian jungle fowl
Gallus gallus

Ceylon jungle fowl
Gallus lafayettii

Indian peafowl
Pavo cristatus

Silver pheasant
Gennaeus nycthemerus

Lady Amherst's pheasant
Chrysolophus amherstiae

CHINA

Tropic of Cancer

INDIA

INDIAN OCEAN

Equator

Ground birds of Asian forests Asia is the home of the majority of the world's species of pheasants. Jungle fowl are widespread throughout the forests

Territorial defense The Ceylon jungle cock maintains its territorial boundaries each day by strutting, crowing, and fighting fiercely with its spurred legs

Brilliantly colored ground birds parade through the forest

The Asian forest is particularly rich in ground birds—mostly jungle fowl and pheasants. Jungle fowl closely resemble domestic bantams. In fact, the Indian jungle fowl is probably the ancestor of all breeds of domestic fowl. The cock is aggressive and polygamous. Its head and neck are bright yellow, its back is purple and red, its wings brown with green tints. Its eyes are orange, the comb is red. The female is smaller and duller. The Indian jungle fowl feeds in flocks on the ground on seeds, insects (particularly termites), and fruit.

Many members of the pheasant family are found in the Asian tropical forests. The best known is the Indian peafowl, which has been kept as a decorative bird in parks and gardens for centuries. In its native forests in India and Ceylon the peafowl is a shy bird. It runs for cover when threatened, and only flies at dusk. It roosts in tall trees. The strong muscles under the tail enable the bird to spread its magnificent long train with the hundreds of brilliantly colored eyespots. The peafowl has an eerie scream and often cries at daybreak. The female, or peahen, lacks the peacock's huge train.

The argus pheasant lives in Malaya and Borneo. It is the giant of the pheasant family, six feet long, including a four-foot tail. The long feathers of the wing and tail are decorated with eyespots similar to the peacock's. To attract the hen, the cock performs an elaborate dance on a patch of ground which he has cleared of all leaves and debris.

The low-canopy mountain forests are the home of some of the more spectacular pheasants. Lady Amherst's pheasant is found in Tibet and Burma, and the silver pheasant in Southeast Asia.

Indian peacock To attract a peahen, this cock fans out its many-eyed train. Then it shakes its wings, making the plumage shimmer and appear iridescent. The female is less spectacular looking

193

Reptiles and amphibians

**The flying frog spreads its long digits,
stretching the webbing between them;
hollows its body into a more concave
shape; then glides 15 yards down**

Reptiles and amphibians are cold-blooded
animals, which means that they are not able
to maintain a narrow range of internal body
temperatures as warm-blooded animals do.
In colder zones cold-blooded animals must
burrow or take other defensive measures
when the temperature drops below a critical
point. But the tropical forest has a constant
warm temperature, and reptiles and amphibians live under ideal conditions. Their
body temperature can remain fairly constant,
since the air temperature under the forest
canopy rarely varies.

Many reptiles and amphibians have
adapted physically, however, to life in the
trees. Many tree-living snakes have long,
thin bodies with angled scales on their
bellies that allow them to cling to tree bark.
The feet of geckos and tree frogs have
hooked claws or hairy pads that give them a
strong grip; and some snakes, lizards, and
frogs have developed "wings" that enable
them to escape predators by gliding.

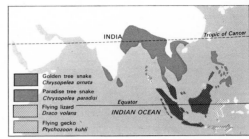

Distribution of gliders In the ideal conditions of
constant warmth and high humidity, many of the
reptiles of the Asian tropical forests have adapted
to living in trees

At home in the jungle: parachuting snakes and flying frogs

When a snake pursues its prey in the trees
it loses the scent trail whenever the fleeing
animal leaps to another branch. Many tree-
dwelling snakes, therefore, have evolved
keener eyesight than snakes that live mostly
on the ground. They can readily follow the
quick movements of their prey and judge
distances accurately.

The majority of forest-dwelling lizards
are well camouflaged by their dull green or
brown coloring, which matches the leaves or
bark of the trees they frequent. As a further
camouflaging adaptation some species are
shaped like a twig or a leaf.

Among the most highly developed gliding
reptiles are the flying lizards. These animals,
which are about eight inches long, can make
directed flights of 20 yards or more by
spreading their gliding membranes.

Many nongliding reptiles live in the trees.
Some snakes have prehensile tails which can
grip a branch firmly while the rest of the
body moves outward, seeking another hold.
Other tree snakes, such as the green whip
snake, have long, slim bodies and green

coloration that merges with the foliage.
Wagler's pit viper is camouflaged by a broken
pattern of bars and spots. The venom of this
three-foot-long snake readily kills lizards,
birds, and small mammals.

The flying frog has longer digits and
more webbing on its feet than other members of the large family of tree frogs to
which it belongs, called the Rhacophoridae.
By spreading its digits and stretching the
webbing, the frog can leap from a branch
and glide on a downward-slanting course for
about 15 yards.

Tree-dwelling members of the widespread
Agamidae family of lizards are well represented in Asian forests. One of the most
common is the green crested lizard. Like the
chameleons, this animal can change color
with startling rapidity, though it appears to
do so as a means of display rather than of
camouflage. When alarmed, it turns dark
brown in seconds; during courtship, the lips
and throat of the male become crimson. Because of its gory appearance at this time, it
is sometimes called the bloodsucker.

Adaptations for gliding

The flying lizard controls
its glide by opening its
flying membranes, which are
supported by elongated
ribs. It begins its glide
headfirst, facing downward,
and lands head
upward, grasping a branch
with all fours

Extendible skin flaps
surround the entire body
of the flying gecko.
When these and its webbed
feet are outspread, the
gecko can make long
glides from tree to tree

Gaining additional support
in the air by drawing its
underside into a concave
shape, the flying frog
can parachute long distances
from branch to branch

Flying frog The night
photograph at the
left shows the frog in
the middle of a
flight between trees.
It has larger feet than
other leaf frogs.
The webbed feet are
used for parachuting
and arresting the
frog's fall as it drops
to the ground

Frog at rest The feet of the flying frog are adapted
for clinging as well as for gliding

Parachuting snake The paradise snake, an accomplished climber, can contract its underside into a
concave surface that acts as a parachute. It sharply
straightens its body as it launches into the air

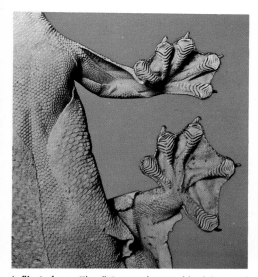

A flier's foot The flying gecko's webbed feet and folded flaps of skin about its body aid it in gliding. Its sharp claws and toe pads give the animal an instant grip on landing

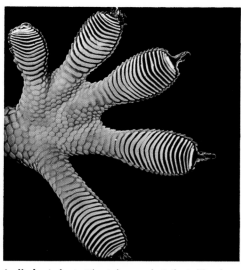

A climber's foot The tokay gecko's feet, like those of most geckos, have pads of microscopic hooks that can grip the smoothest surfaces. This animal's name was derived from its cry

Protected pupils To prevent dazzle during the day and to allow the formation of a precise image, the pupils of the tokay gecko's large eyes close to form four tiny holes

Ground-dwelling skinks, lizards, tortoises, and snakes

Monitor lizards, skinks, tortoises, and snakes inhabit the forest floor. The ground-dwelling Russell's viper, about five feet long, eats mainly small mammals. It is much deadlier than Wagler's pit viper—its venom can kill a man. The nonpoisonous reticulated python can swallow large prey, but feeds mainly on birds and small mammals, seldom tackling anything bigger than a small monkey.

Some of the skinks that live in the litter of the forest floor are particularly well adapted to life underground. Their eyes are protected by transparent "windows" and their eardrums are sunken. Their legs are short—some species have even lost them— and their tails are strong and tapering. Some burrowing lizards and snakes have only rudimentary eyes, and depend entirely on

their keen sense of smell to locate hidden insect prey.

The constant high humidity makes it possible for many soft-skinned amphibians to spend their lives far from water. Wormlike amphibians called caecilians burrow in the humus; and a number of amphibians lay their eggs on the moist ground of the forest floor instead of in water.

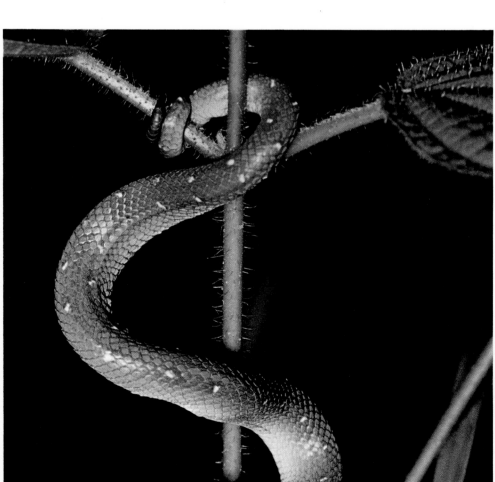

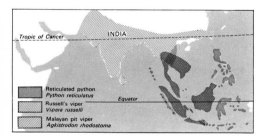

Meeting of two groups Pit vipers and vipers, the two groups of the Viperidae family, meet only in Asia. The Malayan pit viper seems to have replaced Russell's viper in the center of its range

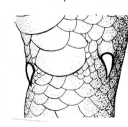

Vestigial legs Pythons have a pair of external spurs on each side of the anal cleft. These are remnants of hind legs that atrophied in the course of the evolution of snakes and some lizards

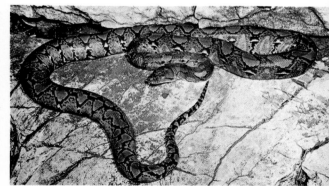

Reticulated python The world's largest snake, it can grow to 33 feet and weigh 300 pounds

Tail anchor Wagler's pit viper (left), unlike most vipers, has a prehensile tail that it can curl around a branch while it reaches to another branch

195

Monkeys

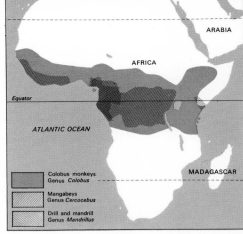

The long, white-tufted tails of colobus monkeys hang down from the trees, marking the boundaries of a troop's territory. The males roar to warn off any intruders

Up to 30 species of monkeys live in the tropical forests of Africa, at all levels, from the ground to the tops of trees. There are four groups: colobus monkeys, guenons, mangabeys, and mandrills.

The colobus monkeys are leaf-eaters. They have long limbs for leaping. Some species are unique among Old World monkeys in that they have no thumbs. The guenons, with up to 20 species, are the largest group of African monkeys. Their range extends from coast to coast north of the equator and down into southern Africa. Mangabeys and mandrills are closely related to baboons. Male mandrills are noted for their coloring.

The baboon's forest relatives In the forests mandrills and mangabeys replace the baboons of the savanna. The colobus monkeys range across Africa

Some monkeys seldom leave the upper forest layers

Leaping guereza All colobus monkeys have long hind limbs that help them leap from tree to tree.

Even when they cannot be seen, they can be heard crashing among the branches of the treetops

Colobus monkeys have complex stomachs that enable them to derive the maximum nourishment from their limited diet of leaves. There are three types of colobus monkeys, grouped by color: black-and-white, red, and olive.

The best-known colobus monkey is the guereza, a strikingly handsome animal: black, with a thick white beard and long white hairs on its flanks and tail. When first born, guerezas are pure white all over; the dark fur grows later. The guereza has long been hunted for its fur, and until recently was in danger of extinction. It is now under protection.

Each troop of 9 to 13 guerezas is led by an adult male, which defends the troop's home territory by roaring loudly, especially at dawn and dusk. The roar, preceded by an explosive snort, lasts up to a minute and can be heard a mile away. Like all colobus monkeys, the guereza can make long leaps through the branches. Its fringe of white hairs functions rather like a parachute to brake its forward movement.

When two troops of guerezas meet they sit glaring at each other, clicking their tongues. The male leader of the troop holding the territory leaps about noisily, sometimes crashing down 20 feet or more through the branches. It then faces the intruding male, and the two monkeys nod their heads and shake branches at each other. The invading troop usually withdraws.

The red colobus monkey occupies the topmost levels of the forest, while the smaller olive colobus occupies the lower forest layer

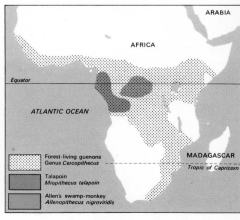

The distribution of guenons These three species are all guenons. The swamp-monkey and talapoin have the most restricted ranges, near the equator

The red colobus These two males belong to the rare Zanzibar race, which is sometimes regarded as a separate species, and now numbers only about 200 individuals. Like all colobus monkeys, the red colobus eats mainly leaves. Lacking thumbs, it grips the leaves between its fingers and palm

Red-tailed monkey One of the guenons, this small monkey has a white, heart-shaped spot on its nose

Owl-faced Hamlyn's monkey resembles an owl. The white stripe on its nose makes its eyes seem closer

Threat display The moustached monkey emphasizes its whiskers by jerking its head sideways

The talapoin This small monkey may be an evolutionary stage between the guenons and the mangabeys

during the day, climbing higher to sleep.

The guenons are widely distributed throughout the tropical forest. Their ranges may overlap, but different species tend to live at different levels of the forest. Guenons come in many colors: some have white whiskers and a dark red belly, others have light-colored patches of cheek hair, a bright spot of color on the nose, or stripes on the thighs.

One guenon, the redtail, lives in small family units in Uganda and the forests of the Congo. When food is plentiful these units join together to form troops of 40 to 50. The troops feed in the morning, split into small groups to rest at midday, and rejoin the large troop for a second feeding session in the afternoon. Redtails eat fruit, leaves, flowers, and insects.

Mangabeys are close relatives of baboons, but have shorter muzzles and longer tails. Like guenons they live mostly in trees.

The collared mangabey of western equatorial Africa lives in troops of 15 to 25 in the lower levels of the trees and on the ground. It eats fruits and nuts, rubbing them on branches to break the skin if it is too tough to bite through.

Instead of sitting on their hands and feet, as most other monkeys do, gray-cheeked mangabeys squat on their rumps, with their hands and feet bunched together in front.

Mandrills are forest monkeys, closely related to baboons and mangabeys. There are two species, the mandrill and the drill. Both species are strong and courageous fighters and their teeth are well adapted for fighting.

The mandrill lives mainly in the humid forests of the western coastal regions. In the male, the nose is bright red and the cheeks are blue. These colors are repeated in the red penis and blue scrotum and red and blue buttocks. The colors become more intense when the mandrill is excited, and serve as a threat display to rival males.

The drill is smaller and less colorful than the mandrill. It has olive-brown fur, a black face with a red chin and white facial fringe. Drills are found farther inland than mandrills, in drier forests.

Colorful male mandrill This species' bright facial colors are not shared by the females, which have duller faces and are only three-quarters the size

Young mandrill Infant mandrills usually cling to their mothers' abdomens. Found in the low-lying forests of West Africa, mandrills live in the shrubs and on the ground. Occasionally they supplement their vegetable diet with small animals they find by turning over stones and pieces of dead wood

Baby-sitting Mangabeys and guenons sometimes live together. Here a gray-cheeked mangabey holds a Wolf's mona as well as her own infant

The chimpanzee

The sociable chimpanzees are the primates that most nearly resemble man. They use a great variety of sounds and gestures to communicate with each other

The chimpanzee is an African ape found in a vast area of more than 1 million square miles straddling the equator. All chimpanzees belong to a single species. Some authorities subdivide this species into four races, the pygmy chimpanzees and three races of common chimpanzees.

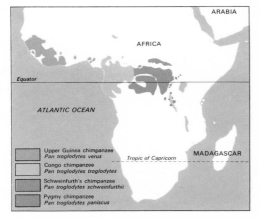

Where the races live Pygmy chimpanzees live only in forests south of the Congo River. Other chimpanzees live in savanna woodland and forest

The chimpanzee is the third largest ape, after the gorilla and the orang-utan. A large male may weigh 120 pounds—about one third of the weight of a gorilla—and stand five feet tall. It has no tail, and its extremely long arms give it a reach half again as wide as it is tall.

Chimpanzees are considered by many scientists to be the most intelligent animal next to man. In the earliest stages of development an infant chimpanzee matures at a rate equal to that of a human baby, and sometimes faster. The animals can distinguish most colors, and can make and use simple tools.

The chimpanzee has a good memory. Individual chimps have demonstrated in experiments that they remembered a person, or place, or how to operate a machine, years after their experience with the person, place, or machine.

In the rain forests, chimpanzees feed mainly by climbing trees to pick whatever ripe fruits are in season. When fruit is in short supply, they eat leaves. They also chew bark and pith for a few minutes and then spit them out.

In the savanna woodlands, where suitable vegetable food is less abundant, chimpanzees eat termites and kill and eat monkeys, pigs, and small antelopes. Forest chimpanzees seldom drink, and when they do it is by dipping a hand into water and then licking the drops of water off. They have also been seen to crush leaves into a "sponge" to soak up water for drinking.

Chimpanzees can travel equally well

Chimpanzees grooming At the top of the tree an adult male is being groomed by another mature male on its left and by an adolescent male on its right. Below sit other males, females, and young

along the ground or through the trees. On the ground they run on all fours, with their weight carried on their feet and on the backs of their curled fingers.

Up to 80 chimpanzees live together in a loosely organized community. The home range varies from about eight square miles, where food is abundant, to 30 square miles in savanna woodlands. Ranges often overlap, but animals from different groups intermingle without hostility. Mothers and young tend to remain together at the core of each community.

When food is extremely plentiful, a large group assembles for a feast. Adult males drum on the buttress roots of trees or on the ground and all the animals join in a loud hooting chorus. The noise, which can be heard up to two miles away, attracts other chimpanzees, and these join in. Small bands of males join together to forage when fruit is scarce. They shout in a similar way to call the infants and females together when they have found food.

A female chimpanzee becomes sexually receptive about one week in every five and mates with several males in turn. There appears to be little or no sexual rivalry over females between adult males in a troop. Social relationships are likely to exist throughout life between members of the same family, but close relatives rarely mate with each other.

Young chimpanzees generally stay with the mother until they are about six years old. Then the adolescents begin leaving the

Building a bed in the trees Every evening at dusk chimpanzees construct a sleeping nest. They stand on a platform of horizontal branches and bend supple, leafy branches into a framework. Then they roughly interweave the ends together, making a bed of leaves and twigs for themselves

mother for longer and longer periods. Young males soon join other adults, but females tend to retain a stronger association with the mother. Other associations, between foraging males or brothers and sisters, lead to "friendships" in which the partners may play together, or may groom each other on what appears to be a regular and reciprocal basis.

The chimpanzees within a group have a particular social status, although there is no true hierarchy like that in monkey troops. Rank among the males is established by dominance displays. The chimpanzees, with hair erect, sway rhythmically backward and forward, hooting loudly. Then they rush about wildly, grimacing, running up and downhill, pounding trees, waving branches, uprooting plants, or throwing rocks.

The male that makes the noisiest and most impressive display gains a degree of dominance, and the other members of the group crouch or bob in front of him, or make way when they meet him. Males of equal rank may groom each other, kiss, or hold hands. They rarely fight.

Facial expressions

Expression in repose   'Grin face'   'Play face'   Pout

Chimpanzees' mobile mouths produce a wide range of expressions. Without equating these expressions with human emotions, zoologists suggest the "grin face" is a reaction to threat, the "play face" with the upper teeth hidden an invitation to play, and the pout a sign of interest

Eating a baboon Although they usually eat fruit, chimpanzees occasionally kill an animal to obtain meat

Holding hands A frightened infant seeks a reassuring touch from its mother. Touching and grooming are an integral part of chimpanzees' lives

Hooting chorus The hoots of chimpanzees express excitement of various kinds

Using a tool Woodland chimpanzees catch termites by poking a trimmed twig or grass stem into a termite nest. When they pull this tool out, the termites are clinging to it (left)

The gorilla

The gorilla, largest of the primates, is usually quiet; the famous chest-beating display rarely presages an attack

Gorillas are the largest and heaviest living primates. A mature male weighs between 300 and 450 pounds, and stands up to six feet high when erect. The female weighs 150 to 250 pounds and lacks the ridge of bone and cartilage on top of the head that adds to the male's height. Differences between the three races of gorilla—the mountain race and two lowland races—are minor. All are black-skinned and black-haired.

Gorillas are the rarest of the anthropoid apes. There are only about 600 mountain gorillas left. The lowland races number in the thousands, but as a result of man's activities there are probably no more than 10,000 gorillas of all races left in Africa.

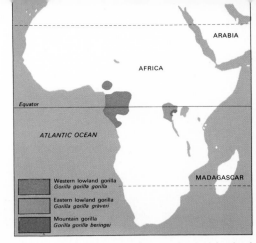

Gorillas' ranges Most live in pockets of lowland forest between the Congo and Niger rivers. The western lowland race is the most numerous

Relaxing in a tree Female gorillas often rest in trees, males rarely. In contrast to their more nimble young, adults climb cautiously because of their bulk

Groups led by gentle tyrants

Gorillas live in groups, with an average of 16 members and a maximum of about 30. Each group is led by a dominant male, at least ten years old. His silver-gray back indicates his maturity. The rest of the group consists of females with their infants and juveniles, and black-backed males which are not fully mature. Other silver-backed males may occasionally join the group.

The dominant male determines the route of the daily foraging expeditions. He stops feeding and stands motionless, legs apart, facing the way he wants to go. The others crowd around him, ready to move on when he does.

Each group keeps within a home range of about 15 square miles, wandering haphazardly through it. The home ranges of different groups overlap, and their members sometimes forage close together. The younger gorillas occasionally mingle, but the adults usually sit aloof. Some groups, however, are more friendly with each other—perhaps because of frequent past contact.

Gorillas are less overtly affectionate toward one another than other apes or monkeys. Occasionally, during a rest period, a female leans her head against the dominant male or a juvenile slides down his back. But the animals rarely groom each other. The dominant male is a tyrant, but a gentle one; if, for instance, one member of the group finds a sheltered spot during a rainstorm, the leader turns him out with a tap of the hand and takes his place.

The gorilla's gait Gorillas usually walk on all fours, their arms supported by the backs of their folded fingers. Occasionally they will move in an upright position but rarely for more than a couple of steps at a time

Gorillas are vegetarians; they eat leaves, shoots, ferns, roots, fibrous bark, and occasionally fruit. After picking their food, they shred it with their hands and teeth, keeping what they like and throwing the rest of the food away.

Tree-dwelling ancestors

Gorillas spend 90 percent of their time on the ground. The weight and massive build of the adults, especially the males, make them unsuited to life in trees. Young gorillas, however, often climb trees, and adult females sit on branches to rest or feed. These activities, and the gorillas' long arms, indicate that millions of years ago their ancestors lived in trees.

Gorillas sleep in nests, both at night and when they take a midday rest. In the lowlands, nests are mainly built in trees. In the mountains, where trees are smaller, most gorillas make ground nests.

The tree nests of gorillas, like those of

Lowland gorillas' nests Female and juvenile gorillas build their nests up to 60 feet from the ground in the treetops, but males sleep on the lower boughs of trees or on the ground

Mother and baby The infant gorilla, more helpless at birth than other apes, cannot cling to its mother's hair. She supports it for the first month with one or both arms

Endangered race Mountain gorillas are in grave danger of extinction

Foraging party Gorillas live on vegetation that is so juicy they have no need to drink

chimpanzees, consist of branches broken and bent inward to form a round, concave, springy mattress. Ground nests usually consist of a few handfuls of vegetation, roughly pressed together. The gorilla makes a new nest every night.

The dominant male

The dominant male builds his nest first, and the others follow suit. Younger animals normally sleep with their mothers, but sometimes they make little nests near them. In the morning gorillas often doze for an hour or two after dawn. But as soon as the dominant male sits up and becomes active, the other animals rouse themselves and cluster around him, awaiting his lead. He will start the troop off on the day's foraging expedition, indicating the direction they are to take by the way he faces. Gorillas soil their nests when they wake up, but the dung is firm and fibrous and does not stick to their bodies.

The leader reacts dramatically to intruders,

including other gorillas, with an elaborate and stereotyped ritual that includes an intimidating display of chest-beating. This display probably helps to strengthen his leadership of the group.

There is a close bond between infant gorillas and their mothers. The mother cuddles a baby gorilla, and it rides on her back from the age of three months. Only when the mother gives birth again—after three or four years—does the juvenile start to become independent of its parent.

Chest-beating
The dominant male gorilla's display against intruders is an intimidating performance. He hoots —slowly at first, then faster. Rising on his hind legs, he plucks vegetation and throws it in the air. The climax is a rapid beating of his chest, followed by a sideways run into the brush

Apart from their occasional noisy chest-beating displays and the short barks and screams that punctuate their infrequent quarrels, gorillas are quiet animals. Members of a group usually feed and sleep within a few yards of each other, so they have no need for the loud location-determining calls of the gibbons.

The gorilla's enemy

The only major predator on gorillas is man. Some African tribes kill the animals for food, or to protect their crops. Hunters capture young gorillas for zoos and laboratories, usually killing the mother in the process. There is only one reliable account of leopards preying on gorillas.

The gorilla faces two major threats to its survival: the inroads made into its habitat by agriculture, and the demand for apes by zoos and research scientists. The gorilla's slow breeding rate makes these threats all the more serious.

Small plant-eating mammals

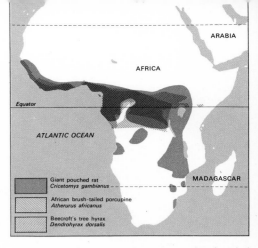

From dusk to dawn the African forest is alive with the noises of myriads of animals; one of the most startling is the tree hyrax's piercing scream

The tropical forest of Africa, with its unchanging climate, provides a year-round supply of plant food for numerous species of small mammals, which live and feed at different levels of the forest. There are climbers and gliders in the trees, and a great number of runners and leapers among the shrubs on the ground. Some of the climbers—the tree hyraxes and the scaly-tailed flying squirrels—are unique to the African forest.

Fruit-eating bats congregate in huge groups to feed on ripe, juicy fruit. Some of them live in caves, others in tall trees.

Rodents are common in the tropical forest. Some burrow; others make grass-lined nests. Some live in the trees. The sun squirrels are among the most interesting forest animals. Their unpatterned coats vary in color from area to area.

Small forest-dwellers The African brush-tailed porcupine is confined to areas near water in the dense forest. It shelters in burrows during the day, and forages in small parties at night for leaves, roots, and insects, its preferred foods

Squabbling bats gather by the thousands to fight for space and food in fruit trees

Many species of fruit-eating bats make their home in the tropical forest, feeding on figs and other soft fruits. The straw-colored fruit bat, one of the largest African bats, measures up to nine inches long and has a wingspan of 2½ feet. Their long, narrow wings enable these bats to fly long distances. Bats of this species live in forest and savanna and feed in gatherings of thousands; but for most of the day they live in groups of 4 to 50. They roost in tall trees, grooming themselves in the morning and sleeping in the early afternoon. Sometimes huge groups will be found roosting together. Groups of 10,000 are not uncommon.

In midafternoon they form compact groups of about 50, and at dusk all the groups fly to fruiting trees. Great gatherings of bats feed together, squabbling over fruit and perching places.

The Egyptian rousette bat, found in both forest and savanna, roosts mainly in caves. Even when undisturbed this bat is noisy and restless. It feeds on juicy fruit and flower nectar, carrying pollen from flower to flower. The females of some species of rousette bats form maternity colonies. The males are very protective toward their offspring, cradling them in their wings whenever the females allow them to approach. Single births are most common; twins are rare.

Straw-colored fruit bats mate in April and May and single offspring are born in February and March. They are carried about by their mother; while in flight, the young cling to a teat.

Colony in a cave Egyptian rousette bats roost in caves in both forest and savanna. Living in colonies, they feed on fruit at night, and rest and groom themselves during the day. They fight often over food and resting places, beating one another with their wings and grabbing with their thumbs

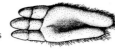

Padded soles The short, thick toes of Beecroft's tree hyrax have little grasping power, but its fleshy soles provide friction

Giant pouched rat Cramming fruit and seeds into its cheek pouches, the rat carries its store to its burrow. When its pouches are tightly packed, it must press them with its forepaws to unload them

Crested rat When threatened, the crested rat mimics skunks by erecting the mane of hair on its back. Although it cannot eject a foul-smelling liquid, it may fool predators

Screaming hyrax Noted for its nocturnal call, the hyrax starts croaking and ends with a high-pitched scream. It is arboreal, but usually descends from the trees to feed on the ground when it is dark

Numerous rodents make their home at different levels of the forest

Rats and mice are the most numerous ground-dwelling small mammals in the forest. Among them are the rufous-nosed rat, which lives in clearings and nests in tunnels just below the forest floor, and the shaggy-haired rat, which is apparently active both day and night. The shaggy-haired rat is semi-aquatic; it swims and dives when it is pursued. It does not burrow, but lives either in holes in riverbanks or in a grass-lined nest in a shallow depression dug out of the matted forest floor. Some ground-dwelling rodents have bristles or spines among their fur.

African striped squirrels live in trees but forage on the forest floor, while sun squirrels forage for fruit and nuts in the shrub layers. Both groups are most abundant in forest fringes where oil palms are common.

The scaly-tailed flying squirrels of the African tropical forest belong to a different family of rodents from the flying squirrels of Asia and North America. They are nocturnal. They feed on fruit, seeds, leaves, and insects, gliding from branch to branch on highly developed gliding membranes. This squirrel has sharp-pointed scales on the un-

derside of the base of its long tail. The scales give support as it climbs or rests on a limb of a tree.

Tree hyraxes have scent glands in the middle of the back, covered by a patch of white hair. When the animal is roused, the hairs stand erect, revealing the glands. Their function is unknown; they may be used in marking out territory.

Tree hyraxes are seldom seen, but when they awake at dusk to feed on leaves and twigs their long repetitive call rings through the forest.

East African dormouse This species feeds in the night on seeds, fruit, insects, and snakes' eggs

Balancing act The African climbing mouse nests on the forest floor, but climbs trees and grass stems in search of seeds. Its fine-scaled, almost hairless tail helps in gripping and balancing while it climbs

Antelopes, pigs, and the okapi

Large plant-eaters, such as the rare okapi, the giraffe's forest relative, browse mainly at night and rely on their acute hearing to warn them of danger

Relatively few species of hooved mammals are restricted only to the African tropical forests. These include several species of antelopes, the giant forest hog, and the okapi, a member of the giraffe family. Each species has features that are not usually shared by its grassland relatives and that help it survive in the forest. Most forest antelopes, for example, have especially sharp hearing and are either small or have smaller horns than

grassland species. Horns are set back against the shoulders to prevent them from becoming ensnared in thick vegetation. Most forest antelopes are solitary.

The African tropical forest is much less favorable for large grass-eating mammals than the savanna, where many antelopes live on grass. There is little grass in the forest, and antelopes browse mainly on the leaves and juicy twigs of the lower branches.

Among the other large plant-eaters in the forest are a few mammals, such as the forest buffalo, or bush cow, and the forest elephant, both of which are forest races of grassland animals. They are smaller than their grass-

land relatives and tend to live in small groups instead of large herds. Bull forest elephants stand about eight feet at the shoulder, compared with 13 feet for the bush elephants of the savanna. Elephants of the forest race have rounder ears and their tusks curve inward or forward instead of outward.

The largest group of forest antelopes are the duikers. There are about ten species. All are small, short-legged animals with stubby, backward-facing horns, which are generally hidden by tufts of long hair. When alarmed, duikers run with outstretched necks and arched backs, then quickly dive into the undergrowth for cover.

Forest antelopes are smaller than their grassland relatives

Wary antelope Duikers are small, alert antelopes that dive for cover into the undergrowth when

alarmed—hence their name, which means "diver" in Afrikaans. All the species are similar in form

Most duikers have an unpatterned red or gray-brown coat, but the zebra duiker, or striped-back duiker, has a bright orange coat with darker stripes; and the yellow-backed duiker has a yellow crest along the ridge of its red-brown back. The crest is erected in times of stress.

The bongo is somewhat similar to the bushbuck in its habits and appearance, although it is more closely related to the elands of the grasslands. Its bright chestnut color is broken by white stripes on the flanks and white blotches on the head and legs. The underside is black and there is a hairy black stripe down the spine. Both sexes have large ears and spiral horns with buff or yellow tips. Unlike most other forest antelopes, bongos feed by day as well as night.

The royal or pygmy antelope is the smallest hooved animal in the world—not much bigger than a rabbit. An adult measures about 11 inches high at the shoulder. The males have tiny, spiked horns less than an inch long, and both sexes are red-brown with white underparts and tail-ruffs. They live in the thick forests of West Africa, feed only at night, and are rarely seen.

Waiting for night The bushbuck (right) rests during the day, emerging at night to feed. When the male moves through dense growth, it holds its horns back so they do not become entangled

Zebra duiker The stripes on the back and light countershading on the underside of this duiker (above) blend with the light and shade of the forest foliage, providing camouflage **for** the animal

Red river hog Often living near water, this pig is a good swimmer. It digs with its snout

Water chevrotain Belonging to a small family of primitive cud-chewing mammals, it resembles the unrelated royal antelope. It is only three feet long and has a small head with a pointed snout

Giant forest hogs In this family group the male is the one with large warts beneath its eyes

The red river hog uses its snout to put a roof over its den

Two species of pigs range throughout the tropical forests of Africa. The red river hog gets its name partly from the red hair of the male and partly from the fact that it is commonly found near water. Males also have a white crest along the spine and white markings on the face. The young are dark with light-colored stripes. Red river hogs, also known as bush pigs, have long, pointed ears with streamers of hairs on the tips. Their two sets of tusks both point downward, and the upper set wears against the lower. Red river hogs live in other types of country, too. In dense forest, they force tunnels through the undergrowth and push up the matted vegetation to make roofs over their dens. They live in groups of up to 20, emerging at night to dig with their snouts for the roots on which they feed. Old boars often live alone, but occasionally they will travel with a young male. The bush pig causes great damage to crops by rooting.

The giant forest hog grows up to five feet long and may weigh 600 pounds. Its body is covered with long, coarse, dark hair, which becomes scantier with age. It seldom digs, and feeds mainly on leaves and tall grass, although it will eat small mammals and birds. Giant forest hogs travel in groups (called sounders) of up to 20 individuals.

The timid okapi, the giraffe's forest relative, was unknown to Europeans until 1900

The okapi lives so deep in the Congo forest that it was not discovered by Europeans until about 1900. It varies in color from deep red or chestnut, to purplish maroon, to almost black, with white stripes on the legs; white shins and face markings complete its camouflage. An extremely timid animal with large ears, the okapi relies mostly on its sense of hearing to detect danger. Bony, skin-covered knobs, much more prominent in males than in females, grow from the top of the skull. Like the giraffe, it has an extremely long tongue that it uses to strip leaves and twigs from trees and shrubs. The tongue is so long the okapi can clean its eyes with it. It feeds on fruit and seeds as well as leaves.

Okapis use smell and hearing to find a mate. The female smells most strongly when in rut and gives a special trumpeting call to enable a male to find her. On meeting, they circle each other before they eventually approach and lick each other's face. Then each raises its head and exposes a white throat patch; mating follows.

Mother and calf Only five feet tall, an adult okapi can reach high foliage by craning its long neck and using its long tongue to grasp branches and strip the leaves from a tree

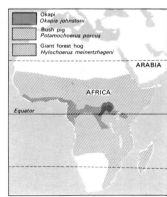

Okapi
Okapia johnstoni

Bush pig
Potamochoerus porcus

Giant forest hog
Hylochoerus meinertzhageni

ARABIA

AFRICA

Equator

Widespread grazers The okapi is restricted to the eastern Congo, while the forest pigs have wide distributions throughout Africa

Small predatory mammals

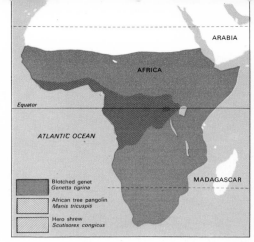

Typical predators of the African tropical forest are the long-snouted genet and the sluggish but stealthy potto— neither any bigger than a domestic cat

The only large flesh-eating mammal in the African tropical forest is the leopard, the same adaptable species that is also found in the bush country of Africa and the forests of southern Asia. Most of the other predators are small and feed on invertebrates.

Since much of their prey inhabits the treetops, many predatory mammals in this biome have become adapted to life in the trees. Even animals which are primarily ground-living are often able to climb trees, and some of them are agile and light enough to hunt in the highest canopy. Most of the small predators live in dense cover and are rarely seen because they hunt only at night.

Confined hero shrews While the blotched genet occurs in both the savanna and the tropical forest, the hero shrew is found only in a small area

Genets, civets, and shrews hunt in the trees and below

Alert for predators The four-toed elephant shrew reacts to the slightest sign of danger by drumming its powerful hind legs on the ground and then rapidly bounding away along its runways

African tree pangolin When alarmed, it curls into a tight ball, protected by its overlapping scales. It defends itself against predators by squirting a foul-smelling liquid from its anal glands

Puzzle of a shrew's backbone

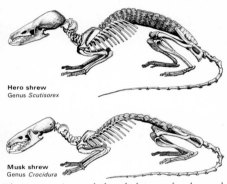

Hero shrew
Genus *Scutisorex*

Musk shrew
Genus *Crocidura*

The comparison of the skeleton of a hero shrew with that of a musk shrew shows the unique, and extraordinarily strong, girderlike backbone of the hero shrew. The reason for this interwoven construction is not known, but, despite the backbone's thickness, hero shrews are able to bend their backs at least as easily as other mammals

The dominant group of small carnivores in the tropical forests of Africa are members of the civet family—civets, genets, mongooses, and the African linsang. Many species of insect-eating shrews live on the forest floor.

Genets are spotted animals, with long snouts and tails, short legs, and round ears. These agile climbers hunt at night, both in the trees and on the ground, for insects, birds, and mice. During the day they rest in hollow trees or in abandoned burrows.

The large African civet eats a wide range of animal and vegetable food. African civets are highly adaptable animals which live in savanna as well as forest. Like other civets, they mark their territories with a strong-smelling secretion from their anal glands.

Mongooses are more typically grassland-dwellers, but there are a few forest species, such as the kusimanse.

The kusimanse is a gregarious animal, traveling in bands of 10 to 24 individuals. The band forages over a small area and then moves on, seldom staying longer than 48 hours in one spot. They have no permanent home, but den up wherever they find a convenient hole, or a burrow abandoned by another animal. The kusimanse makes a chattering noise as it runs about, and occasionally gives a twittering call, like a bird. It eats fruit and insects, and digs larvae out of the soil. The kusimanse is said to hurl eggs and snails against rocks with its front legs, in order to crack the shells.

African linsang This linsang is a nocturnal animal, resting by day in a nest built high in a tree and hunting at night. It preys on birds, small mammals, and insects. Its diet is not totally made up of animals, for it also seeks vegetable food, such as nuts and fruit. It has smaller spots than Asian linsangs

Sluggish pottos and lively bush-babies are good climbers

Pottos and bush-babies, or galagos, are forest predators which feed at night on insects, birds, and fruit. They are small primates belonging to the same group as the lorises of southern Asia. All members of this family have hands which are well adapted for gripping, with opposable thumbs and fingers which splay out and mold themselves to the shape of any twig.

One unusual feature of the potto is a row of visible bumps formed by bony spines projecting from vertebrae in the shoulder. Because pottos are known to groom each other in the neck region with their teeth, it is believed that the spines are sensitive points of contact. One potto often approaches another with its head bent low. From this position it is ready either to give the other potto a friendly neck rub or, if it is feeling aggressive, to raise its head quickly and slash the other potto with its teeth.

The slender angwantibo, or golden potto, is a more agile climber than the potto. The angwantibo weighs about ten ounces, compared with up to three pounds for the potto. It eats mainly insects, whereas the potto is omnivorous.

Bush-babies, long-tailed animals which leap about the branches on powerful hind legs, live in nearly all wooded areas in Africa south of the Sahara. There are six species. The biggest, the thick-tailed bush-baby, weighs only about two pounds. Most species range in color from silver gray to brown. Bush-babies frequently wriggle their large,

almost hairless ears, each of which can be bent independently back, forward, or down almost to the base. All species have flat disks on the ends of their digits to help them climb trees and keep a grip on slippery surfaces. Bush-babies are gregarious; several may sleep together in an old bird's nest. At night, however, when they are active, they forage alone or in pairs. If disturbed during the day, their sleeping time, bush-babies move slowly. But at night they are extremely agile. They can easily leap 13 feet from one branch to another. They hop on their hind legs like a kangaroo when they move on level ground. The bush-baby's favorite food is grasshoppers, but it also eats small birds, fruit, eggs, seeds, and flowers. Bush-babies have the strange habit of constantly licking the soles of the feet and the palms of the hands as they move among the trees.

The smallest species, the 2½-ounce Demidoff's bush-baby, lives among tangled twigs and tendrils. In mature forest it is largely restricted to the canopy and the lianas, but in secondary growth it lives lower down. Demidoff's bush-babies may sleep in groups of up to five in a leaf nest. This species establishes territories.

Bush-babies communicate partly by means of scent markings. Most also make loud calls which are repeated by other bush-babies and echo through the forest. They have a chittering "reunion" call, which they make when they settle into their nests in the morning to sleep.

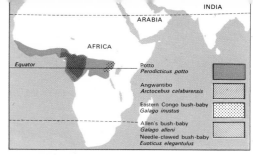

Overlapping ranges Allen's bush-baby and the needle-clawed bush-baby have identical ranges. The potto has a wide range in West Africa

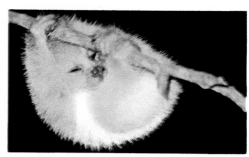

Waiting for its mother A baby potto clings to a branch where its mother has left it while she forages. Angwantibos also "park" their young

Demidoff's bush-babies At the start of the mating season, the female constructs a nest of leaves in a tree. The young are born and reared in the nest. When they leave, several adults may move in

Cautious climber The potto moves slowly, detaching one hand or foot at a time. The index fingers are reduced to stumps and lie along the axis of a branch. When stalking an insect or bird, the potto seems to ooze along a branch, placing each foot so gently that its victim never senses its presence

Needle-clawed bush-babies Living high in the trees, they have broadly padded toes and ridged, sharp-pointed nails on their digits for gripping

A multitude of birds

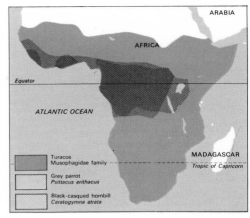

In the dim, green twilight of the tropical forest most birds are inconspicuous— even species that are brilliantly colored when seen in brighter light

About 400 species of birds live in the African forests, but the number of individuals is relatively low. This is in sharp contrast to the savanna, for example, where there are fewer species but birds of some species are very numerous. Single-species flocks are uncommon in the forest. Most birds travel singly, in pairs, or in mixed-species flocks called bird armies.

The great majority of birds in the African rain forests are small, possibly because it would be difficult for a large bird to fly among the dense vegetation. Small birds can make short flights from branch to branch, but large birds need space to get airborne, and their greater wingspan restricts them to cleared areas.

The only levels at which large birds can live are in the treetops or on the ground.

Widespread turaco The turaco family consists of about 18 species of birds that are found throughout Africa south of the Sahara Desert

Large birds fly over the canopy or stay on the floor

A number of hornbills, hawks, and parrots find food in the forest canopy and fly freely above the trees. A smaller group of fairly large birds, such as the bare-headed rock fowl, a few kinds of guinea fowl, and the rare African peacock, have largely given up flight, and remain on the forest floor.

Hornbills have large, often grotesque bills, which in the males are often ornamented by enormous but lightweight casques, or helmet-shaped growths, which seem to protect the bills. The three-foot-long black-casqued hornbill is one of the largest species. Hornbills mate for life. At some point during the breeding season the male seals up the entrance to the nest (a hole in a tree) with mud, until only the tip of the female's bill protrudes. The male brings food to the female, who apparently passes it on to the chicks when they are born. Not until the chicks are half-grown does the female emerge. Either parent cracks open the mud plug so the female can get out.

The bat hawk wheels over the trees at dusk, chasing bats as they emerge from their roosts to feed. Its large eyes give it keen sight in the dim light, and it can trap bats readily on the wing.

Sealed off and fed

The hornbill's nest is built high off the ground within a tree. After mating, the male seals the entrance with mud. Only a small hole is left for the male to pass food through. Some species have a long incubation and the female remains captive for months. During this time, the female grows a new plumage

Black-casqued hornbill *Ceratogymna atrata*

Fruit-eaters Hornbills are primarily birds of the dense forest. Their strong bills help them cut through thick foliage to get at fruit, and the horny casques apparently serve a protective function

Great blue turaco Its colors are brilliant in sunlight, but deeper in the forest it is less conspicuous

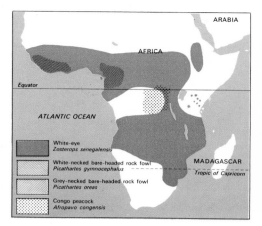

Wide-ranging white-eyes There are four African mainland species of white-eyes in the genus *Zosterops*. One lives up to 10,000 feet high

Hanging nest All white-eyes, which range from Africa to New Zealand, build similar nests. These are suspended from a slender, forked branch

Sunbirds About 60 species of sunbirds live in Africa, Asia, and Australia. Like hummingbirds, they feed on nectar while flying, but they also perch

The bare-headed rock fowl lives in lowland forests, building mud nests beneath overhanging rocks and feeding on insects, crustaceans, and frogs.

Bird armies, made up of dozens of birds of many species, are typical of the tropical forest. They move slowly through the forest, each species seeking its particular food, some on the ground, some in the trees, and others taking insects in flight. One advantage of the bird army is that each bird contributes to a large-scale disturbance of the vegetation. This flushes out many insects which would otherwise be very difficult to find. Driver ant columns disturb even more insects, and bird armies move with them. As the ants search for prey, the more active insects move out—

and many are eaten by the waiting birds.

African forest birds in turn are a source of food for many predators, particularly in the nesting season. Snakes, squirrels, and monkeys all feed on eggs and nestlings, and many birds have evolved means to combat this menace. One of the weaverbirds, the red-vented malimbe, weaves strips of leaves into spherical nests a few inches in diameter. Hanging from the nest is a delicately built entrance tube, up to two feet long and four inches wide, made of the sheathing of palm fruit. The tube is strong enough to support the small weaverbird, but if a snake tried to enter the nest, the tube would probably break away, carrying the predator to the ground far below.

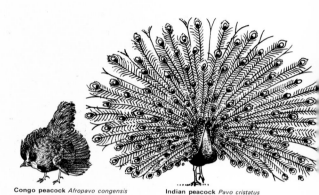

Congo peacock *Afropavo congensis*   Indian peacock *Pavo cristatus*

Different displays The Congo peacock, lacking a train, displays its wings as well as its tail

Birds of the forest floor Crested guinea fowl live in dense cover in eastern and southern Africa. They seldom fly, but run on their exceptionally strong legs. Small parties of guinea fowl travel together, scratching in the leaf litter for their food, which includes white ants, mollusks, and bulbs

Reptiles and amphibians

The gargoyle-like chameleons are the sharpshooters of the animal world; they can hit prey their body's length away with their flicking tongues

Equable temperatures create ideal conditions for many cold-blooded animals in Africa's tropical forests, and the high humidity favors others. Many species are found nowhere else. These include burrowing pythons, tree-living vipers, and the only snakes that subsist entirely on birds' eggs. Climbing snakes, lizards, and frogs abound, though there are fewer families of frogs and toads than are found in the Asian or South American forests.

The humus of the forest floor is almost as full of life as the trees; many types of lizards and snakes burrow there, and toads, tortoises, giant vipers, and other reptiles and amphibians are found on the surface in great numbers.

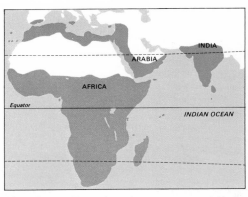

Chameleons True chameleons are essentially an Old World family, and are common in Africa. A great many species are found in Madagascar. Only 3 of the 85 species live north of the Sahara Desert

Tree-climbing lizards can change color in an instant

Visual displays Because sight is important to tree-dwelling chameleons, many have evolved display features. Jackson's chameleon has several horns. Some other species have either crests or dewlaps

Chameleons are among the best adapted of all lizards to life in trees, and fill the same niche as the tree-dwelling agamid lizards of southern Asia and the iguanids of the New World. About 12 species of stump-tailed chameleons live on the ground. All other members of the chameleon family have grasping feet and prehensile tails that help them climb.

The color changes of chameleons are governed by several factors, including the intensity of light reaching the animal, temperature variation, and the animal's behavioral state. A chameleon that is aroused will become darker in color, in a complex process governed by the expansion or contraction of color cells which contain pigment granules. As the granules react to various stimuli, different colors become predominant.

Besides their long, prehensile tongues, all chameleons have eyes that can work independently and move in all directions. Their keen sight and range of vision give them a tremendous advantage in catching insect prey.

The Ituri chameleon changes from a mottled green to brown, to black, under stimuli, and the three-horned chameleon of the Congo forest, starting from the same mottled green, adds white, yellow, and a light red-brown to this color range.

Most chameleons eat insects; but some large species may prey on small mammals.

Tongue for hunting Chameleons capture prey with their long, sticky tongues. The flap-necked chameleon's tongue darts out and retracts with a captured insect enclosed within the hollow tip. The chameleon can scan a wide field of view, because its eyes can swivel through 180 degrees. Its binocular vision gives it precise aim

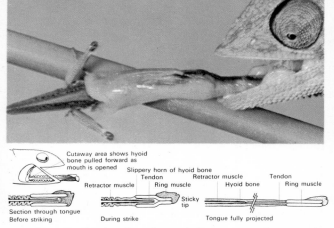

Cutaway area shows hyoid bone pulled forward as mouth is opened

Slippery horn of hyoid bone

Retractor muscle — Tendon — Retractor muscle — Tendon — Ring muscle

Retractor muscle — Ring muscle — Hyoid bone — Ring muscle

Sticky tip

Section through tongue
Before striking — During strike — Tongue fully projected

Muscular control The chameleon's hollow tongue fits over the hyoid bone like a wrinkled sleeve. A sudden contraction of circular muscles rapidly projects the tongue from the mouth and the sticky tip traps the prey. Central longitudinal muscles retract the tongue

Some snakes burrow, others coil around branches

The three-foot-long burrowing python is the smallest python and is found only in Africa. It has the small, compact head of the typical burrowing snake, and when threatened it curls itself into a ball.

The green tree viper grows to a length of 24 inches and preys on leaf frogs and small mammals. It remains motionless when threatened, its colors camouflaging it among the leafy branches. Its prehensile tail enables it to balance on a branch by coiling in alternate loops on each side of its resting place.

Although fat, placid, and weighing as much as 20 pounds at its greatest length of six feet, the Gaboon viper is one of the deadliest snakes of the forest floor. Its highly potent venom paralyzes prey, and can be fatal to man. The remarkable body patterns of the Gaboon viper make it almost invisible as it lies on the ground waiting for prey. Some species have a pair of blunt horns on the snout.

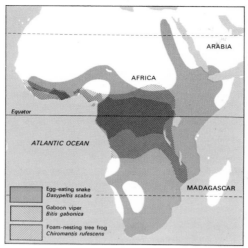

Egg-eating snake
Dasypeltis scabra

Gaboon viper
Bitis gabonica

Foam-nesting tree frog
Chiromantis rufescens

Forest snakes The egg-eating snake is found in the African tropical forest and savanna. The green tree viper and Gaboon viper inhabit the forest

Swallowing an egg

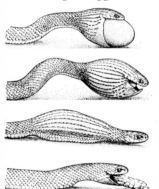

The egg-eating snake, living solely on eggs, has lost almost all its teeth. Its mouth opens to four times its body circumference and engulfs the egg, which is broken in the snake's gullet

Camouflaged in the leaves The Gaboon viper, whose fangs can reach 1½ inches, is the largest of all true vipers and one of the deadliest. It bears live young—often more than 50 at a time. Its markings help camouflage it among the leaves on the forest floor, allowing the snake to wait in ambush for its prey

The bird snake This treetop predator has the elongated snout that is common to many tree-dwelling snakes. Its diet consists of birds and chameleons, such as the flap-necked species that is being devoured here

Tiny frogs that live among the leaves and froth up their own sticky foam nests

Some of the world's smallest frogs—species belonging to the genus *Hyperolius*, which are less than one inch long—live in the Cameroon and Congo forests. These frogs are brightly colored animals.

Many of these frogs, which are often referred to as tree frogs, could be described better as leaf frogs, for they have suction pads on the toes and fingers which give a firm grip on the smooth surfaces of leaves. "Tree frog" generally refers to frogs of the genus *Hyla*, none of which live in Africa.

The foam-nesting leaf frog grips twigs and branches with pairs of opposable fingers as well as suction pads. Like many species of *Hyperolius*, these frogs lay as many as 150 eggs in foam nests that they whip up out of egg jelly on branches overhanging water.

Among the most brightly patterned of the forest frogs are those of the genus *Cardioglossa*, which live on the forest floor and are seldom more than one inch long.

Frothy nest A female and two male foam-nesting leaf frogs beat the egg jelly into a foam with their hind legs. The outer surface hardens into a crust that softens when the tadpoles are born

Suction pads Leaf frogs, such as *Hyperolius marmoratus*, are adapted to living in the trees. They are able to grip leaves with the suction pads at the ends of their fingers and toes

211

Animals in isolation

**In their island isolation descendants of
animals marooned on Madagascar millions
of years ago have "radiated,"
forming new species in new habitats**

Madagascar, part of the Malagasy Republic, is an island more than twice the size of Great Britain, lying 250 miles off the east coast of Africa, from which it is believed to have separated about 200 million years ago.

The island consists of a central plateau, rising from 2000 feet to peaks of more than 9000 feet and surrounded by a strip of coastal lowland. Moisture-laden winds blowing across the Indian Ocean bring heavy rain to the east coast; the western side of the island is drier. As a result, Madagascar has a wide range of life zones, including tropical rain forest, deciduous forest, grassland,

mountains, and some areas of semidesert.

Its long years of isolation have given Madagascar unique animal and plant populations. All vertebrate animals found there today, apart from species brought by man, are descended from a few species which flew or drifted there on logs or other natural rafts. Estimated arrival times for mammals range from 30 million years ago for civets to 60 million years ago for tenrecs.

In the absence of competition, this limited immigrant stock developed into specialized forms that spread into the island's varied habitats. Madagascar is the sole home of more than 70 species of land mammals, several species of bats, 125 species of birds, and numerous amphibian and reptile species.

The island's mammals include all the world's lemurs and the entire Tenrecidae

family of insectivores. Carnivores are represented there by 12 species of civets and mongooses.

Apart from a shrew, *Suncus madagascariensis*, which is a recent immigrant, the remaining land mammals unique to the island are the 15 species of rodents known as Malagasy rats.

Madagascar's bird population includes three families not represented elsewhere: mesites, small, virtually flightless birds; vangas, shrikelike insect-eaters; and asitys, or false sunbirds.

In addition to living birds, Madagascar was until the Middle Ages the home of the now extinct elephant bird, the largest bird ever known. Built like an ostrich, the elephant bird was over ten feet tall and weighed nearly half a ton.

Mammals that resemble those of other lands: tenrecs, Malagasy rats, and mongooses

Madagascar's insect-eating tenrecs have come, by convergent evolution, to look and behave remarkably like insectivores in other parts of the world, though they are not closely related to them.

Spiny tenrecs resemble hedgehogs in appearance, diet, nocturnal habits, and their ability to roll into a ball. Long-tailed tenrecs, of which there are several species, look like shrews. The web-footed tenrec even parallels the water shrew in its aquatic life. Rice tenrecs resemble moles, and live under-

ground. The island's rodents also show similar convergence with forms elsewhere. Different species of Malagasy rats resemble wood mice, house mice, voles, and rats. One even looks like a rabbit.

Among the carnivores are nine species of mongooses. There is also the Madagascar civet, or fanaloka, a cat-size nocturnal hunter. Its scientific name is *Fossa fossa*, but it is very different from its relative *Cryptoprocta ferox,* a much larger, catlike predator whose common name is the fossa.

Spine language Streaked tenrecs are active in the day and night, foraging in groups of about ten. They keep in touch by sounds made by vibrating spines

Forest hunter The Madagascar ring-tailed mongoose hunts in the forest by day for birds, small mammals, lizards, and insects

Prolific tenrec The common tenrec produces more young in a litter than any other mammal in the world. A family of 16 has been sighted and females can have litters of up to 24. Common tenrecs, about the size of a rabbit, have bristly coats. They are nocturnal, and are suspected of finding their way by a primitive form of echo-location, based on sounds produced by rapid tongue clicking

The island's birds

There are 184 species of birds in Madagascar, and 125 of them are found nowhere else. Among small perching birds, the proportion of species unique to the island is much higher: 63 out of 68 species. Most Madagascan birds are descended from African stock, but because they evolved so long in isolation they are now very different from the original immigrants.

Many species have become adapted to carnivorous diets, feeding on insects, lizards, and rodents. Madagascar has few fruit- or seed-eaters, though fruits and seeds abound. Many species occupy a wider range of habitats than do similar birds in Africa, where perhaps because there are more species, birds have become more specialized. The limited number of bird species that have colonized Madagascar are spread thin over the island.

An agricultural pest The seed-eating Madagascar fody bird does serious damage to crops. Dense flocks of these birds descend on rice fields and eat the unripe grain. They are related to the African weavers

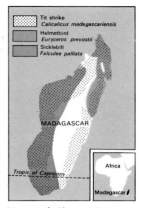

Vanga shrikes These related birds are adapted to different habitats

Among Madagascar's reptiles are both giant and dwarf species

Chameleons are Madagascar's most successful reptiles—about half of the world's 85 species live there. They range from the two-foot-long giant chameleon *Chamaeleo oustaleti* to the dwarf chameleon *Brookesia minima,* which is 1½ inches long and may be the world's smallest reptile.

Geckos are also well represented in Madagascar. About 50 species of these lizards live on the island, including many of the brightly colored diurnal species.

Only three genera of iguanid lizards are found outside the Americas. Two of these, with about seven species, live in Madagascar.

Madagascar's snakes include three species of boas, related to the American boas but without near relatives in Africa except for the sand boas of North Africa.

Iguanas and boas were probably once worldwide groups which reached Madagascar from Africa but were later supplanted on the mainland by the more successful agamid lizards and pythons.

Largest chameleon Madagascar's two-foot-long giant chameleon is feared by the island people because of its fierce appearance. Actually, it eats only insects, small birds, and rodents. It catches these by stunning them with its long tongue that it shoots from its mouth at whiplash speed

The common gecko This is one of several species of Madagascan geckos. It is active in the day, and has bright coloration. Most other geckos are nocturnal and somewhat drably colored

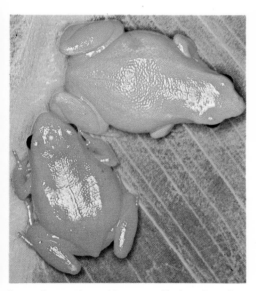

Forest frogs The golden mantella has short legs and a small, broad body. These features are not typical of its family, which also includes the common frogs of Europe and the Americas

Lemurs of the Malagasy forest

For 50 million years lemurs have been isolated on monkeyless Madagascar. They have flourished, while their ancestors in other countries are now extinct

Lemurs are tree-dwelling animals distantly related to monkeys, apes, and man. True lemurs are found only in Madagascar, but their nearest relatives, the bush-babies and pottos of Africa, and the lorises of Southeast Asia, are sometimes referred to as lemurs. All of these animals are classed as lower primates, or prosimians. Man, monkeys, and apes belong to the group known as higher primates.

Most species of lemurs have soft, thick, woolly coats, sometimes patterned with stripes or patches of contrasting color. A lemur at rest often wraps its long, thick tail around itself or another lemur. Some species estivate, or become dormant, during the hottest part of summer, living on the fat that they have stored up in the rump and the base of the tail.

Some species of lemurs are active by day, others by night. Most, particularly the diurnal species, live in family groups or troops of up to two dozen animals.

The nocturnal species tend to be widely distributed throughout wooded areas in Madagascar. Generally, different species do not compete for food, even when their ranges overlap.

Several types of lemurs have become extinct in the last 2000 years, since the arrival of man in Madagascar. One of these climbed like an orang-utan, and another ran on the ground like a baboon. The biggest was the size of a chimpanzee.

Ring-tailed lemurs and sifakas forage by day in troops

There are three families of lemurs—the Lemuridae, the Indriidae, and the Daubentoniidae—containing about 20 species. This variety has arisen from a limited ancestral stock which developed to fill different habitats in Madagascar after reaching the island from Africa 50 million years ago, possibly on driftwood "rafts."

The ancestors of lemurs roamed Africa, Europe, and North America until the time when monkeys evolved and apparently drove lemurs to extinction. But, isolated and free from competition in Madagascar, lemurs flourished to fill the niches occupied by other types of mammals elsewhere.

Lemurs range in size from the mouse lemurs, which are little bigger than mice, to the three-foot-long indri. They live mostly on fruit and leaves, especially those of the tamarind tree.

Unlike monkeys, lemurs become sexually active only once a year. In the case of ring-tailed lemurs, a cat-size species from southwest and west Madagascar, the breeding season is one of the shortest known in mammals. It lasts for about two weeks each year. Each female is receptive to the males for less than a day during this period.

Before the mating season the males of this species work up to a frenzy of aggression, which is expressed in quarrels, chases, and stink fights. In a stink fight, one male threatens another by marking his tail with scent and waving it at his rival. The other male may do the same, or scent-mark a twig and wave it about.

These formal tournaments end when the females come into heat. Then the males fight for females, slashing at one another with their long canine teeth. The males that emerge victorious mate with the females.

Sifakas are large lemurs—about 3½ feet long including the tail—of the Indriidae family. They are usually more docile than ring-tailed lemurs. Within the troop they seldom quarrel except over access to infants. But they fight ritualized battles with members of other troops to defend their territory, which may cover three acres for a troop of five.

Grooming is the social cement of the lemur troop. The members spend much time scraping and combing through one another's fur with specialized dental combs. These consist of all the lemur's lower front teeth, which are flattened and parallel like the teeth of a comb. Lemurs keep the dental comb clean with a kind of built-in toothbrush. This is a fringed structure under the tongue, called a sublingua, which the lemur pushes forward to clear the fur from its teeth.

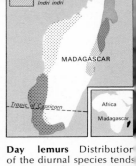

	Ring-tailed lemur *Lemur catta*
	Ruffed lemur *Varecia variegatus*
	Great white sifaka *Propithecus verreauxi*
	Indri *Indri indri*

MADAGASCAR

Tropic of Capricorn

Africa
Madagascar

Day lemurs Distribution of the diurnal species tends to be localized. Few are found in the central plateau

Ring-tailed lemur
Lemur catta

Hand

Scent glands

Grooming claw

Foot

Searching for food Ring-tailed lemurs forage on the ground in the morning and evening. In the mating season a male puts scent from its wrist glands on its tail, then flicks the tail over its head, pointing at another male and spreading the scent. The second toe on each foot has a claw

Ruffed lemur This species, which also has black and red forms, has a tail as long as its body. Ruffed lemurs live in small groups in a confined area within the eastern coastal rain forest

Largest lemur Measuring three feet from head to rump, the indri is not only the largest lemur, but is also the only species without a tail. As its habitat diminishes, it is becoming extremely rare

White sifaka An infant great white sifaka clings to its mother's back. It can travel on its own at six weeks, but remains near its mother for another five months. Sifakas are fully grown at 21 months

Small lemurs that are active at night and store food in their tails

Most of the smaller lemur species are active at night. Mouse lemurs spend the day in nests of leaves hidden in trees. They are social animals—up to 15 have been found in a nest. At the approach of the dry season, when food becomes scarce, dwarf lemurs, which are also called mouse lemurs, eat insects and vegetation voraciously. Extra food is stored in the tail, which becomes club-shaped. The lemurs then go to their nests and stay there, living on the food reserve, until the rains come. This form of estivation is comparable to the hibernation of dormice in more temperate zones.

Strangest of all the lemurs is the aye-aye, which belongs to a family of its own—the Daubentoniidae. Aye-ayes are as big as cats and have huge, batlike ears, rodentlike front teeth, and long, thin third fingers. They listen intently for wood-boring larvae in an old branch, sometimes tapping on the wood in much the same way a woodpecker pecks at a tree. This tapping may help the aye-aye locate the larvae inside. When it finds the larvae the aye-aye pokes into the wood with its long third finger.

Aye-aye's probing finger The skinny third finger is used to catch wood-boring larvae. This finger, longer and thinner than the others, can probe into tunnels where the larvae live and extract them

A tail that stores fat Dwarf lemurs are the only primates that become torpid. The fat-tailed dwarf lemur has a thick base to its tail, where it stores fat that serves as food during its long sleep in the dry season of July and August. It is a solitary, nocturnal animal

Aye-aye
Daubentonia madagascariensis
Red mouse lemur
Microcebus rufus
Greater dwarf lemur
Cheirogaleus major
Grey mouse lemur
Microcebus murinus
Fat-tailed dwarf lemur
Cheirogaleus medius

MADAGASCAR

Tropic of Capricorn

Africa
Madagascar

Night lemurs Dwarf and mouse lemurs each have a species adapted to the wet east and dry west

The rare aye-aye This is one of the world's rarest mammals. Once aye-ayes were found throughout the Madagascan forests. Now no more than 50 are left, and these are restricted to the northern coasts

Insect-eating mammals

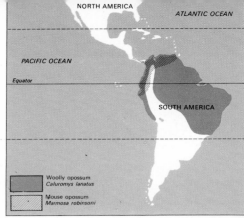

Abundant insects in South American forests provide food for a wide variety of mammals, from toothless anteaters to bats that navigate by echoes

Some mammals of the South American forests feed exclusively on the teeming insect life there. Anteaters and many bats rely entirely on insects for food; most opossums eat fruit as well as a great variety of insects.

The opossums of the New World belong to a different family from the phalangers of Australia, some of which are called possums. Both groups are marsupials—they give birth when their young are at a very early stage of development, and the young continue their development attached to the mother's nipples, generally in a pouch.

Opossums These marsupials are widespread. About 40 species of mouse opossums are found from northern Mexico to Argentina. Woolly species spend more time in trees than other opossums

Tree-climbing opossums and long-tongued anteaters

Eight babies Azara's opossum bears up to eight young. Here, the teats in the mother's pouch have been exposed to show how the young complete their development attached to them

Carrying the young The woolly opossum has a small pouch, so the young are carried on the mother's back when they are old enough to cling

Woolly opossums are more vegetarian than other opossums, eating fruit, seeds, and soft vegetables as well as insects. They are active mainly at night. The pouch of the woolly opossum is little more than a flap of skin, and the young are almost entirely exposed.

Anteaters and armadillos belong to the Edentata (toothless) order of mammals. Edentates, found only in the New World, lack incisor and canine teeth, and the anteaters have no teeth at all. They feed entirely on ants and termites, breaking open their nests with powerful front claws and licking up the insects with long, thin tongues. Forest anteaters are primarily tree-dwellers. The pygmy anteater, which is only about six inches long, stands and fights if attacked, propping itself on its hind feet and tail and lashing out at its attacker with the sharp claws on its forefeet.

Most armadillos live in open country in the savannas and pampas, but the nine-banded armadillo and the giant armadillo are found on the floor of the tropical forests. The giant armadillo has large claws on the front feet, with which it digs up food and makes burrows.

Tiny predator A mouse opossum, only 3½ to 7 inches long, prepares to pounce on a giant grasshopper. It kills insects by biting off their heads

Tree-living anteater   The pygmy anteater, which is only six inches long, rarely leaves the trees

Insect-eating bats and sharp-toothed bloodsuckers

Vast numbers of bats in the forests of South and Central America roost by day in caves, hollow trees, or among branches, usually hanging upside-down. They emerge at dusk to sweep over the trees in search of food.

Most bats, apart from the large fruit bats, emit high-pitched sounds which echo back from objects in their path. By picking up the echo as it bounces back, they locate prey and avoid bumping into objects.

The sounds are emitted in a conical beam, the diameter determined by the shape of the bat's mouth or the "leaf" of skin around the nose. When the sounds strike a "target," such as a flying insect, an echo is reflected back to the bat's ears. In this way, the bat gets a bearing on its prey and is guided toward it. Some bats increase the rate of the sound pulses as they get closer to their prey.

Range of the vampire bat   This bat, found throughout Central and South America, transmits diseases to its prey

The tamandua   This anteater carries its darker infant on its back. Tamanduas can extend their long, sticky tongues through the passages of ants' nests to lick up the insects

Distinctive faces   The nose flaps of insect-eating bats focus sounds emitted by their larynxes. Their large ears pick up echoes reflected from prey or obstacles

Fisherman bat
Noctilio leporinus

Spear-nosed bat
Phyllostomus hastatus

Wrinkled-faced bat
Centurio senex

Sword-nosed bat
Lonchorhina aurita

False vampire bat
Vampyrum spectrum

True vampire bat
Desmodus rotundus

Most species of bats are gregarious and roost in large numbers. Sometimes several species share a roost. One roosting cave may contain thousands of bats of various species, each species choosing a lighter or darker part of the cave according to its habit. Other bats hang from twigs or branches, sheltered by the foliage. Tent-making bats bite partly through the ribs of palm fronds so that the leaves droop down, forming a waterproof covering under which they roost.

Vampire bats have become adapted to a diet of blood. The molar teeth, used by insect-eating bats for crushing prey, are greatly reduced in vampires. Instead, the upper incisors have become developed into two sharp-edged teeth which the vampire uses to scoop out a piece of skin—usually painlessly—from its sleeping prey. It then laps blood from the wound.

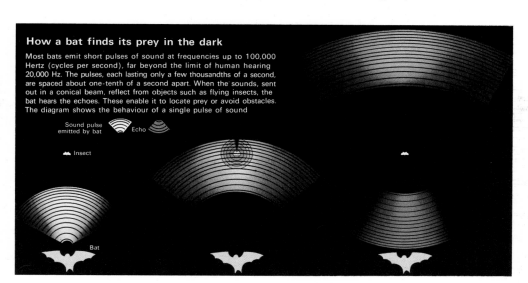

How a bat finds its prey in the dark

Most bats emit short pulses of sound at frequencies up to 100,000 Hertz (cycles per second), far beyond the limit of human hearing 20,000 Hz. The pulses, each lasting only a few thousandths of a second, are spaced about one-tenth of a second apart. When the sounds, sent out in a conical beam, reflect from objects such as flying insects, the bat hears the echoes. These enable it to locate prey or avoid obstacles. The diagram shows the behaviour of a single pulse of sound

Sound pulse emitted by bat   Echo

Insect

Bat

Marmosets and tamarins

In the tropical forests of the New World and the Old World, two groups of monkeys have evolved, similar in appearance, but not closely related

The South American monkeys consist of two families: the cebids, and the marmosets and tamarins. Neither family is closely related to the Old World monkeys, although some species superficially resemble African and Asian monkeys because they have adapted to the tropical forest environment in similar ways.

New World monkeys differ from those of the Old World in three important respects:

they have three premolar (grinding) teeth on each side of each jaw, instead of two; the thumb is not opposable to the rest of the hand, so that they must grasp objects by wrapping them between all five digits and the palm; and their nostrils face sideways instead of downward. This last feature results in their collective name, platyrrhines, which means "flat noses."

All the South American monkeys are tree-living animals, found only in forests. None has a reduced tail, such as the ground-living baboons and macaques of the Old World.

The marmosets and tamarins, of which there are 21 species, are the only higher

primates to have claws instead of nails on all their digits. They are agile climbers, scrambling about the trees like squirrels by digging their long claws into the bark, instead of grasping branches with their hands and feet as other monkeys do. They have thin, flexible bodies and long tails which are not adapted to grasping. On the ground, they usually walk on all fours.

These small monkeys resemble one another in their habits and structure much more than do the members of the cebid family. Multiple births are the rule, and most species live in small family groups. The marmoset family is considered the most primitive group of New World monkeys.

Common marmosets live in the upper levels of trees, feeding mainly on insects. They live in family groups, each consisting of a mated pair and their offspring. The male marks his territory by rubbing scent from his scrotal glands onto branches. He threatens other males by rapidly raising and lowering his ear tufts and arching his back.

Breeding takes place at any time of the year. During courtship, the male displays by walking with his back arched, rhythmically smacking his lips, and sticking out his tongue. The partners lick each other's fur and groom each other.

The young are born after a gestation period of 20 weeks. Twins are common. The young are carried by the male and handed over to the mother for suckling. Young common marmosets begin to wander on their own after about three weeks and are completely independent at five months.

The adult pygmy marmoset, the smallest living primate, is only 5½ inches long and

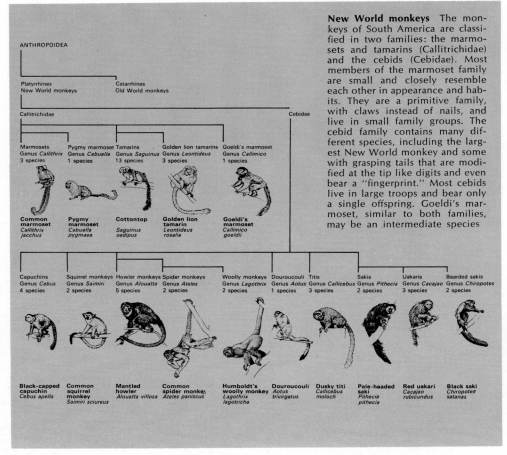

New World monkeys The monkeys of South America are classified in two families: the marmosets and tamarins (Callitrichidae) and the cebids (Cebidae). Most members of the marmoset family are small and closely resemble each other in appearance and habits. They are a primitive family, with claws instead of nails, and live in small family groups. The cebid family contains many different species, including the largest New World monkey and some with grasping tails that are modified at the tip like digits and even bear a "fingerprint." Most cebids live in large troops and bear only a single offspring. Goeldi's marmoset, similar to both families, may be an intermediate species.

Different noses Old World monkeys (left) have downward-facing nostrils, while New World monkeys (right) have nostrils that face sideways

Distribution of South American monkeys Unlike Old World monkeys that have a number of ground-living species, New World monkeys are entirely tree-living. Hence, they are confined to the tropical forests between Mexico and Argentina. The most heavily populated area in terms of variety and numbers is the Amazon basin. Marmosets (extreme left) have the most restricted distribution, being the least adaptable of these monkeys

has an eight-inch tail. Its movements are quick and jerky, and it can travel backward along a branch with short jerks of its body. When startled, pygmy marmosets, like squirrels and other arboreal animals, run to the opposite side of the tree from which danger threatens. The female bears two young, which are carried by the father and returned to the mother only for feeding.

Golden lion tamarins, sometimes called lion-headed tamarins, are large marmosets, with bodies and tails each about 15 inches long. The young are carried by the father, hidden under his long fur, until they are six to seven weeks old. The father crushes solid food between his fingers and feeds it to the young.

Tamarins of the genus *Saguinus* are nervous, aggressive animals, distinguished by the white fur around the mouth in many species and the absence of long incisor teeth.

The golden-handed tamarin, one species of *Saguinus*, lives in the valley of the lower Amazon. It is active in the early morning, when it feeds in the lower levels of the trees. Later in the day, when the temperature rises, golden-handed tamarins climb into the shade of the upper canopy. They are capable of leaping up to 25 feet across the branches.

The cottontop, or pinche, which has notched ears and a white crest of hair on the head, is slightly larger than the other species of tamarins. It too makes tremendous leaps. It rests in the sun by lying face down on a branch with its arms and legs dangling on each side. When aroused it stands erect.

Cottontops form family troops of parents and offspring in which the adult female defends the troop's territory. The animals groom one another with their tongues. During courtship, the female solicits the male by urinating on her tail and scenting it with secretion from a gland at the base of the tail. Twin births are usual.

Goeldi's marmoset is completely black and, like the golden lion tamarin, has a mane of long hair fringing the head. It resembles the other family of New World monkeys, the cebids, in having third molars, or wisdom teeth, and in bearing single offspring.

The young are carried exclusively by their mothers until they are about three weeks old. Only then do the male parents take over. In these respects Goeldi's marmoset can be considered as intermediate between the marmosets and the cebid monkeys.

Geoffroy's marmoset Marmosets of this species spend much time grooming their silky fur

Long fur Cottontops are larger than most tamarins, but their long body fur makes them look larger than they really are

Black-eared marmoset This subspecies of marmoset grips a branch with its long, sharp claws

Leonine monkey The golden lion tamarin (right) gets its name from the large mane fringing its face

Cebid monkeys

The cebid monkeys include some of the largest and noisiest South American monkeys, such as the howler monkeys, which can be heard three miles away

The Cebidae family of South American monkeys contains about 24 species, each with its own adaptations to a specialized way of life. Cebid monkeys on the whole are less lively than Old World monkeys, neither as quarrelsome nor as gay. They tend to be duller, even morose. Most species have bare,

flattened faces, thick woolly fur, and widely separated nostrils. Cebid monkeys tend to be larger than the marmosets, with relatively flat fingernails and toenails rather than claws. They usually give birth to only one offspring.

Titi monkeys occur mainly in the forests of the Amazon basin. The dusky titi resembles the marmosets in the way it sits hunched on a branch with its limbs together and its tail hanging down. Dusky titis live in mated pairs, sleeping with their tails twined together.

Insect-eater This little squirrel monkey is an omnivorous eater. Besides insects, it will forage for flowers, fruit, and nuts

Capuchin and its young This infant is strong enough to ride on its mother's back, but when it was born it clung to the fur on her belly with its

hands and feet. The white-throated capuchins are also known as ring-tails because they carry their tail with the end tightly coiled

Humboldt's woolly monkey Interweaving its forepaws and feet to grasp this short branch, it uses its prehensile tail like a fifth limb for more support

The douroucouli, the only nocturnal higher primate, has large eyes and white eyebrows, which give it an owllike expression. It is active at dawn and dusk, eating mainly fruit and insects, and lives as high as 100 feet. Douroucoulis live in mated pairs and the males defend their territory by "boxing" intruders with their hands, and mark it by rubbing urine on branches.

Sakis and uakaris have long, coarse hair, wide noses, and long canine and lower incisor teeth. The monk saki is named for the "hood" of long hair growing forward over its shoulders.

The bald uakari, an agile climber, has a short tail, a shaggy coat, and an almost hairless face and head. The skull-like face is pale pink in one race and red in another. Uakaris are gregarious, living high in the forest canopy. They rarely descend to the ground. The species that live in a relatively small section of the Amazon basin never intrude on each other's territory or home range.

The squirrel monkeys have white, skull-like faces, with black caps and muzzles. They are found chiefly in riverside forests, living in troops of up to 500, organized in order of rank in each sex. When feeding, squirrel monkeys loop their tails loosely around branches for support. Their tails, however, are not truly prehensile. Squirrel monkeys cannot hang by their tails, as do the larger,

Douroucoulis Also called night monkeys or owl monkeys, they sleep in a hollow tree during the day and emerge at dusk to feed

Head like a skull The skull-like appearance of the bald uakari is due to the nearly hairless skin of its face and head, which has no fat beneath it

Living bridge A female spider monkey bridges the gap between two trees by gripping one branch with its hands and the other with its feet and tail. One young monkey scrambles across the bridge, while an infant clings to the fur on its mother's belly. The young remain with their mother for ten months

stoutly built capuchin monkeys, named after the hooded Capuchin friars. The tufted capuchin has a mat of upright hairs on its head, which may form "horns" on each side. Capuchins are found in groups of up to 50 in the middle layers of the Central and South American forests.

Spider monkeys are much more slender in build than the closely related woolly monkeys. Most have wiry fur. Spider monkeys have no thumbs, so they hook on to branches with the four fingers of each hand. They can walk upright along the ground, on all fours along branches, or swing through the trees, using their prehensile tails as extra limbs. They sleep in groups of up to 100, which split up during the day for feeding. They communicate with sharp barks, and discourage intruders by growling and showering them with branches and feces.

The five species of howler monkeys have a highly modified hyoid bone (a bone at the root of the tongue), which gives the neck a swollen appearance and forms a large voice box. Their howls can be heard three miles away. Howlers live in troops of around 20, with about two adult males to every seven females. They tend to remain in the upper branches, crossing from tree to tree by bridging the gap with their hands on one side and their tails and feet on the other, then swinging across.

Grasping tails

Several species of South American monkeys have prehensile tails, with which they grasp branches. The spider monkeys (above) hook on to branches with their thumbless hands; their main grip is in their feet and tail. The woolly monkey's tail (left) has a flexible tip with a hairless area on its underside. This bears a "fingerprint" similar to those on hands and feet. The howler monkey's tail has the strongest grip of all. The animal can check its plunge when falling from a tree by grasping a branch with its tail

Howler monkey The cries of this monkey can be heard miles away. They howl when competing troops meet and when they locate food

221

Plant-eating mammals

Among many highly specialized mammals in New World forests are the sloths, which live in the trees, hanging upside-down from branches

The South American tropical forests, like those of the Old World, yield an unending supply of vegetable food which provides for a wide variety of plant-eating animals.

Though conditions are similar in both hemispheres, the animals that live in them are hardly ever of the same kind. The place occupied by hooved mammals in the Asian tropical forests, for example, is largely filled by plant-eating rodents in the New World, as the role of pigs is filled by peccaries.

Examples of the plant-eating rodents are the huge capybaras and the smaller acuchis,

pacas, and agoutis. Guinea-pigs are common. They live in burrows which they dig themselves or take over after other animals abandon them. They feed on vegetation at night, following well-worn paths to feeding places.

Peccaries are gregarious, piglike animals which travel in bands. The white-lipped peccary of the South American forests may live in groups of 100.

The largest rodent in the world sometimes grazes with cattle

Giant rodents A group of capybaras search the riverside mudflats for aquatic plants and grasses. The capybara's partially webbed feet are well suited to the animal's life in muddy hollows. Four feet long and a powerful swimmer, it is expert at seeking out floating vegetation

Squirrels, rats, and mice are all represented in South American forests, but the most characteristic rodents of the area are those belonging to the porcupine suborder. They include the capybara, the largest rodent in the world, which weighs up to 100 pounds and has an overall length of four feet. It is a semiaquatic animal with partially webbed feet, spending much of its time half submerged in swamps, or near streams and rivers, where it feeds on plants.

Capybaras live in small family groups or in bands of up to 20 animals. In areas where they are not disturbed they feed in the morning and evening, resting during the day and sleeping at night. But, like some other mammals, they become nocturnal when hunted or disturbed by man or when predators increase in their area. Capybaras sometimes graze with a group of cattle. They rarely fight among themselves or attack predators, relying on their alertness and speed to escape. They are preyed on by jaguars on land and by caymans, relatives of the alligator, in the water. Capybaras are excellent swimmers and divers. They will run to water when frightened, and they mate in the shallows, after first courting on the shore.

Acuchis, pacas, and agoutis are much smaller rodents which also live near water, but feed on roots, berries, and fruit. Agoutis and acuchis make food caches. The paca is rarely seen, since it spends the day in a burrow with two entrances, both plugged with leaves.

The forest shelters a number of species of guinea-pigs of the genus *Cavia*. These gregarious, burrowing animals are about the size of rats, and feed upon plant material by night. They are adapted to swift movement on the forest floor.

Food hoarder The agouti, a slender, long-legged rodent of the forest floor, stores food in scattered caches

Female paca and young Rarely seen rodents, pacas spend the day in riverside tunnels and emerge at night to feed on a variety of vegetable plants. The females have two pairs of teats, but usually produce only one offspring

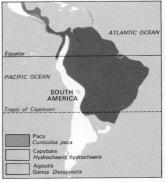

New World rodents These, of the porcupine suborder, all run, swim, climb, and burrow well

Sloths, or life upside-down

Sloths are the most completely tree-living of all South American forest animals. They rarely leave the trees; they eat, sleep, mate, and give birth while hanging upside-down from branches, suspended from powerful, hooklike claws on each foot. Hands and feet are held close together, making the animal look rather like a bunch of leaves, particularly since sloths are often covered with a greenish growth of algae. They are exclusively vegetarian, and some individuals may spend their whole lives lethargically browsing in one tree. Sloths move slowly, hand over hand, from one feeding area to another. They have a keen sense of smell, and depend almost entirely on smell and touch to move about and find food, since their senses of sight and hearing are poorly developed.

Sloths, like armadillos and anteaters, belong to the Edentata (toothless) order of mammals. They have neither incisors nor canines, but the cheek teeth are well developed for chewing leaves and fruit.

Sloths defend themselves against predators with their teeth as well as with their strong, curved claws. They can inflict painful wounds.

They have adapted physically to their upside-down life. Their fur grows in the opposite direction from that of most mammals, so that it points downward when the sloth is hanging from a branch and allows rain to run off. Sloths have long, powerful limbs, which enable them to climb easily, if slowly —their top speed is little more than one mile per hour. They are also strong swimmers, but on the ground they move only with extreme difficulty, struggling forward in a spread-eagle crawl, using their arms to pull themselves onward.

Sloths are unusual among mammals in that they do not maintain a constant body temperature. This is probably why they live only in the warm, humid tropical forests.

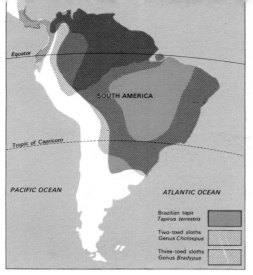

Large herbivores Sloths live only in South and Central America, but tapirs are more widespread and are found in Southeast Asia as well

Clinging for safety A young three-toed sloth clings to its mother as she inches through the branches. This species feeds almost entirely on the leaves and fruit of *Cecropia* trees

Upside-down infancy From birth onward, young sloths cling to their mother's abdominal fur. Two-toed sloths have a long gestation—about nine months—probably due to delayed implantation

Piglike peccaries travel and forage in leaderless herds of up to 100 animals

Peccaries belong to the Tayassuidae family of cloven-hooved mammals, which are related to the true pigs—the Suidae family—of Eurasia and Africa. There are two species— the white-lipped peccary, which lives in South American forests, and the collared peccary, which usually lives in more open country. White-lipped peccaries travel, apparently leaderless, in groups of up to 100, digging for tubers and bulbs. Adults are armed with three-inch tusks. The whole herd may turn on a predator that attacks a member.

Peccary's scent Herd members create a communal scent by rubbing up against one another's scent glands. These are located on their backs

South American tapirs Like the closely related Malayan species, they live close to forest rivers and lakes. They are strong swimmers and have a prefer-ence for water plants. Only two animals prey on the shy, solitary tapir—jaguars on land and caymans, which mainly attack the young, in the water

Carnivores

Carnivores in South America's forests range from the jaguar, a predator on large mammals, to the olingo, a member of the raccoon family

Four families of the carnivore order are represented among South American forest predators—raccoons, weasels, dogs, and cats. Some of these hunt on the ground, but many are good climbers and pursue their prey in the trees.

The representatives of the raccoon family are the coatis, the kinkajou, the olingos of the genus *Bassaricyon*, and the crab-eating raccoon. The weasel family is represented by the tayra. The few members of the dog family that live in the South American forests include foxes and the bush dog.

Killing a snake The jaguarondi preys on a wide range of ground- and tree-living animals, from monkeys and rodents to birds and reptiles. A powerful swimmer, it is known as the otter cat in Mexico

Coatis, kinkajous, olingos, and other forest predators

Olingo Olingos are descended from meat-eating ancestors, like their relatives, the kinkajous. Although they do hunt insects, their diet mainly consists of fruit and shoots. They may descend to the ground, but are mainly tree-dwelling animals

Coatis are slim animals with a head and body length of about two feet, and long, ringed tails. They feed on anything, animal or vegetable, investigating crannies and crevices with their long, sensitive noses. Groups forage largely on the ground by day, keeping in touch with one another by a continuous high-pitched twittering, and sleep in the trees at night. Some species are active at night also. Coatis range in color from reddish brown to black, with paler underfur. Their tail is semiprehensile, and when they hunt in the trees they use it to help in balancing. Females and young go about in bands of 5 to 12. Adult males are solitary, except in the breeding season, when they join a female band. Once in a band the male is subordinate to the females but will drive off other adult males. Females usually bear four or five young at a time.

Kinkajous and olingos are long-bodied, short-limbed animals with long tails which give them an overall length of about three feet. Kinkajous have short-haired, tapering prehensile tails from which they can swing; olingos' tails are not prehensile and are slightly bushier.

Both kinkajous and olingos spend most of their lives in the trees. They are nocturnal, sleeping during the day in hollows in trees and similar shelters. Both are carnivores which have become largely vegetarian. They often forage together, feeding mainly on fruits and shoots, although insects also form part of their diet. Kinkajous eat birds, and olingos will take birds and small mammals.

The weasel family's representative is the tayra, a slender-bodied animal about four feet long, including the tail. Tayras, the South American equivalents of the martens of Europe and North America, are extremely fierce. They sometimes kill deer, but usually prey on rodents, birds, and insects.

Although the dog family is more characteristic of open country, a few species live in the forest. These include a number of foxes. The most common is the crab-eating fox. In spite of its name, crabs form only a small part of its diet, which includes rodents, insects, and fruit. The bush dog, another forest-dweller, is about two feet long, with a sausage-shaped body and short legs. These dogs hunt in packs, preying on large rodents and small forest deer.

Coatis This family group belongs to the most northerly of the three coati species. It ranges from South America to the southern United States

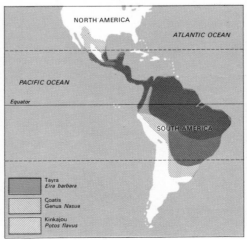

Tree predators The kinkajou and tayra are confined to forests. Coatis, living in trees and on the ground, have a wider range

Fast mover The tayra is extremely agile in trees and moves quickly through branches. Although mainly nocturnal, it may be active in the morning

The magnificent jaguar is almost as strong as a lion

Several members of the cat family hunt in the South American forests. Of the smaller species, two kinds of spotted cat, the margay and the tiger cat, are more numerous than the similarly marked ocelot, which inhabits more open country. All three are golden yellow, white below, and covered with dark spots and blotches. They are agile climbers but also hunt on the ground for small mammals and birds. A larger and more powerful animal than any of these is the jaguarondi, a big, unspotted cat with a long tail. Its total length may exceed four feet.

Jaguarondis, which live on the edge rather than in the depths of the forest, occur in three color phases: black, dark gray, and chestnut. They prey on birds, monkeys, and other animals. Jaguarondis also prey on domestic animals.

The largest carnivore of the forest, and largest of the New World cats, is the jaguar. It looks rather like a heavy-bodied, short-legged leopard, although the rosettes that dot its tawny coat have central spots, unlike the rosettes on the coat of the leopard.

Though jaguars climb trees, fully grown adults are too heavy to be really agile climbers—they may weigh over 300 pounds and grow to more than eight feet including a two-foot tail. A jaguar is nearly as strong as a lion, and will drag a horse or cow a long way over rough terrain to a sheltered spot where it can eat undisturbed.

Jaguars are great travelers, and are sometimes seen on the pampas. But usually they prey on forest animals—deer, agoutis, and, above all, peccaries. They haunt the fringes of peccary herds, watching for a chance to pick off stragglers. Black jaguars are found in dense, wet forest, just as black leopards are found in the wetter parts of the Asian tropical forests.

The jaguar swims well, even when burdened with a tapir between its jaws. It fishes in a leisurely manner, resting by a lake or stream until a fish or turtle swims by. Then the big cat hooks it out of the water with a quick swoop of its powerful claws.

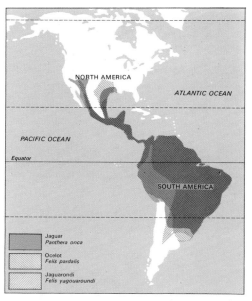

Distribution of the cat family Jaguars, though their spotted coats mark them out as typical forest animals, are sometimes found on the pampas. Their normal range is below the Rio Grande, but they occasionally roam into Arizona and New Mexico. The ocelot also ranges into the drier savanna

Jaguars keeping cool A black jaguar and a normal-colored companion rest in a forest stream. Jaguars are good swimmers and often lurk near rivers where

they prey on animals that come to drink. They also scoop fish from the water. In the tropical rain forests, they live in the more humid areas

Infant margay The margay, a shy, solitary cat, is rarely seen and little is known about its behavior. Its large eyes are thought to be an adaptation to its habit of hunting during the night. It is about the same size as a domestic cat, and is found in northern South America

Speedy hunter The ocelot spends much of its time in the trees, but normally hunts on the ground. It does not ambush prey, but runs it down

Birds of the New World

Among the bizarre birds of South America, none is stranger than the hoatzin. The young have claws on their wings, recalling the reptilian ancestor of all birds

For 70 million years, South America was an isolated area. The majority of its birds evolved there and did not spread far when the two Americas joined up 2 to 3 million years ago. This has resulted in some very distinctive bird groups—such as hummingbirds, toucans, woodcreepers, and others—which are confined to the Americas and are mostly forest-dwellers. Hummingbirds in particular are widespread throughout South and Central America.

One of the most curious of South America's birds is the hoatzin. Young hoatzins have small claws on their wings—evidence of their descent from a reptilian ancestor. These claws, which enable them to scramble through trees in their riverside habitat, disappear after a few weeks. Ant thrushes are common on the South American forest floor. There are about 220 species, mostly insect-eaters. A few of them follow ant armies. Some feed on the ants, and others on insects which the ants flush out.

The hummingbird family Some 300 species of hummingbirds live in the Americas, yet most of them are found south of Texas. The rufous hummingbird migrates as far north as Alaska

Trogons and hummingbirds: a study in contrasts

Rotating wings A Lucifer hummingbird is hovering on wings that rotate in their sockets, while beating more than 80 times a second. The fast-flying hummingbirds can even fly backward

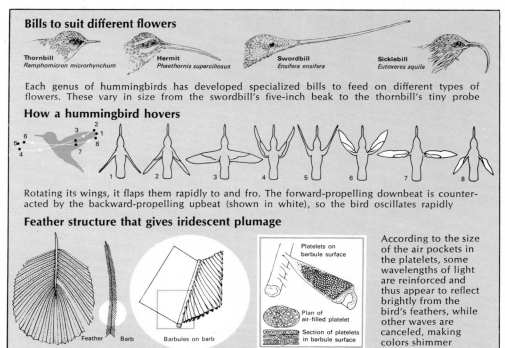

Bills to suit different flowers

Thornbill
Ramphomicron microrhynchum

Hermit
Phaethornis superciliosus

Swordbill
Ensifera ensifera

Sicklebill
Eutoxeres aquila

Each genus of hummingbirds has developed specialized bills to feed on different types of flowers. These vary in size from the swordbill's five-inch beak to the thornbill's tiny probe

How a hummingbird hovers

Rotating its wings, it flaps them rapidly to and fro. The forward-propelling downbeat is counteracted by the backward-propelling upbeat (shown in white), so the bird oscillates rapidly

Feather structure that gives iridescent plumage

Feather   Barb   Barbules on barb

Platelets on barbule surface

Plan of air-filled platelet

Section of platelets in barbule surface

According to the size of the air pockets in the platelets, some wavelengths of light are reinforced and thus appear to reflect brightly from the bird's feathers, while other waves are canceled, making colors shimmer

The trogons have an unusual foot structure: the first and second toes turn back, the third and fourth point forward. They are non-migratory birds, and ornithologists have puzzled over the fact that the several species of the South American tropical forests live in widely separated areas. Trogons are shy birds, seldom seen by man. They are usually solitary and make little noise, living concealed among the closely woven branches. Their soft, downy plumage allows them to fly silently.

The most beautiful trogon is the quetzal, the national bird of Guatemala, which lives at high altitudes in the rain forest. It is brilliantly colored, and many of its feathers have a metallic sheen. The quetzal measures 14 inches, but its tail is lengthened by another two or three feet by long, trailing plumes. Like all trogons, the quetzal has extremely thin, tender skin, and its feathers are loosely attached. Its beauty caused it to be worshiped by the ancient Indians as the god of the air.

There are some 300 species of hummingbirds, almost all confined to South and Central America. The bee hummingbird, the smallest bird in the world, weighs less than $\frac{1}{14}$ ounce and measures only 2½ inches from the tip of its beak to the end of its tail.

The most striking characteristic of hummingbirds is their ability to hover when feeding on nectar from flowers. The birds can hover motionless, fly straight up or down, sideways, and even backward. For years people who thought they saw a hummingbird backing out of a flower were told that this was an optical illusion, but high-speed cameras have proved that the hummingbird really can fly backward for short distances. The hummingbird has tremendously strong flying muscles, larger for its size than those of any other bird. Its wing muscles average 25 to 30 percent of its body weight. The wings rotate in the shoulder sockets, allowing the bird to hover with the body vertical. Hovering in this way makes great demands on a bird's energy. Most hummingbirds are so small that they expend energy very rapidly in the form of heat lost through the body surface. They make up for this by feeding almost continuously throughout the day on nectar, a high-energy food, and insects. They become torpid at night.

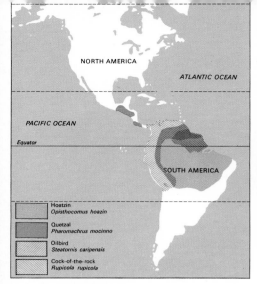

Birds that stay within their range These four rain forest species evolved during South America's 70 million years of isolation. Even though the two Americas have joined up, the birds have not spread

Golden cock-of-the-rock This cock has a helmet-like crest that conceals its bill. These handsome birds stand absolutely still in their courtship areas to attract the drabber-colored females

Navigating by sound and smell Oilbirds build their nest in caves and use an echo-location system when flying in the dark. At dusk, they leave the cave and detect ripe fruit by their sense of smell

An oriole that builds its nest near wasps for safety

Some honeycreepers also feed on nectar, but a large number of families of birds rely on the forest's year-round supply of fruits and seeds. Among these are toucans, macaws, and parrots, which have beaks particularly well adapted to their diet. Toucans have long, thick, colorful bills which they can push through foliage to reach fruit. They also eat small animals. Parrots and macaws, which belong to the same family, crack nuts with their strong beaks. Toucans are seen only in pairs or small family groups, but parrots and macaws often feed in large flocks.

Manakins are found in all the forest layers, but the cotingas live mainly in the canopy. However, the golden cock-of-the-rock, a cotinga, goes through its courtship on the ground, like many manakins. Several cocks clear a court and pose absolutely still for minutes at a time in front of the females.

There are nearly 600 species of tyrant fly-catchers, tanagers, and orioles living on fruits and insects in the tropical forest. The largest species are the orioles, some of which build six-feet-deep hanging nests in the branches. Orioles often build near wasps' nests, where they are less likely to be disturbed by predators. They live in colonies with up to 100 nests, built by the females. The colony is usually located in a tree that stands alone in a clearing, or in the occasional emergent tree that towers above the canopy.

The rare quetzal This aerial feeder rivals the birds of paradise in its colorful plumage. The brilliantly colored male may have tail coverts that extend for three feet. Quetzals seek food in mountain forest trees, flying back and forth from resting perches. They flutter vertically before leaves and twigs, while picking off insects or locating ripe fruit. They supplement this diet with small frogs

Ground birds that fly clumsily, and a vulture with a sense of smell

Most of the larger forest birds are members of the gamebird (galliform) order and live and nest in the treetops. The ground, however, is the home of the tinamous, which fly very little. They belong in an order of their own and are probably related to the flightless rhea of the grasslands.

Above the trees flies the yellow-headed vulture, seeking carrion on the forest floor. It is believed to be guided to its food by its sense of smell, a rare characteristic among birds. This sense is also possessed by the oilbird, which leaves its cave home at dusk to search for ripe fruit in the forest canopy.

The largest and fiercest bird in the upper canopy is the harpy eagle. It swoops through the branches, preying on monkeys and sloths.

Wings with claws The hoatzin has characteristics that closely resemble those of the fossil *Archaeopteryx*, the earliest known bird. The claws on its wings (above) are similar to the clawed toes of its reptilian ancestors. Claws are well developed in the young, but are lost after a few weeks. The fledglings use these hooks to clamber about trees when danger threatens. The adult (right) cannot fly well and usually only glides from the tops of bushes

227

Reptiles and amphibians

Brightly colored "arrow-poison" frogs secrete a paralyzing poison, which Indians of the rain forests collect and put on the tips of their arrows

South American rain forests provide ideal living conditions for a large number of reptiles. Among them is one of the most unusual and puzzling of snake groups, the coral snakes and their mimics. This group consists of nearly 80 species, all of which are marked with bold bands of black, red, and yellow or white.

Lizards of the Iguanidae family are the most numerous of New World lizards, and

have produced forms adapted to most of the continent's land environments. One species, the marine iguana of the Galápagos Islands, has taken to the sea, and there are also ground-living and tree-living species in the rain forests. All are active by day, and have keen eyesight, which offers an explanation for colorful crests and frills on their bodies. The common iguana lives in trees and, unlike most lizards, is largely vegetarian.

Lizards of the Teiidae family live on the ground, some of them burrowing in forest litter. The limbs of many of these lizards are reduced in size—sometimes to the point of disappearance.

Reptile distribution In addition to the 40-odd species of *Micrurus*, one much smaller coral snake lives in Arizona and another in Louisiana

Snakes, some 14 feet long, live in trees and on the forest floor

There are two genera of true coral snakes —*Micruroides*, which has one species, *Micruroides euryxanthus*, and *Micrurus*, with about 40 species. *Micrurus* species live in the litter of the forest floor, and prey on other snakes. The venom of some species is extremely powerful, and it would appear that the brilliant colors have been evolved as a warning to predators. Most coral snakes have at least some bright red color on their bodies. They are burrowing snakes which grow to a length of three to four feet. Coral snakes eat lizards and other snakes, sometimes almost as big as themselves. The snake snaps its body with great force and inflicts several bites on the victim; then the snake moves the prey so that it can be swallowed headfirst.

Living alongside the true coral snakes are many species of false coral snakes with similar color patterns. Some of the false coral

Boa constrictor This snake usually preys on small mammals, especially rodents. Like pythons of the Old World, it kills by suffocating prey in its coils

Waiting for prey With its coils balanced over a branch, the emerald tree boa waits for prey. This

The kill Anchored by its prehensile tail, the emerald tree boa uncoils its six-foot length to seize a

position enables it to strike swiftly, and also helps to distribute its weight evenly on the branch

blue tanager. The normally sluggish boa strikes with great speed. It feeds mainly on birds and monkeys

Giant flower-eater Unlike most lizards, the common iguana is largely vegetarian, eating flowers, fruit, and leaves. It is a day-active creature, and its visual powers are highly developed

How the anole changes color The scales of the green anole contain cells that hold a dark pigment, called melanin. As long as this pigment stays in the center of the cell, light is reflected back from other cells in the anole's scales through droplets of yellow oil, so the lizard appears yellow. When activated by hormones and temperature the melanin expands and masks the yellow oil, giving different colors to the anole

snakes, such as the genera *Rhinobothryum*, *Erythrolamprus*, and *Pseudoboa*, are mildly venomous; others, such as the genus *Simophis*, are harmless. Some false coral snakes look exactly like true coral snakes until they are closely examined together. There has been much popular speculation as to why some nonpoisonous snakes should so closely resemble poisonous ones, and at least one credible scientific explanation has been put forth (see page 161).

Lance-headed snakes are another large group of venomous snakes which inhabit New World rain forests. They are pit vipers of the genus *Bothrops*, and some 50 species have adapted to either ground or tree living.

The largest poisonous snake in South America is the bushmaster, which grows to a length of 14 feet. This snake inhabits forested mountain slopes and is active at night, when cool air descends into the valleys.

Vividly colored frogs produce deadly poison that is used by Indians

Long ago, the Indians of South America discovered that poisonous secretions on the skins of frogs of the Dendrobatinae group could paralyze and kill. They used these secretions to tip their arrows. The secretions are the frogs' defense mechanism, and are accompanied by vivid colors which serve to warn away predators.

Generally, amphibians lay their eggs in standing water; there the young go through the aquatic stage of their development. Many South American forest toads and frogs, however, have evolved other methods of reproduction. Some tree frogs of the Hylidae family lay their eggs in water-filled holes in trees. Females of the genus *Gastrotheca* carry the eggs in a pouch on the back. Other hylid frogs, of the genus *Phyllomedusa*, lay eggs in nests hanging over water. The nests are made of leaves glued together by sterile egg jelly, and when the first egg hatches the whole structure collapses into the water. It is possible that the collapse is triggered by a chemical produced by the tadpole.

Caecilians, secret dwellers in the forest

Caecilians belong to a single amphibian order, the Apoda, consisting of about 75 species in 20 genera which are found in most of the world's tropical regions. One South American genus, *Typhlonectes*, lives in water; the remainder are burrowing animals seldom seen above the ground. Most adults are blind, and have a pair of tentaclelike organs in the sides of the snout, which help them feel their way underground. Little is known of their feeding or reproductive habits, except that some genera give birth to live young. The largest known species is *Caecilia thompsoni* of Colombia, which grows to 4½ feet long.

Genus *Dendrobates*

Genus *Phyllobates*

Genus *Phyllomedusa*

Genus *Gastrotheca*

A wealth of frogs The rain forests of the New World contain an enormous array of frogs. Some genera, like *Phyllobates* and *Dendrobates*, secrete a paralyzing poison in the mucus that lubricates their skins. These are small frogs, only one to two inches long. The female *Dendrobates* lays as many as 20 eggs on the skin of the male, and the growing tadpoles cling to his back until they have developed. Females of the genus *Phyllomedusa* deposit eggs in a leaf nest overhanging water. The nest collapses when the eggs begin to hatch, depositing the young in the water

Caecilian feeding Little is known about caecilians' feeding habits, since they spend most of their lives underground. This rare photograph of a caecilian aboveground shows it eating an earthworm

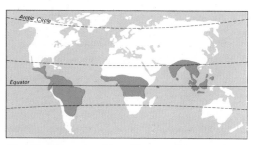

Caecilians' ranges Wormlike caecilians are found in the damp rain forest floor throughout the world, except Australia. South America is their primary range, and has 46 of the known 75 species

Birds

Bizarre and beautiful birds throng the dark rain forests. Some of them flaunt rainbow plumage, others build elaborate pavilions to attract their mates

The fruit- and insect-filled jungle of New Guinea and the broken strip of coastal rain forest in the north and northeast of Australia are rich in strange and colorful birds.

Several families of birds are found only in this region. Their remote ancestors came here from Asia. Examples are the birds of paradise, bower birds, and cassowaries.

Birds of paradise, which are related to crows, are renowned for the male's elaborate and highly colored plumage. The feathers are used in headdresses by the natives of New Guinea, and they were exported for the Western millinery trade until this was prohibited in 1921. There are 42 species.

Forty of them are confined to Australia and New Guinea; the other two live on the neighboring Moluccas islands.

Bower birds are closely related to birds of paradise and they are descended from a common stock which invaded Australasia from Southeast Asia. There are 18 species of bower birds, all found only in Australia and New Guinea.

Bower birds are drabber and shorter-plumed than birds of paradise, but their mating behavior is even more bizarre. The males build structures known as bowers, which they decorate with any small object they can find: flowers, berries, leaves, pebbles, shells, bones, insects, beer-bottle tops, or aluminum foil. Some species paint their bowers with chewed charcoal, grass, or fruit; others plant moss lawns in front of the bower.

Decorative plumage New Guinea tribesmen use the long, broad tail plumes of the male Princess Stephanie's bird of paradise as headdress ornaments

Exotic Australasians—birds of paradise, bower birds, and flightless cassowaries

The mating of birds of paradise is preceded by a flamboyant display of plumage by the male. In species whose males are particularly colorful, the sexes meet only during the breeding season. The male displays, then mates with the females he has attracted. The females fly off alone to make their nests, lay their eggs, and rear their young.

Some birds of paradise prepare their display area carefully. The magnificent bird of paradise, *Diphyllodes magnificus*, clears all leaves and twigs from the ground beneath

the perch tree where he displays and strips the foliage from the branches, with the result that the sun shines through and picks out the displaying bird's bright colors against the cleared forest floor.

The bowers of bower birds appear to be display pavilions to which the male tries to attract as many mates as possible. There are two main types of bowers—the avenue, consisting of parallel rows of upright sticks; and the maypole, an elaborate stick-structure built around the base of a sapling—which

are varied by the different species of birds.

The largest birds of this region are cassowaries; the biggest of the three species is about five feet high and weighs up to 112 pounds. Like emus, to which they are related, cassowaries cannot fly. They are rarely seen; despite their size, they keep well hidden in the thick forest. A study of the two-wattled cassowary revealed that in the laying season the birds occupy territories ranging in size from half a square mile to two square miles, and that they feed on fruit and berries.

A dazzling and acrobatic courtship display high in the tropical forest of New Guinea

Helmeted heavyweights Cassowaries, the giants of the Australian tropical forest, have wings consisting of uncovered, tough quills. These and their bony helmets enable them to run with their heads lowered through the undergrowth without becoming entangled. The males incubate the eggs, which are laid on the forest floor, and also help to rear the young. Two of the three species of cassowaries have brightly colored wattles of flesh hanging from their necks. The young are camouflaged in the undergrowth by long, dark stripes that blend with the light and shadow. Cassowaries attack with their powerful claws

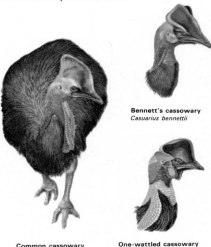

Bennett's cassowary
Casuarius bennettii

Common cassowary
Casuarius casuarius

One-wattled cassowary
Casuarius unappendiculatus

Starting its display on the upper branches of trees, the adult male of Count Raggi's bird of paradise first selects a private perch. Its exhibition begins when it bends forward and raises its wings until they touch. Curving its body until its head is beneath its feet, it claps its wings together and spreads out its flank plumes

Male bower birds build and decorate several types of elaborate pavilions for display and mating

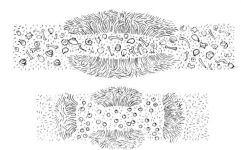

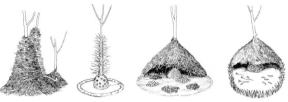

The great gray bower bird builds an avenue bower of two walls of twigs (top). These are either vertical or arching. The avenue of Lauterbach's bower bird has four walls (bottom)

Maypole bowers take varied forms. The golden bower bird builds pyramids; Macgregor's gardener bower, a column surrounded by a moss parapet; the Vogelkop gardener, a hut with a moss garden; the striped gardener, a hut and stockade

The male great gray bower bird (above) displays the vivid pink crest on the nape of its neck. The male of the related fawn-breasted bower bird (below) performs a similar display with a berry instead of a crest. Perhaps this bird had a crested ancestor, and the movement has survived from the past

A cock struts around its bower of interlocked twigs, watched by its mate. Some satin bowers paint their bower with a mixture of charcoal and saliva, using a piece of bark held in their beak as a tool. Flowers and snake skins are used as decoration

Cockatoos and lories are two of the many members of the parrot family

Australia and New Guinea contain many species of parrots. The most widely represented groups are cockatoos and lories. Cockatoos are large birds with long crests that can be erected, and powerful beaks that can crack open the toughest nut or remove a man's finger. The black cockatoo, or great palm cockatoo, is the largest bird of this group. Actually slate gray, it has cheeks of bare pink skin that flush bright red when it is aroused.

Lories have small and comparatively weak bills. They feed mostly on pollen and nectar, which they collect from deep within flowers with the brushlike tip of their tongue.

The pygmy parrots of New Guinea, which are only four inches long, have stiff tails which function like those of woodpeckers—supporting the birds as they climb tree trunks probing for insects.

New Guinea is the home of the largest pigeons in the world—the crowned pigeons, which are almost three feet long. They have large, lacy, fan-shaped crests and live in swamps and on the forest floor. Other pigeons include the wide-ranging, vividly colored fruit doves and the fruit-eating green pigeons. Equally brilliant in their coloring are the pittas, or jewel thrushes—plump, long-legged, short-tailed birds that live on the forest floor and run off at great speed when disturbed.

Other inhabitants of the region include the frogmouths, owllike nightjars that feed mainly on the ground, catching insects in their enormous, gaping beaks.

Animals of isolated rain forests

Kangaroos are usually thought of as ground-dwellers that hop on strong hind legs, but in the tropical rain forests some species live in the trees

Tropical forest covers much of New Guinea, and parts of the east and north of Australia. The animals there have long been isolated, and fewer groups of land mammals are present than in other rain forests. The marsupials and monotremes found in the rest of Australia are also found in the Australian rain forest and in New Guinea. The bats are descended from Southeast Asian stock.

The lizard and snake families are also represented in Southeast Asia, except for the legless lizards of the Pygopodidae family, which live only in Australia and New Guinea.

Tree-living kangaroos jump 60 feet to the ground

Most kangaroos are adapted by their build and by their habits to living on the ground. But in the tropical forests of Australia and New Guinea some seven species, all in the same genus, have taken to the trees.

Tree kangaroos are not rare, but since they live deep in the forest relatively little is known of their life. Strong claws and large, cushionlike pads on their feet give them a good grip. The long tail helps them maintain balance. They can make downward leaps of 20 feet between trees and they may drop 60 feet to the ground without injuring themselves. They are vegetarian.

About six species of wallabies inhabit the forests of New Guinea. Four species live in lowland rain forests and the others live at much higher altitudes in the mountain forests. Like the wallabies of the grasslands, they are ground-living vegetarians.

Cuscuses are tree-living marsupials of the possum family. They have short, heavy limbs and prehensile tails, and eat leaves. Their eyes, which protrude, are rimmed with yellow, and their noses are a bright yellow.

Monotremes are represented by the long-snouted spiny anteaters in New Guinea and the spiny anteaters, or echidnas, in Australia. Both species feed on ants and termites.

During the breeding season, the female develops a temporary pouch in which she lays one or two eggs.

A tree kangaroo Lumholtz's tree kangaroo lives in the Queensland forest canopy. It browses on leaves and climbs easily, balanced by its long brushy-tipped tail. It also has rough pads for climbing

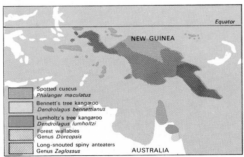

Kangaroos and wallabies These animals are more familiar as plains animals, yet several species have adapted to the tropical rain forest areas. These include seven species of tree-climbing kangaroos

Spotted cuscus
Phalanger maculatus
Bennett's tree kangaroo
Dendrolagus bennettianus
Lumholtz's tree kangaroo
Dendrolagus lumholtzi
Forest wallabies
Genus *Dorcopsis*
Long-snouted spiny anteaters
Genus *Zaglossus*

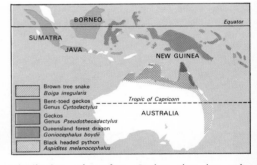

Distribution of geckos Geckos that lay soft-shelled eggs are confined to Australia and oceanic islands to the east. In New Guinea they are replaced by bent-toed geckos, which lay hard-shelled eggs

Brown tree snake
Boiga irregularis
Bent-toed geckos
Genus *Cyrtodactylus*
Geckos
Genus *Pseudothecadactylus*
Queensland forest dragon
Gonocephalus boydii
Black headed python
Aspidites melanocephalus

New Guinea anteater The spiny anteaters of New Guinea have longer snouts and shorter spines than those of Australia—a different genus

Australian forest predator *Dasyurus maculatus*, a flesh-eating marsupial, preys on birds in the trees

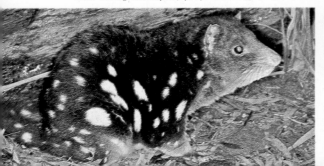

A tropical opportunist The spotted cuscus seeks food at night. It eats leaves, small mammals, and birds

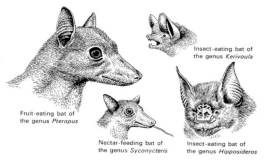

Faces of New Guinea bats The fruit bats have long muzzles; nectar-eaters, long tongues; and insect-eaters, short muzzles. Some of the latter also have nose leaves that are used to locate prey by echo

Fruit-eating bat of the genus *Pteropus*

Nectar-feeding bat of the genus *Syconycteris*

Insect-eating bat of the genus *Kerivoula*

Insect-eating bat of the genus *Hipposideros*

Bats and rodents of the forest

Placental mammals—those in which the young develop to an advanced stage in the mother's uterus before birth—are represented in Australian and New Guinea rain forests only by rodents and bats.

Mosaic-tailed rats have evolved semi-prehensile tails. They live among the branches, where they feed on leaves and berries. Young mosaic-tailed rats hold tightly to the nipples of the mother and are carried about by her for the first two weeks.

Large water rats of the genus *Hydromys* live on riverbanks throughout the region. These aquatic rodents have partly webbed feet, flattened heads, and dense, seallike fur. They feed—on mussels and fish—at night.

From dusk onward, the air above the trees is filled with thousands of bats. Fruit bats roost in forest "camps" by day and fly off together at nightfall in search of flowers and fruit.

A fruit bat and a banana The gray-headed flying fox feeds on juices that it squeezes from fruit

Where venomous snakes outnumber nonvenomous species

Unlike the families of native marsupial mammals, Australia's lizards and snakes appear to have migrated from Southeast Asia. Snakes of the Elapidae family, with fixed front fangs and paralyzing venom, have been particularly successful. Having reached Australia at an early date, they evolved many forms. Australia is the only continent to have more venomous than nonvenomous snake species. Venomous species include the taipan, the blacksnake, and the death adder.

New Guinea is the only part of the world in which the ranges of pythons and boas of similar habits overlap. Small boas of the genus *Candoia* range from Celebes to the Solomon Islands.

Lizards are represented in Australian and New Guinea tropical forests by skinks, agamids, and geckos, many of which live among the branches. So, too, does a monitor lizard, *Varanus prasinus*, which is green and has a prehensile tail. Such adaptations to tree-living are unusual in a monitor. This species resembles the rest of the Varanidae family in eating all kinds of animals.

Salamanders and caecilians have not reached Australia, and the amphibians are represented by only four families of frogs. Two of these, the Leptodactylidae and the Hylidae, also occur in the Americas but have an extremely fragmented distribution in the Old World. This enormous gap in distribution suggests either the existence of a land link between Australia and the Americas in the past, or that the frogs were once very widespread throughout the world, and now survive only in isolated pockets. The other two frog families, Microhylidae and Ranidae, came from Southeast Asia.

Night tiger The brown tree snake, or night tiger, may grow to a length of seven feet. If disturbed, it bites savagely, but its venom kills only small animals

Snake-eating snake A black-headed python is eating a water snake. This python specializes in killing all types of snakes, even the most venomous

Dragon of the trees The Queensland forest dragon is a recent migrant from New Guinea to Australia

Invertebrates

Most invertebrates—animals lacking a backbone—are so small they are rarely seen; yet they make up 95 percent of all species of animals on earth

Most land-living invertebrates, including insects, have rigid external skeletons and jointed limbs; but none except the insects have wings, and most have more than the three pairs of legs of the insects. Although the noninsect invertebrates are more numerous on the forest floor, insects are dominant among the treetops because they can fly.

Invertebrates with rigid external skeletons and jointed limbs, but not soft-bodied invertebrates such as worms and mollusks, are classified together in the phylum Arthropoda—a phylum being one of the major divisions of the animal kingdom. A phylum in turn is divided into classes, which are themselves divided into orders, orders into families, and families into genera. Among the most familiar noninsect arthropods are spiders, which belong to the Arachnida class, and millipedes, of the Diplopoda class.

Fourteen species of ricinuleids, which are blind arachnids, live in American and West African rain forests. Until fairly recently, only a few specimens had been found in the whole order.

A spider that preys on birds and mice, killing them with its poisonous bite

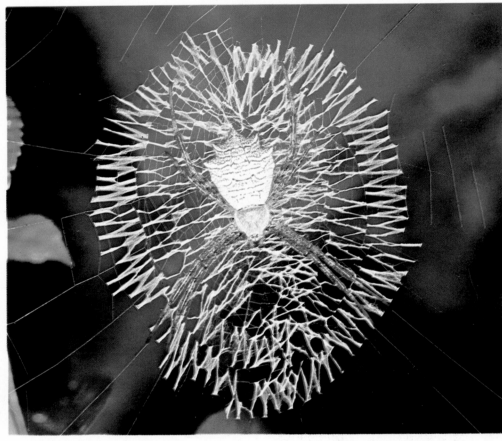

A zigzag web Spiders of the genus *Argiope* are best known for the construction of their webs, which are ornamented with ribbons of white silk. The purpose of this elaborate design is not clear, but it may distract the attention of predatory birds from the spider sitting in the middle. This species weaves its web into a central platform. Other species weave a variety of ribbon patterns

Bird-eating spider This Asian spider is a huge and hairy member of the Theraphosidae family. Though insects and mice are its more usual prey, it can kill a small bird with its poisonous bite

Spiders are the most successful group of land-living arthropods, apart from insects. They range freely through the forest from the canopy down to the ground.

The biggest spiders of all dwell in holes and under fallen timber on the forest floor. They are the bird-eating spiders, sometimes called tarantulas, though the real tarantula is quite a small spider that lives in Italy. Species found in the forests of South America have bodies up to three inches long.

Several species of very primitive spiders live in burrows in the forests of Burma, Malaya, and Sumatra. They belong to the genus *Liphistius* and closely resemble forms that lived in the Carboniferous period, 300 million years ago. Their most obvious primitive characteristic is a segmented abdomen. In all modern spiders the abdomen is bag-shaped and less obviously segmented.

Resembling spiders, but sufficiently distinct to be put in an order of their own, are the rare ricinuleids. Most species live in the rain forest. They are confined to two areas, one in tropical West Africa and the other extending from Texas to the Amazon basin.

Protective spines The sharp spines on the black-and-yellow spiders of the genus *Micrathena* may provide protection from predators

Antlike spider Though it looks and acts like an ant, eight legs make it a spider, not an insect. Several such species live in the tropical forests

Giant centipede The giant centipede *Scolopendra morsitans,* which is common in tropical Asia, grows to a length of eight inches. An American tropical species can be up to one foot long

All-round defense Like all pill millipedes, those of the tropical forest genus *Sphaerobius* roll up into a tight ball when they are molested

Centipede

Giant millipedes These Malayan forest scavengers feed on decaying plant material found on the forest floor. Some may grow up to ten inches long

Millipede (from below)

Two ways of running Centipedes and millipedes each have their own way of moving. In both, the legs are activated by "power waves" that travel forward along each side of the body. In centipedes, the waves alternate, causing them to move with a wriggling motion. In millipedes, the waves are simultaneous, so that opposite groups of legs bunch together or spread out at the same time

One predatory centipede of the tropical rain forest may be as much as a foot long

Scorpions are also arachnids. The biggest are those of the genera *Pandinus* and *Heterometrus* which inhabit the rain forests of Africa and Asia, living on the forest floor under loose bark and fallen timber. These dark green creatures are up to ten inches long, including the claws. Like all scorpions, they use a sting at the end of the tail for self-defense and for paralyzing prey.

Centipedes have 15 to 170 pairs of legs, one pair on every body-segment. They are active and predatory, armed with a pair of poisonous claws, which are simply the first pair of legs transformed to act as a pair of fangs. The rain forest centipedes of the genus *Scolopendra* are formidable; some species reach a length of 12 inches.

Millipedes may have up to 200 pairs of legs, two pairs on each segment. They are slow-moving and nonpredatory, feeding on vegetable matter. They defend themselves by emitting repulsive or even poisonous fluids from pores along the sides of the body, and usually curl up in a spiral or a ball if they are molested.

Velvet worms belong to another class of arthropods known as Onychophora. Though not confined to the tropics, they need a moist environment, and all the tropical species live in rain forests. The best-known genus, *Peripatus,* like all velvet worms, looks like a caterpillar with a soft velvety skin. It has about two dozen pairs of legs and a pair of tentacles on the head. Velvet worms feed on termites and other small insects, and defend themselves by squirting a sticky liquid from their tentacles. This immobilizes small animals such as ants.

Most flatworms, which belong to the phylum Platyhelminthes, are either small water-living animals or parasites, such as the liver-fluke and tapeworm, which live inside larger animals. Like leeches, flatworms need a damp environment. The few species that are free-living (that is, not living inside another animal) on land are mostly found in the rain forests. They glide over the ground with a rippling motion, their flattened and often brightly colored and patterned bodies always moist and shining with a coating of slime.

Each limestone hill has its unique group of tiny snails

In the limestone hills of the Malayan and Bornean rain forests lives a group of minute snails of the genus *Opisthostoma.*

Every isolated limestone hill supports a large variety of snails. Each population group is separated from the others by the surrounding calcium-deficient countryside. Since snails cannot cross such barriers (because they need calcium to live), the populations are as effectively isolated as if they were on islands. This has led to each hill supporting several species of snails that have evolved on it and are found nowhere else.

Bloodsuckers A leech of the genus *Haemadipsa* lives by sucking mammals' blood. At each end of the body is a sucker. It attaches first with the back sucker, then applies the front sucker to the skin

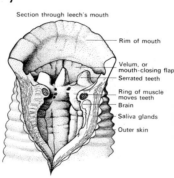

Section through leech's mouth

- Rim of mouth
- Velum, or mouth-closing flap
- Serrated teeth
- Ring of muscle moves teeth
- Brain
- Saliva glands
- Outer skin

Giant snail The plant-eating species *Achatina fulica,* about six inches long, has spread from Africa across tropical Asia to the Pacific. Other members of this genus are widespread throughout tropical Africa

Effects of isolation Separated by calcium-deficient soil, the species of the genus *Opisthostoma* evolved different forms on neighboring hills in Malaya and Borneo. These shells are 20 times larger than life size

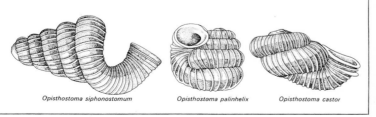

Opisthostoma siphonostomum   *Opisthostoma palinhelix*   *Opisthostoma castor*

The brilliant world of insects

**The warm, humid tropical forests provide
ideal conditions for millions of insects.
The total number of species
there will probably never be known**

Since there is little seasonal variation in the
rain forest, insects breed there throughout
the year. The life cycle of a single insect is
often completed in a few weeks, and 12 to 20
generations may succeed one another in a
year. Evolution can proceed very rapidly
in these conditions, and an enormous diversity of insects is found in the wide range
of habitats which exist between the canopy
and the floor of the rain forest.

Just how many species exist will probably
never be known; one collector in the Amazon forests obtained 14,000 species, and the
1000-mile-long Malay Peninsula has 1000
species of native butterflies alone. The insects are the major consumers of forest vegetation and, in turn, are themselves a vital
food source for large populations of mammals, birds, reptiles, and amphibians.

Leaf insect The entire body of this insect is green,
with markings resembling leaf veins and fungi

Warning colors and camouflage deceive predator birds

The insect communities of the tropical rain
forests contain both hunters and hunted. The
demands of seeking prey or avoiding capture
have led to the evolution of a wide range of
adaptations, one of the most important of
which is camouflage. Many forest insects
resemble vegetation to an astonishing degree.
Some grasshoppers and butterflies, for example, when resting with closed wings,
merge with the leaves that make up their
background, and stick insects, when motionless, look like twigs. Among the predatory
insects, several mantises have evolved forms
like dead leaves, lichen, or flowers. These
adaptations conceal them from predators,
and also assist them when they are ambush-
ing their own prey.

Though camouflage is the more usual result of protective coloration, butterflies
especially make a different use of color. Far
from being concealed, some brilliantly hued
butterflies are the most conspicuous of forest
animals. Their striking colors and patterns
warn predators that the butterflies are poisonous or distasteful. Birds, for example, are
able to distinguish unpalatable species by
color, and leave them alone.

Some butterflies that belong to families
whose members are all edible have developed
colors and patterns similar to those of the

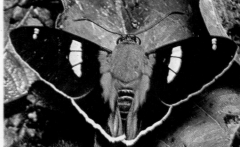

Fast flier Skippers, such as this South American
Pyrrhopyge, are capable of fast, controlled flight,
in contrast to the flutterings of other butterflies

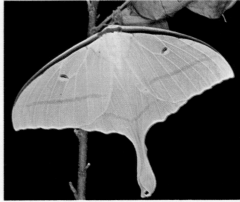

Moon moth The beautiful luna or moon moth
of India is an example of the many spectacular
moth species living in the lower forest zone

Insect or flower? The orchid mantis of the genus
Hymenopus (left) preys on insects and in turn is
the prey of birds. Butterflies are lured within the
grasp of the mantis's forelegs by petallike extensions on its limbs. This mantis is a nymph

A male butterfly Only the males of Rajah Brooke's birdwing butterfly come to the ground. The females live high among the trees

Wanderers at rest Yellow butterflies of the genus *Phoebis* are widespread in the New World forests. All are large, with a wingspan of about three inches. Some are migratory and form traveling swarms

Forest color The South American *Marpesia marcella* is typical of brightly colored forest butterflies

unpalatable butterflies, and so they gain the same protection against predatory birds as the unpalatable species.

More butterflies and moths are found in the rain forests than in all other environments put together, and in these forests are the largest and most brilliant species. The biggest, Queen Alexandra's birdwing butterfly, lives in the New Guinea forest canopy and has a wingspan of ten inches.

Female butterflies of many species spend their lives in the treetops and are seldom seen by man. The males, however, often crowd in hundreds beside rivers or mineral springs. Possibly they are attracted by dissolved salt; those found near rivers usually congregate at drinking places where animals have urinated on the sand.

Huge night-flying moths, and brightly colored beetles that shine like gold

Moths are even more numerous than butterflies, but since most species are nocturnal, they are less in evidence. Many moths equal, and even surpass, the butterflies in size. The noctuid moth, for example, has a wingspan of 11 inches, and the atlas moth is only an inch smaller. The biggest moth, and the largest of the moth and butterfly order, or Lepidoptera, is the Hercules moth, which lives in tropical Australia and New Guinea; its wings may cover a total area of nearly 100 square inches.

The countless beetles of the rain forests are remarkable for size and color. Beetles of the Buprestidae family, whose larvae tunnel in wood, have metallic green or copper-colored wing cases which are used as ornaments by people of both the Old and New World tropics. Tortoise beetles of the Cassidinae subfamily shine like golden drops among the leaves, but their luster fades quickly after death.

Ants mainly inhabit the jungle floor, though leaf-cutter ants of the genus *Atta* forage in the trees, where they cut segments of green leaves with their scissorlike mandibles. The leaf fragments are carried back to the underground nest, where the ants chew them into compost. They feed this compost to the fungus that forms their food supply.

The Hercules beetle This New World giant lives in South American rain forests and is one of the world's largest beetles. Almost half of the male's length consists of two enormous horns that curve forward from the head and thorax. Their function is unknown, but they may be of sexual significance

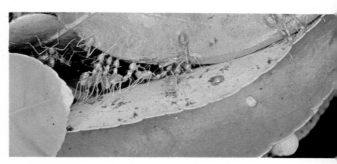

The leaf weavers Worker weaving ants begin their nest building by drawing the edges of leaves together before they are bound by silk-spinning larvae

237

MOUNTAINS

**Constantly eroded by wind and rain—and, over the millennia,
slumping, buckling, or arching as the plates of the earth grind against one
another—the mountains are not as solid and eternal as they seem**

The higher mountains of the world, whether isolated peaks such as Mount Kenya or continent-dividing ranges such as the Andes and the Himalayas, lack to some extent the protection afforded by the earth's atmosphere. This blanket of air protects plants and animals from the full force of solar radiation during the day, and at night prevents the rapid escape of heat from the earth's surface.

Air contains oxygen, which all animals use in respiration—"burning" food with it to obtain energy. But the higher a mountain rises, the less dense (or "thinner") and less insulating the atmosphere becomes. There is more space between the air's molecules of oxygen, so there is less oxygen available. For every 500 feet a mountain rises, the temperature falls about two degrees Fahrenheit. Also, wind speeds tend to increase with altitude. Such conditions hardly favor the growth of plants; and soil is constantly being eroded: washed away by rain, broken up by frost, and carried downhill with falling rocks.

Above timberline, a snowbound zone

The timberline marks the limit above which trees cannot survive. The altitude of the timberline varies throughout the world, according to local soil and climatic conditions. As the forest climbs, trees become smaller, more stunted, and then disappear, giving way to shrubs. These in turn give way to alpine grassland, followed by mosses and lichens. Finally, at the greatest heights, there is a permanent snow belt, where hardly any food exists to support plant or animal life.

There are as many life zones on a 20,000-foot mountain at the equator, rising less than four vertical miles, as there are in the approximately 6200 miles at sea level that extend between the equator and either pole.

For the relatively few species that live in the high mountains, food is scarce, the climate is bitter cold for much of the year, and—particularly over 16,000 feet—there is a lack of oxygen. Many mountain vertebrates have more oxygen-absorbing red blood cells than their lowland counterparts. Some animals can live nowhere but on a mountain. Such highly adapted mountain species are as effectively isolated as if they lived on an island.

Mountains cover only a small proportion of the earth's surface, yet they have a major impact on climatic conditions. Winds and rain patterns are in-fluenced by mountains and in turn erode the mountains, washing down soil materials to more temperate zones, where they nourish plant life.

Winds are air movements caused by hot air rising and cold air moving in to take its place. Basically, the direction of winds is determined by the rotation of the earth; and wind patterns would be simple and predictable if mountains did not get in the way. Mountains create eddies in the flow of air, and these eddies produce variations in temperature and rainfall that can affect climate thousands of miles away. Moisture-bearing winds rise with the mountain contours to higher altitudes, where the moisture cools and condenses into rain. On mountains' leeward side (the side sheltered from the wind), little condensation occurs. In this "rain shadow" an arid area develops.

How the mountains were formed

The layer of dense basaltic rock that forms the earth's crust has been found to consist of six huge, irregularly shaped plates that lie on a layer of rock called the mantle. Continents are carried on these basaltic plates.

The plates have been moving continuously for the past three billion years. At the point where two plates meet, the edge of one descends into the earth's mantle and the other's edge buckles up to form a chain of islands, such as the Aleutians, or, if it has a continent on its edge, a mountain range, such as the Andes.

Continents are too buoyant to be forced down into the molten interior, since they consist of less dense rocks. Earthquakes along the Andes chain are caused by a sudden displacement of the rocks, jarred by the descending plate's grinding against the continent's edge.

The great frictional heat produced by the descent of a basaltic plate can cause volcanoes: the basalt melts and escapes upward.

Mountain-building of the Himalayan kind occurs when plate movement pushes together two continental blocks and causes buckling of both plates.

Solid and immovable though they seem, mountains are in a constant state of flux. The growing or shrinking is almost imperceptible year by year, but over a thousand-year period the change in them is considerable.

Sediment washed from continents accumulates on the seabed, particularly near continents. When two plates collide, this accumulated sediment may be scraped off the descending plate onto the mountain range or island chain. This is another way in which mountains "grow."

Monarch of the peaks An ibex pauses on an alpine crag to survey his mountain kingdom. Below, on the snow-covered lower slopes, is the beginning of the timberline

Islands in the sky

**In the barren soil and punishing climate
between the timberline and the zone
of permanent snow, only shrubs, dwarf
trees, and a few other plants grow**

The mountain life zone, or "alpine" biome, comprises those areas that lie above both the timberline and an altitude of 8200 feet. At this height the air is only three quarters as dense as at sea level.

The ice-capped peaks and barren slopes of the world's higher mountains have a polar-like appearance, though many mountains are thousands of miles from either pole. But life in the mountains is far different from life in polar regions.

Four factors largely determine the nature of plant and animal life in mountain zones: thin air, low temperature, low humidity, and high winds.

Mountain ranges act both as barriers and as refuges

Where large mountain chains run from east to west, they cause a sharp division between the climatic areas on each side of them. One such chain, formed by the Caucasus range, the Hindu Kush, and the Himalayas, obstructs the movement of tempering winds, subjecting Siberia to excessive cold and India to excessive heat. The chain also prevents the north-south movement of animals. Similarly, mountain chains running from north to south bar the east-west movement of animals.

The Rockies, the Sierra Madre, and the Andes form a north-south chain through both North and South America, so that different animals are found east or west of the barrier. In Africa, where there are no high mountain chains south of the Atlas range, plant and animal species often have very wide ranges.

Timberline in the tropics

A mountain can make its own climate to a remarkable extent. For example, a mountain's timberline generally occurs above the altitude where the average monthly temperature never exceeds 50° F. (10° C.). Citlaltepetl is an isolated 18,696-foot peak, well inside the tropics, at 19° N, in Mexico. Mount Everest, on the Nepal-Tibet border, 29,028 feet high, is part of the massive Himalayan range and lies 600 miles farther

north than Citlaltepetl; yet the timberlines of both mountains begin at the same level, about 13,000 feet.

Mountains cut Sumatra in two

The effectiveness of an unbroken mountain barrier is clearly demonstrated on the island of Sumatra. The island is divided by the Barisan range, with peaks rising to 13,000 feet. Many animals found in the southwest of Sumatra are not found in the northeast of the island, although the climate is similar in both sections.

In other high ranges, mountains that have been barriers to the spread of other species provide a refuge for isolated "pockets" of animals such as the ibex of Eurasia and the bighorn of North America

The sun's rays reach the high mountains after a relatively short journey through a thin layer of atmosphere. But the sun's rays also radiate quickly back from the mountains into the atmosphere because of the high altitude and thin atmosphere. This heat loss is intensified by the low density of air at high altitudes. Air pressure is also low at high altitudes because there is less atmosphere pressing down from above.

Low-density, low-pressure air influences every other factor of the high-altitude environment. Low-density air cannot retain

much water—so humidity (the moisture-content of the air) is low. This absence of moisture makes the air clearer than it is at sea level, which in turn permits the passage of more ultraviolet rays in solar radiation.

In addition, there is a wide divergence between ground and air temperatures during the day, since the ground absorbs more heat from the sun than the low-density air. Because frictional drag with the earth's surface is reduced, winds tend to attain high speeds in mountains, increasing evaporation and leading to even lower temperatures.

Shelter under a rock

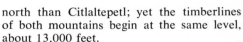

Beneath mountain rocks the temperature variation between day and night is least, and small animals can find shelter there. Ground surface temperatures vary more than air temperatures. The low-density mountain air can absorb only a limited amount of the sun's heat, so that much of the heat reaches the ground

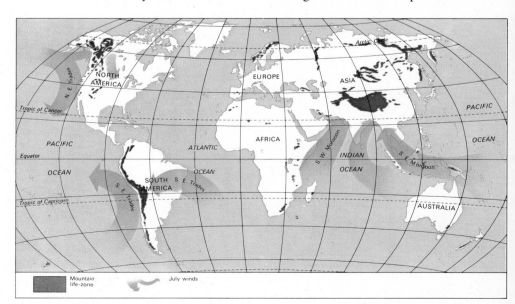

Wind patterns The principal winds of the world are influenced by mountains. The moisture-bearing monsoons of southern Asia cool as they rise against the barrier of the Himalayas and spill vast quantities of water on the land to the south of the range. On the other side are the deserts

Zones of rocks and lichens Coming just before the permanent snowline of Mount Sir Donald in British Columbia is a typical zone of lichen-encrusted rocks, tussocks of grass, and patches of snow

Alpine grassland Heath and tussocks of grass, as well as stunted shrubs, form part of the alpine zone above the timberline of the Beartooth Mountains in Montana. Higher still are lichen-covered rocks

Above the clouds Snow-capped mountains form inhospitable islands. At more than 12,000 feet these glaciers and ragged pinnacles of the Savoie Alps in France cannot support the growth of vegetation

The many zones of a mountain

A mountain situated on an equatorial coast typically would have mangrove swamps at sea level. These would merge into tropical forest which, at about 3000 feet, would give way to deciduous and broad-leaved evergreen forest. At 9000 feet coniferous forest would begin.

The height at which different zones of vegetation begin is partly determined by the exposure of a particular slope. In Nepal at 10,000 feet the cool north-facing slopes are covered with conifers. At the same level the dry, sunny southern slopes are grassland.

The timberline may occur below 2000 feet in Scandinavia and above 13,000 feet at the equator. Above the timberline there is typically, first, a zone of shrubs and dwarf trees —miniature, moss-draped versions of local forest trees. Above this is alpine-type grassland, with tundra vegetation (see page 21). Immediately below the snowline, in the subsnow zone, a few hardy flowering plants grow, and rocks are crusted with lichens.

In the Himalayas these three above-timberline vegetation zones are succeeded by a fourth—the aeolian zone. Here, organic debris windborne from the plains below supports some tiny plants and scavenging insects.

Vegetation zones linked to altitude and latitude

Vegetation layers From the grass and deciduous forest of this Tyrolean valley, the vegetation changes with increasing altitude

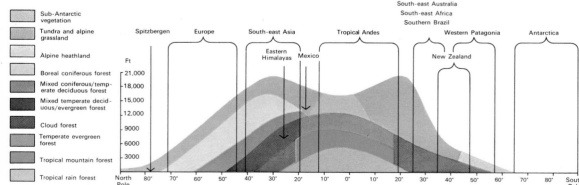

In humid parts of the world, an increase in altitude can create vegetation zones in the same way new zones arise with distance away from the equator.

Because there are smaller land areas in the southern hemisphere, the zone systems are far less complex than those in the northern hemisphere

241

Survival above the tree line

Mountains present a formidable challenge to life: oxygen shortage, low humidity, high winds, glaringly bright light, and poor soil. Yet many species thrive there

Any plant or animal that has established itself successfully above the tree line, in an alpine habitat, shows adaptations that set it apart from related species living in the more hospitable environments afforded by the lowlands. These adaptations have made alpine species different from the lowland forms in shape, size, color, and internal physiology, including reproductive patterns.

Mountain conditions prevent the sexual production of seeds in the manner associated with most familiar plants; mountain plant species reproduce themselves by other means. The drooping saxifrage forms little buds, or bulbils, at the junction of leaf and stem. These bulbils drop off, winter beneath the snow, and produce new plants the following spring. Some species, such as the mountain buttercup, can develop seeds without being fertilized. Others, including the mountain grass, have seeds that germinate, or sprout, while still attached to the parent plant.

Mammals have adapted to the shortage of oxygen by developing large lungs and hearts. Alpine species also tend to have relatively more oxygen-carrying red blood cells than lowland creatures.

Protection against extremes of climate

The North American deer mouse lives in habitats ranging from low-lying deserts to high mountains. At the higher altitudes, deer mice have larger hearts, and their circulating blood contains more red cells and hemoglobin. These adaptations enable mountain deer mice to absorb and circulate sufficient oxygen to survive in the thinner air. At 4500 feet, the ratio of heart weight to total body weight is approximately .007, and a pint of the animal's blood would contain about 1.7 ounces of hemoglobin. At 14,500 feet the animal's heart-body ratio is .01—a heart proportionately half again as big—and a pint of blood has 3.4 ounces of hemoglobin—or twice as much oxygen-carrying capacity as at the 4500-foot level.

Many mountain animals grow thick coats that protect them from extremes of temperature. Other warm-blooded species are larger than their lowland relatives, and the reduction in the ratio between body surface and body size reduces the rate at which these animals lose heat.

Some cold-blooded animals can be frozen without dying. Roundworms have survived in laboratory experiments at temperatures of −457° F. (−272° C.). Springtails have revived after being frozen for three years in a glacier.

A bird that digs a hole

Some mountain animals, including deer, sheep, and ibexes, move to lower altitudes in winter. Others hibernate, like the alpine marmot, or store food, like the Tibetan pika. Several South American ovenbirds, such as the shaketail, dig their own holes in which they shelter from high winds and snow.

The Patagonian earthcreeper, living high in the Andes, is about the size of a finch. It has strongly developed feet and legs and digs a three-foot-long underground passage into the slope of a hill to its spacious nesting chamber.

Small mountain animals tend to breed less often than their lowland relatives, and favorable seasons for the growth of young are often short.

Adapted to high altitudes In the Andes, the vicuna can cope with the thin atmosphere at 14,000 to 18,000 feet because its blood absorbs large quantities of oxygen. Vicunas have 14 million oxygen-carrying red cells per cubic millimeter of blood compared to man's 5 million. Even at an altitude of 15,000 feet, they can run 30 miles per hour. Vicunas also have thick coats that keep out the cold

Bimaculated calandra lark
Melanocorypha bimaculata

Long-billed calandra lark
Melanocorypha maxima

Longer bill for mountain life Two species of calandra larks are found in India. The mountain species, which probes for insects in hard ground, has a longer, sharper bill than the lowland species

How plants survive

Most alpine plants are small. They are also perennial, but each year brings only a brief season in which growth can occur. Year by year, bit by bit, mountain perennials attain sufficient size—and sufficient resources of energy and nutrients—to reproduce. Of 300 species found above the timberline in the Rockies, only two are annuals—plants that grow for one season and then die, after producing seeds that will germinate the following spring.

Some alpine plants are protected from frost by their rich cell fluid, which acts like antifreeze in lowering the point at which the plants freeze. Others conserve heat. The cushion pink is surrounded by a dense mat of stalks. The matted stalks form a microclimate, in which the temperature can be 18 degrees higher than the surrounding air. A few plants can actually produce heat. One is the alpine soldanella, which melts snow by converting its carbohydrates into heat that radiates from its shoot.

High winds affect plants and animals

Some mountain plants belonging to different families have similar adaptations for coping with high winds—for example, cushion shapes that offer minimum wind resistance.

Flight is hazardous in the mountains—especially so for small birds and insects, which are likely to be blown off course or swept along at the mercy of the high winds. Most small mountain birds rarely fly, and 60 percent of insects found above the timberline are wingless. Even those that have wings seldom use them. The American cockroach has wings, and in tropical lowlands both sexes fly. But in low-lying temperate zones, only males fly; while in the mountains, neither sex leaves the ground.

Low humidity and high solar radiation

Humidity is low in alpine areas, and snow is the main source of moisture, so most animals live along the snowline, or near glaciers, glacial lakes, and torrents of water from melting snow and ice.

High solar radiation causes many alpine animal species to develop dark colors that absorb potentially dangerous ultraviolet wavelengths. The darker color protects the underlying tissues. The pearl-bordered fritillary butterfly found in the mountains of Finland is darker than the lowland varieties. Dark colors also help many insects to absorb more heat during the day. Mountain insects are rarely active unless the sun is shining.

High ultraviolet radiation causes many alpine plants to develop more chromosomes—the structures in cells that carry genetic information—than lowland species. (The extra chromosomes sometimes result in greater adaptability.) For example, the crowberry *Empetrum hermaphroditum*, found high on mountains, has twice as many chromosomes as its lowland relative, *Empetrum nigrum*, which is found on European moors.

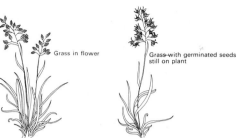

Protection for grass The mountain grass *Poa alpina* first flowers and then germinates while still attached to the parent plant. This gives it a good start in the rugged alpine conditions

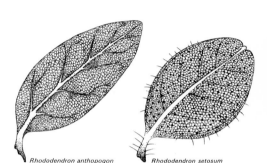

Conserving moisture Structures underneath the leaves of Himalayan rhododendrons prevent water loss in dry alpine areas. *Rhododendron setosum* has fine hairs; *Rhododendron anthopogon*, scales

Amphibian adapted to a dry climate Most salamanders reproduce by laying eggs in water. But the alpine salamander (right), living in an arid habitat, has adjusted to the scarcity of water by bearing live young. It is much darker than lowland species

Flowers that resist frost The mountain crowfoot blooms on mountains in Iceland, Greenland, and Europe. It is protected from frost damage by its rich cell fluid, which acts like antifreeze

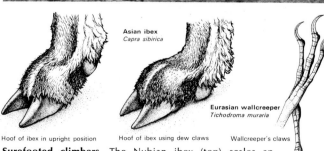

Surefooted climbers The Nubian ibex (top) scales an almost sheer mountain face. When climbing, ibexes grip with the dew claws, toes at the back of the foot, which are not used on level ground. Most hooved animals have dew claws, but never use them. The Eurasian wallcreeper (right) climbs by gripping with its sharp claws

Large mammals above the timberline

Alpine conditions influence the hunting methods of big cats—the snow leopard will stalk its prey rather than ambush it, as lowland leopards do

Most of the large mammals that live above the timberline are plant-eaters. There are few true carnivores—only the puma, wolf, snow leopard, and, on Mount Kenya, the common leopard—since mammalian prey is scarce.

Predators that roam the mountainsides

The only true alpine cat is the snow leopard, which is found up to 20,000 feet in the Altai Mountains in Mongolia, and in the Himalayas. A full-grown male is about 7½ feet long, including the tail, and weighs 100 pounds. The snow leopard's thick coat is gray-brown, shading to white underneath, and marked with blurred black rosettes. During the day they emerge from their dens to hunt over large territories for yak calves, sheep, goats, and small mammals.

The mountain pumas are much larger than the lowland races—nearly eight feet long, including the tail, and weighing 250 pounds, compared with five feet and 100 pounds. Males usually occupy home ranges that over-

Bears are common in the mountains, but their diet is not limited to flesh; they eat berries, moss, ants, and fish as well.

The only mountain representative of the cattle family is the yak, an expert climber. A few species of deer and antelopes live above the timberline in Asia and Africa, while in the Andes the camel family is represented by the vicuna, the guanaco, and the domesticated llama and alpaca.

lap the home ranges of several females. In the Rocky Mountains, females occupy a range of 5 to 20 square miles and males one of about 25 square miles.

Some pumas do not establish ranges, but wander about freely. When a wanderer enters the range of another puma, the two seem to avoid each other, using scratches and scent on trees or rocks as warning markers. Puma cubs are born at any season and hunt with their mothers until they are two years old.

The spectacled bear is the only South American bear. It lives in the Andes in Ecuador and northern Peru, but is now in danger of dying out as a species. Fruit, leaves, and roots form its basic diet.

Large cats of the mountains Snow leopards are the only truly alpine big cats, for pumas are found also in lowland areas throughout the New World

Leopard that stalks The snow leopard, unlike its lowland relative, relies entirely on stalking its prey

Hunting in the day In the mountains, the puma hunts above the timberline during the day, when its prey—deer, sheep, and rodents—are active. It hides the remains of a large kill and returns later to feed. These caches keep fresh for weeks in the low temperatures. Lower down, pumas are nocturnal

Hardy grazers and browsers

Small herds of wild yaks still exist in Tibet and Kansu Province in northwest China, although they have been domesticated for centuries in Tibet. Males and females form small, separate herds until the rut in September and October. Like musk-oxen, adult yaks form a protective circle around the young, with horns facing outward, when threatened by predators such as wolves or snow leopards.

The musk deer of central Asia is one of only two deer species that lack antlers—the other is the Chinese water deer—but the males have daggerlike upper canine teeth, which they use as weapons. Rarely are more than two or three musk deer found together. They are active in the morning and evening, and sleep during the day in "forms," like the hare. The male is highly prized by hunters for the brownish, waxlike musk secreted in its abdominal gland, which is used in making perfume and soap. Musk deer mark their territories by rubbing this substance on rocks and trees.

White-lipped or Thorold's deer, now becoming rare, travel in herds during winter over large areas of Tibet and China's Szechwan and Kansu provinces in search of their plant food.

Antelopes, vicunas, and guanacos

Only two species of antelopes are restricted to mountains, and both live in Tibet. The chiru grazes along glacial streams up to 15,000 feet, and protects itself from the cold winds by scraping shallow trenches in which to lie. This habit is shared by the Tibetan gazelle, or goa, which feeds in areas of scant vegetation as high as 18,000 feet. This gazelle is swift and agile in its rocky habitat.

Vicunas, the smallest members of the camel family, are found in the Andes between 14,000 and 18,000 feet. Guanacos, which are not good climbers, keep to the plateaus. Both species live in bands of about a dozen animals led by a male, which defends a grazing territory of 20 to 100 acres. The male vicuna warns off rivals by standing stiffly on a mound holding its ears and tail erect. Vicunas and guanacos both are swift runners, relying on speed to escape pumas, their chief predators.

Sharp eye for danger The leading male guanaco acts as a sentinel for a browsing herd. When danger threatens, it emits a sharp bleat. It remains as a rear guard as the herd moves off. Guanacos, the largest wild members of the South American branch of the camel family, often attack intruders

Survival in the cold The yak's coat is so dense and matted that the animal can live in temperatures as low as −40° F. (−40° C.). When no other food is available, the yak lives on mosses and lichens, and eats snow to obtain water. In spite of its bulk, the yak is an agile and surefooted climber

Wool from vicunas Herds of vicunas are rounded up annually for their wool, which is claimed to be the finest and lightest in the world. These animals cannot be successfully domesticated

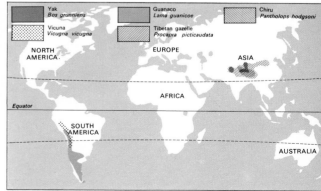

High-altitude survival Several mammals have adapted to living over 15,000 feet above sea level

Yak *Bos grunniens*	Guanaco *Lama guanicoe*	Chiru *Pantholops hodgsoni*
Vicuna *Vicugna vicugna*	Tibetan gazelle *Procapra picticaudata*	

NORTH AMERICA

EUROPE

ASIA

AFRICA

Equator

SOUTH AMERICA

AUSTRALIA

Sheep and goats

Grazers and browsers of the high mountains extract a living from tiny, isolated pastures far beyond the reach of predators

Mountain-living wild species of sheep and goats are very similar in appearance. Typically, true sheep—genus *Ovis*—have scent glands between the hooves of both fore and hind feet and on the face. True goats—genus *Capra*—have these glands on the front feet only. Male goats are bearded and have a pungent odor. But in the wild, few species are typical. Particularly in the mountains, sheep and goats have become adapted to the

same harsh conditions in similar ways, and they often resemble one another, which is rare among lowland sheep and goats.

Sheep and goats belong to one of the four tribes of the Caprinae subfamily of hooved animals. The three other tribes are the Saigini, which includes the saiga and chiru; the Rupicaprini, which includes the chamois and the Rocky Mountain goat; and the Ovibovini, consisting of the takin and the musk-ox. This subfamily is found mainly in the Old World. It is absent from the southern hemisphere, and only three species live in North America.

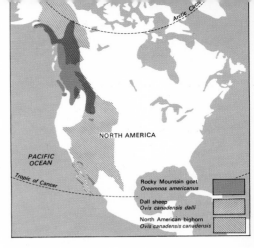

Shrinking range Until the last century, bighorn sheep were found from British Columbia to northern Mexico. Their present diminished range is partly due to their own inability to expand into new habitats. Young bighorns learn routes between mountain grasslands by following their elders. The memory dies out when man interrupts the routes

Agile sheep of the high mountain crags live where few predators can follow

Among the largest of the true sheep is the North American bighorn. Bighorns are tremendously agile and can leap easily among the rocks and crags. Mature males have massive horns that sweep back in a curve for three feet or more. The horns do not reach their full length until the ram is seven or eight years old, when it also becomes sexually mature and is ready to round up or defend a harem.

The northern race of bighorn is called the Dall sheep. These animals often have white coats. The glands on their feet leave scent trails that keep the sheep in contact with each other during the long winter nights and in mountain mists.

The Rocky Mountain goat has a dense whitish coat over a thick hide and several layers of fat—insulation against mountain cold. On its short, stocky legs and small hooves, it can pick its way over the most impassable-looking crags. These animals live far out of reach of most predators except human trophy-hunters.

The largest Eurasian wild sheep is the argali of the central Asian plateau. It weighs up to 350 pounds and has five-foot, curving horns. Argalis winter in herds in the valleys. In summer they may graze as high as 18,000 feet, and may venture even higher if threatened by snow leopards or wolves. When alarmed, argalis strike the ground

sharply with their forefeet as a warning to the herd. Older males tend to live on their own for most of the year, but return to the herd to mate in early winter.

Another Eurasian inhabitant, the bharal, seems to be an intermediate species between sheep and goats. It has neither the sheep's face glands nor the beard and strong smell of typical goats. Like the sheep, it grazes on open ground, and it can climb Himalayan rock faces with the agility of a goat. The bharal avoids woods and forests—so much so that in the valley of the Yangtze River a race of dwarf bharal has evolved only 500 yards from the main parent stock because the dwarf herd will not cross a belt of forest.

Sparring for supremacy Two bighorn rams begin their aggressive display by stretching out their necks and slightly turning their heads so that the

horns are seen to the best advantage. Rams will not fight unless their horns are of similar size. If they are, the rivals crack their heads together

Dall sheep Another race of the North American bighorn, it is smaller and its horns have a wider spread. The hoof scent glands mark a trail and this helps to keep the herd together

Inaccessible and safe The Rocky Mountain goat, a relative of the chamois, roams the most inaccessible peaks, where few predators can pursue it

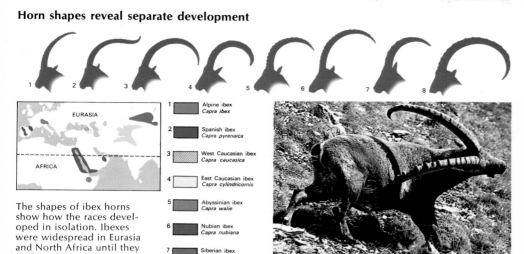

1 2 3 4 5 6 7 8

	Alpine ibex *Capra ibex*
1	
2	Spanish ibex *Capra pyrenaica*
3	West Caucasian ibex *Capra caucasica*
4	East Caucasian ibex *Capra cylindricornis*
5	Abyssinian ibex *Capra walie*
6	Nubian ibex *Capra nubiana*
7	Siberian ibex *Capra sibirica sibirica*
8	Himalayan ibex *Capra sibirica sakeen*

The shapes of ibex horns show how the races developed in isolation. Ibexes were widespread in Eurasia and North Africa until they took to the mountains in isolated groups during the Ice Age

Fighting horns The horns of the male ibex—about three feet long—are used in battles with other rams

Goats of Eurasia migrate to mountain peaks in summer

The markhor is a true goat, the largest member of the genus *Capra*. It is almost as big as an argali, with curving, four-foot-long horns, a heavy beard, and a rank odor. Lacking insulating underfur, markhors abandon the high cliffs of the Himalayas and Hindu Kush in winter and descend to sheltered valleys, where they gather in large herds. In summer, the males separate and migrate to heights where females with dependent young cannot climb.

The Himalayan tahr, which resembles a goat, has a magnificent, shaggy mane. It is often found below the timberline—sometimes so low that it falls victim to tigers that roam the forest, hunting for prey.

The eight forms of ibex, so closely related that they interbreed in captivity, are most reliably identified by their horns. All live at high altitudes and feed on grass and lichens, in winter seeking snow-free patches of rock warmed by the sun. When the adults

descend to lower levels to feed, the young stay behind, hidden in holes and crevices.

The chamois, like the Rocky Mountain goat, lacks scent glands on both the face and feet, but has glands just behind the horns. Chamois use their glands to scent-mark shrubs and rocks in their territories. The males, solitary for most of the year, rejoin the herds during the November breeding season. They threaten one another by erecting the hairs along the ridge of the back.

The takin, a member of the Ovibovini tribe, has only one close relative—the musk-ox of the Arctic. The takin resembles a short-legged gnu, and lives in rhododendron thickets near the timberline in Assam and western China. Four feet long, but extremely agile, it can elude predators in steep, broken country. Most takins are brown with black faces, but one race in the Shensi mountains of northern China is entirely covered with golden hair.

Mountain habitat (right) Three distinct races of the sheep *Ovis ammon* live in the mountains of central Asia. There are eight other races, including the mouflon, which lives on Mediterranean islands, and the urial of western Asia. Their massive horns are deeply wrinkled

Formosan serow This serow inhabits wooded rocky ridges in Taiwan and Japan. It is not particularly agile, but its solid hooves give a sure grip, especially when descending steep slopes

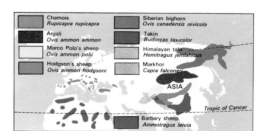

Chamois *Rupicapra rupicapra*	Siberian bighorn *Ovis canadensis nivicola*
Argali *Ovis ammon ammon*	Takin *Budorcas taxicolor*
Marco Polo's sheep *Ovis ammon polii*	Himalayan tahr *Hemitragus jemlahicus*
Hodgson's sheep *Ovis ammon hodgsoni*	Markhor *Capra falconeri*
	Barbary sheep *Ammotragus lervia*

ASIA

Tropic of Cancer

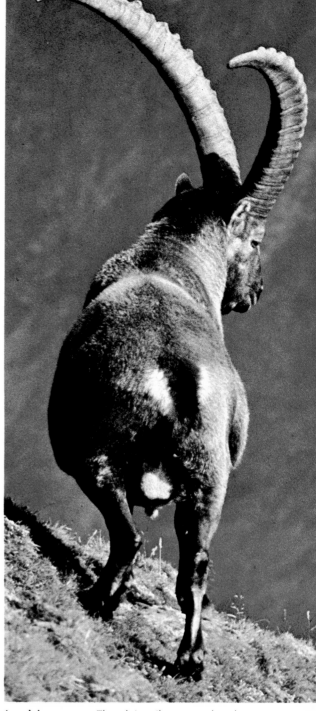

An alpine grazer The alpine ibex, now largely restricted to the Italian Alps, grazes on high-altitude vegetation in summer, but descends to avoid deep snow during the winter months

Mother and kid High on a mountain ledge, a female chamois guards its young. Almost from birth, chamois kids can follow the mother, and within a few days they leap from rock to rock

Birds and small mammals

Because so few species are adapted to live high in the mountains, there is not the fierce competition among species found in the temperate and tropical lowlands

Birds and small mammals are the most successful vertebrates in alpine areas. Their warm blood, of course, is an advantage. But this alone would be inadequate for survival in the worst cold. Then, birds can simply fly away, while small animals shelter in crevices and holes.

In the mountains, each species' niche or habitat is usually all its own, and there is little or no overlapping of food preferences. In lowland biomes, on the other hand, there are usually several species competing with one another for food and territory within a given area.

The higher a mountain altitude the less food (plants and prey) there is. Perhaps as a result, mountain species, both birds and mammals, tend to be quite aggressive, hold large territories, and have low reproductive rates. Alpine birds and mammals rarely produce offspring more than once a year.

Mountain vulture The lämmergeier, a member of the vulture family, can fly above 30,000 feet

Birds of prey and perching birds live in a world where the wind is master

Birds in the high mountains must cope with savage, buffeting winds. The birds of prey (including the scavengers) are usually big enough, heavy enough, and strong enough for flight in strong winds. Some perching birds, however, rarely fly; and all keep close to the ground away from the full force of the wind. Their feet are adapted to cling firmly to rocky surfaces.

One of the strongest fliers among the birds of prey is the lämmergeier, which has been seen flying at more than 30,000 feet. This eaglelike member of the vulture family inhabits the mountains of Africa and Eurasia.

Lämmergeiers are scavengers. Their blunt talons, like those of other vultures, are unsuitable for killing prey. But, unlike other vultures, lämmergeiers can lift and carry food. They are said to drop bones onto rocks from heights of several hundred feet. The bones shatter on impact, exposing the edible marrow.

Another mountain scavenger is the Andean condor of South America. Its relative, the Californian condor, once widespread in the mountains of North America, is now reduced to a population of about 40 birds in southern California.

Golden eagles range throughout Eurasia and North America. They often make long journeys from their nesting sites, which are usually on rocky ledges, to their hunting grounds. They prey mainly on small mammals, but also eat carrion.

Perching birds of the mountains include alpine choughs, the Eurasian wallcreeper, and accentors. Alpine choughs, which live in the mountains of Eurasia and North Africa, occupy the highest habitat on earth. They have been seen at 27,000 feet on Mount Everest, and they probably reach the 29,028-foot summit. Choughs move in flocks of 20

Giant scavenger With a wingspan of up to ten feet, the Andean condor is one of the largest flying birds. Like other vultures, it is a carrion-eater

Golden eagle and its prey In winter golden eagles fly many miles in search of food. This bird is looking up from its half-eaten prey lying in the snow. Its victims include birds and small mammals

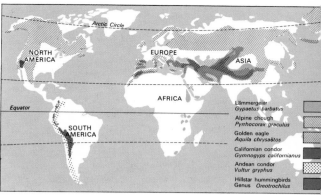

Contrasting ranges Though widely distributed, the golden eagle is rare over most of its range. The Andean condor is more common in its range

to 30, foraging for worms and insects. They store surplus food in crevices to eat later.

Eurasian wallcreepers, small, square-tailed birds related to nuthatches, cling to cliff faces at heights up to 18,000 feet. They climb up a rock face obliquely, supporting themselves with their stiff tail feathers. They climb down headfirst, their thin, curved bills probing into cracks in search of insects.

Several accentors, small sparrowlike birds related to thrushes, live in the high mountains of Eurasia. Accentors are solitary, unobtrusive birds that hop and creep over the ground and rarely fly. In summer they live on insects, but in winter they migrate to lower altitudes to feed on seeds and berries.

The Himalayan accentor breeds above 17,000 feet.

South America's 300-odd species of hummingbirds include some that live only high in the Andes. One entire genus, *Oreotrochilus,* is confined to altitudes between 10,000 and 16,000 feet. One species is found only on the slopes of 20,000-foot Mount Chimborazo, in Ecuador. Flowers are rare in the high Andes, so these mountain birds, called hillstar hummingbirds, feed mostly on insects. They build their nests of feathers, fern fronds, and cobwebs, either on cliff edges, where they get the most sunlight, or deep inside caves, where they are sheltered from the wind and cold.

Clinging on Eurasian wallcreepers cling to cliff faces at altitudes up to 18,000 feet. They nest in deep crevices, where the young remain until they can fly and climb. Then they become independent

The ubiquitous rodents burrow and store food at high altitudes

Rodents are the most numerous small mammals in the mountains, as they are in most lowland zones.

Their habits of burrowing and storing food for winter enable several species of mice to live at high altitudes—for example, the European snow vole and the groove-toothed rat, which is found above the timberline on Mount Kenya. Like all mountain rodent species, they have longer fur and shorter breeding seasons than their relatives that live in the lowlands.

Marmots and ground squirrels are distributed over the mountains of North America and Eurasia. All species dig long burrows with grass-lined nesting chambers, up to ten feet underground. Unlike other squirrels, these species do not hoard food. Instead they build up reserves of fat in summer, and hibernate in their burrows during winter.

Relatives of porcupines and rabbits

In South America a number of species of chinchillas, cavies, and pacas—members of the porcupine group—fill mountain habitats occupied elsewhere by mice, squirrels, and pikas, which are small animals related to rabbits. They live at heights of up to 17,000 feet, and feed on shrubby plants.

Pikas live on rocky slopes in the mountains of North America and Asia. All 14 species collect green plants in summer, dry them in the sun, then store them in hollows under the rocks for winter food. The Tibetan pika lives in one of the highest habitats of all those occupied by mammals: 18,000 feet up in the Himalayas.

A hay-stacker The pika will lay out this freshly picked sprig of columbine to dry in the sun before adding it to its haystack of winter supplies

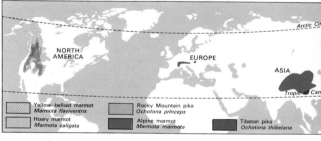

Ranges of mountain mammals Pikas have a scattered distribution, suggesting that they are the remnants of a more widely distributed group

Chipmunks with their own mountain zones

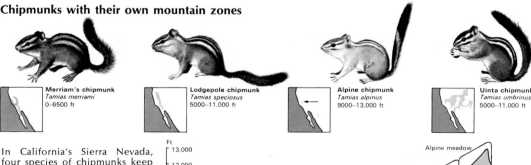

Merriam's chipmunk
Tamias merriami
0–6500 ft

Lodgepole chipmunk
Tamias speciosus
5000–11,000 ft

Alpine chipmunk
Tamias alpinus
9000–13,000 ft

Uinta chipmunk
Tamias umbrinus
5000–11,000 ft

In California's Sierra Nevada, four species of chipmunks keep fairly strictly to separate altitude zones. The sizes of both plants and chipmunks diminish with the altitude. On the western side, the 9-inch Merriam's chipmunk inhabits the lowest zone. The 8½-inch lodgepole chipmunk lives mainly in the mountain forest, and the alpine meadow is occupied by the 7-inch alpine chipmunk. On the drier eastern side of the mountains lives the 8-inch uinta

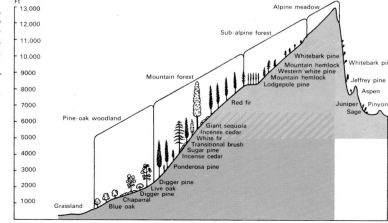

High-living communities of invertebrates

Tiny wingless insects called springtails, found up to 20,000 feet, are a basic link in many food chains above the timberline

The most populous group of animals above the timberline are insects and other invertebrates. They survive the high, dry altitude and winter cold because of, not in spite of, the snow. Snow provides them with a protective blanket not only against extremes of temperature, but also against ultraviolet radiation and desiccation in the dry air.

Snow keeps the ground from freezing in winter and supplies the moisture that stimulates plant growth in summer. Without snow, there would be no alpine communities of any kind much above the timberline. With it, the region can support a unique, complex system of life.

Mountain insects rely for much of their food on a constant airlift from the lowlands. All year round, the warmer lowland winds lift pollen, seeds, insects, and spiders into the cold upper air, where the animals are instantly frozen to death. Icy winds then carry this refrigerated food supply hundreds of miles to the mountains and deposit it on the snowfields.

In some parts of the Himalayas, a dead lowland insect is deposited on each square yard of snow every 30 seconds. All this organic debris builds up in the snow, providing a larder that keeps a large number of alpine animals alive.

Pockets of dense populations

The active feeding period of mountain insects is limited to the short summer of six to eight weeks. For some species the total feeding period is no more than a few sunny hours in the whole year.

As altitude increases, food supplies decrease, and with them the number of animal species. But, in the absence of competition, the population of each species becomes larger. Enormous numbers of individual animals are packed into each available habitat. Up to 30 insects, ranging as big as 1½ inches long, have been counted squeezed, curled, and tucked into a square inch of ground.

Animal habitats above the timberline include snow, glacier, and ice surfaces, as well as snow-earth mixtures. These areas are also visited by many wandering birds and insects.

Generally, the food chain in the snow

Butterflies that fly high The Apollo butterfly, restricted to mountainous regions, flies mainly at altitudes of 2500 to 6000 feet. In the Himalayas other members of the same genus—*Parnassius*—fly at more than 17,000 feet, and some of these breed at altitudes over 15,000 feet

Mountain mating A pair of day-flying moths *Zygaena exulans* mate high in the Alps. This species lives at 6000 to 8000 feet

Numerous butterflies The marbled white butterfly *Melanargia galathea* is abundant throughout the mountains and lowlands of western Europe and Russia, as far south as the Caucasus. The larvae feed on a variety of grasses and the adults are found in the grasslands

Asp viper This snake lives in the Pyrenees and most of southern Europe at altitudes up to 9700 feet. It feeds on small birds, lizards, and insects

Alpine butterflies Idas blue butterflies *Lycaeides idas* are small. The spots on the wings may deter predators from striking a vital part

Migrants on the march The larvae of several species of midges make mass migrations, in columns up to 100 feet long and ten inches wide. The function of these migrations has not been determined. The larvae, known as heerwurms or snakeworms, feed on rotting vegetation

community rests on several species of tiny, wingless, pollen-eating creatures called springtails, some of which are found as high as 20,000 feet in the Himalayas. Swarms of mites, beetles, and flies congregate to feed on a population of springtails.

Water from melting snow softens the bodies of dead insects, and their juices are sucked by small hairy flies, *Limnophora triangulifera.* Among the mites that prey on springtails in Eurasian mountains are some species that are so hardy they can survive being frozen solid.

Rock habitats range from bare stone surfaces, cracks, and fissures, to screes—loose stones and debris left by glaciers. Nunataks —peaks of barren rock projecting above the permanent snow—provide the harshest environment on earth. No animal can exist there until pioneer lichens and mosses take root and provide some shelter. Enough windblown organic dust may slowly accumulate in cracks to permit growth of a few

high-altitude plants. These in turn will support springtails and thrips, closely followed by mites, flies, and even a few species of butterflies.

A comfortable place for many creatures above the timberline is under a stone. Humidity is usually higher; temperatures more constant; light and wind absent.

One species of scorpion, *Chaerilius insignis,* is found up to 13,000 feet in the Himalayas, sometimes under stones covered by 50 feet of snow.

Soil is rare in the mountains above 16,000 feet. But where it is deep and moist enough, alpine soil contains a complex community supported by springtails, and including mites, weevil larvae, and other beetles.

Most soil animals live well below the surface, where more moisture is retained, and feed on organic debris and the roots of alpine plants. Soil-dwelling insects are adapted to burrowing and are usually hairless, with poor eyesight and short digging legs.

Hibernating in a mass Many species of ladybugs of the genus *Adonia* assemble in vast numbers and fly thousands of feet above the tree line to huddle under the snow for the entire winter. Inevitably, many perish from the cold. Others are eaten by insects, birds, or even bears

A living thermometer The mountain frog *Rana wittei* is found in the marshes of the Ethiopian highlands and the northern slopes of Mount Kenya. It is said that it still calls when the temperature is as low as one degree above freezing but is silent the instant it drops to freezing

Flightless grasshopper Like many mountain grasshoppers, *Miramella alpina* has greatly reduced wings and cannot fly. Its long, powerful hind legs enable it to move in a series of short or long jumps. This grasshopper is distributed from the Alps in Europe to the western Ukraine in Russia

OCEANIC ISLANDS

An oceanic island, surrounded by a vast expanse of water, is the most isolated habitat on earth. On such an island there may develop species of plants and animals that are unknown anywhere else

The world has many isolated habitats, such as ice-capped mountains rising from tropical forest, oases in the desert, and the frozen wasteland of Antarctica. But the most isolated habitats of all are islands, because the sea is the greatest barrier to the movement of land animals.

Continental islands are a part of adjacent land masses. The most common type, of which the British Isles and Newfoundland are examples, is a section of continental shelf protruding from the sea. Some continental islands, however, are more isolated and are surrounded by deep water. Examples of this type are Madagascar, Kerguelen, New Zealand, and South Georgia—which are all fragments of continental material that at one stage may have been closer together.

Oceanic islands, on the other hand, have been built up by underwater volcanic eruptions. The actual cause of such eruptions is still shrouded in mystery. One theory is that since these volcano-born islands lie above the ridges of underwater mountains on the sea floor, pressure building up along the cracks radiating from the ridges caused shifts and eruptions. The islands built up gradually from deposits of basaltic rock spewed out by the volcanoes.

At no stage in their history were oceanic islands linked to the continental masses where most land plants and animals evolved. The plant and animal communities of these islands are based on a few original forms that managed to cross great expanses of ocean.

Oceanic islands, therefore, have scanty plant and animal life. Successful plant and animal colonizations are rare—perhaps one in 10,000 years. Amphibians and most land mammals, apart from bats, are usually absent, and reptiles are few. On many islands birds and bats are the only nonaquatic vertebrates. Many groups of insects are missing, especially those such as dragonflies, whose young stages live in freshwater.

Difficulties of colonization

Many land and freshwater animals on oceanic islands have evolved directly from sea-dwelling ancestors. Land crabs and freshwater fish are examples.

Despite the reduced competition faced by an animal or plant that reaches a remote island, colonization is not easy. Oceanic islands are generally wetter, cloudier, and more windswept than conti-

nents. These differences in climate may hamper plants—especially those that need plenty of sunshine to ripen their fruits. Insects may be unable to survive because their food plants are missing; this is why the Brazilian moths occasionally seen on Tristan da Cunha cannot establish themselves.

Birds, blown off course, may arrive exhausted, and find no suitable food. This happened to a South American gray heron seen by the fishless streams of Gough Island in the mid-Atlantic in May 1968. And unless the lone arrival is a fertilized female, in most animal species a male and a female must be present in order to colonize an island.

Some colonists flourish

Oceanic islands are small, with fewer habitats than continents, and this is another reason why they support fewer kinds of plants and animals. But these islands also offer advantages. Plants that are usually restricted to marginal habitats on the mainland may thrive on an island where dominant species of forest trees are absent. Grasses can grow unchecked, because there are no grazing mammals. There are usually no predatory mammals either, so colonies of seabirds and ground-nesting land birds can extend over accessible open ground.

Once a species has colonized a remote island, it is unable, because it is isolated by the surrounding water, to interbreed with its parent stock. This fact, coupled with the animals' adaptation to different conditions and different competitors, often leads to the evolution of new species peculiar to the island. These are called endemic species. In birds and insects the new forms are often flightless.

Disrupting the delicate balance

Man, the first land mammal to overcome all ocean barriers, has endangered the very existence of many unique plant and animal communities on oceanic islands by introducing competitive continental species. He has planted crops; inadvertently introduced many new insects; imported cattle, goats, sheep, and pigs to feed upon vegetation never before exposed to grazing; and let loose such predators as dogs, cats, and rats among creatures powerless to resist them.

In recent decades new forms of destruction and disruption have been added to the old. Guano deposits laid down by seabird colonies over thousands of years have been removed for use as fertilizer, destroying the plant and animal life of some oceanic islands. And hydrogen bomb tests have blasted other islands out of existence.

The first arrivals When a new island is formed, seabirds, such as these Dominican gulls, are usually the first animals to arrive and colonize successfully

The birth and death of islands

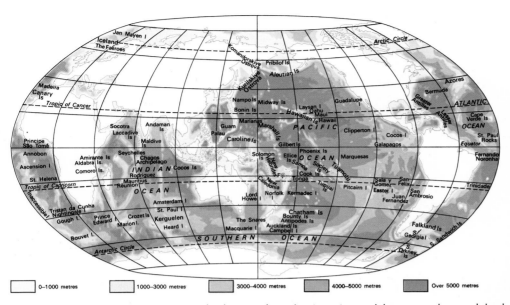

Islands created by volcanoes Oceanic islands are scattered throughout the oceans, particularly the Pacific. They have arisen directly from the seabed by volcanic action and have no submerged land links with any continents, in contrast to continental islands, which may be offshore or remote

Oceanic islands, produced by volcanoes, are doomed to live geologically short lives. As soon as they are "born" they come under attack by the sea

The oceans form a continuous body of water covering seven tenths of the earth's surface, and making an island of even the largest land mass—the linked continents of Africa and Eurasia. All land is bounded by the sea. This limits the spread of land plants and animals and helps to shape patterns of evolution.

Islands, in the ordinary sense of the word, are of two kinds: continental and oceanic. Continental islands arose as—and most still remain—part of the great blocks of land. Oceanic islands have arisen directly from the sea as a result of volcanic action and have therefore never had links with any of the continents.

A fiery birth from the seabed

True oceanic islands burst from the sea as fuming, sterile volcanic cones, rising from water often 10,000 feet deep and 1000 miles from the nearest land mass. Most oceanic islands are associated with the submarine ridges that run down the center of the Atlantic and Indian oceans, and in a much more complex latticework of north-south and east-west ridges that lie under the Pacific.

Some volcanic islands are built up around one or two volcanic vents, while others, such as Tahiti, are formed by a whole series. The age of an island can be judged from its structure. Young islands have perfectly formed cones and craters and lack deep soil, while older islands become eroded and have areas of rich soil.

Volcanic islands are uninhabitable at first, but gradually, as the lava cools, they become capable of supporting life. Soils are formed as crumbled rock is enriched by the droppings of seabirds and seals. Young volcanic rocks are normally very permeable and much of their drainage is subterranean. But as the surface layers are washed away, less permeable layers may be exposed and water begins to run in streams.

It takes hundreds of thousands of years to build up substantial plant and animal communities. Hawaiian vegetation consists of about 400 basic types and it has been estimated that, since the islands are 5 to 10 million years old, successful colonizations may have occurred on an average of only once in every 12,500 to 25,000 years. The majority of plant species, however, were probably established during Hawaii's early period.

Oceanic islands are under constant attack by the sea. If they are small, and composed of soft volcanic materials, they may last only a few years. Even large islands may be greatly reduced by rain and sea after some 10 million years, and after 20 million years many will be submerged.

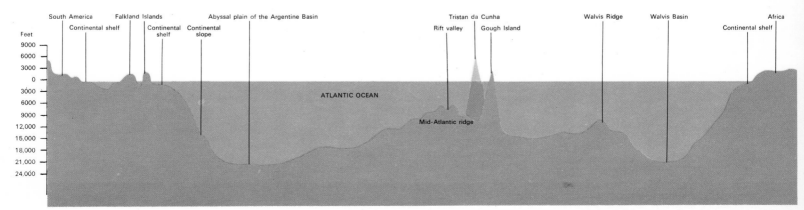

The South Atlantic The Falklands, continental islands, rise from the South American continental shelf. Beyond, the seabed dips into the Argentine Basin and then rises slowly to the mid-Atlantic ridge, from which the volcano of Tristan da Cunha towers. Submerged peaks crown Walvis Ridge

How an island is formed

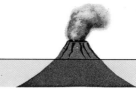

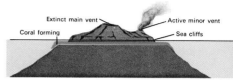

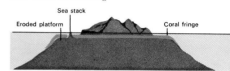

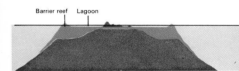

A volcano erupts from the sea-bed, thrusting its cone above the water to form an island with steeply sloping sides, scored by gullies and wreathed in vapor

In the next stage the main vent is extinct, but a lesser one is still active. The sea has eroded cliffs and coral is forming

Erosion continues to extend the coral platform, leaving an off-shore stack. The reef also extends. On shore, rocks crumble and soil is forming

Eventually, the island begins to sink. Only the tip of the original volcanic rock remains, surrounded by a lagoon and guarded by its barrier reef of coral

An island is born Amid boiling seas and sulfurous fumes, the volcanic island of Surtsey erupts out of the Atlantic, 20 miles southwest of Iceland. This photograph was taken when the island was just 14 days old and still growing bigger every day

Attacked by the sea Seven months after its birth Surtsey was still emerging from the waves. Yet Atlantic storms were already eating into it, eroding cliffs and forming beaches

Mature island Bora-Bora, one of the Society Islands, is sufficiently eroded to supply a good base for plant life. But it has already started to sink and soon it may be an atoll around a lagoon

Sinking island Only a small remnant of this sinking volcanic island still breaks the surface of the Pacific. Eventually this part will also subside into the water and only a coral fringe, or an atoll, will remain visible

Sunken island Takin, in the Caroline Islands, is a dead volcanic island. Its rocky mass now lies under the sea's surface. Only its coral fringe survives as an atoll on the sunken rock, marking where the main island was

255

Colonization by plants and animals

The colonization of all oceanic islands follows a pattern—microscopic soil animals must establish themselves before most insects and birds can survive

A newly formed volcanic island presents a hostile environment to animals and plants.

Until the rocks are broken down by weathering and the chemical action of rainwater, there is neither soil nor water. As time passes, seabirds bring in nutrients.

Plants and land animals usually drift to oceanic islands in sea or air currents. Their chances of reaching an island depend on

how isolated it is, the speed and direction of the currents, and the species' ability to survive away from its original habitat. Once individuals reach an island, the establishment of the species depends on the habitats and food supplies available, the climate, and competition from other species.

Air currents or birds carry seeds and insects to oceanic islands

The atmosphere is always full of drifting material, including pollen and spores of plants, small spiders, and insects.

Mosses, lichens, and ferns have lightweight spores, easily dispersed by wind, and are proportionately more numerous in the lush vegetation of temperate islands than in continental areas. A high proportion of flowering plants on many remote islands have lightweight seeds. Other seeds are dispersed by birds, carried internally, in the

gut, or externally, on feathers or feet.

Many invertebrate animals also reach islands in air currents. Samples of aerial flotsam collected by aircraft have been found to contain the same main groups of insects, in much the same proportions, as those that live on oceanic islands.

Bats are the only other vertebrates which are obviously adapted for crossing the sea. There are five species on Aldabra, all probably immigrants from Madagascar.

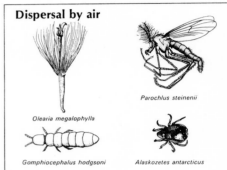

Dispersal by air

Olearia megalophylla

Parochlus steinenii

Gomphiocephalus hodgsoni

Alaskozetes antarcticus

The seeds of a member of the dandelion family float on a parachutelike carrier (top, left). Also dispersed by the wind are flying insects (top, right) and tiny wingless creatures smaller than pinheads (bottom)

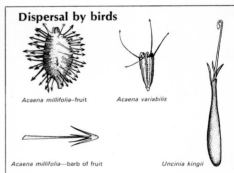

Dispersal by birds

Acaena millifolia—fruit

Acaena variabilis

Acaena millifolia—barb of fruit

Uncinia kingii

Many plants are dispersed by animals because they have hooked or barbed seeds that cling to fur or feathers. All three of the seeds shown here have been found in the feathers of the wide-ranging yellow-nosed albatross

Wind-blown visitor South American purple gallinules, blown off course, often land on Tristan da Cunha

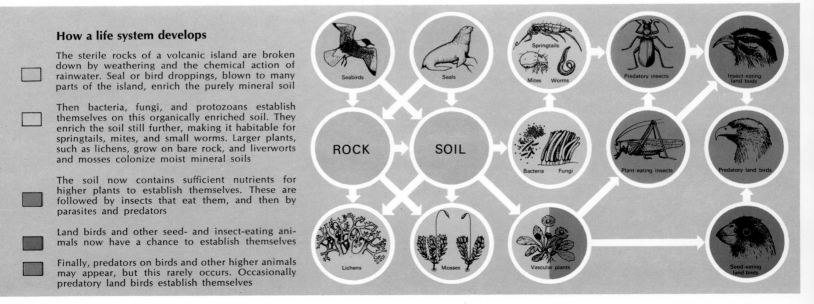

How a life system develops

The sterile rocks of a volcanic island are broken down by weathering and the chemical action of rainwater. Seal or bird droppings, blown to many parts of the island, enrich the purely mineral soil

Then bacteria, fungi, and protozoans establish themselves on this organically enriched soil. They enrich the soil still further, making it habitable for springtails, mites, and small worms. Larger plants, such as lichens, grow on bare rock, and liverworts and mosses colonize moist mineral soils

The soil now contains sufficient nutrients for higher plants to establish themselves. These are followed by insects that eat them, and then by parasites and predators

Land birds and other seed- and insect-eating animals now have a chance to establish themselves

Finally, predators on birds and other higher animals may appear, but this rarely occurs. Occasionally predatory land birds establish themselves

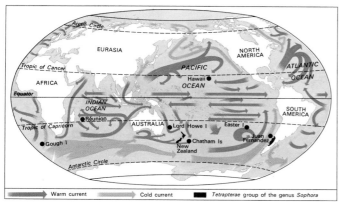

Colonization by sea Species of *Sophora*, plants of the sweet pea family, are common on riverbanks in southern Chile. Their seeds have been carried by currents in the Pacific, Indian, and Atlantic oceans. The seeds are buoyant because of an air space between the embryo and the seed coat

Tree-climbing crab The mature robber crab of the Pacific islands does not carry a shell

On driftwood and seaweed come eggs and invertebrates

The easiest means of transport to an island is by ocean currents. Some seeds can survive afloat for months; driftwood may provide a vehicle for eggs or adult invertebrates; and seaweed may carry the spores of shore plants, the eggs of shore animals, or even the animals themselves. Just as wind-dispersed plants and animals are related to mainland species upwind of them, so those that reach islands by sea are related to mainland species up-current of them. For example, Ascension Island, which lies in the course of the Benguela Current, receives species from the African coast to the south.

Reptiles have also colonized islands by sea. The marine iguanas of the Galápagos Islands, for instance, probably arrived from South America, where iguanas are common. On the Galápagos the marine iguana gave rise to a land species, found only in the interior of the islands. The ancestors of the giant tortoises of the Galápagos and Aldabra also arrived by sea, possibly floating on driftwood "rafts," for tortoises can survive without food and water for months.

Crabs are uncommon on remote islands, but there are some land crabs in places such as Trinidade, off Brazil, and the Galápagos.

Land iguana This Galápagos species, related to the marine iguana, is found only in inland areas

Marine iguanas These shore-dwellers of the Galápagos bask on the rocks, returning to the sea to feed on seaweed. This species colonized the islands by sea, possibly from South America

Living on land The Galápagos land crabs have abandoned the sea and adapted to life on shore

Giant land tortoises Found on Aldabra, a small island off southeast Africa, these tortoises may be descended from members of an extinct Indian species

Seabirds

Even the bleakest and loneliest islands, dotting the vastness of the world's oceans, are havens where seabirds breed, protected from predators by the sea

Seabirds are usually the first animals to colonize an island formed by a new oceanic volcano, for they are in the area before the island emerges. Seagulls were among the first living creatures to land on Surtsey, the volcanic island that arose from the sea off the southern coast of Iceland in November 1963. They even rested on the warm cinders during lulls between eruptions.

Young seabirds tend to return to breed in the place where they were reared. Once a new colony is established it will grow rapidly. The size of seabird populations is thought to be regulated by competition for food within easy foraging range of the breeding site. A new island opens up a new area of sea.

Seabird colonies are generally crowded. Nests are less than three feet apart, for seabirds, unlike land birds, do not need to feed in their breeding territories—the sea is their source of food. This crowding provides some protection against predatory seabirds, such as skuas and great black-backed gulls.

Wandering albatross
Diomedea exulans ☐
Lays its egg on open boggy plateaux above the scrub

Grey-backed storm petrel
Garrodia nereis
Nests in forested regions, among grass

Coastal zone   Grassland
Forest   Moorland

Dusky or sooty shearwater
Puffinus griseus
Lays eggs in holes in ground among tussock grass at edge of forest

Atlantic petrel
Pterodroma incerta
Lays single egg in burrow on fern-clad or grassy slope

Yellow-nosed albatross
Diomedea chlororhynchos
Builds nest-mound of soil in forest clearings

Pediunker
Adomastor cinereus
Nests on high ridges; also called grey petrel

Great skua
Stercorarius skua
Nests in open ground along the coast from September to January; adults prey on young of other birds

Rockhopper penguin
Eudyptes crestatus
Nests in large colonies, laying eggs in shallow holes on rocky flats

Greater shearwater
Puffinus gravis
Nests on coasts of Gough Island before migrating northwards

Antarctic tern
Sterna vittata
Nests in the coastal region; very similar to Arctic tern in appearance

Sharing the habitat There are four main vegetation zones on Gough Island, which lies southeast of Tristan da Cunha in the South Atlantic. At various times of the year, different seabirds nest in each zone. This means the whole island is occupied by nesting birds in all seasons

Lofty nursery Northern gannets breed on island crags in the North Atlantic. The young are fed by the parents for two months. Then they glide to the sea, where they live on stored fat until they fly

Crowded colony Murres bunch together on the high cliffs of a remote Arctic island. These clustered nesting sites do not lead to a food shortage, for the birds seek food far from land

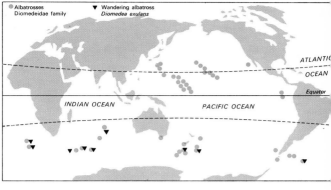

Effortless soaring Albatrosses, such as the light-mantled sooty albatross (right), soar for miles without once flapping their wings. Going into the wind, on the upward leg of its zigzag path, the bird encounters an increasingly strong headwind. This provides lift, which enables it to maintain its air speed. It slows as it turns at the top of its climb, then accelerates downwind

Where albatrosses nest All 13 species of albatrosses travel vast distances out of the breeding season. Some wandering albatrosses spend the entire winter 8000 miles from their nest sites

The wandering albatross, giant of the seabird family, flies 8000 miles to nest

The safest breeding sites in a seabird colony are those in the center, and over the years birds gradually work their way to these favored locations. The oldest breeders in an Adélie penguin colony, for instance, occupy the central sites. They lose fewer eggs and chicks than the young birds on the fringes of the colony.

On some islands one bird species predominates, but other islands have vast mixed colonies. On Beauchêne Island, off the Falklands, more than 5 million black-browed albatrosses and rock hopper penguins breed in an area covering about half a square mile, while shags of the genus *Phalacrocorax* nest on the island's cliff ledges.

Larger islands provide more varied habitats. On Gough Island, in the South Atlantic, different species occupy different nesting sites at different altitudes during various times of the year. Their arrival and departure times are phased so that one species takes over a site when another has finished with it.

At night such an island is loud with the sound of birds. The smaller burrowing petrels locate their nests by sound. An incubating adult or chick calls from the burrow to the partner or parent circling above. By flying at night, to relieve their mates or ob-

tain food, these birds keep to a minimum the losses inflicted by the great skua.

Though skuas feed at sea for much of the year, during breeding seasons they go to land to take penguin eggs, chicks, and small petrels. Their nests are often surrounded by neatly cleaned breast bones that linked pairs of petrels' wings.

The wandering albatross, with a wingspan of 10 to 11 feet, is the largest and most spectacular of all flying seabirds. There are 13 species of albatrosses, and 9 breed on the oceanic islands of the southern hemisphere.

Albatrosses usually mate for life, but they participate in elaborate courtship displays at the beginning of each breeding season.

Outside the breeding season, many seabirds roam widely over the oceans. Wandering albatrosses that feed near Sydney, Australia, in winter travel 8000 miles to nest on Bird Island off South Georgia in Antarctica. Like all albatrosses, they are magnificent gliders, able to cruise for hours on end with hardly a flap of their wings. Greater shearwaters, which breed in the Tristan da Cunha island group, migrate to the northern hemisphere during the southern winter. They follow a rough figure-eight course around the North Atlantic before returning to their southern breeding grounds in spring.

Ritual threat With bills agape, male waved albatrosses confront each other in a threat display. Such encounters occur only during the breeding season and precede the long courtship ritual

Courtship accomplished Male and female waved albatrosses bow to each other, signaling the end of the complex courtship display, which includes "sky-pointing" (with the beak) and wing-raising

Dramatic courtship display Two male wandering albatrosses, with wings outstretched, display before a female. One is probably her former partner, since albatrosses, once paired, usually mate for life. When a male and female pair up, they begin displaying by leaning forward and clattering their bills together. At the height of the ritual, they circle each other with outstretched wings, alternating with periods of mutual preening

Seabirds of the tropics

Braking its dive just above the surface, a frigate bird snatches a fish from the water and soars up again without even getting its feet wet

Some of the most spectacular members of the major seabird families are confined to the warmer seas. These include pelicans, tropic birds, frigate birds, and boobies.

Birds as outwardly different as pelicans and frigate birds belong to the same group. The Pelecaniformes order includes both these families, as well as the boobies, tropic birds, and cormorants. Big-billed, ponderous pelicans, weighing up to 16 pounds, are tied fairly closely to the coasts; cormorants and frigate birds roam more widely; and boobies and tropic birds are more truly oceanic.

Three species of albatrosses are found in the North Pacific, and one breeds in the Galápagos Islands, which straddle the equator. The world's most northerly species of penguin, the Galápagos penguin *Spheniscus mendiculus*, also breeds there.

Members of the cormorant and shag, gull and tern, and skua and jaeger families are found in both hemispheres. Birds of these families live in both cold and warm seas, and are familiar sights in most coastal areas of the world.

Huge flocks of boobies plunge together into the sea after fish

Young red-footed boobies Different races of red-footed boobies differ in color. This race, brown in youth, turns white with dark wings when adult

Blue-footed boobies The legs and feet of these boobies may be any color from turquoise to ultramarine. Males generally have slightly paler feet than the females, and the chicks' feet are almost white. They usually raise two or three chicks; red-footed and white boobies raise only one

Strutting blue-footed boobies
1 The male advertises his arrival with a flash of blue feet. **2** The male parades with raised bill, while the female inclines her head. **3** The male sky-points before the interested female. **4** The female displays by rattling her wings. **5** The pair goose-step; mating begins soon

Boobies, tropical relatives of the North Atlantic gannet, were given their name by old-time sailors who mistook their lack of fear of man for stupidity.

The variegated booby breeds along the edge of the Humboldt Current on the southern Peruvian and Chilean coasts. Because of its spectacular stabbing dives in search of food, it also bears the local name *piquero* —Spanish for "lancer." Variegated boobies, like blue-footed boobies, often feed in immense flocks, and thousands may dive together from the sky, striking the ocean like a hailstorm.

Red-footed boobies, which breed on islands and coasts throughout the tropical and subtropical zones, are unusual among seabirds and unique among boobies in that they nest in trees. On Laysan, in the Hawaiian group, a colony once tried to maintain itself in the crown of the single surviving tree. The red-footed booby usually lays a single egg. Even if two are produced, the second egg is rarely hatched unless the first chick is lost.

Blue-footed boobies, which inhabit the Galápagos and Lobos islands off Peru, and mainland coasts northward to California, do not build elaborate nests. The nest is usually little more than a slightly rubbed spot on the ground, and even nests that have been used for years are marked only by a ring of guano.

Solitary wanderer The red-billed tropic bird nests on islands from the Galápagos to the Indian Ocean. During the mating season, the birds form colonies, making their nests in holes in cliffs. Once the young are independent, tropic birds roam alone or in pairs, traveling far over the ocean

Sharing a colony Terns often nest in vast colonies. Here royal terns and the smaller elegant terns are sharing the same nesting site

A tropical tern The white noddy, or fairy tern, never leaves the tropics. It lays a single egg on a bare branch or cliff ledge. The chicks can cling

even when they are upside-down. The young bird remains in its precarious perch for several days until it finally jumps or falls to the ground

Frigate birds, awkward on land and wary of water, are superb performers in the air

Frigate birds, or man-o'-war birds, of the genus *Fregata,* measure eight feet across from wing tip to wing tip. With this wingspan, and their long, forked tails, they are magnificent gliders. Their wings are larger in proportion to their bodies than those of any other bird, and the flight muscles account for a quarter of the body weight, which in spite of the bird's size is no more than two or three pounds.

Called the most aerial of water birds, frigate birds seldom if ever enter the water—although their feet are fully webbed, they take much of their food from the ocean, and their closest relatives are good swimmers. They are as inept on land as they are in the water. Since they need either a strong wind or a high perch to take off, they roost on bushes or trees.

Frigate birds take fish by diving to the sea but, unlike boobies, they brake above the surface, strike downward with their four-inch-long beaks, and rise with their prey without wetting feathers or feet. Their plumage is probably not completely waterproof, and they have never been seen to settle on water.

A pirate among birds

The birds' piratical habits caused sailors to name them man-o'-war birds. Like skuas and jaegers, they pursue other species, especially boobies, until the pursued bird regurgitates the food in its crop. The frigate bird then catches the food in midair. The frigate bird is not only a hunter in the air, but also a scavenger and general predator, taking newly hatched turtles from beaches, and any kind of food it can find around human settlements.

Frigate birds often nest near the colonies of their prey birds, such as boobies, pelicans, gulls, and cormorants. They soar above the crowded colony, watching for a chick to be left unattended. Then, with lightning speed, they swoop down and snatch the young bird from the nest.

Unlike albatrosses, frigate birds do not wander the oceans. They are rarely recorded at any distance from coasts. It may be this attachment to land which keeps their breeding populations separate and accounts for the complex range of species and subspecies.

Bizarre breeding behavior

The breeding behavior of frigate birds is as bizarre as that of boobies. The male develops a brilliant red inflated sac on its throat. During the breeding season this sac remains inflated even while the bird is sleeping. When the female approaches, the male rises to face her, displaying the sac. Both raise their bills, spread their wings, and gurgle to each other. Mating takes place at the climax of this demonstration. After the single egg is laid, the male's sac deflates and its color fades.

Both partners build the nest, the female doing most of the foraging for twigs, and the male matting them together to form a flimsy platform. Both parents incubate the egg and feed the chick, which stays in the nest for many months. The breeding cycle may last a year or more. It is likely that frigate birds nest only in alternate years, and then at any time of the year. This means that the small, scattered nesting grounds are used continuously—as one pair moves out, another pair takes its place.

Attracting a mate The inflated sac on the male frigate bird's throat develops in the breeding season as a courtship display. It remains distended until the female lays its egg; then the sac deflates and returns to its usual dull orange color. Male and female take turns incubating the single egg

The emergence of island species

Almost completely isolated from the competitive pressures of the rest of the world, island animals have evolved into many strange forms

There are two ways in which an island may acquire distinctive species. First, the island population may evolve along different lines from its mainland relatives. Second, all the mainland stocks of a species may become extinct, leaving the island inhabitants as the sole representatives.

Animals that colonize remote oceanic islands, cut off from interbreeding with mainland parent stocks and forced to live under different conditions, become adapted so that they can survive in their new environment. For example, the trend toward flightlessness among island birds and insects may have stemmed from the fact that flying could result in a creature being blown out to sea by the wind, leaving behind those animals with a reduced tendency to flight. Also, if animals can find food without having to take to the air, or if there are no land predators, being flightless is no longer the handicap it would be on the mainland.

Birds and insects that have lost the power of flight

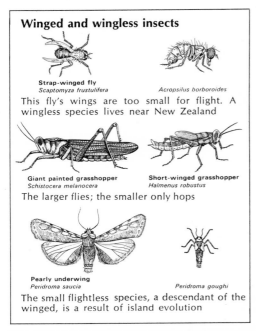

Winged and wingless insects

Strap-winged fly
Scaptomyza frustulifera

Acropsilus borboroides

This fly's wings are too small for flight. A wingless species lives near New Zealand

Giant painted grasshopper
Schistocera melanocera

Short-winged grasshopper
Halmenus robustus

The larger flies; the smaller only hops

Pearly underwing
Peridroma saucia

Peridroma goughi

The small flightless species, a descendant of the winged, is a result of island evolution

Flightless cormorant A clumsy and vulnerable bird on land, it nests near the shore. Like its flying relatives, it is more adapted to life in the sea, and is a good swimmer and diver

Losing the power of flight This land rail of Aldabra, related to a flying species on nearby Madagascar, can barely fly. Even greater distinctions arise when islands are more isolated

Aldabra land rail
Dryolimnas cuvieri

Gough Island gallinule
Porphyriornis nesiotis comeri

Inaccessible Island rail
Atlantisia rogersi

Flightless birds of the islands Rails are particularly prone to lose the power of flight during their evolution on islands. Aldabra land rails can barely fly, while Gough Island gallinules only flutter a few feet with their short wings. The Inaccessible Island rails, with even smaller wings and a simplified feather structure that gives them the appearance of fluffy chicks, cannot fly at all

The island forms of land rails seem particularly prone to lose the power of flight, depending on the isolation of the island and the length of time the birds have been there. The Aldabra land rail, which is barely able to fly, differs so little from its relatives in nearby Madagascar that it can be regarded as belonging to the same species. On the other hand, the Gough Island subspecies of gallinule is distinct from the American purple gallinule, a flying bird from which it has diverged over a long period of time. The Gough Island bird has short wings and can flutter only a few feet. The flightless Inaccessible Island rail is such a distinct species, with its tiny wings and hairlike plumage, that its ancestry has not yet been determined.

The trend toward flightlessness is rarer among seabirds. One example is the flightless cormorant of the Galápagos Islands, with its ragged, poorly feathered wings, not much bigger than a penguin's flippers.

Many insects have become flightless, or even wingless, on islands. Galápagos Islands grasshoppers and moths on other islands are examples. The moths *Peridroma goughi* of Gough Island and *Dimorphinoctua cunhaensis* of Tristan da Cunha, with their tiny wings, large abdomens, and strong legs, hardly look like moths at all.

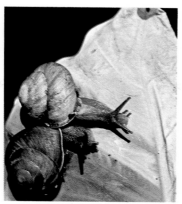

Rare amphibian The frog *Megalixalus seychellensis* is common on two islands in the Seychelles, a group of continental islands in the Indian Ocean, but is found nowhere else. Five or six other species of frogs are peculiar to the group

A minute range This snail of the Seychelles is now found only around Valé du Mai on Praslin Island, where it lives in local palm forests

Decrease in size In the Seychelles, day geckos of the genus *Phelsuma* illustrate the trend of some island reptiles to become smaller. Their relatives on Madagascar are over two inches longer

Giant carnivorous lizards Komodo dragons, reaching a length of nine feet, are the largest lizards in the world. Highly voracious monitors, they often kill animals as large as goats and small deer. The Komodo dragons shown here are probably scavenging, since the deer is a large one

Reptiles have lost limbs or rattles and grown larger or smaller on isolated islands

Reptiles and amphibians have generally been less successful than birds and insects in reaching oceanic islands, but skinks and geckos have colonized many island groups near the mainland, and are fairly widespread in the Pacific. The skink genus *Brachymeles* in the Philippines contains species that show a progressive tendency toward limblessness. This may result from an evolutionary change to burrowing, since the legless species live mostly underground.

The reasons for some adaptations are obscure. On Santa Catalina, in the Gulf of California, the rattlesnake *Crotalus catalinensis* has lost its rattle. One theory is that, in continental species, the rattle acts as a warning signal to large animals that might be about to trample on the snake. If large mammals are absent, there may be no selective pressure to retain the rattle.

Many island reptiles—perhaps because of the absence of mammalian competitors—have become unusually large. The Komodo dragon, a carnivorous monitor lizard confined to Komodo and a few nearby continental islands in the Sunda group in Indonesia, is the world's largest lizard. Males are often nine feet long, and females six feet.

Some iguanas on the islands in the Gulf of California are also larger than their mainland relatives, as are those that have colonized the Galápagos. On the Galápagos, these lizards have diverged in their development. The tawny-colored land iguana feeds inland on cactus fruits, while the marine iguana is amphibious, and eats the seaweed *Sargassum*.

Tortoises are no exception to the trend toward enlargement. The giant tortoises on Aldabra, Mauritius, and the Galápagos have probably evolved from much smaller colonist ancestors.

Some island reptiles, on the other hand, have become smaller. A West Indian gecko of the genus *Sphaerodactylus* is only 1½ inches long, and can easily hide in rock crevices. Such increases or decreases in size are adaptations to changed ways of life on islands with few or no land mammals, and with new habitats available for reptiles.

While most animals confined to particular islands have evolved in their present haunts, some are probably true relics of ancient species that formerly lived in many parts of the world.

The giant Aldabra land tortoises are the last survivors of populations that were once widespread on more than 30 islands in the Indian Ocean, while the tuatara, a lizardlike reptile of the offshore islands in New Zealand, is the only survivor of an order that was widespread throughout the world about 200 million years ago.

The variety of island life

Once a species is established on a group of oceanic islands, its descendants often radiate, producing a whole series of related but different forms

Many island species not only diverge from the parent stock to become new species, but also radiate and produce daughter species, each adapted to exploit a different habitat.

This process is called adaptive radiation.

All animals show genetic variation—that is, the offspring differ from their parents and from one another. There is some evidence that variability is higher and mutations— the changes in genetic material that produce new variations—more frequent in island populations. These populations are often small and descended from a few

initial colonists that may have lacked some of the characteristics of the mainland stock of the species. These characteristics will also be lacking in their descendants.

In small populations it is easier for a new characteristic to spread to all members or for the normal processes of genetic variation to lead to the complete disappearance of a characteristic.

Over 1000 species of Hawaiian land mollusks evolved from 24 colonist species

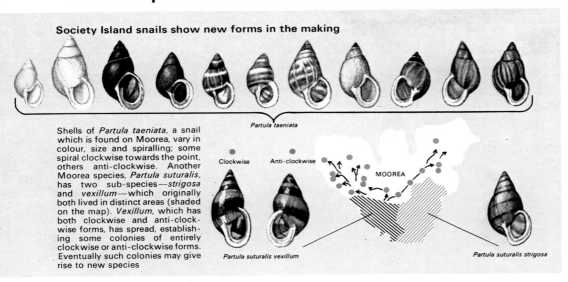

Society Island snails show new forms in the making

Shells of *Partula taeniata*, a snail which is found on Moorea, vary in colour, size and spiralling; some spiral clockwise towards the point, others anti-clockwise. Another Moorea species, *Partula suturalis*, has two sub-species—*strigosa* and *vexillum*—which originally both lived in distinct areas (shaded on the map). *Vexillum*, which has both clockwise and anti-clockwise forms, has spread, establishing some colonies of entirely clockwise or anti-clockwise forms. Eventually such colonies may give rise to new species

Good examples of genetic variability are found among the land snails of the genus *Partula*, which exist on many Pacific islands, but nowhere else. In Samoa the single species *Partula actor* ranges in color from white to dark brown and also shows great variation in the patterning of its shell. On Moorea and other islands in the Society group, *Partula* snails vary widely in color, size, and shell patterns.

Hawaii has 1064 species of land mollusks, including more than 1000 species of land snails with a very large range of colors and forms. One genus, *Achatinella*, confined to the island of Oahu, has 42 species and 75 subspecies.

All the Hawaiian land mollusks are believed to be derived from only 24 colonist species. A single colonist species is thought to have given rise to the islands' Amastrinae subfamily, which has 294 known species.

Galápagos tortoises tell a story on their backs: many species from one ancestor

When Darwin visited the Galápagos Islands in 1835, the great land tortoise *Geochelone elephantopus* was present on all the main islands in the group. The ancestral immigrant, perhaps a pregnant female and probably closely related to *Geochelone denticulata* of South America and the West

Indies, may have reached the islands either by floating in the water or on a driftwood "raft." Once established, the species radiated, and distinctive forms evolved on different islands.

On some islands, the tortoises have saddle-backed shells and long necks. The long necks

may be adaptations that allow the tortoises to browse on cacti and low shrubs. On most of the other islands shells are dome-shaped.

All these races of island tortoises are larger than their mainland relatives. They weigh up to 500 pounds, and are very slow-moving, covering only 1000 feet an hour.

Land tortoise Galápagos tortoises can survive droughts because they drink copiously when water is available, then store some of it

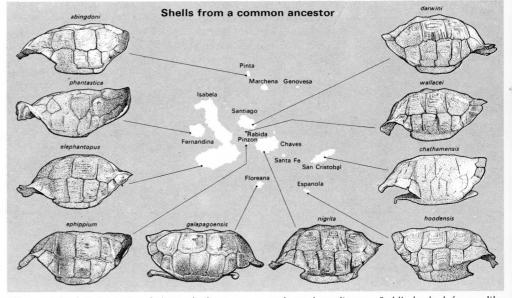

Shells from a common ancestor

The great land tortoise *Geochelone elephantopus* of the Galápagos Islands has subspecies confined to particular islands. Differences between their shells show how isolated populations of a single

stock tend to diverge. Saddle-backed forms, like *phantastica*, are found on some islands and dome-shaped forms, like *nigrita*, occur on others. All came from one ancestor; some forms are extinct

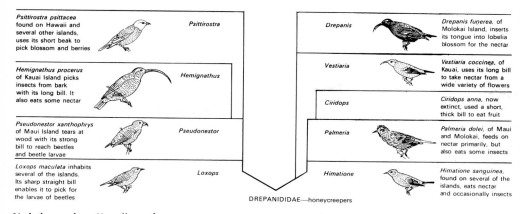

Variations in Hawaiian honeycreepers Nine genera of Hawaiian honeycreepers have evolved from a warblerlike or tanagerlike ancestor. Vari-

ations in the sizes and shapes of their beaks and their tongues probably arose from their various diets. They also differ in size, color, and shape

Diagram labels:

Psittirostra psittacea found on Hawaii and several other islands, uses its short beak to pick blossom and berries — Psittirostra

Hemignathus procerus of Kauai Island picks insects from bark with its long bill. It also eats some nectar — Hemignathus

Pseudonestor xanthophrys at Maui Island tears at wood with its strong bill to reach beetles and beetle larvae — Pseudonestor

Loxops maculata inhabits several of the islands. Its sharp straight bill enables it to pick for the larvae of beetles — Loxops

Drepanis — *Drepanis funerea*, of Molokai Island, inserts its tongue into lobelia blossom for the nectar

Vestiaria — *Vestiaria coccinea*, of Kauai, uses its long bill to take nectar from a wide variety of flowers

Ciridops — *Ciridops anna*, now extinct, used a short, thick bill to eat fruit

Palmeria — *Palmeria dolei*, of Maui and Molokai, feeds on nectar primarily, but also eats some insects

Himatione — *Himatione sanguinea*, found on several of the islands, eats nectar and occasionally insects

DREPANIDIDAE—honeycreepers

Adaptive radiation in finches and honeycreepers

Seventy species of land birds have been recorded in Hawaii. About 42 of these belong to one family, the Drepanididae, or honeycreepers. Several species have become extinct, but the group as it now exists displays a remarkable range of forms, the result of adaptive radiation.

The delicately curved bills of *Hemignathus* and *Drepanis* are used to probe flowers for nectar and to sift through moss, soft bark, and rotting wood for insects. *Pseudonestor* tears the bark from branches with a powerful curved beak in search of insects. *Loxops, Vestiaria, Palmeria,* and *Himatione* feed mainly on nectar from the blossoms of the ohia, a tree that has a long flowering season. The extinct *Ciridops* fed on palm fruit with its short, thick bill.

Members of the genus *Psittirostra* crack large, tough seeds with thick, parrot-type bills, and, as in the other genera, the bills of individual species show further variation. The stoutest-billed species of *Psittirostra* takes hard, dry seeds; the lightest-billed species specializes in more fleshy seeds.

The tongues of most of the honeycreepers are also closely adapted to their diets. The original tongue was probably of medium length, fork-tipped, fringed, and capable of curling up along the edges to form a tube for sucking up nectar. Now the seed-eaters have short, round tongues.

Although the Hawaiian honeycreepers are the best example of adaptive radiation in a family of island birds, the Galápagos finches have become even more famous because they provided the stimulus for Darwin's speculations on the origin and evolution of species.

The ancestor of these finches, a small American finch living on the ground and feeding on seeds, is thought to have invaded the Galápagos while there were still unfilled habitats in the islands. This species has given rise to a distinct subfamily with 14 species. Like the Hawaiian honeycreepers, Galápagos finches have evolved to feed in different ways. There are seed-eaters, plant-feeders, cactus-feeders, insect-feeders, and woodpeckerlike finches. The beaks of each species have become modified to fit the species' eating habits.

Stout bill for seeds The Nihoa finch of the Hawaiian honeycreeper family has developed a strongly muscled parrotlike beak for cracking the large, tough seeds that are the staple of its diet

Beaks for different diets The anianiau (left), an insect-eater, has a short beak and a fringed tongue. The related Amakihi honeycreeper (right) has a long, curved bill for drinking nectar

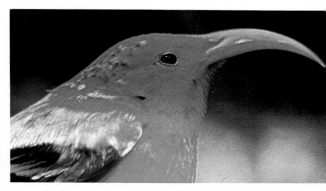

Nectar feeder The long-billed iiwi honeycreeper, of Kauai Island in the Hawaiian Islands, sucks up the nectar of ohia flowers with its long tongue that curls at the edges, forming a tube

A small insect-eater This Galápagos tree finch feeds on small insects. Two larger species of the same genus feed on the larger insects

Tool-using bird A Galápagos finch digs for insects in bark with its beak, then holds a cactus spine or stick to dislodge the prey

265

THE WORLD OF WATER

**The oceans, seas, rivers, and lakes, in which most of the earth's
water is stored, were the original home of life on earth, and the habitats they
provide still contain the greatest number and variety of living things**

The collective name for all the earth's waters, including the water in the atmosphere and the frozen sheets of ice, is the hydrosphere.

The oceans can be divided into several natural regions, each of which supports its own forms of plant and animal life. Some of these organisms are restricted in range; others, more adaptable, move freely from one region to another. A number of factors, including the depth and temperature of the water and its content of nutrient salts, determine the kinds of plants and animals that can live in a given section of ocean.

The deepest known part of the ocean is the Marianas Trench in the Pacific, where a sounding of 36,198 feet has been made. Light cannot penetrate to such a depth, and many deep-sea creatures are luminous, providing their own illumination.

The sea floor has its mountains and valleys, just like the land. Under the great oceans are steep canyons, sloping hills, and immense mountain ridges —formations that greatly influence life forms.

Temperature barriers

The greatest variety of animals occurs in tropical waters, but the seas surrounding the polar regions usually support a greater weight of animals to the square mile. There are many exceptions to this general rule, however, especially in deep tropical waters where cold currents well up from the bottom.

Erratic currents can have a disastrous impact on the plant and animal life of what would otherwise be a stable natural region. The cold upwelling waters of the Humboldt Current, which washes the coasts of Ecuador and Peru, are sometimes invaded by a warm current called El Niño. The cold-water fish and other aquatic animals cannot tolerate the warmth of this current and when it reaches them they die in vast numbers, as do the seabirds that rely on them for food.

Some groups of animals are restricted to waters of certain temperatures. Reef-building corals, for example, cannot exist outside the tropics, whereas many species of fish used as human food are found only in colder waters.

Some regions of the oceans have clearly defined temperature barriers that separate different forms of animal and plant life. One of the best known is the Antarctic Convergence, at a latitude of about 50° S, where the cold water of the West Wind Drift meets the warmer and saltier waters of the sub-Antarctic

seas. The forms of life that exist on each side of the convergence differ from each other as much as the animals of the grasslands differ from those of the forests.

Inland waters include both standing and running waters. Standing waters range from small pools with fairly simple plant and animal communities to great sheets of water such as the 12,700-square-mile Lake Tanganyika, which has life forms that are found nowhere else.

Running waters, or rivers, provide an even greater variety of habitats than the oceans and support a highly complex plant and animal life.

Saltwater and freshwater fish

Most water-living animals are not waterproof. Water can enter or leave their bodies through the skin or the gills. A fish must maintain a balance between the dissolved salts in its blood and body fluids and the degree of salinity in the water surrounding it. Freshwater fish have a higher proportion of salt in their body fluids than the surrounding water, which means that water constantly seeks to enter their bodies. To maintain the proper balance, freshwater fish must continually excrete water.

Most saltwater fish, on the other hand, have a lower salt content in their body fluids than the surrounding seawater, and must constantly swallow water, lest they dry out.

Fish with skeletons of cartilage, such as sharks and rays, avoid such water loss by retaining much excretory urea in their blood, so that the concentration of dissolved substances in their body fluids is equal to that in seawater. But bony fish, such as mackerel and herring, do not retain urea. They must drink large quantities of salt water to maintain their fluids at a concentration of salt roughly equal to that of the sea.

Many bony fish have a swim bladder—an enclosed sac into which gas is secreted until the density of the fish is about the same as that of the surrounding water. Such fish expend little energy remaining buoyant.

The oceans and freshwaters differ so much as environments that most water-living animals do not move from one to the other. Some fish, however, do live in both worlds. Eels are born in the sea and migrate across the ocean to rivers and streams, where they complete their growth; and the Atlantic salmon feeds in the sea and breeds in the upper reaches of rivers. Similarly, some amphibians, reptiles, and mammals move readily back and forth between land and water. Turtles and crocodiles breed on land but feed in the water.

Fish of the tropical seas From the shores to the depths, from the poles to the tropics, the oceans teem with life. These perchlets live in the waters around Australia's Great Barrier Reef

Water as a medium of life

Seven tenths of the earth's surface is covered by oceans. These vast reservoirs, together with inland waters, ice, snow, and water vapor, form the hydrosphere

Water was the original home of life on earth, and all forms of life have a high proportion of water in their bodies. About 65 percent of the total body weight of a human being is made up of water.

Water has some remarkable properties that have had far-reaching effects on the way life has developed. Between 32° F. (0° C.) and 212° F. (100° C.) it is liquid—the only inorganic liquid, apart from mercury, that occurs naturally at normal pressure on the earth's surface. Below 32° F. water freezes and becomes a solid. It is the only substance on earth that expands when it freezes. Because of this unique property, water has played a major role in shaping the surface of the land; by freezing and expanding in rock fissures, it forces the cracks wider apart, breaking up the rocks. As a liquid, it erodes the rocks and eventually helps form soil. Many substances dissolve easily in water, so it usually contains a range of food materials in a form that allows them to be readily absorbed by the cells of living organisms.

Meeting of the waters This river flows into the sea near Cape Cod, carrying with it a weak solution of mineral salts washed off the land. These river salts are mixed with the concentration of salts already in the sea. All form essential nutrients for the oceans' plant and animal growth

How rain and snow are formed and move around the world

Water is not confined to rivers, lakes, and oceans. As a liquid, it soaks into the earth's crust or lies on the surface, where it is transformed into vapor by energy from the sun. Precipitation is most commonly caused by the upward movement of moisture-laden air. As the land is warmed by the sun, the air in contact with it becomes warmer, and rises. As it rises, sometimes ten miles into the atmosphere, it cools. Wind carries the vapor-laden air over the earth's surface, and water condenses out of the vapor and falls to the earth as rain or snow, permitting the plant growth on which all animal life on earth ultimately depends. Precipitation also occurs when air currents are forced upward by mountains and when air currents meet.

This worldwide system of water exchange between earth and atmosphere is called the water or hydrological cycle. The water vapor forms a partial barrier to the loss of heat from the earth's surface.

Most precipitation on land evaporates directly or through the transpiration of plants. Some of the remainder, called runoff, feeds streams and rivers and flows into the sea; some seeps through the soil to form underground lakes and streams; and some remains stored in ponds, lakes, and swamps, and as snow on mountains and polar ice caps.

	Per cent
Seas, including floating ice	93·6
Underground water	4·2
Continental ice	1·8
Surface inland waters	0·36
Vapour in the atmosphere	0·001
Water contained in plants and animals	0·00004

Where water is stored Most of the earth's water is stored in the oceans and the polar sea ice. Also, more water is held under the ground than in all the lakes, rivers, snow caps, and glaciers together. During the ice ages so much water was locked in ice that the sea level fell

Major constituents of water	Sea	Lake Windermere
Calcium	400·1	7·0
Magnesium	1,272·0	0·85
Sodium	10,556·1	4·5
Potassium	380·0	0·6
Chloride	18,979·9	8·2
Sulphate	2,648·6	7·0
Carbonate	71·0	11·8
	Parts per million	Parts per million

Chemicals in salt and fresh water Seawater contains a much higher proportion of salts than fresh water. In the sea, chlorides are the dominant chemicals, while fresh water contains more carbonates. The salt content is extremely variable in inland waters, which range from almost pure waters to salt-saturated solutions such as the Great Salt Lake, which can contain up to 270,000 parts of salt per million parts of water. In the oceans, the salt content ranges from 7200 parts per million in the Baltic to 40,000 in the Red Sea

Why warm or cold water rises Water has its greatest density at 4° C. (39° F.) and becomes lighter as the temperature rises or lowers. For this reason, ice floats on top of warmer water

Density in grams per cc.

0·9980
0·9985
0·9990
0·9995
1·0000

0°C   4°   8°   12°   16°   20°   24°

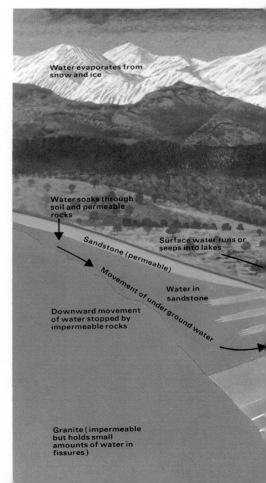

Water evaporates from snow and ice

Water soaks through soil and permeable rocks

Sandstone (permeable)

Surface water runs or seeps into lakes

Movement of underground water

Water in sandstone

Downward movement of water stopped by impermeable rocks

Granite (impermeable but holds small amounts of water in fissures)

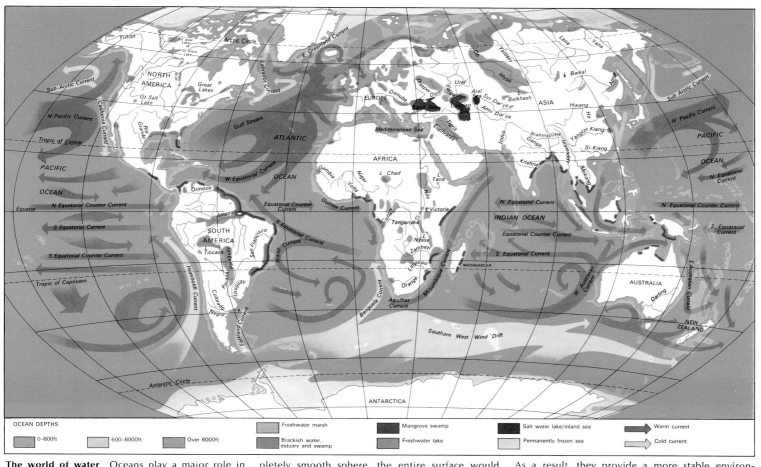

OCEAN DEPTHS

0–600ft	600–6000ft	Over 6000ft

Freshwater marsh | Mangrove swamp | Salt water lake/inland sea | Warm current

Brackish water, estuary and swamp | Freshwater lake | Permanently frozen sea | Cold current

The world of water Oceans play a major role in the water cycle, covering about seven tenths of the earth's surface. The volume of water in the oceans is so great that if the earth were a completely smooth sphere, the entire surface would be covered by water to a depth of 885 feet. Because the oceans act as storage basins for heat, they warm and cool more slowly than the land. As a result, they provide a more stable environment for the growth of living things than land. Inland freshwaters, although small in total area, contain the widest variety of water habitats

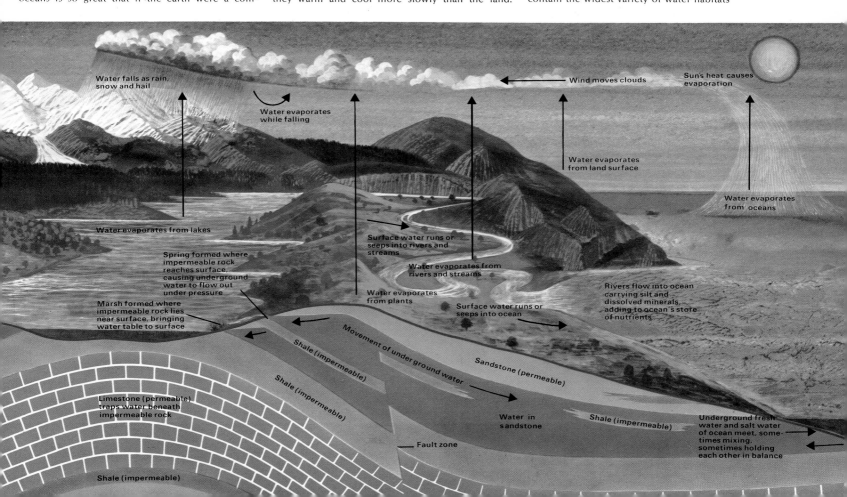

Life in the standing waters

The life forms supported by standing waters are often determined less by climate than by such factors as the age and depth of the lake, pond, or swamp

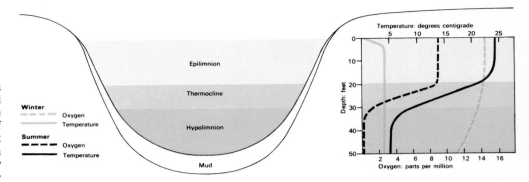

Standing waters range from small puddles a few inches deep to great lakes and inland seas. The largest inland waters are the Black Sea and the Caspian Sea, remnants of a vanished part of the ocean. The largest area of fresh water is Lake Superior, which covers 31,810 square miles. Lakes also vary in depth; a very few are known to be over 1200 feet deep.

The size and depth of standing waters partly determine the nature of their inhabitants. Some deep lakes support a profusion of plant and animal species, and may have existed for thousands, even millions of years. But a rain pool in the Sahara may dry up in less than a week, and harbors only a few animals, whose short life-spans are completed within a few days.

Layers of lake water in summer The waters of a deep lake in a temperate zone form distinct layers when warmed by the sun. The sun's rays penetrate only the upper layer, the epilimnion. Since warm water floats on cold water, mixing does not take place between this and the bottom layer, the hypolimnion. As the temperature rises further, the difference between these two layers increases, and the thermocline, an intermediate zone, is created. In autumn the surface cools and the water of the lake begins circulating until

it is thoroughly mixed. It remains like this through the winter, except when there is a temporary surface layer of colder water or ice. In summer the stratification of oxygen nearly matches that of temperature. That is, oxygen is most plentiful in the top layer, with little mixing below. Because these definite boundaries disappear in winter, the oxygen reaches all levels. At this time, the nutrients are also recycled and they rise to the epilimnion. This mixing of warm and cold waters and recycling of oxygen and nutrients occurs yearly

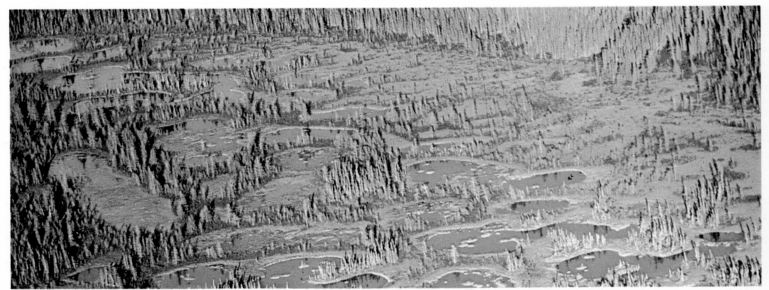

Canadian muskegs In the coniferous forest of Canada, where there are vast undrained areas, ponds and lakes form in hollows. Stands of spruce, fir, and pine grow on the higher ground. Many lakes silt up with decaying material and form swamps, or muskegs, that support mosses and sedges in the summer. These lakes are a rich source of food for musk-ox and caribou, and for smaller mammals such as lemmings and hares

Sterile lake Lake Maclure in California is an oligotrophic, or "young," lake—deep and sharply sloped, with a V-shaped bottom. Such lakes are poor in nutrients and little vegetation can grow

Rich waters Eutrophic lakes have gentle slopes and are rich in nutrients and living matter. In time, the water becomes shallower, and plants, such as water lilies, slowly spread in toward the center

Silted-up lake Dystrophic lakes, the oldest kind, are boglike areas that are rich in organic matter, but often poor in oxygen. Decaying plant and animal material makes the water highly acid

As a lake bottom changes, so does the life it supports

The bottoms of the larger, deeper lakes have several distinct environments. The shore slopes down to a depth where light cannot penetrate; the sublittoral, a region below the shore, is filled with accumulated plant debris and empty shells; and the profundal, or deep bottom, consists of soft mud. The water itself has its own distinctive regions: the limnetic zone, along the shore, and the pelagic zone, or open water.

The factors that influence plant and animal life in all these regions are solar radiation, which provides light and heat, and the amount of mineral and organic nutrients in the water. These substances are carried into lakes by streams, rain, and wind.

The most varied and densely populated area of a lake is the shore. Rooted plants provide shelter and food for a host of flatworms, segmented worms, mollusks, crustaceans, and insects and their larvae.

As the water deepens, plant food becomes scarcer, and animal life poorer. Insect larvae, some snails, and a variety of segmented worms inhabit the plant debris and mud at the bottom of most lakes.

The all-encompassing name for the minute animals and plants that float in the open water is plankton. The animals are called zooplankton, and the plants—mainly algae such as diatoms and blue-greens—are known as phytoplankton. Organisms living on the shore and on the lake bottom are termed benthos, a Greek word for depths of the sea; and the larger animals, such as fish living in the open water, or pelagic zone,

are classified as nekton, or free swimmers.

Most planktonic animals and plants are small. The smaller the organism the greater its surface in relation to its volume; and the greater the surface the greater the friction with the surrounding water, so the easier it is to float. Many planktonic animals are star-shaped, with fine filaments and long limbs which increase their surface area.

Changes in ponds and lakes

Ponds are small bodies of water, often artificial, usually shallow, and lacking an underlying rock layer. Some ponds dry up for part of the year, and the organisms that live in them must be able either to survive in a dormant state during dry periods or to move in and out of the water, as do insects and amphibians.

A lake may undergo three stages in thousands of years of development—the oligotrophic, eutrophic, and dystrophic. Oligotrophic lakes, the youngest, usually have steep, barren sides and clear water containing only a small amount of dissolved nutrients. In time, these lakes may begin to silt up and develop into eutrophic lakes. These shelve less steeply, and are richer in dissolved nutrients and therefore in plant and animal life. Dystrophic lakes have a high proportion of organic material, and often develop into peat bogs. Many lakes, however, become arrested at one stage or another, and others may show some features of all three stages at the same time.

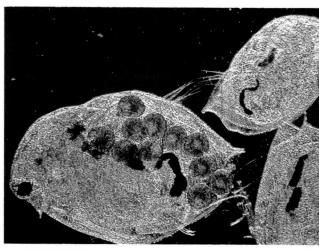

Brood chamber A female water flea, a member of the zooplankton, produces eggs every two or three days and carries them in a brood chamber located between its body and its transparent shell

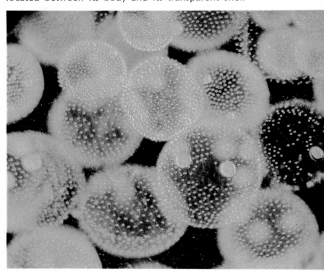

Plant plankton Colonial algae of the genus *Volvox* are typical members of the phytoplankton. Tiny threadlike structures on their bodies help to propel them through the water

Swarming predators Voracious spotted gars are found in weedy waters in the eastern United States

Freshwater shrimps These fertile crustaceans—one inch long—of the genus *Gammarus* live in ponds and streams. They mate and lay eggs from spring to autumn, producing many offspring

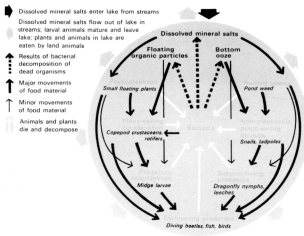

Dissolved mineral salts enter lake from streams

Dissolved mineral salts flow out of lake in streams; larval animals mature and leave lake; plants and animals in lake are eaten by land animals

Results of bacterial decomposition of dead organisms

Major movements of food material

Minor movements of food material

Animals and plants die and decompose

Dissolved mineral salts

Floating organic particles — Bottom ooze

Small floating plants — Pond weed

Copepod crustaceans, rotifers — Snails, tadpoles

Midge larvae — Dragonfly nymphs, leeches

Diving beetles, fish, birds

The food cycle in a lake Plant growth occurs in part because of nutrients in water. Animals eat the plants and transform plant tissue into animal tissue. The animals are eaten by predators, which eventually die and are decomposed by bacteria into simple mineral and organic compounds

271

Life in streams and rivers

Few plants or animals can gain a foothold in fast-flowing mountain streams, but lower down, the river slows and broadens, and many species can flourish

The current is a strong influence on the animals and plants that exist in running waters. Animals must expend much of their energy to stay in one place. Rooted plants cannot take hold on the beds of torrents, so they are confined to the slower reaches of rivers. Floating animals and plants can thrive only in the slowest-running waters.

In a typical river system, torrential headstreams and highland brooks join to form quickly flowing upland streams with currents strong enough to move rocks and gravel. These streams converge into fairly swift rivers, where patches of silt are deposited. The next phase occurs where the land slopes more gently. The current is moderate, and sandbanks and mudbanks form. Finally, when the land flattens out, the river broadens, and meanders through the lowlands to meet the sea. Each zone of running water has its own challenges and opportunities for animal life.

The waters of mountain torrents and streams are cold, and rich in oxygen. The only plants are microscopic algae, which

Trout stream Few fish can breast the torrential currents of these waters. They must be strong-swimming, streamlined species, such as trout. Other fish find shelter on the bed

The minnow stream This part of a stream is more constant in flow than headstreams. Minnows live among the water crowfoot, and many other animals are adapted for clinging on rocks

Lowland river On the lowland plains, an old river is usually slow and meandering. The river is shallow and lacks strong currents, so its course has many loops before arriving at the sea

cling to boulders and the stony riverbed. Animals in this zone feed on organic waste that falls from the banks, or prey on other animals.

The speed of the water prevents most animals from establishing themselves in mountain streams. Fish that are found there are often strong swimmers, like the brown trout. Other fish survive by clinging or creeping over the surface of stones, using suckers on their undersides. Some fish protect their eggs by laying them in hollows scooped in the riverbed or, like trout, burying them in the gravel. Others lay sticky eggs that adhere to stones and are not swept away in the current.

Invertebrates in fast-moving currents have strong claws, suckers, and flattened bodies. When some caddisfly larvae are ready to pupate, they build cocoons of silk threads and weight them against currents by adding sand particles and sometimes stones. Some species construct nets, which they use to catch food.

Plants and fish of swift rivers

Where mountain streams converge to form rivers, the current is still swift, though silt may be deposited in protected places. This permits plants such as crowfoot and bur reed to grow.

The temperature of the water in the upper reaches of rivers is higher than in the mountain streams, but there is still plenty of oxygen. The fish of mountain streams are replaced or joined by species adapted to warmer waters.

In these less exacting conditions, there is more animal life. Added to the stonefly nymphs, mayfly nymphs, and beetles found in the mountain streams are animals such as dragonfly nymphs, snails, and mussels. These invertebrates, and the increased amount of plant material, provide more food sources for the fish living here.

In the next phase of the river, the slope is gentle and the current is moderate. In North American rivers the dominant fish are suckers, catfish, and chub. Predatory fish such as bass, perch, and eels are common. Submerged and floating plants growing at the river edge provide a spawning ground for the fish as well as food and shelter for their young, or fry.

Rich waters of the lowland reach

In the lowland reach, rivers are usually wide and bordered with dense vegetation, which provides food for animals. Rivers often meander in great loops, and the water is clouded with organic waste. In temperate latitudes the water temperature may reach 68° F. (20° C.) in summer and the current may be so slow that plankton can develop.

In the estuary, where the waters of river and sea meet, the water is brackish. Most freshwater animals cannot live in estuaries, though some species that live in both fresh and salt water, such as the three-spined stickleback, are found there.

River divider Waterfalls, like the 210-foot-high Iguassú Falls in Brazil, form barriers across rivers, and on either side the animals are different. Only clinging animals can survive near the falls

European river zones and the fish that live in them

Trout stream
Only well-muscled trout and fish that shelter among stones can live in swift mountain streams. Fish feed on insects that fall in the water. These waters are rich in oxygen

Brown trout — *Salmo trutta*
Bullhead — *Cottus gobio*
Stone loach — *Nemacheilus barbatulus*
Salmon about 2 years old — *Salmo salar*

Minnow stream
Here the riverbed is less steep. Although it is still swift, cool, and well oxygenated, it is slow enough for plants to root. Trout- and minnow-stream fish mingle

Dace — *Leuciscus leuciscus*
Minnow — *Phoxinus phoxinus*
Grayling — *Thymallus thymallus*

Barbel reach
Here the land slope is gentle and the water flows more slowly. Deeper-bodied fish, such as barbels and perch, swim among the plants that grow in muddy patches

Barbel — *Barbus barbus*
Chub — *Squalius cephalus*
Roach — *Rutilus rutilus*
Perch — *Perca fluviatilis*
Pike — *Esox lucius*

Bream river
Its vegetation is like that in the barbel river, except in the muddy depths where poor light inhibits plant growth. The warm water has little oxygen. Flat-bodied fish swim among reeds

Tench — *Tinca tinca*
Bream — *Abramis brama*
Roach — *Rutilus rutilus*
Perch — *Perca fluviatilis*
Pike — *Esox lucius*
Carp — *Cyprinus carpio*

Feeding in swift streams The dipper feeds in the waters of Eurasian streams. It walks along the stony bed, held down by the force of the current, or swims, using its wings, as it forages for insects

Adaptations to torrents

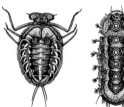

Bornean sucker fish — *Gastromyzon borneensis*
Water penny — (Psephenid beetle larva)
Mayfly nymph — genus *Iron*
Blepharocerid fly larva

The Bornean sucker fish, water penny, and mayfly nymph are shaped so that the underside acts like a sucker against the rocks. Blepharocerid fly larvae have six suckers that help them cling

Mountain stream frog The tadpoles of the mountain torrent frog of the genus *Staurois*, from Southeast Asia, have sucking disks below their mouths, and these are used for clinging to rocks

Holding on against the current A stonefly nymph has long legs with two claws on each foot, enabling it to grasp stones in fast-moving streams. Its body is flat and offers little resistance

Invertebrates

Single-celled protozoans are a vital link in the inland waters food chain; they devour bacteria and are themselves eaten by larger and more complex animals

Invertebrates are the most prolific forms of animal life in inland waters, far outnumbering the more familiar vertebrates in both species and individuals. They range in size from microscopic protozoans to crayfish more than 18 inches long. They live in mud and gravel, between sand grains, under stones, among vegetation, and in open water.

Some invertebrates are carnivorous and prey upon smaller animals. Others are plant-eaters. A large third group feeds upon decaying organic matter in the water.

The most numerous and widespread group are the protozoans, single-celled animals, most of which move freely in the water and feed upon bacteria. Protozoans can survive within protective cysts when temporary pools dry up, waiting until the pool fills again. Other groups common in most fresh-waters are the microscopic rotifers and the nematode and segmented worms. Segmented worms live deep in the sediment at the bottom of lakes and ponds.

Many water-living invertebrates have evolved special structures that allow them to exist in a medium which has a lower oxygen content than air and is 800 times more dense.

The smaller, simpler water invertebrates do not have special organs for respiration, but absorb oxygen and excrete carbon dioxide through the skin. This gas exchange is helped by the circulation of water over the respiratory surface. In the case of more complex animals, such as mollusks, the exchange is also aided by the circulation of internal fluids, in the form of a blood system.

Many larger animals have developed special respiratory organs called gills, the surface areas of which are richly supplied with blood vessels. The comblike gills of freshwater mussels are also used to filter particles of food from the water moving through them. Freshwater crustaceans such as crayfish breathe through feathery filaments on the limbs.

Insects are typically air-breathing animals. Many species that seek food underwater must have access to air. Some, such as

Small diving predator The fisher spider of North America catches minnows by walking down submerged plant stems. Tiny hairs covering the spider trap sufficient air to last for a 45-minute dive

mosquito larvae, have hair-fine snorkels, while others, such as the giant diving beetle of the genus *Dytiscus,* draw on a reservoir of air trapped beneath the hard wing covers. Most aquatic insect larvae, such as those of dragonflies and mayflies, breathe in the water by means of gills.

Movement in water calls for adaptations very different from those needed on land. Amoebas move along the bottom by flowing into extensions of their fluid bodies, while flagellates vibrate their long, whiplike flagella.

Some insects, particularly those living in strong currents, crawl on mud and plants, but the majority have oarlike swimming ap-

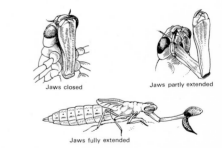

Jaws closed   Jaws partly extended

Jaws fully extended

Methods of trapping prey Dragonfly nymphs (above) seize prey with their hinged mouth parts. Caddisfly larvae (below) remain on the bottom and feed on animals washed into upstream-facing traps

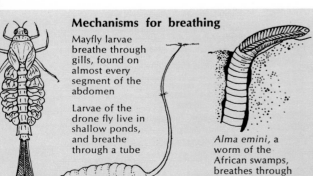

Mechanisms for breathing

Mayfly larvae breathe through gills, found on almost every segment of the abdomen

Larvae of the drone fly live in shallow ponds, and breathe through a tube

Alma emini, a worm of the African swamps, breathes through its tail, which acts as a simple gill

The whirligig beetle of the genus *Gyrinus,* like other water beetles, carries an air bubble beneath the wing cases. This allows it to remain submerged for several minutes, while it seeks larvae or other prey. However, the air bubble makes the beetle so buoyant it must cling to plants or other fixed objects

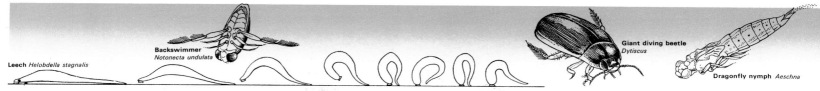

Leech *Helobdella stagnalis*

Backswimmer *Notonecta undulata*

Giant diving beetle *Dytiscus*

Dragonfly nymph *Aeschna*

How invertebrates swim Leeches move along the bottom of a pond in a series of loops by alternately attaching their front and rear suckers to the ground. Backswimmers of the genus *Notonecta* swim upside-down, propelled by means of their oarlike rear legs. They are so buoyant that they move in a series of arcs and return to the surface after each stroke. A smooth, streamlined shape helps the giant beetle to swim. The gills of the dragonfly nymph are located in its rectum, from which water is expelled so violently that the animal is driven forward by jet propulsion

pendages. Most freshwater insects have at least one pair of legs with undersides flattened for swimming.

The tiny protozoans and rotifers feed on even smaller organisms, such as algae and bacteria. They use hairlike structures known as cilia to create currents and filter out food particles from the water.

Many invertebrates, including water snails and some leeches and insect larvae, browse upon vegetable matter, while others, like the planktonic crustaceans, filter minute plants from the water. These invertebrates are eaten by carnivorous predators such as coelenterates of the genus *Hydra*, which catch them in their stinging tentacles.

Many insect larvae also are carnivorous, and are adapted for such a diet. Dragonfly nymphs, for example, have hinged mouth parts which shoot forward to grasp prey.

Suspended on the surface Mosquito pupae, breathing through tubes, hang from the surface film of a pond, where the water molecules tend to stick together. Pond film is the habitat of many insect species

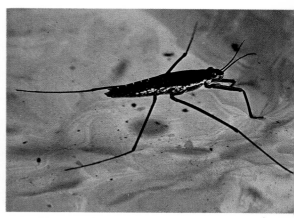

Water strider The pond skater, or water strider, walks across the surface film of a pond. It is so light that its feet hardly dimple the water as it moves

Freshwater invertebrates reproduce in a variety of ways

Reproduction in freshwater invertebrates ranges from the simple nonsexual division of the body, as in some protozoans and flatworms, to the highly complicated life cycles of many insects. Some invertebrates can reproduce either with or without sexual processes. Female water fleas and rotifers can produce eggs without being fertilized by males, which, in any case, appear only at intervals of several generations. Females alone can ensure a rapid population increase. The relatively few eggs fertilized by males help maintain the species' genetic health.

Freshwater sponges, hydras, threadlike nematode worms, and ectoprocts—mosslike animals that cling to leaves—produce eggs that are resistant to drought and cold.

Most aquatic insects leave the water at the adult stage, though by then the greater part of their life-span may be over. From the egg, which is laid in water, an insect may undergo a dozen stages of development over two years before emerging into the air for its brief adult life. The function of the adult, in these cases, is simply to reproduce and disperse the species.

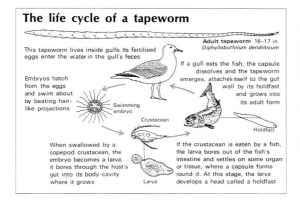

The life cycle of a tapeworm

Adult tapeworm 16–17 in.
Diphyllobothrium dendriticum

This tapeworm lives inside gulls. Its fertilised eggs enter the water in the gull's feces

Embryos hatch from the eggs and swim about by beating hairlike projections

Swimming embryo

Crustacean

When swallowed by a copepod crustacean, the embryo becomes a larva; it bores through the host's gut into its body-cavity where it grows

Larva

If a gull eats the fish, the capsule dissolves and the tapeworm emerges, attaches itself to the gut wall by its holdfast and grows into its adult form

Holdfast

If the crustacean is eaten by a fish, the larva bores out of the fish's intestine and settles on some organ or tissue, where a capsule forms round it. At this stage, the larva develops a head called a holdfast

Splitting in two
The coelenterate *Hydra* reproduces asexually by growing a bud, a replica of itself. Initially, the bud is fed by the parent; then it begins to catch mites and worms in its own tentacles. Finally, as the point of attachment constricts, the young hydra breaks away from the parent. Hydras also are able to reproduce sexually

Two-year transformation During its two-year larval stage (above), the damselfly lives underwater, breathing through leaflike gills on the tail. In its adult stage (right), lasting only a month, the damselfly mates, lays its eggs, and then dies

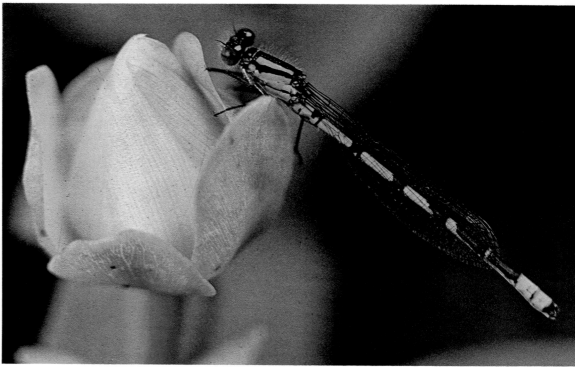

275

The fish

About a third of the 20,000 known species of fish live in inland waters, eating an immense variety of food, ranging from sediments in mud to other fish

There are three classes of fish: jawless fish; those with skeletons of cartilage; and those with bony skeletons. The jawless fish are the least abundant in inland waters, where they are represented by lampreys, eellike parasites with sucker mouths. Cartilaginous fish are also more common in the sea than in inland waters, although there are about 50 species of sharks and rays that live in estuaries and freshwaters.

Bony fish are the most numerous and successful class in inland waters. They fall into two main types: the fleshy-finned fish, represented by lungfish; and the ray-finned fish, of which there are three groups. The most primitive group of ray-fins, the chondrosteans, is represented in inland waters by the sturgeons and the bichirs of Africa. The more advanced holosteans are represented by garpikes and the bowfin. The most advanced group, the teleosts, has many freshwater members, including carps.

The earliest bony fish had air-breathing lungs that opened off the gut. Most teleosts have evolved to the point where this primitive lung has become sealed off, forming a gas-filled swim bladder that provides buoyancy to keep the fish afloat without effort.

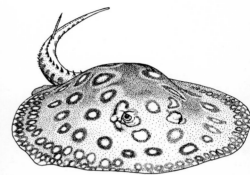

Stingrays Members of the genus *Potamotrygon*, among the few freshwater cartilaginous fish, live in South American rivers. Like marine stingrays, they have venomous spines, sheathed in skin, on the upper sides of their long, pointed tails. Stingrays eat crustaceans; the venom is only for defense

Mud-stirring fish The paddlefish, a relative of the sturgeon, is found only in the Mississippi river system. It stirs up muddy river bottoms with its paddle, which accounts for one third of its five-foot length, and filters out minute animals with gill rakers in its enormous mouth

Freshwater predators Spotted gar lurk among plants and, protected by bony plates, ambush other fish

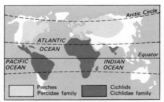

Salt water limits range Perch, characins, and carp live only in fresh water, and are as effectively restricted by sea barriers as land animals. But cichlids are able to make short sea crossings

Mouth brooder The bony tongue, a fish of the Amazon basin, holds its eggs in its large, prominent mouth until they hatch. It generally cruises just below the surface of the water

Upside-down swimmer This African catfish swims and floats near the surface with its belly uppermost. This adaptation helps it, and other members of its genus, to feed easily from the surface film

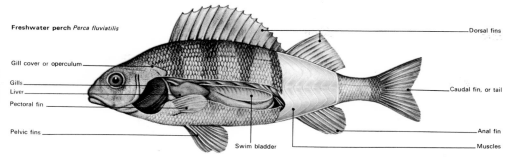

Freshwater perch *Perca fluviatilis*
Dorsal fins
Gill cover or operculum
Gills
Liver
Pectoral fin
Pelvic fins
Swim bladder
Caudal fin, or tail
Anal fin
Muscles

Elements of a bony fish This perch, cut away to show the internal organs, has the advanced aquatic adaptations of typical teleost bony fish. The gills extract oxygen from the water, and the gas-filled swim bladder provides buoyancy. The fins and tail stabilize the fish and help it to swim

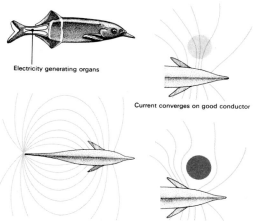

Electricity generating organs
Current converges on good conductor
Undisturbed electric field
Current diverges from bad conductor

Navigation by electricity Fish of the mormyrid family find prey by means of sense organs in the head and electric discharges from organs near the tail. The sense organs record any distortions

Some fish feed on anything from plants to organic sediments and animal matter; others feed only on plants—even on one particular kind of plant; and still others are hunters, and feed only on animals. This variety in feeding habits is made possible by an immense variety of jaw and mouth shapes, and by the formation of gill rakers, the filter apparatus with which some fish collect particles of food that are suspended in the water.

In Lake Victoria, in central Africa, more than 170 species of cichlids have evolved different eating habits, and each species differs from the others in its physical adaptations for eating. Some have strong, blunt teeth and eat mollusks; others, with chisel-shaped incisors, eat weeds or rasp algae from rocks. A third group, with reduced teeth and wide-opening jaws, take the eggs and young of other cichlids from their parents' mouths. There are even some species that eat only the scales of other fish.

Breeding habits vary almost as much as feeding techniques. Many species simply discharge the unprotected eggs into the water, where most of them are lost to predators. Other fish, such as the three-spined stickleback, lay eggs in a nest and defend the nest against intruders. In certain parts of Africa and South America, where ponds and streams dry up completely during the hot months, some small tooth-carps lay their eggs in the mud at the bottom before the dry season begins. The adult fish die, but the fertilized eggs survive in the mud and, with the coming of rain, hatch to repopulate the pond or stream until the next drought.

Fish, like other vertebrates, have organs of sight, taste, smell, touch, and balance. But, unlike land-living vertebrates, fish also have a pressure-sensitive system called the lateral line, which spreads over most of the body and enables the fish to sense disturbances in the water and to locate the objects that cause them.

Some fish have organs that discharge electricity. The discharge, which can be of a force up to 550 volts, comes from disklike cells embedded in a jellylike substance. These cells, which have developed from muscle cells, are used both for defense and for creating an electric field that gives the fish information about its position in the water. Three families of electric fish live in inland waters—the African snout fish, the South American knife fish and electric eels, and the African electric catfish.

Safety in mother's mouth Young cichlids swim close to their mother's mouth, ready to dart inside the instant danger threatens. Many cichlids hatch their eggs in their mouths

Deadly piranhas *Serrasalmus piraya* grows up to two feet long and is the largest piranha of the Amazon. A school of piranhas has stripped the flesh from a 120-pound capybara in minutes

Trailing sense organs Some catfish, such as *Ictalurus nebulosus*, live on the bottom and detect food with chemical sense organs in their whisker-like barbels. Some species have venomous spines

277

Air-breathing and migratory fish

Some species that are classed as freshwater fish spend much of their lives in the sea, and others at times leave the water altogether, to journey over land

Not all fish that live in inland waters spend their entire lives there. Salmon migrate to the sea and back again, and eels make similar migrations in reverse. Other fish, adapted to breathing air, can live temporarily out of water, and move about on land.

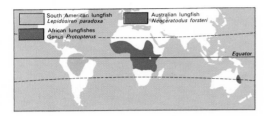

Distribution of lungfish Lungfish once had wide ranges, but today they are restricted to parts of tropical Africa, South America, and Australia. Three species of the genus *Protopterus* live in Africa

The lungfish, primitive survivors of the mid-Devonian age, have air-breathing lungs like the amphibians. Some species can survive periods of drought, when a river dries up, by becoming dormant in the mud. African lungfish spend the dormant period in cocoons, while the South American species merely covers itself with slimy mud. The lungfish's paired, slender fins resemble the limbs of amphibians, and one species, in Australia, uses these fins to "walk" over the mud much as an amphibian does.

The Chinook salmon, or king salmon, is, like the Atlantic salmon, a migrating fish. It begins its migration as a young silvery smolt, swimming down the rivers out to the Pacific, feeding on plankton. When it matures it becomes a predator, feeding on small fish, such as herring. In its four years of wandering the Chinook may travel more than 700 miles from its home stream, past the Queen Charlotte Islands off the British Columbia coast, before returning to spawn in the creek where it was born.

African lungfish Both the African lungfish (above) and the South American species have similar life cycles. In the dry season they lie dormant in mud, emerging to breed when the rain comes

Fish out of water—lungfish and climbing perch

Lungfish, like many of the earliest bony fish, have primitive lungs that allow them to exist in oxygen-deficient swamps, or in seasonally dry river and lake beds where other fish could not survive.

Three species of lungfish live in Africa, one in South America, and one in Australia. The Australian lungfish cannot survive long droughts, but the other species are so well adapted to breathing air that gill respiration accounts for less than 5 percent of their oxygen consumption. They can withstand drought by becoming dormant.

The dormant state normally lasts two to three months, but African lungfish have survived for several years, and been revived almost instantly by moisture.

Some other fish are able not only to breathe air, but also to travel across land. In India climbing perch of the genus *Anabas*

can travel several hundred yards over land from pond to pond. These fish have developed structures in their gill chambers that absorb oxygen from air. When they are in water they must surface to breathe air. Climbing perch do not actually climb; their name comes from the fact that they are often found in trees, where birds of prey have carried them.

The climbing perch travels on land by spreading out its gill covers, anchoring them to the ground with their sharp spines, and pushing itself forward with its pectoral fins and tail.

Asian snakeheads can also survive long periods out of water because they have cavities behind their gills that are filled with oxygen-absorbing blood vessels. Other air-breathing fish have respiratory organs in the mouth or even in the intestine.

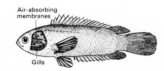

Breathing chamber Lunglike membranes in a chamber linked to the gills of climbing perch absorb oxygen from air

Cocooned fish African lungfish pass dry seasons in mud burrows, protected against moisture loss by cocoons of mucus

Gills that vanish Young lungfish absorb oxygen from water with external gills that later vanish—adults breathe air

The incredible migrations of salmon and eels

The vast migratory journeys of the eels and the salmon, and their incredible "homing" abilities, are still not fully understood.

Most is known about the Atlantic salmon, which spends the first one to three years of its life in freshwaters. During this period it is called a parr. Then comes a transition to the silvery smolt stage and migration down the rivers into the sea, where the fish lives for several years, traveling thousands of miles across the Atlantic.

At maturity comes another migration, in which the adult salmon returns to spawn in the very river or stream where it was hatched. The most likely explanation for the salmon's ability to find its home stream is that it navigates by the sun to reach coastal waters, then is guided to the river where it was born by its sense of smell.

Many scientists think that migration in

the salmon is triggered by hormone changes, which first demand salt water, then reverse and demand fresh water again. Salmon usually die after spawning, but a small proportion, called kelts, survive and return to the sea, where they gain strength before migrating to fresh water to spawn again.

The migration of eels is even more mysterious. For both the European eel and the American eel, life begins in the Sargasso Sea. From here ocean currents carry the young either toward North America or toward Europe.

At this stage the larval eel bears so little resemblance to the adult that until the turn of the century it was placed in a separate genus and named *Leptocephalus*. After two years the larvae go through another change and become elvers, which move in mass migrations to rivers and inland waters. There

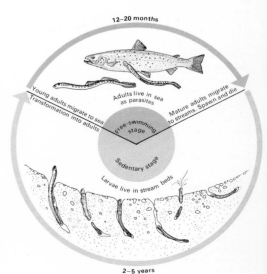

Adult European eel

Eel larva

Elvers

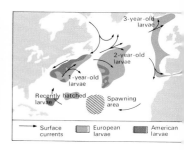
Surface currents | European larvae | American larvae

From sea to river and back

American and European eels are both born in the Sargasso Sea and may be the same species. The larvae drift with ocean currents to North American and European coasts. Then they change into young eels, or elvers, and swim up rivers to spend 7 to 20 years inland before returning to the sea. Some think that the European eels may never reach the Sargasso Sea again to breed, but American eels do, and produce a new generation

they live for anywhere from 7 to 20 years.

The great reverse migration of eels begins shortly before sexual maturity. At this time digestive organs atrophy, reproductive organs develop, and the eels begin their last journey, back to the Sargasso Sea. After spawning there, they die.

There is, however, some doubt as to whether the European eels complete the return journey. If this is the case, it may be that all eels belong to the American species. The breeding population would be derived from American eels, and the differences between American and European eels due to factors influencing the European larvae during the early stages of their life cycle.

Another migratory fish is the ayu, which breeds in rivers in Japan, Korea, and Taiwan but spends most of its life in the sea near the shore. It spawns on gravel in the upper reaches of rivers, where a strong current aerates the water and the temperature is never higher than 54° to 59° F. (12° to 15° C.). When the fry hatch they float down the river into the sea. After about 15 months' development in the sea the adult ayu swims up a river to the spawning ground. Soon after spawning, it dies.

Parasitic sea lamprey

Sea lampreys spend their adult lives, lasting from 12 to 20 months, in the sea as parasites on other fish. At the end of this time they migrate up rivers to spawn on the gravel bottoms. The female lays about 60,000 eggs. These are fertilized by the male and buried, after which the adults die. Some 10 to 12 days later, the eggs hatch. After another ten days the larvae, about a quarter of an inch long, leave their nests and drift downstream, eventually finding a muddy bottom in which they burrow. After two to five years, the larva, now about six inches long, changes into an adult, developing a rasplike tongue and a round, suckerlike mouth ringed with teeth. Finally it leaves its burrow and moves downstream to begin its parasitic life in the sea. The life cycle of the sea lamprey *Petromyzon marinus* is shown in the drawing to the left.

A hard-fought journey Mature salmon, after spending several years in the sea, return to the rivers in which they were born, fighting the strong currents, and spawn in shallow streams

Amphibians

Some species of amphibians never leave the water; among them is the five-foot-long Japanese giant salamander, which must continually surface to breathe

Most amphibians are creatures both of land and of freshwaters. They cannot live in the sea because its saltiness would cause the water in their body fluids to flow out through their skins. Like fish and reptiles, amphibians are cold-blooded, incapable of regulating their body temperatures in-ternally. If the temperature of their surroundings is too low, they become sluggish. They are most numerous in the tropics.

Amphibians are an ancient group whose primitive ancestors evolved from fish some 300 million years ago. Some early amphibians in turn evolved into reptiles, but despite this relationship the surviving amphibians are a quite distinct group. Reptiles have scaly, waterproof skins; most amphibians' skins are soft, permeable, and moist.

Amphibians lay eggs that can develop only in water or in damp places, and so for the first part of their lives most of these animals are aquatic. Some remain in the water, but most go ashore at some time.

To cope with this dual existence, amphibians have three different breathing methods. Gills, which extract dissolved oxygen from water, are present in the young and in some adults; many adults have lungs; and all amphibians have skins that are richly supplied with blood vessels that can absorb oxygen from the air or water.

Salamanders, toads, and frogs wriggle their way through several life stages

There are three orders of amphibians—the Urodela, which have tails; the Anura, which do not; and the Apoda, the strange, legless caecilians which live in tropical forests. The Urodela are often called newts, but the word is correctly used only for the aquatic members of one family in the order, the Salamandridae. All members of the order are best called salamanders. The Anura order consists of 12 families of what are commonly called toads or frogs. In strict scientific usage, however, the word "frog" applies only to the Ranidae family, and "toad" only to the Bufonidae.

After hatching, the majority of amphibians go through several distinct stages of development in which the young differ in appearance and structure from adults. Frogs undergo several changes—from spawn to tadpoles with outer gills and then, as the legs develop and the gills and tail are lost, to small frogs. This cycle may take up to three months to complete. Most salamanders, including newts, go through similar changes.

Species that remain in water all their lives sometimes keep their tadpole characteristics of gills and flattened tails. One example is the axolotl of Mexico. It does not leave the tadpole stage unless the water in which it lives dries up. Then it loses its external gills.

Adult amphibians are well equipped for their double lives. Salamanders can walk across the floors of ponds, or swim by undulating their tails. Frogs and toads have powerful hind legs, often with webbed feet, which enable them to swim strongly.

Anchored eggs Italian spectacled salamanders fix their eggs to stones or plant debris in slow-moving water. The eggs are fertilized inside the female

Old World toad The green toad ranges from central Europe to the Mediterranean region and Asia. It nests near the shore in a sandy slope and will eat almost any small animals that it can find

Hidden eggs The female great crested newt of Europe spends most of the year on land, but lays its eggs in water during the spring. The eggs are attached singly to water plants

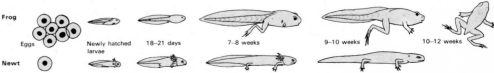

Frog — Eggs — Newly hatched larvae — 18–21 days — 7–8 weeks — 9–10 weeks — 10–12 weeks

Newt

Stages toward an adult form Newts and frogs go through similar stages from egg to adult, but the newt tadpole is slimmer and more closely resembles its adult form. Newts, unlike frogs, lay single eggs. In both cases the larvae hatch with external gills that disappear before maturity. The newt's forelegs appear before its hind legs, but in the frog this order is reversed

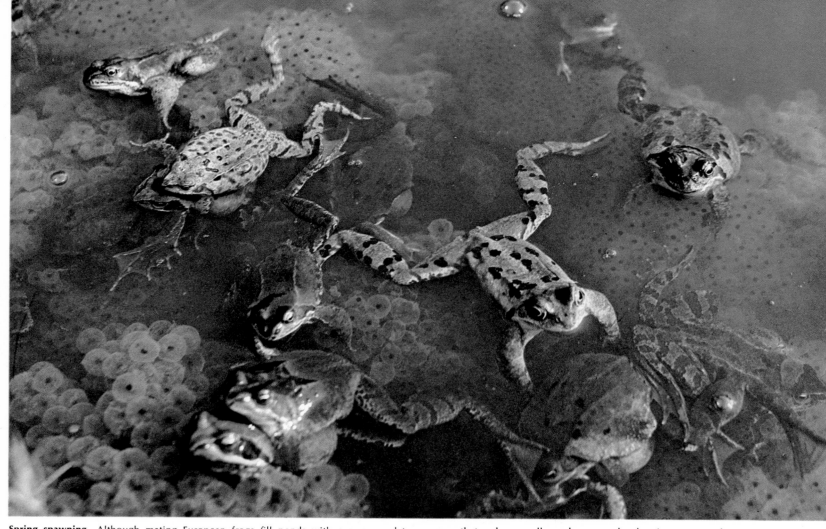

Spring spawning Although mating European frogs fill ponds with spawn, predators ensure that only a small number ever develop into mature frogs

Male midwife toad This toad takes strings of eggs from the female and winds them around its legs. It carries them like this for several weeks, then deposits them in a pond, where they hatch

Edible frog The hind legs of the widespread edible frog have been considered a delicacy since Roman times. Like other members of its genus, *Rana*, it is widely distributed throughout Europe

Clawed toad The South African clawed toad avoids drought by burying itself in mud as its pond dries up. It remains there until rain refills the pond. It uses its claws to dig food out of mud

Some frogs, living high in the Andes, never leave the lake where they were born

Amphibians have exploited a number of surprising habitats. The American grotto salamander lives in subterranean waters. It never sees light, and its eyes are covered by skin. Salamanders, the most aquatic of amphibians, include the mud puppies of the genus *Necturus*, which live on lake bottoms in North America and keep their external gills and flattened tails all their lives.

Salamanders of the Sirenidae family are even more adapted to water. They have evolved an almost eellike appearance; their hind legs have disappeared and their forelegs are only rudimentary. One, *Amphiuma means*, which lives in running water in Virginia and Florida, has legs so small and useless it is known locally as the Congo eel.

The largest amphibian is the Japanese giant salamander, which grows to over five feet. It lives in mountain streams, feeding on fish, worms, and crabs.

Many frogs spend their entire lives in water. Members of the genus *Telmatobius* live in high-altitude rivers and lakes in the Andes, notably Lake Titicaca, never appearing on shore and rarely on the surface.

Mud is a favored habitat of anurans. The aquatic Pipidae family contains species such as the Surinam toad, which lives in rivers in the Amazon and Orinoco systems and gropes through the mud with its long fingers to find food. During the breeding period, the female lays eggs and the male helps attach them to her back, where rough skin grows over them. The young do not emerge until they are fully developed.

The largest of all frogs is the Goliath frog, which when its legs are extended reaches an overall length of about three feet. It lives in deep river pools in western equatorial Africa, emerging at night to feed in the riverside forest.

Bird-eating frog The common bullfrog, the largest North American frog, can grow up to eight inches long. It sometimes eats small birds and turtles, in addition to insects and crustaceans

Reptiles

The dominant predators in inland tropical waters are crocodiles—reptiles so powerful they can overcome and dismember an antelope in a matter of minutes

Only a small proportion of the world's 5000-odd species of reptiles live in inland waters; but turtles, snakes, and lizards all have forms that have adapted to this habi- tat, and crocodiles are almost completely restricted to it.

Most water-going reptiles resemble other present-day reptiles: they are dependent on the land. The majority breathe with their lungs and, with the exception of some water snakes, the young begin life on shore.

Crocodiles are found mainly in inland waters, where they live in lakes, rivers, swamps, and estuaries, and breed on the shores. There are two families—Croco- dylidae, comprising true crocodiles, alli- gators, and caymans; and Gavialidae, with only one member, the gavial, or gharial, which is found in India.

The only lizard known to live in fresh water is the South American cayman lizard, which looks like a small crocodile.

Tortoises and turtles—reptiles in armor plate or leathery shells

The armor-hard shell that protects tortoises and turtles is usually composed of scales of keratin, the substance that forms the basis of mammalian hair and the feathers of birds. Beneath this shell, and fused to it, are plates of bone joined to the ribs and shoul- der girdle.

Soft-shelled turtles do not have horny scales, but instead are protected by a tough, leathery skin over their reduced bony shell.

It is sometimes possible to estimate the age of a young tortoise or turtle by count- ing the rings on its scales. In temperate regions, where there is a seasonal variation in climate, a new ring is added each year.

Turtles have two ways of withdrawing the head as a defensive measure: folding the neck sideways, as do members of the two families of side-necked turtles, or fold- ing it vertically, as is the case with the majority of turtles. One side-necked species, the Australian snake-necked turtle, catches fish with a quick lunge of its long neck.

Among freshwater turtles that fold their necks vertically is the common snapping turtle, an aggressive animal widespread in North American waters.

Fishing turtle The matamata of South America has a long nose and fleshy fringes on its jaws. These move in the water and attract small fish and other prey. The matamata then opens its mouth suddenly and the prey is sucked in

Adult and young The largest South American turtle is the 30-inch-long side-necked turtle that inhabits the Amazon and Orinoco river systems

Florida soft-shelled turtle Because of its elon- gated snout, it is able to breathe while largely submerged. The leathery shell has lost the outer covering of horny plates. Its name, *Trionyx ferox*, is derived from its habit of biting viciously

Florida cooters These freshwater turtles are com- mon in the southern United States and Mexico, where they browse on riverbed debris and floating vegetation. They are sluggish and frequently bask on logs. It is thought that the sun's heat may speed up their digestive processes

South American killer The black cayman ranges from the Amazon and Orinoco basins north to Guyana. It is the largest and most dangerous of all caymans, and is widely hunted because it preys on domestic cattle

Fish-eater The gavial of India catches fish with a sideways sweep of its slender jaws

Hatching Young Nile crocodiles emerge from eggs that have been incubated in a covered nest

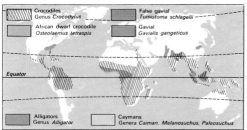

Crocodiles Only a few species live outside the tropics. These hibernate for half the year

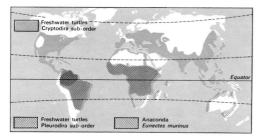

Turtles Pleurodiran turtles, once widespread, now live only south of the Tropic of Cancer

Crocodiles can eat underwater and move quickly on land

The two families of crocodiles are similar in their habits, but can be distinguished by their external appearance. True crocodiles, alligators, and caymans have enlarged fourth teeth in the lower jaw. In true crocodiles, these enlarged teeth fit into a notch on the outside of the upper jaw and are visible when the mouth is closed. In alligators and caymans, however, the enlarged fourth teeth fit inside the jaw. The most obvious feature of the gavial of India is its long beaklike snout—an adaptation for catching fish.

All crocodiles have raised nostrils that protrude above water, allowing them to breathe while the rest of the body is submerged. They can also feed while submerged and are adapted to this habit by having an air passage that runs from the nostrils into the throat, behind a valve that can exclude water from the windpipe.

In water the crocodile's swift movements are powered mainly by the tail. They can move faster on land than is generally supposed. Crocodiles eat any birds, mammals,

or fish they can drag from the shore or overcome in the water. Large crocodiles will attack animals as big as deer or cattle. They drag their prey into the water and tear it limb from limb.

True crocodiles lay their eggs in a pit on the shore, while alligators lay them in a heap of decaying vegetation, where the heat generated by the process of decay helps hatch the eggs. The Nile crocodile buries its eggs in a pit, and the newly hatched young chirp until the mother digs them out.

Snakes that live in freshwaters have evolved nostrils on top of their snouts

Most snakes swim well and will take to the water when necessary, but only a few species actually live in freshwaters. Many of these have evolved nostrils on top of their snouts that enable them to breathe while swimming. Members of one such genus, *Grayia*, are fish-eaters, and live in rivers in the African rain forests and savanna. In the case of the Southeast Asian Acrochordidae family, the young are born live in the water. This means that the snakes need never come ashore at any point, and most probably remain in water all their lives.

Riverside strangler The anaconda is the largest boa in the world. It hunts along riverbanks and kills its prey, such as mammals, birds, and small caymans, by constriction, squeezing it in the coils of its body until it suffocates

Mammals

Most mammals of the inland waters are land-based species, but there are also members of marine groups, including a dolphin that lives 1000 miles inland

Only a few species of mammals spend all or most of their lives in inland waters. Most of them are members of predominantly sea-going groups, such as dolphins and seals. Many other mammals, such as otters, water voles, and water shrews, live on land but spend much time in inland waters, seeking food. They usually have thick fur which traps air and keeps their skins dry, while their feet may be webbed and hair-fringed. Some have special muscular flaps for closing ears and nostrils when submerged.

Among the most widespread Eurasian freshwater rodents are water voles. They live in burrows along the banks of streams, with entrances below water level. Voles have dense fur, hairy fringes on the feet, and hairy tails.

The muskrat, native to North America and introduced in Europe, is particularly well adapted to freshwaters. It has partially webbed hind feet covered with stiff hairs, and a scaly, rudderlike tail. Its home has underwater exits, and it can remain submerged for up to 12 minutes.

Inland aquatic mammals include the platypus, some dolphins, and the hippo

The platypus belongs to the group of primitive egg-laying mammals called monotremes, found only in Australia and New Guinea. It swims and dives, mainly in the morning and evening, in search of food such as shrimps and insect larvae. Soft, dense fur, a broad tail, and webbed feet equip it for aquatic life. Its eyes and ears are closed by skin flaps underwater, and it relies on a well-developed sense of touch to locate prey. Platypuses live in burrows in riverbanks, where the females lay their eggs.

The marsupials—mammals whose young are born at an early stage of development and suckled in the mother's pouch—have only one species adapted to aquatic life, the

water opossum, or yapok, of Central and South America. This densely furred animal has webbed hind feet. The female has a watertight pouch in which the young are carried. Water opossums hunt at night for crayfish, shrimps, and small fish. During the day they shelter in ground nests of leaves or in dens reached through holes in riverbanks.

Among the insect-eating animals living in freshwaters are three species of African otter shrews. The largest species, *Potamogale velox*, is about 13 inches long and is found in western and central equatorial Africa. It lives in lowland rivers and mountain streams, feeding on fish, crabs, and amphibians. Its feet are not webbed, but even without that

adaptation the otter shrew is a speedy and agile swimmer, propelling itself through the water with its thick, powerful tail. Its nostrils close when it submerges.

The northern Eurasian water shrew is an excellent swimmer. It has large, hair-fringed feet and a slightly flattened tail, with a keel of stiff hairs along the underside. It is active both day and night, feeding on insects and other small aquatic animals.

Even the burrowing mole family has two aquatic members—the Russian desman and the Pyrenean desman. Both species have webbed feet. Like all moles, desmans burrow extensively, and they make their homes in riverbanks. In the water they seek out in-

Built for water The water opossum, which hunts in rivers, has a watertight pouch for its young

Foraging shrew The northern Eurasian water shrew feeds day and night on small aquatic animals

Riverbed feeder The platypus detects invertebrate prey in riverbeds by touching with its snout

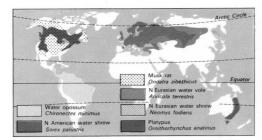

Widespread small aquatic animals Shrews, rats, and voles are among a large range of mammals that have become adapted to living in inland waters, which encompass a great variety of habitats and offer many different types of food

Active all year The northern Eurasian water vole lives in riverbank colonies, feeding mainly on grass. It stores food for the winter, when it tunnels under the snow, but does not hibernate. Under the snow the temperature is warmer

Freshwater dolphin When swimming rapidly and when feeding, Amazon dolphins come to the surface every 30 seconds and roll to breathe. Although they seem to scan their surroundings above water, their senses of hearing and touch are probably more acute than their vision. They use an echo-sounding system to avoid underwater obstacles and locate prey—fish and crustaceans

Sensitive paws The oriental small-clawed otter feels under mud and stones for mussels, snails, and crabs with its sensitive front feet

sects, crayfish, snails, and amphibians with their flexible, spatulate snouts.

The coypu, also called the nutria, a large, ratlike rodent weighing about 18 pounds, is well-equipped for aquatic life, with its webbed hind feet. It is native to inland waters in central and southern South America, but has colonized many parts of Europe and North America after escaping from commercial fur farms.

Truly marine mammals that have become adapted to fresh water in estuaries and large rivers include several dolphins, one of which —the Amazon dolphin—may be found up to 1000 miles from the sea.

Among the carnivorous mammals, several species of otters—members of the weasel family—are distributed throughout the world's inland waters. Their aquatic adaptations include dense fur, flattened, webbed feet, and small ears and nostrils that can close when the animals are submerged. Otters feed mainly on crayfish, frogs, and fish, and they also prey occasionally on a variety of birds and mammals.

Seals and hippos

The only seal that lives exclusively in fresh water is the Baikal seal, found in Lake Baikal in southern Siberia, about 1000 miles from the sea. There are about 60,000 Baikal seals, which are believed to have evolved from Arctic ringed seals that reached Lake Baikal by river.

The saltwater Caspian Sea is the home of a similar seal, the Caspian seal, which is also thought to have evolved from the ringed seal of the Arctic.

The largest freshwater mammal is the common hippopotamus, which may weigh up to three tons. Common hippos have nostrils and ears which they can close when submerged. They normally stay underwater for four or five minutes but are believed to be capable of remaining submerged for half an hour. Common hippos are grass-eaters.

The pygmy hippo of West Africa weighs about 500 pounds and is less aquatic than the larger species. Its nostrils are large and almost circular, and its eyes do not protrude.

Freshwater seal The Baikal seal, about 4½ feet long, lives mainly at the north of Lake Baikal

Hippo ranges Common hippos generally live in rivers and head for water when frightened on land. Pygmy hippos live in swampy forest and take refuge among the trees if danger threatens. They eat tender shoots, leaves, and fallen fruits

At home in water Common hippos spend practically their entire day sleeping and resting in or near water. When molested they will move into deep water or reed beds where they can lie unobserved, with only their eyes and nostrils above the surface of the water. They sometimes travel 20 miles on land, but stay near the shore

Swimming and diving birds

Birds have many methods of obtaining food from streams and lakes. Some dabble at the surface; others dive and chase fish; and pelicans cooperate in scooping them up

Lakes, rivers, and swamps offer a greater variety of habitats for birds than do the oceans, so inland waters have a greater variety of birdlife. Thirty-seven families of birds are composed wholly or mainly of species that live close to water. Fifteen of these families belong wholly to inland waters. Seven other families are composed mainly of birds that live on freshwaters. The remaining 15 are principally seabirds.

Water birds can be divided into four main groups, according to the way they feed. The surface swimmers dive only in emergencies, such as when escaping from a predator, and their aquatic food is limited to what they can reach when up-ended.

Divers, such as grebes and loons, swim on the surface, but dive for food, propelled by their feet or wings or both. Loons, called divers in Europe, are fairly common on northern lakes and coastal waters in the United States. Their harsh, laughing call is unforgettable. When threatened, a loon expels the air from its lungs and feathers and sinks into the water like a stone, hardly making a ripple.

The third group is composed mostly of nonswimming birds that obtain their food from water, either by diving into it momentarily or by swooping down and snatching prey from the surface with their feet.

The fourth and largest group of water birds are the wading birds; they are nearly all limited to shallow water.

Non-swimming plunging birds, such as some kingfishers, dart into the water, seize their prey, and immediately return to the air

Snake birds swim underwater, using wings and feet for speed in pursuing prey

Surface-swimming ducks are limited to the food they can reach when dabbling

Waders, such as herons, wait in the shallows for prey to come near

How water birds feed The upper layers of some inland waters are rich in food. Because different birds have evolved various methods of feeding, they can exploit the same area without competing. These birds can be divided into four main groups: nonswimming birds, underwater swimmers, surface swimmers, and waders. They also range from plant-eaters, such as herons, to fish-eaters, such as pelicans

Surface-swimming birds search the waters for food

Feather care A graylag goose preens itself, waterproofing its plumage with an oily beak. The oil comes from a gland in the goose's rump

The most characteristic surface swimmers, and the most numerous in temperate regions, are the swans, geese, and dabbling ducks. Among them, these birds will eat anything from minute plants and animals sifted from the mud to larger plants and invertebrates and even newly hatched fish. They obtain some of their food from land, or even most of it, as in the case of the grass-eating geese. Some surface swimmers are specialist feeders, such as the shoveler duck, which has a huge, broad bill adapted for sieving small organisms from mud.

These swimming birds tend to move from one body of water to another in search of food. Many species spend part of their time on the sea. Others make regular migrations, traveling great distances along well-established flight lines. The snow goose flies 3000 miles from its Arctic breeding ground to winter on the Gulf of Mexico.

The tropics are especially attractive to migratory wildfowl. In the upper Nile, resident species, such as tree ducks of the genus *Dendrocygna*, are joined periodically by huge flocks of ducks from the north, including shovelers and pintails. Southern migrants such as the knob-billed goose may also use the area.

Another typical group of surface swimmers are the pelicans, which feed almost exclusively on fish. They usually fish from a swimming position, dipping their great pouchlike lower jaw in the water like a scoop. A dozen or more pelicans may form a circle around a shoal of fish, driving the fish before them, and scoop up almost the entire shoal.

Cooperative fishers White pelicans congregate in large numbers in their feeding grounds. Sometimes a group surrounds a shoal of fish and shares the catch

Sharing a tree African spoonbills, sacred ibises, long-tailed cormorants, and snake birds live side by side at Lake Naivasha in Kenya. The species are able to share the habitat because each is adapted to exploit a different sector of the food resources. Some are waders, some underwater swimmers

Breeding plumage The male great crested grebe grows a crest on its head and a ruff on its neck in the breeding season, which attract the female

Birds that forage for food and chase prey underwater

The birds that swim underwater as well as on the surface are a larger and more varied group than the surface swimmers. They include diving ducks, and many of these, such as the North American redhead and the Eurasian tufted duck, have broad bills like those of dabbling ducks. Diving ducks feed on underwater plants.

Another group, the mergansers, or saw-bills, have serrated bills that are adapted to catching slippery fish. Even more specialized fish-catchers are the cormorants, darters, and divers. Cormorants, which have long necks and short wings, are particularly numerous in tropical freshwaters. In temperate regions, however, most cormorants are visitors from the sea.

The snake bird, or African darter, is at home underwater. It often swims with its narrow body and wings submerged, using its long neck and narrow head like a periscope. The snake bird spears fish with its long bill.

The grebes specialize in diving from the surface to obtain a varied diet that includes mollusks, frogs, and small fish. The great crested grebe displays remarkable courtship behavior, which reaches a climax when male and female dive simultaneously, then surface breast to breast. The female accepts a small "present" of waterweed from the male.

Many species of the rail family, which includes moorhens and coots, are aquatic. The aquatic types are good swimmers, although, unlike most waterfowl, they do not have webbed feet. Instead, they have flaps of skin on their toes that open as the bird swims to assist propulsion. Rails feed on small animals and plants.

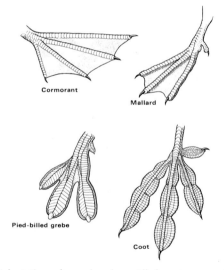

Adaptations for swimming All four toes on the cormorant's foot are webbed together, while only three of the mallard's toes are webbed. The pied-billed grebe and the coot have toes with lobes on them that open on a power stroke through the water and close on the recovery stroke

A toothed bill Saw-billed ducks, such as the red-breasted merganser, have serrated, slightly hooked bills. These birds hunt fish under the water. The toothed edge of the bill ensures that once a fish is caught it cannot get away

Snake bird This bird, the most specialized of freshwater fish-catchers, captures its prey with its bill. It is also called the anhinga

287

Birds that feed in water without swimming

**Not all waterside birds swim to feed.
Some make spectacular plunges to
seize prey from the surface; slow-stepping
waders sieve food in the shallows**

In addition to swimming waterfowl, two
other large groups of birds find their food
in inland waters. These are birds that catch
prey while flying, plunging, or swooping
at the water, and birds that feed while wading in shallow water.

The most widespread of the birds that
plunge to seize prey from near the surface of
the water are kingfishers. Most species perch
on branches over the water, then plunge like
arrows into a shallow dive, snatching up
prey in their beaks. Others, such as the pied
kingfisher of tropical Africa and southwest
Asia, hover first, like hawks spying from the
air. Not all kingfishers eat fish; some tropical species, such as the pygmy kingfisher of
Africa, feed on insects and live away from
water.

Fishing eagles and ospreys swoop feet-
first on their prey, clutching it in their talons.
Skimmer birds skim small invertebrates
from coastal inlets and backwaters, their
wings nearly dipping into the clear, shallow
water as they fly over seeking insect prey.

Bird that digs for fish With its hooked bill, the
shoebill digs in muddy swamp bottoms for lungfish. Standing motionless in the water, it also waits
for fish or frogs to come within its reach. About
3½ feet high, it lives in eastern tropical Africa

The bald eagle Named after its white head, it
catches fish with its sharp talons and dismembers
them with its strong beak. A scavenger, it often
steals carrion from other predators. It ranges from
North America to northeastern Siberia

Long-legged wading birds forage in the shallows for plant and animal food

Wading birds are found in most parts of the
world where there are shallow waters, which
usually offer an abundant supply of plant
and animal life for food. Most wading birds
have long legs and adaptations to their bills
related to various methods of feeding in
shallow water. They include such birds as
storks, ibises, spoonbills, and herons.

One stork, the openbill, has a gap between
the upper and lower mandibles of its beak,
which enables it to collect and hold water
snails, its only food.

Ibises and spoonbills belong to the same
family but have differently shaped beaks for
different uses. Ibises have long, curved beaks

with which they probe mud in search of
worms and small shellfish. Spoonbills have
flattened bills, broadening out to spoonlike
tips. They feed by sweeping the bill from side
to side, sieving the mud for small animals.

The shoebill has a heavy, hooked bill with
which it forages for worms, frogs, and
lungfish in tropical African swamps. Another storklike African wading bird, the
hammerkop, or hammerhead, has shorter
legs than most wading birds. It walks along
the edge of the water searching for small
fish and insects.

Herons are one of the most widespread
groups of wading birds. They are found in

North and South America, Eurasia, Africa,
Australia, Madagascar, New Zealand, and
some oceanic islands. They range in size
from night herons, some of which are only
12 inches high, to the Goliath heron of
tropical Africa, which measures about five
feet from head to toe. All herons have long
bills, necks, and legs, which enable them
to wade in shallow waters, feeding on fish,
amphibians, insects, and worms.

Jacanas, or lily-trotters, feed in freshwaters of the New and Old World tropics,
stepping nimbly from one water-lily leaf to
another on extremely long toes that distribute their body weight evenly.

Returning to its nest The common kingfisher will
dig as deep as eight feet into steep riverbanks
to make its nest. It eats mainly minnows, swallowing the fish headfirst. When minnows are scarce,
it will eat small crustaceans and insects. It is
found in Eurasia, Africa, and New Guinea

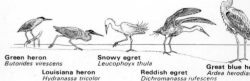

Green heron
Butorides virescens
Louisiana heron
Hydranassa tricolor
Snowy egret
Leucophoyx thula
Reddish egret
Dichromanassa rufescens
Great blue he
Ardea herodias

Sharing the water These herons all share the
same Florida habitat. The green heron waits on
a branch for prey to appear; the Louisiana heron
wades in very shallow water; the snowy egret
flushes prey out of the mud; the reddish egret
stirs the water to alarm small fish that collect in
the shadows formed by its outspread wings; and
the blue heron wades at the greatest depth

A skimmer's bill Tropical skimmers have bills
adapted for taking food from the surface of inland
waters. The lower mandible skims insects and
other small animals from the surface film

Louisiana heron It has the long, thin legs and beak typical of herons, but its neck is very slender

Great blue heron This bird stalks shallow waters by day and by night in search of food. It is found in southern Canada and most of the United States, nesting high above the ground in large stick nests. Both parents feed the young

Green heron In breeding season, the green heron undergoes a color change. The irises of its eyes turn from yellow to orange and its yellow legs become coral pink. The green heron is distributed mainly in the eastern and central United States, in small ponds and along wooded streams. It is a short-legged heron, only about 14 inches long, and often dives into the water after its prey. It lives in small colonies and builds its nest in trees or shrubs near the shoreline

Flamingoes use their tongues to sieve microscopic food from water and mud

Flamingoes, long-legged waders that may stand over five feet high, feed entirely on microscopic plants and animals. These are abundant in shallow saline or alkaline waters in the warm regions of both the New and Old Worlds. Flamingoes form huge colonies, sometimes containing more than 2 million birds.

Flamingoes feed with their heads between their legs, facing backward, and with their bills underwater. The bird sweeps the bill from side to side, sucking in mud or water, and food. The liquid is pumped out by the bird's tongue, but the food is trapped on featherlike filters in the bill.

Filter feeding

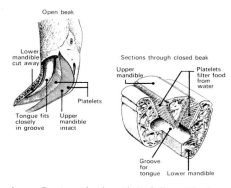

The lesser flamingo feeds with its bill upside-down and closed, the upper mandible fitting into the lower. Swinging its head from side to side, the bird pumps water through its mouth by moving its tongue back and forth. Minute plants are trapped in filterlike platelets inside the bill. The bills of all species of flamingoes are adapted for sieving food in this way

Greater flamingoes These birds congregate in large colonies with their young. Most flamingoes feed by filtering through the surface water, but the greater flamingoes of the genus *Phoenicopterus* feed by submerging their entire heads, since they filter through the mud for their food

Animals in unusual habitats

Few areas of water are devoid of animal life; even pitch-black underground lakes, hot mineral springs, and water-filled hollows in plants support animals

Any new area of water, including land-locked inland waters, gradually becomes colonized by plants and animals. Flooded craters, quarries, and gravel pits, initially devoid of life, are soon occupied by crustaceans and insects. These animals crawl or fly to their new habitat, or their eggs are transported there by other animals. Such colonization processes have been taking place for millions of years.

Changes in climate and other evolutionary pressures have forced some animals to live in isolated and unusual watery habitats, such as wet sand, wells, and lakes in caves. These species, left in isolation by upheavals of the surface of the earth, or other changes, are known as relict fauna.

Other animals have evolved adaptations that enable them to survive in such unlikely places as hot springs and salt lakes.

The specialized animals living in wet sand include single-celled protozoans, threadlike nematodes, rotifers, mites, crustaceans, and segmented worms. They are called interstitial fauna because they live in the tiny spaces, or interstices, between grains of sand. Most of them are wormlike and can squeeze between the grains. They are thought to have originated in the sea, and to have reached their inland water habitats through the ground.

Pale, blind animals dwell in the inky blackness of caves

Blind fish The cave characin, growing up to three inches long, lives in chilly underground waters of limestone caves. Skin covers its rudimentary eyes

Hunting by vibration A blind North American fish, *Typhlichthys subterraneus* locates its prey and avoids obstacles by a sense that detects vibrations

Hidden sanctuary Limestone deposits decorate this huge cavern, which stretches for miles 200 feet beneath Arkansas' Ozark National Forest. There are similar caves in many parts of the world, where a limestone layer is overlaid by harder rock. Over millions of years, rainwater seeping through fissures in the upper layer dissolves the limestone and forms caves with underground rivers

The best-known underground water habitats are in caves. No light penetrates these cool waters, so there are no green plants. Animals that live there feed on fungi, bacteria, and plant litter carried by underground streams or introduced by other cave-dwelling animals such as bats.

Several species of fish live their entire lives deep in caves. These fish have adapted in similar ways to their environment. Vision is a useless sense in the blackness of caves, and cave-dwelling fish either have greatly reduced vision or none at all. And since visual markings serve no purpose where there is no light, skin pigmentation is reduced or missing. As a result most cave species are pink or white.

The same reduced vision and lack of pigmentation is a feature of cave-living amphibians, like the Texas blind salamander and the olm of Europe.

North American fish of the Amblyopsidae family show a gradation of these features, from the small-eyed pigmented forms that live in dark corners of surface streams, to the white, completely sightless Kentucky blindfish, which lives in caves.

Most fish of the Brotulidae family live in deep oceans, but two genera in Cuba, *Lucifuga* and *Stygicola*, inhabit rivers that flow into cave rivers, and one species lives in caves in Mexico. There are also cave-living barbels and catfish in Africa, and in North and South America.

Invertebrates that live in hot springs and desert pools

Underground crustaceans Isopod crustaceans, looking like bleached wood lice, are blind and almost transparent. Both features are typical of animals that spend their entire lives in dark caves

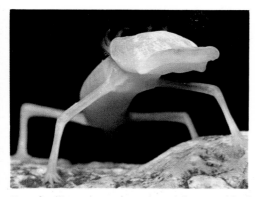

Cave-dwelling salamander The adult Texas blind salamander's eyelids are fused together, and its skin has virtually no pigment. Its larva lives aboveground and has normal eyes and good vision

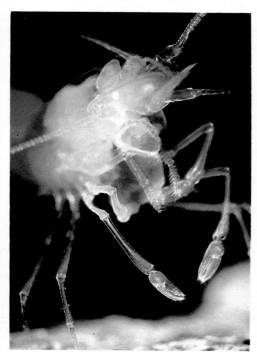

Sightless shrimp The Texas blind shrimp scavenges on the bottom of shallow lakes in dark caves. Food particles are dropped by bats, sleeping above

Tiny animals of the hot springs Small crustaceans and insects can inhabit such improbable places as this hot spring on the slope of a volcano in Isabela Island in the Galápagos group (right). In some hot springs, a few fish are able to tolerate the heat

Prolonged immersion in very hot water will kill most animals, yet the hot springs in desert and volcanic regions are inhabited by a few life forms. Single-celled flagellates and some tiny crustaceans and insect larvae can tolerate very warm water. Even a few fish live in warm freshwater springs. The North American desert pupfish swims in water as hot as 120° F. (49° C.) and another fish, *Tilapia grahami*, lives in the warm mineral waters of Lake Magadi in Kenya at 109° F. (43° C.).

Deserts and other arid regions often have salt lakes, which may contain fish if the mineral concentration is not too high. Another small North American pupfish lives in Salt Creek in Nevada, where it tolerates water twice as salty as the sea.

Deserts also have freshwater ponds, which last for only a few days after the erratic rainfall in such regions. No animal with an extended active life cycle can survive in such conditions, but a few tolerate the high mineral content and temperature extremes, often by producing drought-resistant eggs or larval stages, or by developing extremely rapidly. Some rotifers, crustaceans, and insects have acquired these qualities.

Life in desert rain pools is often a race against time. Eggs of some crustaceans, for instance, may lie dormant for several years between heavy rainfalls and then, in seven

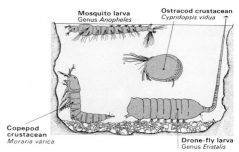

Tree-puddle inhabitants These adult crustaceans and insect larvae are some of the many animals that dwell in flooded tree holes. The crustaceans have gills, but the larvae require access to the air. Many of these small animals lie dormant for a long time until rain comes

to ten days, hatch, grow to adulthood, feed, breed, lay their own eggs, and finally die, when their temporary desert pool evaporates in the sun.

Few watery habitats, however small or hazardous, remain unoccupied for long. Insects probably search actively for them, but protozoan cysts usually arrive by chance, blown on the wind. Even the puddles between the stems and leaves of some tropical plants are colonized. The Mexican flat-toed salamander quickly moves in and lives in such puddles as long as they last, feeding on the insects that also live there.

Life in estuaries and mangroves

The prop roots of red mangroves form a network in which mud accumulates, building up the land and sheltering mud-burrowing animals

The waters of river estuaries, too salty for freshwater animals and not salty enough for most sea creatures, have their own specially adapted inhabitants

An estuary is the mouth of a river where fresh water meets the sea and the saltiness of the water varies. It is also a place where creatures from land, inland waters, and sea meet. In large estuaries currents, tides, and crosswinds often mingle muddy river water with salt water, causing the mud to settle and form shifting sandbanks, which are alternately exposed and covered by the tide.

The abruptness of the transition from salt water to fresh depends mainly on the slope of the riverbed. In many parts of the world this transition takes place fairly rapidly; but on the northeastern coast of South America, where the coastal plain is wide, the tides can affect the river waters nearly 100 miles away from the sea.

Estuary-dwellers have adapted to mud, tides, and varying salinity

Flocks of waders After feeding at low tide on shellfish and worms, buried just below the surface, crowds of wading birds congregate on the remaining exposed mud flats. Most of the birds in this group are knots, but near the edges are some curlews, godwits, oystercatchers, and redshanks

Burrowing crab When the tide comes in, the soldier crab digs an airtight chamber in the sand and remains sheltered there until low tide

Basking manatees Two American manatees lie sunbathing in the shallow water of an estuary. They eat, sleep, and give birth in the water

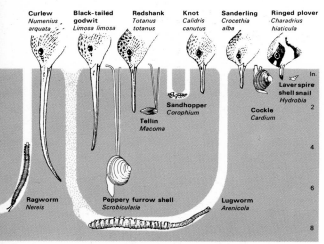

Waders' bills The prey available to a wading bird depends on the length of its beak. Even the curlew's long bill cannot reach a lugworm unless the worm climbs into the vertical part of its burrow

Curlew *Numenius arquata*
Black-tailed godwit *Limosa limosa*
Redshank *Totanus totanus*
Knot *Calidris canutus*
Sanderling *Crocethia alba*
Ringed plover *Charadrius hiaticula*
Laver spire shell snail *Hydrobia*
Sandhopper *Corophium*
Tellin *Macoma*
Cockle *Cardium*
Ragworm *Nereis*
Peppery furrow shell *Scrobicularia*
Lugworm *Arenicola*

Salt water is denser than fresh water. When it enters a river, therefore, it often lies beneath the river water flowing to the sea. This helps bottom-living marine animals to travel up-river. The mixture of salt water and fresh water in estuaries means that inland water animals living there must tolerate more salt, and creatures of the sea must adapt to less.

Animals that live between the tides—between the high- and low-tide marks—are mostly of marine origin. Since most of them are filter-feeders, they can eat only when the bottom is covered by water. Many of the larger crustaceans carry their eggs or young with them to protect them from the tide.

Many animals that live in estuaries feed mainly on organic waste matter carried downstream by the current, or on plant litter from salt marshes or mangrove swamps. Filter-feeders may also eat the bacteria that thrive on such plant waste.

Visual signals cannot be seen through the muddy waters of estuaries, and the animals that live there have evolved other ways of communicating. Several species of fish, such as croakers, drums, and grunts, communicate by sound.

The four-eyed fish, which live in Central and South America, have a pair of two-lensed eyes on the top of the head, one set of lenses for viewing in air and one set for seeing underwater.

Another unusual adaptation is that of the archer fish, found in estuaries in India, Malaya, the East Indies, and the Philippines. It shoots down its insect prey by squirting water from its mouth.

Among the few mammals found in estuaries are seals and manatees. Manatees grow up to 11 feet long, have paddle-shaped forelimbs, and live entirely in the water, feeding on water plants. There are three species, one of which is found in Florida.

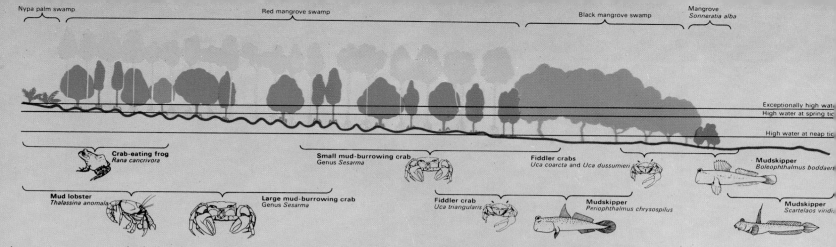

Nypa palm swamp   Red mangrove swamp   Black mangrove swamp   Mangrove *Sonneratia alba*

Exceptionally high water
High water at spring tide
High water at neap tide

Crab-eating frog *Rana cancrivora*

Mud lobster *Thalassina anomala*

Small mud-burrowing crab Genus *Sesarma*

Large mud-burrowing crab Genus *Sesarma*

Fiddler crabs *Uca coarcta* and *Uca dussumieri*

Fiddler crab *Uca triangularis*

Mudskipper *Boleophthalmus boddaerti*

Mudskipper *Periophthalmus chrysospilus*

Mudskipper *Scartelaos viridis*

In a mangrove swamp, the higher the ground the less frequent the flooding and the firmer the soil. Each level supports different animals and plants.

The mudskipper *Scartelaos viridis* lives where the mud is semifluid; *Boleophthalmus boddaerti* on firmer mud; and *Periophthalmus chrysospilus* on

the firmest mud. Mud-burrowing crabs of the genus *Sesarma* live on higher ground; larger ones prefer clayey soil and live in mud lobsters' holes

Swamps at the ocean's edges provide many animal habitats

The deltas and estuaries of many tropical rivers are lined with forests of evergreen mangrove trees. The animals that live there, like those that live in the estuaries, come from land, freshwaters, and the sea.

All mangrove swamps are much alike. There are two major groups: the Atlantic swamps of western Africa and eastern America, and those of the Indian and Pacific oceans, found in eastern Africa, Asia, and Australia. Many swamp animals are distributed throughout both areas.

A typical mangrove swamp is hot and steamy, inhabited by many insects, including mosquitoes and midges, which breed in stagnant pools in rotten tree stumps. Barnacles and spiny oysters live among the prop roots, and snails live in the trees. The mud between the tides houses animals that can tolerate seawater or have ways of maintaining an air supply. Some crabs and ants plug their burrows as the tide rises, and stay in air pockets until the water recedes.

The swamps also provide homes for many species of crabs which keep to their own particular zones of mud. Large crabs of the genus *Cardisoma* live along the landward fringe, next to mud-burrowing crabs of the genus *Sesarma,* to be replaced by other species at the edge of the sea. Xanthid crabs live in crannies along eroded shores, and the mud lobster makes deep burrows and mounds on clayey, waterlogged soil.

Birds, less numerous in swamps than in estuaries, nest in the upper branches of the mangroves. They include a number of herons and the scarlet ibis, which now is common only in Trinidad. Waders perch in the trees at high tide. Fishing birds include cormorants, darters, fishing eagles, kingfishers, and ospreys.

Most amphibians avoid brackish water, but the crab-eating frog lives in Indonesian mangrove swamps. The tadpoles and adults can tolerate water with salt in it.

Mammals are scarce in mangrove swamps, but include otters and occasional small cats. Crab-eating raccoons in South America visit the swamps, generally at dusk; and in Africa, Syke's monkey sometimes eats crabs. Leaf-eating monkeys are found in the mangroves of Southeast Asia, and colonies of the bats called flying foxes roost in the trees of Australian swamps during the daytime.

The fish of mangrove swamps include gray mullet, tarpons, and tripletails, whose young drift in the water, mimicking fallen leaves. Mudskippers, fish of the goby group, live in Indian Ocean, West African, and Pacific swamps. They have eyes on the top of their heads and "elbowed" fins, on which they "walk" across the mud; some species climb into the trees above the rising tide. While out of the water they keep their respiratory chambers full of water to allow breathing through the gills.

Courtship display   Male mudskippers of the genus *Periophthalmus* erect their dorsal fins to attract females

Scarlet ibis This colorful bird is found in the mangrove swamps of South America. Although it once had a wide range along the Guianese coasts, it is now common only in Trinidad

The regions of the sea

The vast, seemingly inexhaustible storehouse of the oceans supports a greater variety of life than any of the habitats on land

The sea covers 139 million square miles—71 percent of the earth's surface—and it extends to depths in which Mount Everest could be buried with thousands of feet to spare. The sea is also continuous, whereas land and freshwater habitats are separated by intervening water and land.

Variations in light, pressure, temperature, tides, currents, waves, and salinity all interact to create a range of natural regions, each with its typical forms of life.

Plants form the basis of all food chains in the sea, as they do on land, and the conditions that affect plant growth determine the areas where marine life is most abundant. The most important of these conditions is light penetration. Since all plants need the energy of sunlight in order to grow, marine plants are limited to the layer of the sea illuminated by the sun. This layer is called the euphotic zone.

The chief types of marine plants are tiny, free-floating phytoplankton, found in the lighted surface layers of open water. The phytoplankton is eaten by small floating animals, or zooplankton, and by small fish which, in turn, support a succession of actively swimming, or nektonic, predators.

Light penetration varies considerably, but light of sufficient intensity for photosynthesis—the process by which plants use sunlight to manufacture food from carbon dioxide and water—reaches down to a maximum of about 650 feet in summer. In winter, or in coastal areas where water is clouded by sediment, the limit may be much less than this.

Mineral salts, particularly nitrates and phosphates, are essential for plant growth. The distribution and concentration of these salts greatly affect the growth of marine plants. Close to the shore, salts are carried from the land by rivers, while in open waters, upwelling currents carry nutrients from the seabed. For instance, off the west coast of Africa the mineral-rich Benguela Current supports an abundance of plant and animal life in the sea, while off the Peruvian coast the Humboldt Current also supports a rich marine life, the basis for a major commercial fishery.

The temperature of the sea plays its part in the formation of natural regions. In some areas, such as the Antarctic, there are sharp changes of water temperature, known as convergences, which form barriers that separate different communities of plants and animals on each side.

As the sea becomes deeper, the pressure increases. Marine animals cannot range far beyond the depth to which they are adapted. If fish from shallow water are taken too deep, their bodies will collapse under the increasing pressure. Similarly, if deep-sea fish are brought rapidly to a higher level, their tissues are damaged because the balance between the fish's internal body pressure and the pressure of the surrounding water has been destroyed.

Lush rock pools In the littoral zone, permanent hollows are formed by the daily ebb and flow of tides. Here plants and animals are abundant, contrasting with the bare surrounding rocks

The sea's rise and fall

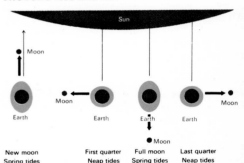

| New moon | First quarter | Full moon | Last quarter |
| Spring tides | Neap tides | Spring tides | Neap tides |

When sun and moon are in line, their combined gravitational pulls cause spring tides; rise and fall are greatest. When pulls are opposed, neap tides occur

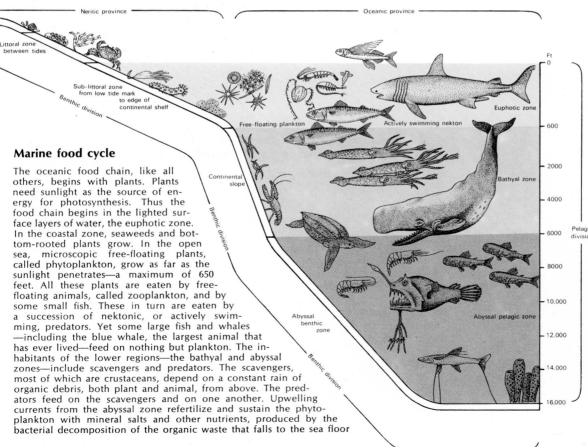

Marine food cycle

The oceanic food chain, like all others, begins with plants. Plants need sunlight as the source of energy for photosynthesis. Thus the food chain begins in the lighted surface layers of water, the euphotic zone. In the coastal zone, seaweeds and bottom-rooted plants grow. In the open sea, microscopic free-floating plants, called phytoplankton, grow as far as the sunlight penetrates—a maximum of 650 feet. All these plants are eaten by free-floating animals, called zooplankton, and by some small fish. These in turn are eaten by a succession of nektonic, or actively swimming, predators. Yet some large fish and whales—including the blue whale, the largest animal that has ever lived—feed on nothing but plankton. The inhabitants of the lower regions—the bathyal and abyssal zones—include scavengers and predators. The scavengers, most of which are crustaceans, depend on a constant rain of organic debris, both plant and animal, from above. The predators feed on the scavengers and on one another. Upwelling currents from the abyssal zone refertilize and sustain the phytoplankton with mineral salts and other nutrients, produced by the bacterial decomposition of the organic waste that falls to the sea floor

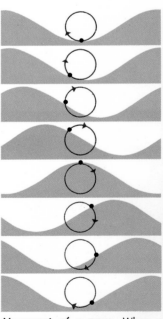

Movement of a wave When a wave travels through water, the particles of water do not move with it. A particle, represented by a black dot, travels in a circle up the front of the wave and then slides down the back of the crest. When the wave has passed, the particle will have gone a full circle. Waves mix the surface waters of the sea

Muddy shores Silt is deposited on coasts where the forces of currents and waves are small. The water is unfavorable to most animal and plant life because it is low in oxygen and restricts light

Flowerlike animal In spite of its plantlike appearance, this is an animal—a hydroid coelenterate. Hydroids, like this *Lampra microrhiza*, spend most of their lives embedded in the sea floor,

feeding on plankton that falls from above. This rooted existence is typical of bottom-dwelling animals. Some hydroids, however, grow on shells occupied by hermit crabs and move around with them

The various divisions of the sea: the surface, the depths, and the sea floor

The sea floor itself presents a varied environment. Its inhabitants live on a rain of waste matter from the regions above. From the tidal region on the shore, the seabed slopes down a gentle gradient known as the continental shelf. At a depth of about 600 feet, the shelf falls away sharply down the continental slope to the deep sea floor, which is marked with mountain ranges, valleys, and undulating plains. Some of the valleys, or submarine trenches, are very deep—the Marianas Trench in the Pacific, for example, plunges down 36,198 feet, the deepest known part of any of the world's oceans.

These mountains and trenches are impassable barriers to the movement of animals that live at great depths. The continents present additional barriers and account for the marked differences between creatures in, for example, the Atlantic and the Pacific, which are separated by the land mass of the Americas.

The open waters of the sea, called the pelagic region, are divided into two provinces. The waters above the continental shelf are known as the neritic province, and the remainder as the oceanic province.

The pelagic region is also divided into depth zones: the euphotic zone extends from the surface to the limit of light penetration, about 650 feet. The bathyal zone extends down to 6000 feet. Beyond this depth to the ocean floor is the abyssal pelagic zone.

The sea bottom, called the benthic region, has four main zones: the littoral, consisting of the shore between the high and low tide limits; the sublittoral, extending from the low tide mark to the edge of the continental shelf; the continental slope, from the edge of the shelf down to 6000 feet; and the abyssal benthic zone, consisting of the remainder of the seabed.

The power of the sea Waves, constantly breaking on the shore, gradually wear down even the hardest rocks, forming beaches of pebbles or sand

Life between the tides

The many animals that live on the shore, between the high and low watermarks, face a twice-daily change in environment from wet (or damp) to dry

In order to survive the often rapid changes of climate and chemical conditions caused by the rise and fall of tide, the animals of the seashore must be exceptionally adaptable. They must withstand wave action when the tide is in, desiccation by sun and wind when it is out, and different degrees of light, heat, and salinity between their immersion and their exposure. The ways in which they have become adapted fall into two main categories: physiological resistance, and behavior that helps them to avoid the extremes—for example, by moving into dark, moist crevices when the tide is out.

The problems of avoiding desiccation are severe for an animal that spends its life in varying proportions above and below water. A shore animal may spend five or six hours a day in cool water and, in the space of minutes, be exposed to the full heat of the sun, protected only by a thin film of water, or none at all. Also to be overcome are the variations of salinity in the water caused by evaporation or the addition of fresh water from rivers, streams, and rain.

The seashore, the region between the highest and lowest tides, varies greatly in different parts of the world. Where the land descends precipitously to the sea, the intertidal zone is quite narrow, and may even be almost nonexistent.

In other places, where the exposed land forms part of a permanent plain, tides normally ebb and flow at astonishing speed, and may expose a shore a mile or more wide twice every lunar day (which consists of 24 hours, 50 minutes).

There are three principal types of seashore—rocky, sandy, and muddy. Each provides a different environment to which characteristic groups of animals have become adapted.

Rocky shores are exposed to the assault of waves. Battered by the water and by the pebbles it dashes against them, even the hardest rocks are slowly eroded. Here, the sea makes an abrasion platform—a strip of rock, eroded into pools and grottoes that support an array of animals and plants.

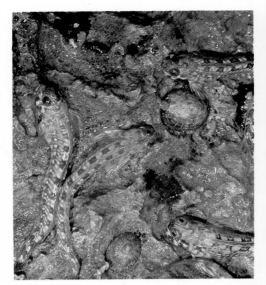

Fish out of water When the tide is out, blennies, or rockskippers, are exposed. They keep their gills and bodies moist by spending most of the time in rocky crevices, under weeds, or in the shade. Blennies have a worldwide distribution, though the majority of them are found in tropical waters

Slow movers Needle-spined sea urchins move slowly over the sand on tiny, tubelike feet with suction tips. These tips can also cling to rocks, and, when submerged, can extend to grasp prey

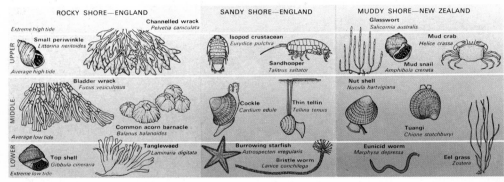

Zones of a shore Plants and animals of the seashore have adapted both to the terrain—rocky, sandy, or muddy—and to the amount of water present. Those living at high-tide level spend more time out of the water than at any other level. Animals on rocky shores usually cling or bore to avoid being washed away by the sea, while those on sandy or muddy shores are burrowing animals

ROCKY SHORE—ENGLAND / SANDY SHORE—ENGLAND / MUDDY SHORE—NEW ZEALAND

Extreme high tide
Channelled wrack *Pelvetia caniculata*
Small periwinkle *Littorina neritoides*
Isopod crustacean *Eurydice pulchra*
Sandhopper *Talitrus saltator*
Glasswort *Salicornia australis*
Mud crab *Helice crassa*
Mud snail *Amphibola crenata*
Average high tide

Bladder wrack *Fucus vesiculosus*
Cockle *Cardium edule*
Thin tellin *Tellina tenuis*
Nut shell *Nucula hartvigiana*
Common acorn barnacle *Balanus balanoides*
Tuangi *Chione stutchburyi*
Average low tide

Tangleweed *Laminaria digitata*
Top shell *Gibbula cineraria*
Burrowing starfish *Astrospecten irregularis*
Bristle worm *Lanice conchilega*
Eunicid worm *Marphysa depressa*
Eel grass *Zostera*
Extreme low tide

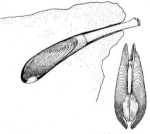

Rock-borers The common piddock is a bivalve with a bean-shaped shell. Protruding from the shell and opposite the hinge is a suckerlike foot. By constantly opening and closing its shell, the piddock uses rasplike teeth around its foot to cut into rock, slight movements of the foot ensuring that a round hole is bored. The hole is made larger as the animal grows and penetrates the rock

Camouflaged shrimp The anemone shrimp, a native of the South Pacific, is camouflaged by having the outline of its partly transparent body varied with vivid patches of different colors

Venus's necklace This seashore plant, an Australian alga, is made up of knobby, fluid-filled bladders that protect it while it is exposed to the air. It grows best when protected from waves

Plantlike animal A sea anemone looks like a harmless plant, swaying gently in shallow water, but it is a carnivorous animal whose graceful tentacles have stinging cells that paralyze small fish

Fan worms With their bodies buried in corals, fan worms of the genus *Spirobranchus* intercept and filter microscopic particles of food, which are collected by their colorful fringed crowns

Amphibious crab The ghost crab lives high above the watermark in burrows. Although it lives on land, it regularly returns to the sea to fill its gill chamber with water in order to breathe

Burrowing into the sand Razor clams are bivalve mollusks with shells shaped like straight razors. At one end of the shell are siphons for feeding; at the other is a flexible foot, used for burrowing. When burrowing, the razor clam elongates its foot, pushing the tip into the sand until it is fully extended. Then the tip swells, forming an anchor, and the foot muscles contract, pulling the shell vertically down into the sand

During low tide the animals living here face desiccation unless they live in pools, hide in crevices, or have thick shells. Consequently there is severe competition for the more protected sections of rocky shores.

The animal population of a crevice may include sponges, sea anemones, hydroids, sea urchins, starfish, mussels, limpets, oysters, chitons, sea mice, shrimps, crabs, lobsters, barnacles, sea squirts, and rockskippers.

Among the animals most highly adapted to rocky shores are the acorn barnacles, which live in unimaginable numbers on exposed rock faces. A barnacle is enclosed and protected from drying and wave action by a moisture-retaining shell made of six hard plates with a hinged cover of four more plates. When the tide rises, the cover opens to allow six pairs of feathery legs to extend and sweep the water for the minute organisms of the plankton on which the animal feeds.

Sandy shores consist of rock, but in pulverized form. The minute particles eroded from the land are at first held in suspension in the water and then deposited by the action of crosscurrents to make sandy beaches. The majority of animals on a beach burrow in the sand in order to avoid the extremes of the tides.

Though sand is easy to burrow in, it is difficult to prevent burrow walls from collapsing. Sand-burrowing animals have various ways of overcoming the danger of suffocation. Polychaete worms form tubes to the surface, and lamellibranch mollusks have long siphons.

Sand-dwellers obtain their food by drawing in water and filtering off the organic matter when the tide is in; by collecting detritus—organic debris—from the sandy surface, again when the tide is in; by taking in sand and digesting the organic matter it contains; or by preying on tiny animals that live in the spaces between grains of sand.

Muddy shores consist of fine particles of inorganic matter, and often a considerable proportion of organic debris. The fine particles are easily carried in suspension in water and tend to clog an animal's feeding and respiratory structures. Animals that are adapted to combat this hazard include the bivalve mollusks known as gapers, which live deep in the mud and maintain contact with the surface only by means of siphons.

Mud flats can support vast numbers of animals. The lugworm lives at the bottom of a U-shaped tube with two surface openings. It draws mud and sand down the head shaft for food, and a continuous current of water down the tail shaft for respiration. At intervals the lugworm backs up the tail shaft to deposit casts (wormlike coils of sand) on the muddy surface.

The plankton

The plankton—billions of drifting plants and the tiny animals that graze on them—make up the pasture of the sea and are the food of a host of larger animals

All life in the sea depends ultimately on plankton, the multitude of microscopic organisms that drift in the surface waters. Many planktonic animals can swim, but their movements are insignificant in relation to the sea's currents.

Plant life in the sea is restricted to the top or euphotic layer where there is adequate light for photosynthesis. With few exceptions, the drifting plant life, called phytoplankton, is made up of single-celled organisms. Some, like the flagellates, swim actively, but the larger diatoms are encased in shells. Some diatoms have spines and other fine projections which increase the surface area of the plant in relation to its weight. This increases their frictional resistance to water, so that they tend to sink only very slowly. Other diatoms have horizontally flattened bodies which act in the same way. Their large surface area also allows mineral salts and sunlight to be absorbed efficiently.

The tiny drifting animals called zooplankton feed on the phytoplankton, or on one another. They must keep swimming to remain near the surface, where their food is. Many have the same adaptations for buoyancy as the phytoplankton. Some have gas-filled chambers and oil droplets that reduce their density.

Animals of the plankton can be divided into two types: those that spend their lives as permanent members of the plankton, and those that are only temporarily planktonic.

Plant-eating crustaceans of the Copepoda subclass are among the giants of the permanent plankton. The copepod, about the size of a rice grain, is common in northern seas, and there are many smaller species.

Many animals in one The Portuguese man-of-war, one of a large group of marine animals called hydrozoan coelenterates, is a complex colony of individuals that can exist only when together, and each has its own job: digestion, reproduction, defense (by stinging), or keeping the colony afloat

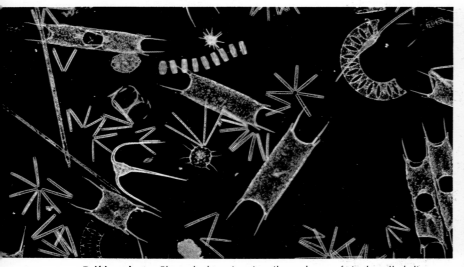

Drifting plants Plant plankton is primarily made up of single-celled diatoms, which have variously shaped shells and are often linked. When the daylight hours increase in the spring, the plant plankton multiplies and tints the sea brown. The stretcher-shaped organisms are diatoms *Biddulphia sinensis*, and those like wheel spokes are *Thalassionema nitzschioides*. Dinoflagellates, like the anchor-shaped *Ceratium horridum*, swim by lashing hairlike flagella

Drifting animals Zooplankton, or animal plankton, feed on the often smaller phytoplankton, such as diatoms and dinoflagellates. They, in turn, are eaten by larval and adult fish and other larger organisms. The copepods are the most important of the zooplankton in the food chain. They are the animals with two antennae at right angles to their bodies. Also visible are the larvae of bottom-living worms, crustaceans, and acorn barnacles

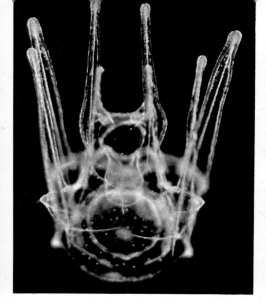

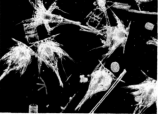

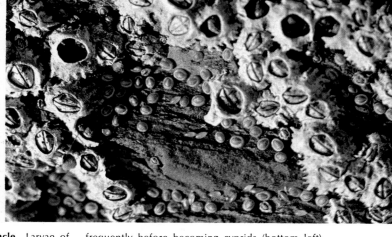

Sea urchin larva The fully developed larva of the common sea urchin has eight arms, bearing hair-like cilia which the animal beats in order to move. The mouth and gullet leading to the stomach can be seen in the center of the arms. These arms disappear when the sea urchin reaches maturity

Stages in the life of an acorn barnacle Larvae of the acorn barnacle (top left), called nauplii, are released from the adults' shells, where the eggs are brooded. The temporarily planktonic nauplii have hornlike spines at the front of their bodies, a single eye, and swimming "limbs." They molt

frequently before becoming cyprids (bottom left). Cyprids have two antennae to detect, on contact, adult acorn barnacles, and thus find the correct environment to occupy. The yellow cyprids above are settling on a rock covered with brown young acorn barnacles and large, whitish adults

Another major group of planktonic crustaceans are the euphausiids. One species is the krill, a shrimplike animal about two inches long, which is found in dense shoals in Antarctic seas, and is eaten by several species of whales.

Arrow worms of the genus *Sagitta* and comb jellies are members of the carnivorous permanent plankton; they prey on the copepod crustaceans. Arrow worms "twitch" themselves through the water by contracting their trunk muscles. A comb jelly has eight rows of plates running around its body from front to back. These plates, with hairlike fringes resembling the teeth of a comb, beat like paddles to move the animal through the water.

Many species that live in deeper water, on the bottom, or on the shore live in the plankton during their larval stages. Such temporary members of the plankton include the larvae of segmented worms, clams, and snails, squids and octopuses, starfish, sea urchins, and very young fish.

The need for light

The distribution of plant plankton in the sea depends on factors such as light for photosynthesis and the supply of nutrient salts. These salts are used up by the phytoplankton and must be replenished by salts dissolved in river water flowing into the sea or by upwelling water from the nutrient-rich lower depths.

In temperate latitudes the surface water is warm in summer and forms a layer over the cold waters that restricts the upwelling and the supply of nutrients to the surface phytoplankton, which then declines in quantity. In autumn cooling of the surface water breaks the layers down and allows turbulence to bring nutrients to the surface again. In tropical waters the layering is more permanent, and plant plankton is less abundant.

The abundance and distribution of all ocean life are tied to the quantity of phytoplankton. These plants form the first link in the ocean food chains, since the zooplankton which feed on them form the staple food of many other animals. These in turn are preyed upon by larger fish, which are themselves eaten by seals and some whales.

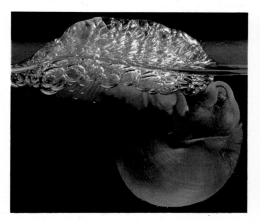

Raft of bubbles The planktonic snail of the genus *Lanthina* creates its own raft of gelatinous bubbles and clings to it beneath the surface of the water

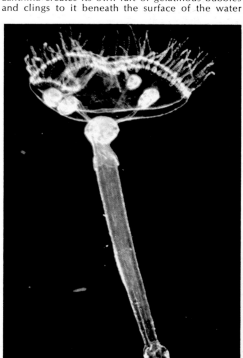

Carnivore eats carnivore With its bell turned inside-out, a jellyfish of the genus *Obelia* has captured a carnivorous arrow worm *Sagitta* with its stinging tentacles. The arrow worm now hangs from the jellyfish's mouth, its tail inside the stomach. Jellyfish have complex life cycles

Abundant copepods Copepods are one of the most numerous zooplankton. This plant-eating species is eaten by many actively swimming predators

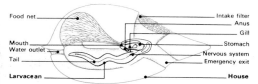

Food-sieving "house" The larvacean *Oikopleura*, a plankton plant-eater, produces a gelatinous house. Water flows constantly through this structure, entering by a filter that excludes large particles. Smaller particles are sieved out by the food net

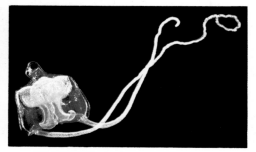

Voracious predator The medusa of the hydroid genus *Amphinema* has two tentacles that can be extended when searching for small crustaceans or other hydroids. They bear stinging cells called nematoblasts which can paralyze prey. *Amphinema* moves by jet propulsion

Sharks and rays

**There are far greater differences
between fish than between mammals—an
elephant is more closely related to
a mouse than a shark is to a mackerel**

The fish of the sea belong to the same three widely separated groups as the freshwater fish. These are the cartilaginous fish, which have skeletons of gristle or cartilage; the bony fish, with skeletons of bone; and the jawless fish, the smallest and most primitive group. Species such as the jawless lampreys and hagfish have changed very little over millions of years.

Water is a dense medium, and in order to swim efficiently and to find food or shelter many fish have evolved shapes and fins which tend to minimize their water resistance, or increase their swimming powers.

The three orders of cartilaginous fish all have distinctive shapes. The sharks swim with streamlined bodies, elliptical in cross-section, and large tail fins. The chimaeras, which swim mainly by flapping their large pectoral fins, have stout bodies tapering to long slender tails. The skates and rays, the third order, have wide, flat bodies and move slowly across the ocean floor. Rays often have beautiful markings, but those that live in the depths of the sea are pitch black.

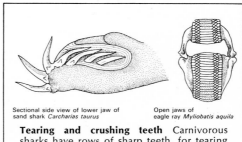

Sectional side view of lower jaw of sand shark *Carcharias taurus*

Open jaws of eagle ray *Myliobatis aquila*

Tearing and crushing teeth Carnivorous sharks have rows of sharp teeth, for tearing and cutting flesh. The front rows are gradually replaced as they wear down. Rays have many rows of teeth for grinding and crushing

A boxfish Also known as a trunkfish, this species swims slowly, flapping its anal and dorsal fins, for its body is enclosed in a rigid shell

Rudder in front The hammerhead shark seems to gain greater maneuverability than other sharks by using its T-shaped head as a forward rudder

Sharks, less buoyant than many fish, swim constantly to keep from sinking

Among the bony fish, body shapes are much more varied. The fastest-swimming fish, such as mackerel, live in open water. Their streamlined shapes contrast with the squat forms of fish such as the gurnards, which live on the seabed.

A gas-filled swim bladder in most of the bony fish influences their body form and swimming methods. The swim bladder gives the bony species buoyancy in the water, and their paired fins are used mainly for steering.

The cartilaginous fish, with no swim bladder, are heavier and less mobile in the water. Most sharks and rays must swim constantly to keep from sinking. Their bodies and fins are shaped to provide lift. A few species have large, oil-filled livers which give them buoyancy.

Feeding habits also affect body shape. The cylindrical, streamlined species are mostly active predators. Many feed on other fish and cephalopods, such as squid, and they usually have sharp teeth and strong jaws. Flattened and rounded shapes are associated with bottom-feeding habits. These fish often have blunt teeth and feed on bottom-living invertebrates such as clams.

The eyes of cartilaginous fish detect little more than movement. In hunting, these fish use their acute sense of smell and probably the nervous system, which sends impulses to the brain when it picks up vibrations in the water.

Sharks, in spite of their streamlined shapes, are not particularly maneuverable in the water. Fast and agile fish can escape them, and consequently sharks eat mostly slow-moving or wounded fish. Some species, such

Man-eater The whaler shark lives in the coastal waters of southeast Australia, where it is held responsible for more attacks on man than any other species. It was named for its habit of following whaling ships to feed on dead whales. The similarly named whale shark is a harmless plankton-eater

as the basking shark, which is 20 to 40 feet long and weighs up to seven tons, feed only on microscopic plankton. Sharks swim in leisurely curves and circles when they are hungry. If smell or vibrations indicate that food is near, their movements become increasingly animated until they actually make contact with the prey.

The ferocious white shark may reach a length of 15 to 20 feet, and weigh over a ton. It will attack large prey such as sea lions or other sharks. A kill may arouse a shark to a frenzy, and the white shark in particular becomes so uncontrolled after a kill that it thrashes about in all directions, attacking any other prey within reach.

Profile of a ray A spotted eagle ray is silhouetted against the sky as it swims near the surface. These big rays, which are sometimes eight feet across, have been seen giving birth by leaping from the water and releasing the young one at a time. Rays and other cartilaginous fish are fertilized internally and either give birth to living young —usually between 7 and 32 at a time—or lay eggs protected by thick-walled capsules

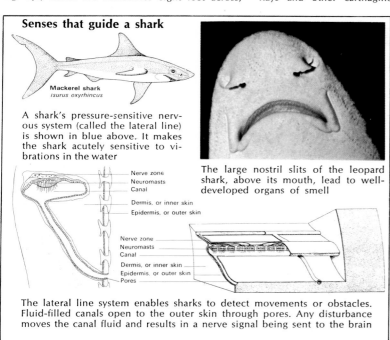

Senses that guide a shark

Mackerel shark
Isurus oxyrhincus

A shark's pressure-sensitive nervous system (called the lateral line) is shown in blue above. It makes the shark acutely sensitive to vibrations in the water

Nerve zone
Neuromasts
Canal

Dermis, or inner skin
Epidermis, or outer skin

The large nostril slits of the leopard shark, above its mouth, lead to well-developed organs of smell

Nerve zone
Neuromasts
Canal
Dermis, or inner skin
Epidermis, or outer skin
Pores

The lateral line system enables sharks to detect movements or obstacles. Fluid-filled canals open to the outer skin through pores. Any disturbance moves the canal fluid and results in a nerve signal being sent to the brain

Camouflaged shark The tasseled wobbegong, or carpet shark, is a sluggish fish that often lies on the sea floor in wait for its prey. Its coloring and barbels give it the appearance of a weed-covered rock

Some rays give electric shocks, others sting, and lampreys and hagfish cling

There are about 350 species of rays, compared with some 200 species of sharks. The biggest are the devil rays, which spread as much as 20 feet from wing tip to wing tip. They feed on plankton and small fish. Smaller rays feed mainly on mollusks and other invertebrates from the seabed. Some, like the torpedo ray, administer electric shocks for defense and to stun prey. Other rays have poisonous stings.

The jawless fish are very ancient vertebrates. They belong to an order of animals called cyclostomes, or round mouths. The only survivors are hagfish and lampreys.

Besides their lack of proper jaws, hagfish and lampreys differ from the jawed fish in that they have thin, horny structures rather than true teeth, and lack paired fins. Hagfish live on the sea bottom, usually feeding on dead and dying fish, and sometimes on worms. Lampreys are eel-shaped. They usually remain attached to a fixed object, ready to dart out and fasten their sucker mouths onto some unwary passing fish.

Fish with bony skeletons

Most sea fish are bony fish—an immense class that includes such contrasting animals as swordfish and small cleaner fish that act as "servants" to sharks

The most important food chain in the sea begins when the microscopic animals known as zooplankton feed on the plants known as phytoplankton. The animal plankton in turn often become the food of small fish. These are eaten by bigger fish, and so on, until the greater fish are preyed upon by giant carnivores such as sharks, seals, and whales. Most of the fish in this food chain are fish with bony skeletons.

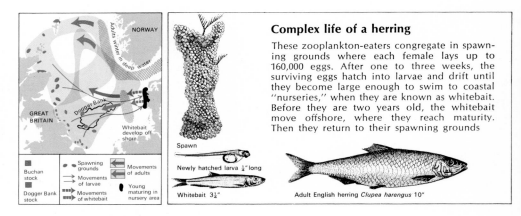

Complex life of a herring

These zooplankton-eaters congregate in spawning grounds where each female lays up to 160,000 eggs. After one to three weeks, the surviving eggs hatch into larvae and drift until they become large enough to swim to coastal "nurseries," when they are known as whitebait. Before they are two years old, the whitebait move offshore, where they reach maturity. Then they return to their spawning grounds

Spawn

Newly hatched larva ¼" long

Whitebait 3¼"

Adult English herring *Clupea harengus* 10"

Adaptations of bony fish include color change, spines, scales, and swordlike jaws

Many bony fish are rendered less conspicuous to potential predators by their coloring. Active-swimming open-water species such as the tuna, or tunny, and the mackerel are striped in dark green and blue on the back, making them difficult to spot from above, while their undersides are pale, making them hard to see from below.

These active, fast-moving fish can also escape from predators by swimming. Bottom-living fish are slower-moving and more vulnerable to attack. Many, such as plaice and turbot, have developed protective mechanisms, including the ability to change their color to match that of the bottom.

Color and color changes often proclaim fish as distasteful or dangerous, and thus warn off potential predators. Bright spots and stripes camouflage fish living among coral. In some fish, bright colors are an integral part of courtship. Many deep-sea fish have luminous organs that produce flashes of light, and probably confuse approaching predators.

Slow-moving fish may be covered with spines or tough scales. The lesser weever is protected not only by its habit of burrowing in the sand for concealment but also by poisonous spines on its fins and gill covers. Boxfish are well protected from attackers by bony coverings that are formed from thickened scales.

Among the big carnivorous fish of the oceans are members of the swordfish and sailfish families. Swordfish, the largest members of this group, may grow to a length of

15 to 20 feet and are widely distributed in all warm seas.

These fish have long upper jaws, forming in the swordfish a flattened swordlike weapon, and in sailfish a rounded, tapering spear. They appear to hunt by slashing about with this weapon among schools of smaller fish, stunning and maiming victims, and then eating them at leisure.

All members of the sailfish family, which includes spearfish and marlins, have a dorsal fin that is folded into a groove along the back except when the fish is swimming on the surface. When raised, this "sail" helps the fish to steer a steady course in the more turbulent surface waters.

Other large bony fish found in the warmer seas are the barracudas, ferocious predators

Grouping for protection Many fish, such as these jacks, also known as turrums, apparently school for collective defense and finding food

which may reach as much as eight feet in length and weigh up to 100 pounds. They have thin bodies, large tails, and powerful jaws armed with sharp teeth.

Underwater sounds

The sea is not a silent world. Fish produce a rich medley of grunts, gurgles, barks, murmurs, and bubbling sounds in a variety of ways. The simplest method is by stridulation —the rubbing together of two parts of a fish's body to produce a grating noise.

The horse mackerel and the sunfish stridulate by gnashing their teeth. Others, like the surgeonfish, stridulate the spines in their fins. Drums and croakers use their swim bladder as a resonator, or use muscles which set the bladder wall vibrating. A fish may use sounds to communicate with others, to warn off predators, or as part of an echo-location system to determine the position of objects in the water.

Little fish that clean big ones

Fish of one species often associate with members of a different species, to their mutual advantage. For example, a variety of species of small fish known as cleaners or barbers associate with bigger fish whose bodies carry parasites on which the cleaners feed. The cleaners are rarely eaten by the bigger fish, even though they often enter the larger fish's mouth and may be the same size and shape as the host's normal prey.

Twelve species of small fish called remoras form close relationships with sharks and many other big fish. The remora attaches itself to the host fish's body by means of a sucker disk on the top of its head. It normally feeds on parasites on the shark's body, but when the shark makes a kill it detaches itself and feeds on the scraps.

The pilot fish, which is only nine inches long, also associates with sharks and rays. With rays it acts as a cleaner. With sharks the relationship is one-sided—the pilot fish feeds on scraps left from the shark's kill, but seems to be of no benefit to the shark.

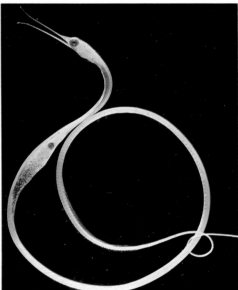

Needlelike jaws This snipe eel lives in the deep waters of the tropical and temperate seas. It uses its jaws to deadly effect: this one has just swallowed another snipe eel of about its own size

Escape flight Chased by an oceanic predator, a young two-winged flying fish, seen here from above, leaps from the water and glides to safety

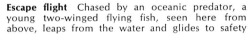

Takeoff Vigorously beating its tail to gain speed, a flying fish breaks the surface, immediately spreads its winglike pectoral fins, and glides forward. When speed slackens, it repeats this entire process

Cleaner fish The tiny blue wrasse on the head of this grouper is removing parasites from its host

Sucker disk A modified dorsal fin forms the sucker disk on top of the remora's head; it is used when the remora attaches to a host fish

Porcupine fish Sharp spines protect many slow-swimming fish, such as this porcupine fish of the genus *Diodon*. It defends itself by swallowing air or water and inflating itself to erect long spines

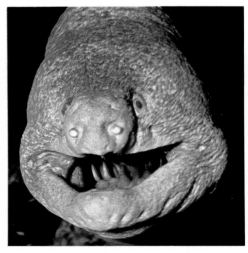

Night predator Like all moray eels, the California moray eel usually lurks in holes and crevices during the day and emerges at night to forage for its prey—small fish and crustaceans

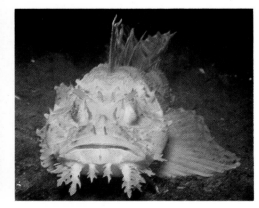

Camouflaged hunter As a defense or when seeking food, the sea raven, or sculpin, is able to vary its color to match that of its environment. This bottom-dwelling carnivore inhabits cold waters

Squid and octopuses

Though squid are descended from snail-like ancestors, some reach enormous size, and others propel themselves as fast as the fastest-moving sea animals

Squid, cuttlefish, octopuses, and nautiluses belong to the group of mollusks called cephalopods—animals whose legs (or arms) are attached to their heads. Most other mollusks are slow-moving. But many cephalopods can move quickly, and their greater mobility enables them to live as predators.

Squid live mainly in the open sea, often at great depths. They have eight short arms and two long, thinner ones—the tentacles with which they seize prey. Like those of all cephalopods, the squid's arms have a flat inner surface bearing rows of cuplike suckers. Many species are less than twelve inches long, but giant squid of the genus *Architeu-*

this may grow to a length of over 50 feet.

Most squid are powerful swimmers. Their streamlined bodies are stiffened by a thin, horny internal skeleton. This gives them the rigidity they need to reach speeds high enough to overtake the fish and invertebrates on which they prey, and to escape their own enemies, such as whales and seals. Some small species can move fast enough to leave the water and fly for about 50 yards. Other species have a fluid in their bodies that is less dense than seawater and so makes them more buoyant.

When hunting, the squid usually darts into a shoal of fish, such as mackerel, and seizes a young fish behind the head. It bites until the head drops off, and then eats the rest of the fish.

Cuttlefish, like squid, have ten arms, eight short and two long, but are usually much

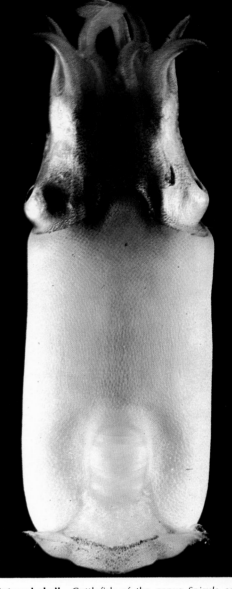

Internal shell Cuttlefish of the genus *Spirula* are the only living cephalopods with an internal spiral shell, containing a gas that keeps them from sinking

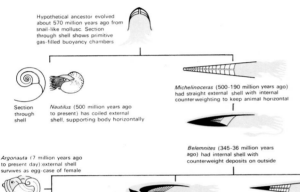

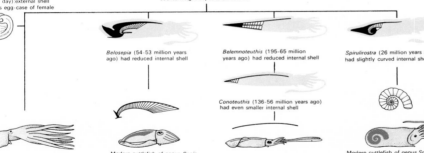

Hypothetical ancestor evolved about 570 million years ago from snail-like mollusc. Section through shell shows primitive gas-filled buoyancy chambers

Section through shell

Nautilus (500 million years ago to present) has coiled external shell, supporting body horizontally

Michelinoceras (500-190 million years ago) had straight external shell with internal counter weighting to keep animal horizontal

Argonauta (7 million years ago to present day) external shell survives as egg-case of female

Belemnites (345-36 million years ago) had internal shell with counterweight deposits on outside

Belosepia (54-53 million years ago) had reduced internal shell

Belemnoteuthis (195-65 million years ago) had reduced internal shell

Spirulirostra (26 million years ago) had slightly curved internal shell

Conoteuthis (136-56 million years ago) had even smaller internal shell

Octopus (136 million years ago to present day) has no shell

Modern cuttlefish of genus *Sepia* has shell reduced to gas-filled cuttlebone (section above)

Modern squid of genus *Loligo* has shell reduced to horny pen (section above)

Modern cuttlefish of genus *Spirula* has smaller, coiled, gas-filled internal shell (section above)

The vanishing shell Cephalopods —squid, octopuses, cuttlefish, and nautiluses—evolved from snail-like ancestors having gas-filled chambers within their shells. Later types had more complex shells that kept the animals horizontal in the water, allowing them to swim. Coiled shells remained external and protective, as in *Nautilus*. Straight shells first became enclosed, then reduced, until in *Octopus* the shell has vanished

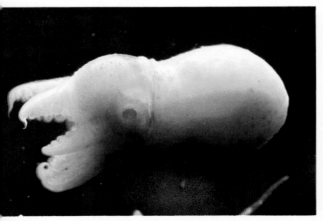

Male and female octopuses The female of the genus *Argonauta* (right) grows horny flaps on her two back arms. When the flaps are brought together, they form a shell in which she keeps the bulk of her body and lays her eggs. The male of this genus (the male above is of a different species), like all other octopuses, has no shell

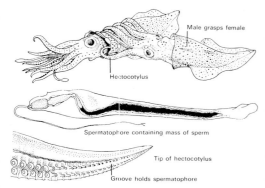

Mating arm During mating, the male cephalopod uses an arm, called a hectocotylus, to take a package of sperm from its storage sac and deposit it in the female's mantle cavity, leading to the oviduct

Male grasps female

Hectocotylus

Spermatophore containing mass of sperm

Tip of hectocotylus

Groove holds spermatophore

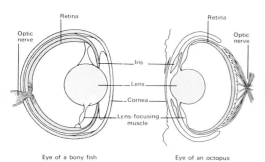

Retina
Optic nerve
Iris
Lens
Cornea
Lens-focusing muscle
Optic nerve
Retina

Eye of a bony fish

Eye of an octopus

Highly developed eyes Like vertebrates, cephalopods' activities rely greatly on vision, and their eyes have developed like those of vertebrates. In this they are unique among invertebrates

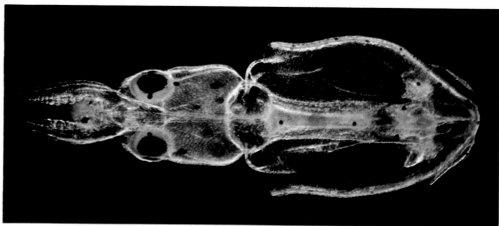

Baby squid *Alloteuthis subulata*, only one-quarter inch long when hatched, will grow to seven inches

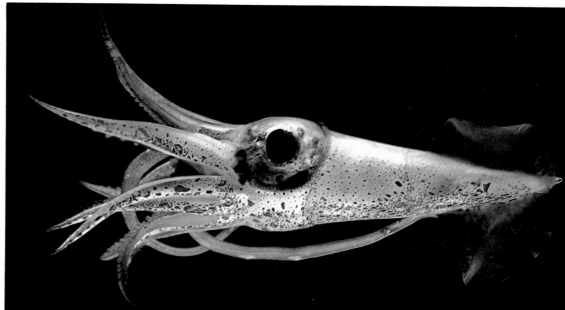

Hunting arms Tucked under the body of this squid are the two long arms with which it seizes prey

smaller than squid. They live on the seabed, fairly close to shore. The cuttlefish hunts at night for fish and invertebrates, often near the surface. It obtains the buoyancy control it needs to move between the surface and the bottom by regulating the proportions of fluid and nitrogen gas in its hollow-chambered internal shell.

Octopuses have only eight arms. Most live on the seabed near shore. The northern Pacific species reaches 30 feet across, but most octopuses are much smaller. They crawl rather than swim, and stalk their prey —mainly shellfish—or ambush it from rock lairs. This method of hunting requires neither streamlined bodies nor buoyancy control, which explains the octopus's flabbiness and lack of an internal shell. Unlike squid and cuttlefish, octopuses can subdue their prey with a poisonous bite.

Nautiluses, which are found in tropical waters, are the only surviving cephalopods with an external shell. The chambered nautilus described in Oliver Wendell Holmes's famous poem of that name is a member of this family.

All cephalopods have a mantle of skin and muscle compressed into a collar just behind the head. Between this mantle and the body there is a cavity into which the animal can draw water by relaxing the mantle muscles. It then locks the water in by contracting the muscles and closing the mantle. When a cephalopod needs to move quickly it propels itself by blowing out a jet of water through a flexible funnel which leads out from the mantle cavity.

Nearly all cephalopods squirt a dark fluid into the water when alarmed. This "ink" is released from a sac through the anus. Once in the water it spreads in a dense cloud that may function as a smokescreen, a diversionary "dummy," or a repellent.

Suckers that can grasp Octopuses use the suckers on their arms to seize prey and to crawl. Like all cephalopods, octopuses can change color for camouflage. This is the deadly *Hapalochlaena maculosa*

Animals of the sea floor

**Among the many strange creatures adapted
to life on the sea floor are animals
that look like plants and lead sedentary,
plantlike lives, fixed to the bottom**

All animals in the sea depend on plants for
food either directly or indirectly. Plants in
turn depend on sunlight for the process of
photosynthesis, by which they convert carbon dioxide and inorganic nutrients from
the water into organic matter.

Most plant life in the ocean consists of
phytoplankton, microscopic floating plants,
different types of which flourish at different
depths down to 650 feet. Phytoplankton is
eaten by zooplankton, almost equally small
animals, and the two types of plankton support many sea creatures, including bottom-
dwellers.

The sea floor can be divided into three
zones—the continental shelf, down to approximately 600 feet; the continental slope
leading down from it to 6000 feet; and the
deep ocean floor, or abyssal benthic zone,
which is deeply fissured but has an average
depth of about 15,000 feet. Within these
live three main kinds of sea-floor animals.

First there are the creatures fixed to the
bottom. Besides oysters and mussels, these
include many that look more like plants than
animals—such as sponges, sea mats, sea
anemones, and sea squirts. Many have tentacles or sieves for trapping or filtering food.

The second group is composed of animals
that crawl over the sea bottom or burrow beneath it, such as lobsters, crabs, starfish,
brittle stars, and many kinds of sea slugs and
worms. The third group consists of bottom-
feeding fish, like rays, turbots, and halibuts.
Unlike the crawlers, they swim great distances over the bottom in search of food,
though many of them spend long periods
motionless on the sea floor.

Moving out from the shore along the continental shelf, the first region of the sea floor
is the sublittoral. Here, bottom-attached sea
plants have enough light to grow, and they
support many animals. Seaweeds of the genus
Laminaria, for instance, create an underwater jungle in which many creatures make
their homes, including sea mats, hydroids,
several kinds of limpets, snails, and worms.
Eelgrass, a flowering plant, also grows in
this zone.

Living vase The vase sponge is a typical sponge—an organism that lacks an
integrated nervous system

Animated sieve The red finger sponge, like all sponges, is
immobile after the larval stage. It feeds by filtering microscopic organisms and dead matter from the water

Fan worm These spectacular worms
are named after the plumelike tentacles
through which they breathe and feed

Baglike animals Sea squirts take in water through one opening in their bodies, filter out its food content, then expel
it from another opening. They squirt water when handled

Giant scavenger The American lobster is one of
the world's largest crustaceans, weighing up to 35
pounds. Like other lobsters, it is omnivorous

Shellfish-eater The cobalt starfish has five arms; if one arm is lost, another will grow in its place. It uses its arms to pry open bivalves

Stationary killer The banded anemone is engulfing a silverside *Hepsitia* that has ventured too close

to the animal's tentacles. Anchored to the sea floor, this anemone must wait for such blunders

Black-backed flounder This fish lies on its side but its eyes face upward

Primitive inshore animals

The sublittoral zone is home to lancelets, small translucent creatures that inhabit sandy bottoms. Although they look like fish, they are much more primitive; animals very like them lived more than 400 million years ago. An animal of this type was possibly the ancestor of all living vertebrates.

Mud-living creatures of this zone include brightly colored sea anemones, which, instead of displaying their colors, are hidden under the mud, only mouths and tentacles exposed.

Farther down the sublittoral zone, in the still well-lit waters of the continental shelf, crustaceans such as lobsters are common, and mollusks are abundant. Sponges are another group typical of this region. In spite of their plantlike appearance they are animals. The ordinary nonsynthetic bath sponge is simply the skeleton of a sponge that has

been dried in the sun and then processed.

At the border of the continental shelf, and for some way down the continental slope, animal life is again different, although many of the same groups are represented. Starfish and brittle stars are common. The complex-looking *Gorgonocephalus agassizi* is one of the most striking. This brittle star, three to four inches across, has tentacles that divide and subdivide so that it looks like a writhing mass of red worms.

The floor of the abyss, the deepest zone of all, is a world of darkness. The bottom is covered with a layer of soft mud and is subject to enormous pressure—more than three tons per square inch at 20,000 feet. Bottom-dwelling animals must adapt not only to the pressure, but also to the mud. The sea spider, for example, has legs up to 24 inches long, and sea lilies grow on long stalks that keep them clear of the ooze.

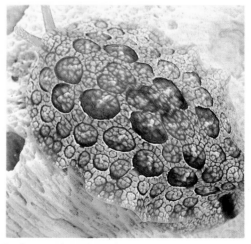

Predatory slug Sea slugs, distantly related to snails, are often brightly colored. Most feed on stationary animals, such as hydroids and sponges

307

Animals of the deep sea

Deep-sea animals feed in bizarre ways—anglerfish lure prey with "rod" and luminous bait, and black swallowers gulp victims twice their size

The deep sea constitutes the greater part of the ocean. It begins at a depth of about 600 feet and is divided into two zones. The first, down to 6000 feet, is called the bathyal zone; the second, below 6000 feet, is called the abyssal pelagic zone, or simply the abyss.

The floor of the abyss is a vast plain about 15,000 feet deep, interrupted by trenches up to 36,000 feet deep.

Enormous pressure—6½ tons per square inch at 30,000 feet—is exerted on deep-sea animals and is counteracted by equal pressure within their bodies. If any creatures from these depths were brought rapidly to the surface the change in pressure would cause them to burst.

No plant tissue is produced by photo-synthesis in the abyss, because of the absence of sunlight. A rain of dead animal and plant material from the productive layer above provides the chief food for many deep-sea planktonic animals. These are then eaten by predators such as fish and squid.

The remains of dead organic material from above, ranging from plankton to large sea animals, sink to the sea floor and are eaten by the creatures that live there. Most animals that live in the abyss are small.

Light-producing lantern fish stay below on moonlit nights

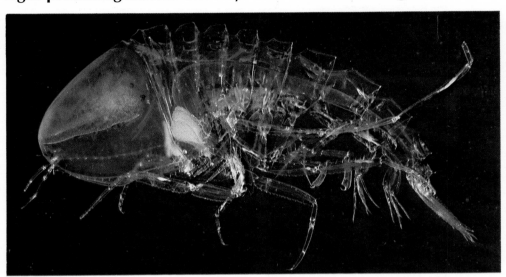

Drifter in the depths *Cystosoma pellucidium* is an amphipod, a shrimplike animal with enormous eyes, and is related to sand fleas. It lives at depths as great as 13,000 feet. Like all amphipods, the young, small replicas of the adults, are hatched from brood pouches. Its six pairs of legs are adapted for different uses: the first three pairs are for swimming and the last three for springing

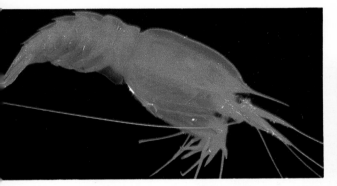

Luminous prawn The caridean prawn (left) about eight inches long, lives in temperate and tropical waters to depths of 15,000 feet. Like many deep-sea animals, it is red and can produce light

Lantern fish, four to six inches long, are an important link in the deep-sea food chain. On moonless nights they rise near the surface in great numbers to prey on the abundant planktonic animals there. When they return to the depths the nourishment they carry back in their bodies becomes available to the creatures that prey on them.

The bodies of lantern fish carry rows of light-producing organs called photophores. The function of the glow produced by the photophores is uncertain, but lantern fish normally shun light from other sources, and on moonlit nights far fewer rise to the surface waters to feed.

Another group of light-producing fish are the hatchetfish. The body resembles a hatchet and the mouth is a gaping slit. Some species are almost as thin as coins.

Anglerfish descend to great depths; one species was caught at around 12,000 feet. These fish "angle" with a luminous lure, attached like a fisherman's bait to a modified fin ray at the front of the head. The lure tempts prey within reach of the fish's jaws.

Anglerfish feed on hatchetfish, lantern fish, and invertebrates. Their highly elastic stomachs enable them to swallow prey larger than themselves.

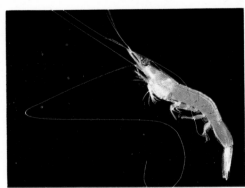

Three-inch predator *Funchalia villosa*, a carnivorous crustacean, lives at depths down to 1350 feet

Young squid At this stage squid have eyes of equal size, but when mature, their left eye is about four times larger than the right one. Deep-sea squid often have elaborate luminous organs

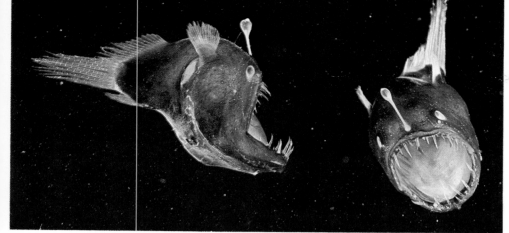

No escape Anglerfish, like *Melanocetus johnsoni*, lure prey into their enormous jaws with luminous "bait." They can swallow fish almost as big as themselves. Backward-pointing teeth hold in prey

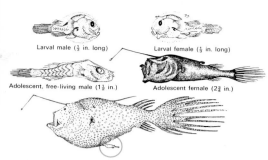

Larval male (⅓ in. long)   Larval female (⅓ in. long)

Adolescent, free-living male (1½ in.)   Adolescent female (2¾ in.)

Adult female (39 in.) with parasitic male (4 in.)

A male that lives on its mate The female angler-fish *Ceratias holboelli* can be 20,000 times heavier than the male, who attaches to her with his jaws and lives on her as a parasite. The jaws gradually fuse to the female's skin. His sole function is to fertilize the eggs when they are spawned

Fish of the continental slope The small *Diretmus argenteus* lives in shoals on the edge of the continental shelf at depths of 900 to 1500 feet

Luminous fish *Margarethia obtusirostra* (top) and the hatchetfish below it are among the many species of luminous fish living at 1000 to 2000 feet

Telescopic eyes The headlamp fish *Winteria telescopa*, related to salmon, has tubular eyes with overlapping visual fields, giving it binocular vision

The gutless Pogonophora of the deep sea were once mistaken for horsehair

Gulpers and swallowers live below 8000 feet. Their heads consist mainly of jaws and are enormous in relation to their slender abdomens and whiplike tails. The black swallower, which is three to six inches long, engulfs victims twice its size. Food is relatively scarce in the abyss, and these large meals may have to sustain the fish for long periods before they eat again.

There are many invertebrates in the deep sea. Most of them are some shade of red. Since only a little blue light penetrates to any depth in the sea, red creatures look black, and have a better chance of avoiding predators in the near-total darkness. In the deepest regions the only light is the luminescence of animals; this is predominantly blue-green and it is totally absorbed by red pigments.

Among the most remarkable inhabitants of the deep-sea floor are the tripod fish of the genus *Bathypterois*. These fish have two elongated rays running down from their pectoral fins and a third from the tail. They have been photographed at a depth of 23,000 feet, perching on these rays like a camera on a tripod. They use the rays for walking and as feelers for locating prey.

Another strange group are the Pogonophora or beard worms, a distinct phylum (a major division of the animal kingdom) discovered only at the beginning of the century and at first mistaken for horsehair. These wormlike animals, found in soft sediment on the seabed, live inside a thin tube, from one end of which projects a mass of tentacles. They have no gut; food is absorbed through the tentacles and possibly through the body surface as well.

Many sea cucumbers and sea lilies live on the deep-sea bottom, together with glass sponges, which look like bundles of hay; sea pens, luminous animals that resemble plants; and sea spiders, whose legs may be two feet long.

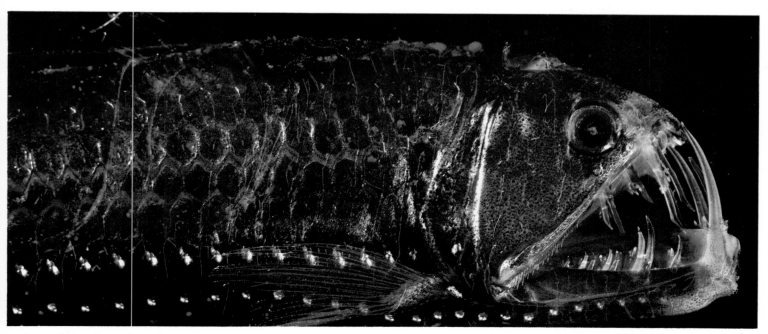

Predator of the deep The viperfish *Chauliodus danae* is only a few inches long, but it is as predatory as it looks. Because food is scarce in the ocean depths, when predatory fish do find victims they are likely to be their own size. As a result, many have developed huge, gaping mouths

Corals and coral reefs

**Skeletons of numberless minute animals
form a coral reef, providing homes
for many other marine creatures, some of
which prey on the reef-building corals**

Coral reefs are formed by colonies of millions of tiny carnivorous animals called coral polyps. Coral polyps have soft, saclike bodies, with one end closed and the other opening at a mouth surrounded by tentacles bearing stinging cells.

The term "coral" is generally applied to any polyp that produces a skeleton of some sort—a hard, stony skeleton, a horny one, or even a mosaic of particles inside the body.

Some types of corals are solitary individuals, but most are colonies of many individuals. All types, however, begin as a single polyp, produced by sexual reproduction, which emerges from the parent's body as a free-swimming larva no bigger than a pinhead. The larva develops a tentacle-fringed mouth leading to a gut. Then it settles on a firm support, its undersurface forming a base that begins to produce the skeleton.

If it is a solitary coral, its development is now complete and it has only to maintain and reproduce itself. But if it is a colonial, reef-forming coral, it is only at an early stage of development.

Reef-building corals develop by asexual budding. Side polyps sprout from the original polyp and these in turn sprout so that a vast colonial structure arises. As the earlier polyps die, the living polyps of the outer layers are supported by the skeletons of their predecessors.

Polyps tend to follow characteristic growth patterns, which give corals the varied shapes suggested by their common names: brain, staghorn, lettuce, and whip corals, sea fans, sea pens, sea feathers, and sea pansies.

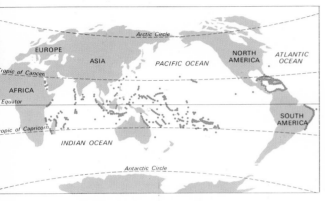

Reef-forming corals Corals also exist in other warm places, but they do not form large reefs

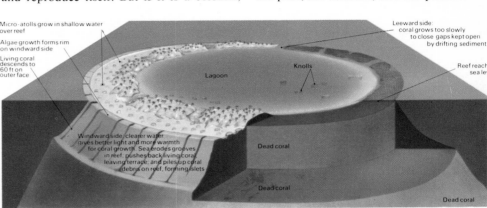

Coral atoll Coral around an oceanic island may be left as an atoll, or circular reef, if the island sinks or the sea rises. Knolls (pinnacles of coral) grow from the lagoon floor, perhaps 200 feet below

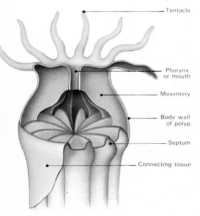

Structure of a coral
The individual chalk skeletons of stony coral polyps are formed around cupped base plates, from which radial divisions, called septa, project upward into the polyp's body. Mesenteries, internal walls, divide the polyp and contain digestive glands that break down the food caught by the tentacles. The food is passed into the body cavity through the pharynx, or mouth. In a colony, all the polyps are interconnected by sheets of tissue

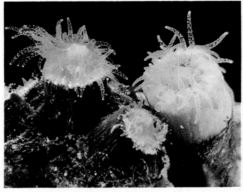

Colonial and solitary corals The large coral at the right is a star coral, a reef-building species; and the smaller ones are solitary corals. The two types of coral are found together in warm waters

Staghorn coral Named for its antlerlike branches, it provides shelter for many different fish. This reef-building stony coral belongs to the genus *Acropora*. It is found only in shallow water

Splitting in two This soft coral is in the final stages of reproducing by budding. Its skeleton consists of splinters embedded in the body

Stinging coral *Millepora dichotoma* gets its common name from the stings of the polyps, which project through the dense, chalky skeleton, and are painful to man. It is also called fire coral. Although it resembles coral and contributes to reef-building, it is not a true coral, but a hydrozoan

The rise and fall of reefs

There are three main forms of coral reef: the fringing reef close to shore; the barrier reef, which is separated from the mainland by a broad channel; and the coral atoll of the open sea. All thrive only where the water temperature is above 70° F. (21° C.) and the water is no deeper than 250 feet.

Solitary corals are found in most waters, but warmth and light are necessary for the reef-building species. Light is particularly important because it allows tiny plants, which are believed to help in skeleton-building, to grow in the polyps' bodies.

Many species of vividly colored tropical fish are adapted to living in coral reefs. Other animals add to the growth of a reef. Mollusks and chalk-shelled protozoans called foraminiferans, for example, die and leave their shells as part of the structure.

But even while a reef is building up, forces are working toward its destruction. Marine worms and mollusks burrow into the coral. Fluctuations in the water level may either bury a reef too deeply for the polyps to grow or expose it to erosion by waves and wind.

Many reefs in the Pacific are threatened by the crown-of-thorns, a large starfish that feeds on the polyps, leaving a bare coral skeleton in its wake. Enormous numbers of these starfish have destroyed the living coral on parts of Australia's 1200-mile-long Great Barrier Reef, which was laid down many thousands of years ago.

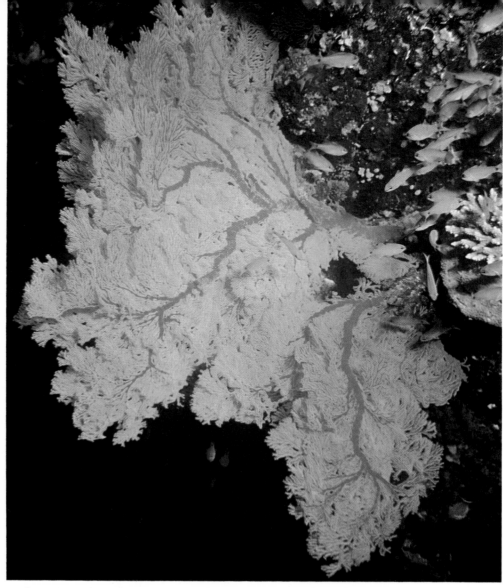

Sea fan All sea fans belong to the subclass Alcyonaria. Their skeletons of horny material are internal. This red gorgonian supports a colony of millions of polyps. Its body contains a central horny rod

Reef destroyer The crown-of-thorns starfish feeds on coral polyps, leaving the reef as a bare skeleton that faces destruction by erosion

Small fish of the reefs Damsel fish, like many tropical inshore fish, have brushlike teeth, with which they feed on invertebrates and tiny plants

Cleaner of reef fish The banded coral shrimp *Stenopus hispidus* cleans the bodies of reef fish, picking parasites off their skin with its claws and eating them. They live in pairs in coral crevices and are widely distributed throughout the tropical waters of the Indian and Pacific oceans

311

Sea reptiles

None of the reptiles that live in the sea are completely adapted to marine life. All must surface to breathe, and the turtles lay their eggs on shore

Reptiles form only a small part of the oceans' animal life. There are about 60 species of sea snakes, six species of marine turtles, and a single marine lizard. All of these species belong to groups more widely represented on land, and all live almost exclusively in tropical and subtropical seas, although some may drift farther north.

Plant-eating turtle   The green turtle, found in the tropics, is entirely vegetarian, feeding on seaweed

Flesh-eating turtle   The common loggerhead turtle feeds mainly on mollusks, crustaceans, and fish. Most other sea turtles eat plants as well as animal food

Female turtles lay their eggs above the high-tide mark

The largest marine reptile is the leatherback turtle, which may reach a length of seven feet and weigh up to 1500 pounds. Its name comes from the leathery skin that covers its shell. The normal turtle shell consists of a shell and breastplate of bony plates covered by horny plates, or scutes. The scutes are the substance known as tortoiseshell. The leatherback turtle has no scutes, and the large bony plates of the shell are replaced by a mosaic of small plates in the leathery skin.

The 900-pound, four-foot-long loggerhead is the second largest marine turtle.

Although turtles spend most of their lives in the open sea, the females of all species must come ashore to lay their eggs. This is always done at night. The female drags herself ashore on a sandy beach with ungainly heaves of her flippers. Well above the level of the highest tide, she scrapes out a hole with her flippers and lays about 100 eggs in it. Then she covers the eggs with sand and returns to the sea.

When the young turtles hatch, after seven to ten weeks, they scratch their way to the surface and head unerringly for the sea, probably guided there by the light, which is brighter over the sea than over the land. But only a fraction of the young ever reach their goal. Wheeling seabirds, attracted by the sudden supply of fresh meat, swoop down and take many young turtles, while, on the beach, scuttling crabs and lizards take many more.

The green turtle is the only reptile known to migrate over long distances. Green turtles marked after nesting on Ascension Island have been found feeding 1400 miles away off the coast of Brazil. Other turtles' feeding grounds are much closer to the beaches where they breed.

Leaving the nest A newly hatched green turtle emerges to run the gauntlet of predators that are awaiting its journey to the sea. Few young survive

Laying eggs The female green turtle, her back smothered with sand, lays eggs on a sandy beach. She comes ashore at night, making great sighing noises as she moves her enormous weight up the beach. Then she digs a hole, lays 100 or more eggs, covers them, and returns to the sea

Returning to the sea A female turtle struggles back toward the sea after laying her eggs high on the beach of an island on Australia's Great Barrier Reef. She visits the beach about six times during the breeding season, and each time lays a clutch of eggs that take seven to ten weeks to hatch

Venomous snakes, and a lizard that hugs the shore

Most sea snakes have evolved in the waters off Southeast Asia. From there they have spread through the warm coastal waters of the Pacific and Indian oceans. Sea snakes, like the cobras, their land-living relatives, are highly venomous.

The largest sea snakes may be ten feet in length, but three to five feet is more usual. Their bodies are often marked with alternating bands of light and dark colors, and their scales have a metallic sheen. The upper sides of their bodies are darker than the undersides, making them difficult to see both from above and from below—an asset when hunting fish. Sea snakes swim with a

sinuous side-to-side motion, propelling themselves with their tails. Many have vertically flattened bodies, which give them more thrust in water.

The nostrils of sea snakes are set on top of the snout, so they can breathe with the head only slightly out of the water. They can remain underwater for up to two hours by closing valves in their nasal passages. The lung extends the full length of the trunk and gives the animal buoyancy.

Most sea snakes breed at sea, bearing living young. The few species that come ashore to lay eggs have large scales, or ventral plates, on the undersides of their bodies

that aid them when they move on the land.

The marine iguana is the only lizard that is found in the sea. It is about five feet long, and has long fingers and toes terminating in claws. Its skin is black and scaly, and it has a ridge of small spines along its back and the upper edge of its flattened tail. It propels itself in the water with its tail.

Marine iguanas are found only around the shores of the Galápagos Islands, where they feed entirely on a type of seaweed which grows just below the low-tide mark. They are good swimmers and take refuge in the sea when frightened, but they never swim far from the shore.

Tail of a sea snake Like most sea snakes, the olive brown sea snake *Aipysurus laevis* swims with an oarlike tail. All sea snakes are venomous; this one strikes only at its natural prey—small fish

Sea snake that breeds ashore The yellow-lipped sea krait *Laticauda colubrina* lays its eggs on land in caves and crevices. Large scales on its underside aid this snake in moving on land

Giant mammals of the sea

The blue whale, the largest animal ever known, may grow to more than 100 feet long and weigh 140 tons — the weight of 30 average-size elephants

Whales are mammals that have returned to the sea and taken on a fishlike form. Their external hind limbs have disappeared, their front limbs have evolved into flippers, and they propel themselves by moving their massive tail flukes up and down.

There are two groups of whales—the toothed whales and the whalebone whales. Both groups have embryonic teeth when young, but in whalebone whales the teeth never develop. Baleen, or whalebone, a flexible, horny substance, grows from the whale's upper jaw in finely separated plates, the inner surfaces of which are frayed into fine, whiskery fibers. Shoals of plankton are sucked into the whale's mouth and trapped in the baleen. The huge tongue forces water back out. In this way the blue whale eats two tons of shrimplike krill a day.

In toothed whales, the embryonic teeth grow into adult teeth, enabling these whales to prey on a variety of fish and squid.

The whale family

CETACEA

Odontoceti — Toothed whales

Mysticeti — Whalebone whales

Platanistidae — River dolphins
La Plata River dolphin *Stenodelphis blainvillei*

Monodontidae — White whales
Narwhal *Monodon monoceros*

Delphinidae — Dolphins and porpoises
Harbour porpoise *Phocaena phocaena*

Balaenopteridae — Fin whales
Humpback whale *Megaptera novaeangliae*

Ziphiidae — Beaked whales
Bottle-nosed whale *Hyperoodon ampullatus*

Physeteridae — Sperm whales
Sperm whale *Physeter catodon*

Eschrichtiidae — Grey whales
California grey whale *Eschrichtius gibbosus*

Balaenidae — Right whales
Biscayan right whale *Balaena glacialis*

Toothed whale The sperm whale *Physeter catodon*, like other whales, has a fishlike body that conceals the skeleton of a four-legged mammal. The flipper bones are those of the front legs, while a vestigial pelvic bone shows that there were once rear legs. The 60-foot-long sperm whale, largest of the toothed whales, has about 40 teeth in the narrow lower jaw, but none in the upper jaw

Vestigial pelvis

Whalebone whale The Greenland right whale *Balaena mysticetus* has no teeth; instead, fronds of baleen hang down from the rim of the upper jaw. It feeds by swimming open-mouthed into shoals of plankton. Then it closes its mouth and raises its tongue, forcing the water through the whalebone and out through its lips. The plankton is left behind on the whalebone and then swallowed

Vestigial pelvis

Whales, once legged land-dwellers, have adapted to the sea

Perhaps the whale's most striking adaptation to the sea is its ability to withstand long, deep dives. The sperm whale, for instance, can descend more than 3000 feet and remain underwater for up to 75 minutes. This is made possible to a large extent by a slowing of the heartbeat and a very efficient system for transporting and storing oxygen within the body.

Finding air is an immediate problem for the whale calf, which is born underwater. If the calves do not swim to the surface themselves, the adults will nudge them upward to take their first breath through their nostrils, or blowholes.

The blowhole has a valve that closes when the whale dives, keeping the seawater out.

The windpipe can be sealed off from the throat so that water cannot get into the lungs while the whale is feeding.

Whales are social animals and nearly always travel in groups called schools.

There are about 70 species of toothed whales and 10 species of whalebone whales. Toothed whales range from 5-foot-long dolphins to the sperm whale—a 60-foot, 50-ton giant.

Although some dolphins have up to 260 teeth, more than any other mammal, other toothed whales not only have far fewer teeth, but have them on one jaw only. For example, all of the sperm whale's 40 or so teeth lie along its lower jaw.

There are three families of whalebone

whales—the rorquals, or finbacks; the right whales; and the gray whales.

The rorquals have furrows one or two inches deep on their throats and chests. When the whale opens its mouth these furrows expand, increasing the mouth's capacity and enabling it to take a greater scoop of plankton-rich water. Rorquals are the fastest of the large whales; the common rorqual can reach a speed of 30 miles an hour.

Other rorquals include the humpback whale and the 100-foot-long, 140-ton blue whale, the largest animal known to have lived on earth, larger even than the biggest prehistoric animals.

Whalers coined the term "right whale" for the second family, because its members were

White whales of the Arctic The 12-foot-long beluga, or white whale, *Delphinapterus leucas* changes color from gray to white at maturity. Belugas usually roam in schools of five to ten, and sometimes travel far up large rivers

Common rorqual in polar waters In summer the polar waters are rich in planktonic food, and rorquals of both hemispheres migrate poleward to breed. The common rorqual is second in size to the blue whale

High-powered swimmer A 40-foot-long humpback whale, weighing 30 tons, erupts from the depths, displaying its throat furrows and long front limbs

the right whales to kill. With their stockier, less streamlined bodies, right whales are not only slower and more easily overtaken than rorquals, but also have longer, more flexible baleen, which was once of great commercial value. The Greenland right whale has up to 700 baleen plates, each one 9 to 12 feet long, whereas the rorquals' baleen rarely exceeds two feet in length.

Greenland right whales are now rare because of hunting by whalers. Their tragic history underlines the plight of the larger whales. Many, such as the common rorqual, are being overhunted—250,000 common rorquals have been killed in the last ten years. Some species, such as the blue whale, even face extinction. Its numbers have been reduced from 400,000 to about 1500 in the last 60 years.

Whales now are hunted principally for their oil, which is obtained from the blubber and fat stored in the body tissues and bones. A large specimen will yield more than 20 tons of oil. The blubber is a layer of fat several inches thick between the skin and the muscles of the whale. Ambergris, a rare secretion that forms occasionally in the intestines of sperm whales, is used as a fixative for perfumes. Oil from the head cavities of sperm whales is used as a lubricant.

Rorqual in warm waters All whales must surface to breathe. In the colder waters much of the "blow" is fine mist consisting of condensed exhaled moisture. But a mist also occurs in warmer areas. The mist might be a nitrogen-laden foam that the whale must expel after a dive

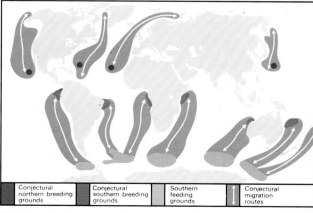

| Conjectural northern breeding grounds | Conjectural southern breeding grounds | Southern feeding grounds | Conjectural migration routes |

The humpback's realms The northern and southern hemispheres have separate stocks of humpback whales. Within each hemisphere, the populations can be further divided into distinct groups. There is little movement between these groups. During their migration poleward, they tend to stay close to continental coasts. Humpbacks stay in polar waters longer than other rorquals

315

The realm of dolphins and killer whales

The largest member of the dolphin family, the killer whale, is a voracious predator that travels in packs and detects prey by echo-location

Dolphins and porpoises are the most numerous members of the largest family of toothed whales. They are sometimes difficult to tell apart, but dolphins generally have beaklike snouts and longer, more slender bodies than those of the stocky porpoises. Many dolphins are eight to nine feet long, whereas porpoises rarely exceed six feet. Much larger members of the family are the pilot whales of the genus *Globicephala* and the killer whale, which has been known to grow to 30 feet long.

All these whales travel in herds or schools, often of 100 or more. Different species sometimes congregate together. Pacific bottle-nosed dolphins and Pacific white-sided dolphins, for example, often accompany schools of pilot whales which leave colder waters in the autumn for warmer seas where they mate and breed.

The bottle-nosed dolphin, which is also called a porpoise, was netted by commercial fishermen off the North Carolina coast for its oil, in the years before the First World War. These dolphins are the star performers at many marine attractions.

Killer whales, which are found in all seas, travel in packs of 5 to 50 animals. They are voracious predators, armed with interlocking teeth that give them a tight grip on such slippery prey as squid.

Pilot whales These sociable whales travel in large schools. Like other whales, they navigate by echo- sounding the seabed; but they can be confused by gently sloping coastal shelves and become stranded

Killer whales are able to produce sounds and to judge distances from the echoes reflected off the bodies of possible prey. It is likely that they also maintain contact with one another by sound. The echo-location sense is present in other toothed whales, and perhaps in whalebone species as well.

This ability to estimate the distance and the size of underwater objects from echoes enables whales to avoid steeply shelving shores and other obstructions. The bottle-nosed dolphin, for instance, navigates by sending out clicking sounds at rates up to 400 per second, although it makes whistling noises to maintain contact with its young or other members of the school.

Marine dolphins and porpoises feed on fish and squid. A six-foot-long dolphin can reach speeds of more than 25 miles an hour. But, unlike whales, they do not dive very deep, nor do they remain underwater for more than five or ten minutes.

Dolphins bear single offspring after 10 to 11 months' gestation. The young are born tailfirst; if they were born headfirst, like most other mammals, they might drown. As soon as the baby dolphin is born, the mother lifts it to the surface to take its first breath.

Killer whales A pair of killer whales rises between thin floes to survey the surface. Found in all the world's oceans, they are most common in polar waters

High jumpers Dolphins, like these Pacific white-sided dolphins, often leap high above the water when they come to the surface in order to breathe

Advanced offspring Dolphins, like many sea mammals, bear large, highly developed young. The baby dolphin here is less than a day old

The resourceful sea otter sleeps tight in a bed of seaweed

The smallest sea mammal is the sea otter, a member of the weasel family. Males grow to just over four feet in length and weigh up to 80 pounds. The sea otter has a shorter tail and a stockier build than the freshwater otter. Its markings range from light gray to cream on the head and throat, to dark brown or black over the rest of the body.

Even at mating and breeding times sea otters rarely leave the sea. They usually live about half a mile from the shore, congregating in and around beds of the thick seaweed

called kelp. At night they wrap strands of the ribbonlike plant around themselves, apparently to keep themselves from drifting out to the open sea while they sleep.

During the day, sea otters stay in open water, swimming and diving after shellfish, sea urchins, and small fish. When a sea otter returns to the surface with shellfish, it lies on its back and cracks the shells open with its cheek teeth. If the shells are too thick, the otter places a stone on its chest and crushes them against it.

Sea otters do not have blubber, the insulating layer of fat that retains heat in the other sea mammals. They are kept warm by a jacket of air, trapped between the hairs of their dense fur.

The demand for sea otters' fur led to their near extermination by the early 1920s. Only a century ago they were numerous along western and eastern Pacific coasts, from the Bering Strait south to Japan and California. Now they are confined to a few scattered areas.

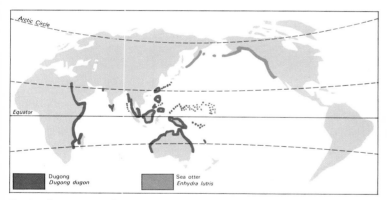

Arctic Circle

Equator

Dugong
Dugong dugon

Sea otter
Enhydra lutris

Contrasting ranges The sea otter's insulating fur protects it in polar waters. The dugong, although it has blubber, is restricted to tropical waters

A tool user Sea otters often balance flat stones on their chests, and crack open shellfish on the stones before scooping or licking out the soft parts

The dugong grazes in shallow water safe from predators

The dugong is a slow-moving vegetarian found only in the Indian Ocean, the Red Sea, and the western Pacific. Its only defense is that the coastal waters in which it lives are usually too shallow for sharks and killer whales. It is a large mammal, with a heavy, tapering body, eight to ten feet long, covered with a thick layer of blubber. Individuals weighing as much as 400 pounds are not unusual.

Like whales, the dugong is highly adapted to the sea and never leaves it. Its hind limbs

have completely disappeared during the course of evolution, to be replaced by two rounded tail flukes. It uses the flexible, overhanging upper lip of its bristly muzzle to grasp and uproot clumps of sea plants. The female bears one calf every other year.

The head of a marine grazer The dugong feeds underwater on sea plants at night. The broad nostrils on top of its muzzle can be shut tightly to keep out water. It can remain submerged from one to ten minutes, and frequently surfaces to breathe

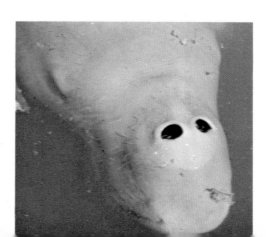

Seals and sea lions

The biggest herd of mammals in the world is made up of northern fur seals, creatures that come ashore only to breed, molt, and bask

There are three families of seals—true seals, fur seals and sea lions, and walruses. All three are carnivorous, eating mainly fish and shellfish. True seals have no external ears and cannot turn their hind flippers forward; fur seals and sea lions have external ears and their hind flippers can be swung forward, making them nimble on land. Some species can move as fast as man.

Seals come on land only to breed, molt, and bask in the sun. Land assembly guarantees mating, which would otherwise depend on chance meetings at sea. Breeding usually takes place on islands because they are free of predatory land mammals.

Common or harbor seal pups are born on sandbanks

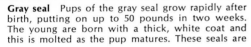

Gray seal Pups of the gray seal grow rapidly after birth, putting on up to 50 pounds in two weeks. The young are born with a thick, white coat and this is molted as the pup matures. These seals are rare toward the southern limit of their range, and they prefer rough water around cliffs and reefs. The young are weaned at about two weeks, after which the adults' mating season begins

About a month before the breeding season, male and pregnant female gray seals gather on or near their chosen beaches. When the first pups are born, the older bulls establish large inland mating territories; the younger bulls are restricted to the water's edge. Mating occurs two weeks after pupping.

The common or harbor seal is more completely adapted to life at sea than the gray seal. Common seals do not gather on breeding territories, and the interval between pupping and mating is several weeks longer than with gray seals. Pups are often born on an exposed sandbank or ledge, and swim off when the tide rises to cover it.

Northern fur seals form one of the world's largest herds of mammals. About 1.5 million of them come ashore to breed on two islands of the Pribilof group in the North Pacific. The dominant bulls, known as beachmasters, establish territories in early June. The females arrive in mid-June, and pup a day or two later. The adults mate when the pups are about a week old. In October the northern fur seal migrates more than 3000 miles to Japan and California, and returns in early spring. Each year sealers kill about

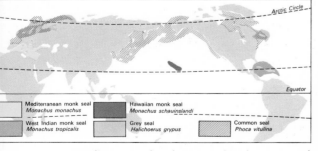

Breeding grounds of true seals The gray seal breeds only on islands and on floating ice. The common seal, or harbor seal, comes ashore to breed on mainland temperate and Arctic coasts of the Atlantic and Pacific oceans

Reproductive cycle A feature of the gray seal's reproductive cycle is a two-to-three-month gap between the fertilization of the female's egg and its implantation in the womb, a process that is called delayed implantation

Mediterranean monk seal *Monachus monachus*
West Indian monk seal *Monachus tropicalis*
Hawaiian monk seal *Monachus schauinslandi*
Grey seal *Halichoerus grypus*
Common seal *Phoca vitulina*

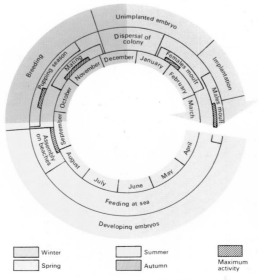

Winter
Spring
Summer
Autumn
Maximum activity

Arctic Circle

ATLANTIC OCEAN

Equator

PACIFIC OCEAN

Antarctic Circle

Distribution of fur seals and sea lions Three quarters of the world's 2 million northern fur seals breed on two islands of the Pribilof group in the North Pacific, north of the Aleutian Islands

Harem on a beach Dominant Hooker's sea lion bulls establish territories, regularly spaced on the beaches. The surplus bulls are forced to stay on the margin of the colony or in the sea. Cows ar-rive later and each dominant bull forms a harem of about a dozen. The cows pup in December and January, and mating takes place soon after. Harems break up early in February

Shallow divers Like other sea lions and fur seals, this male southern sea lion does not dive as deeply or stay submerged as long as true seals, since it feeds on fish, shellfish, and squid in surface waters

60,000 young bachelor bulls, which congre-gate away from the breeding colonies. But despite this annual kill the total population has remained stable for some time at around 2 million individuals.

The males are polygamous, and a beach-master may have a harem of 50 females. Southern fur seals have much smaller harems —four or five cows to each bull.

The rare monk seals are the only seals that breed in tropical and subtropical waters. There are two species, the Mediterranean and the Hawaiian.

Sea lions are the largest of the eared seals, and there is a greater difference in size be-tween the sexes than in other species. The male Steller's sea lion, for example, is a heavy, thick-maned animal which can reach

a length of 11 feet and weigh over a ton. Females are only about 7½ feet long and a third as heavy as males. Sea lions, like fur seals, are polygamous, the bulls guarding territories and small harems. They eat squid, a wide range of fish, and, very rarely, sea-birds. These animals will swim and dive to escape attackers, although they are able to fight with their canine teeth.

Sheltering in the sea Frightened by the photographer's low-flying plane, a colony of Steller's sea lions in the Aleutian Islands rushes to the safety of the water

PART TWO
THE PAST, PRESENT, AND FUTURE OF ANIMAL LIFE

Evolution traced in stone Fossils, such as this ammonite, provide information on the probable course of evolution. These petrified remains can be dated by the ages of the rocks in which they occur

Intensive care This Weddell seal will nurse her pup continuously for its first six to seven weeks—not even leaving it to feed herself. Such behavior is typical of mammals living in exposed habitats

How does one account for the present-day distribution of animals? Why does one species live here and another there? Part of the answer is neatly supplied by the theory of continental drift, explained on the following two pages. Next, the whole sweep of evolutionary history is portrayed: from single-celled animals to early man. An investigation of animal behavior follows, tying together the many facets of behavior described in Part One. Finally, "Animals and Man" explores the close links that exist between animals and the human race.

Ensuring the future of a species Although man has exterminated many species, in some cases the slaughter was stopped. This happened with the Manchurian crane. Because the Japanese government set up a reserve in 1924, the number of cranes in Japan increased from 20 to 172 by 1965

The distribution of animals

There are many reasons for the present distribution of animals, including great changes in climate and the infinitely slow but steady shifting of the continents

Since life began, at least 3.5 billion years ago, the face of the earth has undergone immense changes. Seas have risen and fallen, drowning or exposing vast areas of land. Continents themselves, parts of rigid plates floating on less solid rock, have drifted apart and moved together again. Tremendous forces have pushed up chains of mountains, many of which have since been leveled by erosion. Polar glaciers have advanced and retreated, leaving behind deep, carved valleys thousands of miles from the present-day poles.

The animals on earth today are those whose ancestors survived these immense changes, in many cases evolving as they met new challenges and spread into new areas. As they spread, they came up against impassable barriers: mountains, deserts, seas, and differences in climate—barriers that have largely determined the current distribution of animal groups.

In the sea, where life probably originated,

there are fewer obvious barriers to movement, and many marine animals are widely distributed throughout the oceans. Birds, too, are limited more by barriers of habitat and climate than by mountains, deserts, or seas, so that bird families and species are often more widespread than other vertebrates that live on land.

In the last million years, the northern temperate regions have several times been locked in the grip of ice. Each time, the general temperature of the earth has been lowered and sea levels have fallen as the ocean waters were converted to mountains of ice. Many animal species became extinct during these times because they were trapped by the advancing ice and did not have time to adapt. But the ice provided a way to cross the frozen sea for those animals that were adapted to the cold. By reducing the level of the sea at various points, the advancing ice also exposed land links.

It was such a land link—a bridge across what is now the Bering Strait—that was used by the ancestors of the modern members of the horse family when they crossed from North America into the plains of Eurasia more than 1.5 million years ago.

The plates on which the continents rest are moving

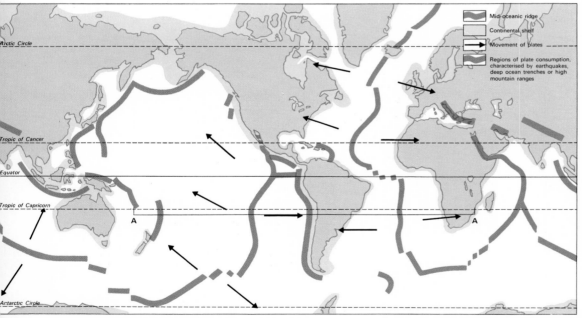

	Mid-oceanic ridge
	Continental shelf
	Movement of plates
	Regions of plate consumption, characterised by earthquakes, deep ocean trenches or high mountain ranges

The earth's crust—forming both continents and ocean basins—is a series of rigid plates floating on the more plastic rock of the earth's mantle. The plates' boundaries are at midoceanic ridges, where

new rock from the mantle wells up between the plates, forming new ocean floor. When the plates move apart, they carry, like conveyor belts, continents and new ocean floor

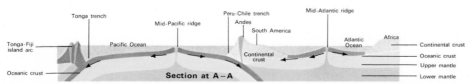

Section at A–A

Where the old ocean floor sinks, the plate material returns to the mantle at deep-sea trenches, causing earthquakes and volcanic activity. Sometimes undersea volcanic activity builds chains of islands, such as the Tonga-Fiji arc. If a continent is at the

edge of a trench, a range of volcanic mountains is formed, such as the Andes. When continents are on the edges of plates and they collide, a mountain chain forms. The Himalayas were thrust up by the collision between India and Asia

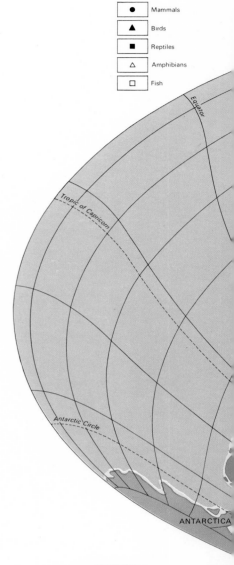

●	Mammals
▲	Birds
■	Reptiles
△	Amphibians
□	Fish

Continents 200 million years ago

Continents 60 million years ago

The continents were probably grouped closely together as recently as 200 million years ago. Since then, the movements of the plates have carried them apart. This separation of the continents isolated large groups of animals

The zoogeographical regions of the world

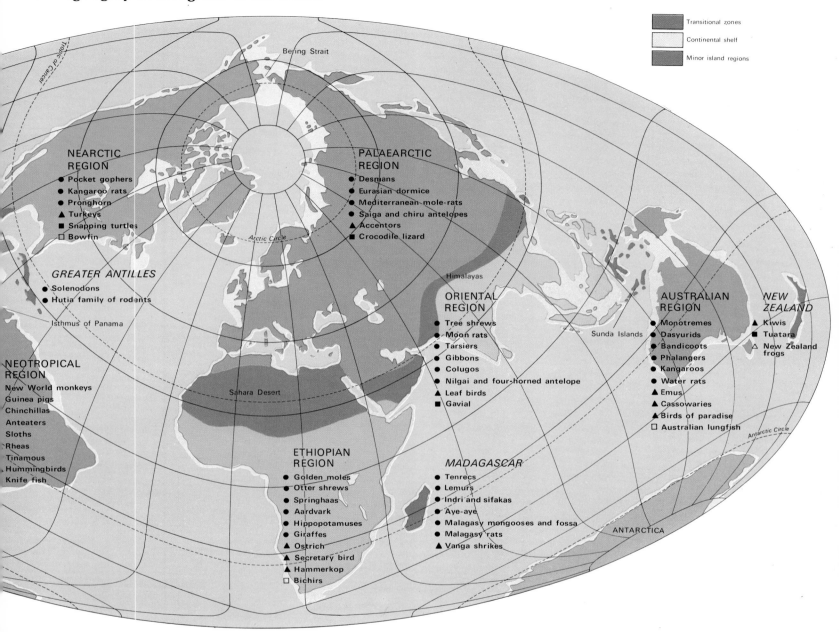

Transitional zones

Continental shelf

Minor island regions

NEARCTIC REGION
- Pocket gophers
- Kangaroo rats
- Pronghorn
- ▲ Turkeys
- ■ Snapping turtles
- ▢ Bowfin

GREATER ANTILLES
- Solenodons
- Hutia family of rodents

NEOTROPICAL REGION
- New World monkeys
- Guinea pigs
- Chinchillas
- Anteaters
- Sloths
- Rheas
- Tinamous
- Hummingbirds
- Knife fish

PALAEARCTIC REGION
- Desmans
- Eurasian dormice
- Mediterranean mole-rats
- Saiga and chiru antelopes
- Accentors
- ■ Crocodile lizard

ORIENTAL REGION
- Tree shrews
- Moon rats
- Tarsiers
- Gibbons
- Colugos
- Nilgai and four-horned antelope
- ▲ Leaf birds
- ■ Gavial

ETHIOPIAN REGION
- Golden moles
- Otter shrews
- Springhaas
- Aardvark
- Hippopotamuses
- Giraffes
- ▲ Ostrich
- ▲ Secretary bird
- ▲ Hammerkop
- ▢ Bichirs

MADAGASCAR
- Tenrecs
- Lemurs
- Indri and sifakas
- Aye-aye
- Malagasy mongooses and fossa
- Malagasy rats
- ▲ Vanga shrikes

AUSTRALIAN REGION
- Monotremes
- Dasyurids
- Bandicoots
- Phalangers
- Kangaroos
- Water rats
- ▲ Emus
- ▲ Cassowaries
- ▲ Birds of paradise
- ▢ Australian lungfish

NEW ZEALAND
- ▲ Kiwis
- ■ Tuatara
- △ New Zealand frogs

Scientists studying the distribution of animals have divided the world into areas called zoogeographical regions, each with types of animals that are not found elsewhere. New seas and oceans have been barriers to the movement of land animals, and account in part for the present distribution of animals. Some of the regions are named on the map. The minor regions are large islands that have land vertebrates found nowhere else in the world. Madagascar's unique animals have evolved in isolation since their ancestors were separated from Africa. At the borders of all land-linked regions are transitional zones where some animals from different regions mix. Barriers, such as the Sahara and the Himalayas, hinder the movement of most animals and yet there is some mixing. In the Sunda Islands primates and civets of the oriental region and marsupials from the Australian region are found together on Celebes. Most of the indigenous animals of Cuba and Hispaniola, in the Greater Antilles, have become extinct

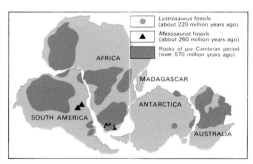

Adjoining continents Matching layers of old rocks show that the southern continents were once closer together. The distribution of fossils of freshwater reptiles, which could not have crossed oceans, confirms this theory

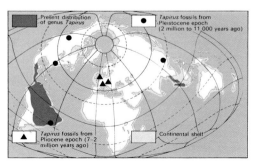

Former land link Today, tapirs live only in America and Asia, but fossils show that their ancestors were once widespread in the northern hemisphere, at a time when there was a land "bridge" across the present Bering Strait

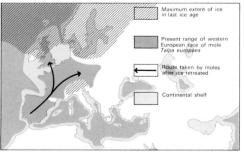

Sea barrier During the last ice age, western European moles died out, except in Spain. When the ice retreated, they moved back northward, reaching England before the Channel formed, but were blocked from Ireland by the Irish Sea

The evolution of animals

Charles Darwin's theory of evolution has been called the greatest unifying theory in biology. It was reinforced by Mendel's experiments with pea plants

For centuries most people believed that animals and plants never changed and that all living things had appeared on the earth in exactly the same forms that they have at present. Then in 1859 the British naturalist Charles Darwin (1809–82) published a book that revolutionized the science of biology. This book, *On the Origin of Species by Means of Natural Selection,* outlined the theory that today's animals have evolved from earlier, different species. It was based on many years' observation of animals from all parts of the globe, and particularly on what Darwin had seen and noted more than 20 years earlier when he traveled the world on the H.M.S. *Beagle.* During the voyage he spent over four years studying plant and animal life on the coasts of South America.

Theories of Darwin and Mendel

Darwin based his theory on three central observations: (1) All members within a species vary. Some are taller than their fellows, some are faster, some have longer claws or keener eyesight or thicker fur, and so on. (2) Most creatures produce large numbers of offspring—more than will survive to become breeding adults. (3) The total numbers in a particular species tend to remain constant. From these observations he deduced that all living creatures are involved in a struggle for existence, and those that survive this struggle and breed are those whose variations give them some advantage over their fellows. They are the fittest, in the sense that they are the best adapted to their environments. Over thousands of generations, natural selection gives rise to new species, as forms from a parent species become adapted in different places to different conditions.

Although Darwin's theory of evolution assumed that characteristics are inherited, he did not know how inheritance works. In the 1860s, a monk named Gregor Mendel

(1822–84), living in what is now the Czechoslovakian town of Brno, was experimenting with pea plants. Mendel's experiments convinced him that inherited characteristics are carried from generation to generation by what he called factors. Each characteristic —whether a pea is smooth or wrinkled, for instance—depends on a pair of such factors, one passed on through the male reproductive cell and the other through the female. Mendel announced his findings to his local natural history society, but his work went unnoticed until it was rediscovered by the Dutch botanist Hugo de Vries in 1900.

Genetics in action

Today biologists call Mendel's "factors" genes, and the science of heredity genetics. Genes are units in DNA (deoxyribonucleic acid) molecules (or, as in some viruses, RNA, or ribonucleic acid). The genes lie along rodlike bodies, called chromosomes, found in the nuclei of living cells. When a cell divides, the molecules of DNA duplicate themselves so that identical genes are formed in the resulting daughter cells.

The modern view of evolution combines Darwin's theory with a knowledge of genetics. The genes of individual animals in a population are part of the gene pool of that population. New variations in the gene pool arise by sporadic mutations—chemical or structural changes in the chromosomes. The enormous genetic variety of the gene pool is recombined into new patterns in the individuals of each new generation. This genetic variation is expressed in the unique structure and function of each individual.

The evidence for evolution is overwhelming. Fossils provide a record of changes in the world's animals over immense periods of time. A study of embryos reveals primitive structures even in today's highly evolved animals. Biologists compare similar structures in groups of related animals to deduce whether they share a common evolutionary origin. The new science of molecular biology has gone a long way to reveal how the mechanism of genetic inheritance works.

The DNA molecule

In Britain, in the early 1950s, scientists Francis Crick and James Watson discovered the structure of DNA, the material that carries the genetic information of the chromosomes. The DNA molecule turned out to be shaped like a double helix (a helix is the shape of the thread on a screw) of long-chain molecules, linked sideways by weak chemical forces called hydrogen bonds. The whole molecule resembles a twisted ladder, with hydrogen-bonded organic bases as rungs and alternating chains of phosphate and sugar groups forming the sides. The order of bases on the chains can vary, and it is this order that constitutes the "code" that controls the development of an individual by dictating the sequence of amino acids in proteins made by each cell.

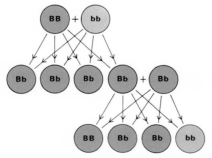

Inheritance of eye color in man The gene for brown eye color is dominant—that is, it overrides the contribution by the gene for blue eye color. All the children of a pure brown-eyed (BB) and a pure blue-eyed (bb) parent have brown eyes. But each carries the gene for blue eyes and may pass it on. If two such brown-eyed people with these genes (Bb) have children, on the average one out of four children will have blue eyes

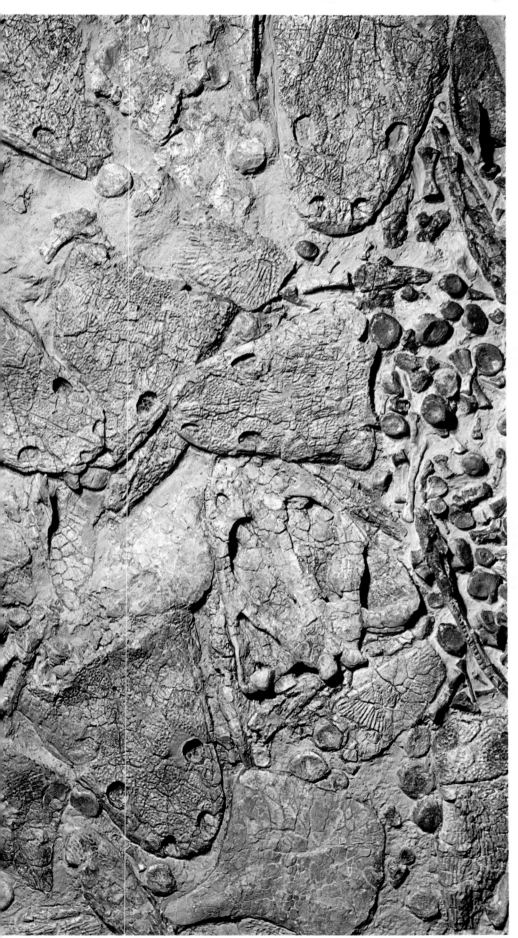

Evolution shown by evidence

Scientists learn much about evolution by studying fossils—the preserved remains of plants and animals. The stone slab at the left contains the remains of about a dozen alligatorlike amphibians that died about 200 million years ago in New Mexico. They are preserved as they died, crowded into the last pool in their drought-hit swamp. Sand and mud covered their skeletons and over the years compressed into rock

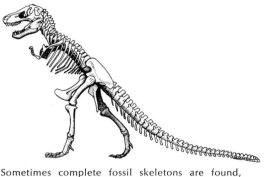

Sometimes complete fossil skeletons are found, especially those of the larger animals, whose massive bones tend to defy destruction. This carnivorous dinosaur is 50 feet from nose to tail

Few early mammals left complete fossils, but scientists can reconstruct creatures such as this planteater of about 75 million years ago from just a few fragments. Conjectural bones are in color

The peppered moth of Europe originally lived on lichen-covered trees where its coloring was an effective camouflage. During the last 100 years, trees in industrial areas have become sooty, and the once-rare dark form of the moth is now common

The evolution of the horse

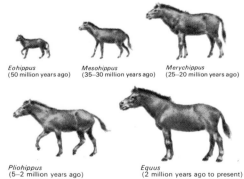

Eohippus
(50 million years ago)

Mesohippus
(35–30 million years ago)

Merychippus
(25–20 million years ago)

Pliohippus
(5–2 million years ago)

Equus
(2 million years ago to present)

The fossil record of the evolution of the horse family shows how natural selection leads to the survival of the form best suited to its environment. The ancestor of the modern horse was a terrier-sized browser with feet well suited to its life in the soft soil of the forest. It had four toes on its front feet and three on its hind feet. Gradually, with the spread of grasslands, new forms arose that were adapted for swift movement. Their legs grew longer and their toes disappeared

The origins of life

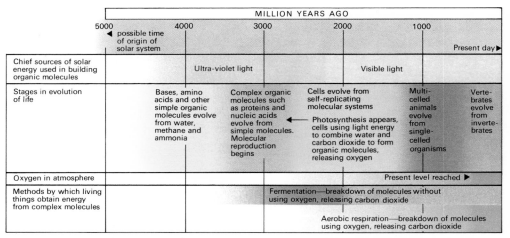

MILLION YEARS AGO					
5000 ◀ possible time of origin of solar system	4000	3000	2000	1000	Present day ▶
Chief sources of solar energy used in building organic molecules		Ultra-violet light		Visible light	
Stages in evolution of life	Bases, amino acids and other simple organic molecules evolve from water, methane and ammonia	Complex organic molecules such as proteins and nucleic acids evolve from simple molecules. Molecular reproduction begins	Cells evolve from self-replicating molecular systems ◀ Photosynthesis appears, cells using light energy to combine water and carbon dioxide to form organic molecules, releasing oxygen	Multi-celled animals evolve from single-celled organisms	Verte-brates evolve from inverte-brates
Oxygen in atmosphere				Present level reached ▶	
Methods by which living things obtain energy from complex molecules			Fermentation—breakdown of molecules without using oxygen, releasing carbon dioxide		
				Aerobic respiration—breakdown of molecules using oxygen, releasing carbon dioxide	

Sources for the evolution of life Under the action of the sun's ultraviolet rays, simple molecules probably combined to form self-duplicating complex ones, and cells evolved. Then photosynthesis appeared, releasing oxygen for respiration. The ultraviolet light converted some oxygen to ozone, which blocked further ultraviolet radiation and left visible light as the main source of energy

Basic chemicals of life

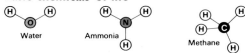

Water   Ammonia   Methane

Originally the organic compounds in the atmosphere and oceans of the world were simple ones formed from hydrogen (H), oxygen (O), nitrogen (N), and carbon (C)

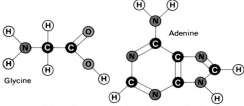

Glycine   Adenine

Activated by the sun's ultraviolet radiation, simple molecules probably combined to form amino acids, such as glycine, and bases, such as adenine

Structure of the DNA molecule

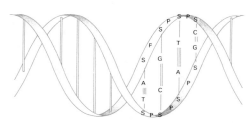

The DNA molecule consists of a double helix of long strands bonded together like a twisted ladder. The strands are made up of alternate phosphate and sugar groups (P and S), linked by pairs of bases (A = adenine, G = guanine, T = thymine, and C = cytosine). When DNA unwinds to form RNA, the double helix "unzips" by splitting down the center. Each separate strand then duplicates its missing half. In this way, genetic information carried by DNA is passed unchanged

Life probably began among the collection of chemicals in the primeval seas; from simple, single-celled organisms the whole of the animal kingdom evolved

About 4.5 billion years ago, the earth and its oceans were without life, and surrounded by an atmosphere of ammonia and methane. Erupting volcanoes hurled ash and molten rock upward, violent electrical storms thundered across the sky, and the sun blazed down with an intense heat, bathing the earth in ultraviolet as well as visible light.

Although there was no life on earth, chemical reactions were taking place in the oceans. Bombarded by lightning and by the sun's rays, simple substances combined to form amino acids, organic bases, and sugars —the building blocks of living matter.

In the next phase the organic compounds must have linked together to give rise to even more complex substances; for proteins are formed of long chains of amino acids, and nucleic acids are formed from a combination of bases and sugars. The concentration of ingredients necessary for life to arise has been called the primeval soup. This "soup" may have accumulated at the surface or on the fringes of the seas. Some of the larger molecules that formed out of these organic compounds were probably able to reproduce themselves and to evolve by a process similar to natural selection, only the best-adapted forms surviving.

A living organism can reproduce itself and can convert energy either from sunlight, as in a plant, or from food, as in an animal, to drive its own life processes. The key to the formation of a true life form was the appearance of a membrane, a skinlike layer of proteins and fats that enclosed and concentrated groups of nucleic acids and other

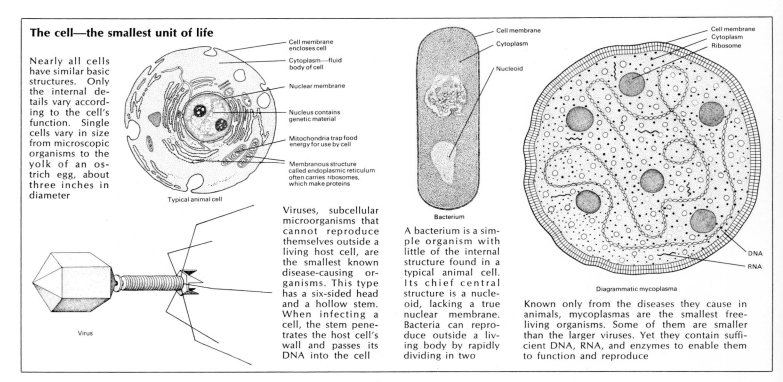

The cell—the smallest unit of life

Nearly all cells have similar basic structures. Only the internal details vary according to the cell's function. Single cells vary in size from microscopic organisms to the yolk of an ostrich egg, about three inches in diameter

Cell membrane encloses cell
Cytoplasm—fluid body of cell
Nuclear membrane
Nucleus contains genetic material
Mitochondria trap food energy for use by cell
Membranous structure called endoplasmic reticulum often carries ribosomes, which make proteins

Typical animal cell

Viruses, subcellular microorganisms that cannot reproduce themselves outside a living host cell, are the smallest known disease-causing organisms. This type has a six-sided head and a hollow stem. When infecting a cell, the stem penetrates the host cell's wall and passes its DNA into the cell

Virus

Cell membrane
Cytoplasm
Nucleoid

Bacterium

A bacterium is a simple organism with little of the internal structure found in a typical animal cell. Its chief central structure is a nucleoid, lacking a true nuclear membrane. Bacteria can reproduce outside a living body by rapidly dividing in two

Cell membrane
Cytoplasm
Ribosome
DNA
RNA

Diagrammatic mycoplasma

Known only from the diseases they cause in animals, mycoplasmas are the smallest free-living organisms. Some of them are smaller than the larger viruses. Yet they contain sufficient DNA, RNA, and enzymes to enable them to function and reproduce complex molecules. The resulting arrangement would resemble a simple cell, the basic unit of all living things. Other membranous structures have evolved and are found within most living cells today. They include the mitochondria, which trap energy from food materials. A membrane surrounds the nucleus which contains DNA (deoxyribonucleic acid), the substance that carries the cell's genetic information in the form of a chemical code. Another nucleic acid, RNA (ribonucleic acid), is responsible for transcribing and carrying this information to particles called ribosomes. Ribosomes manufacture proteins necessary for the cell on the basis of instructions carried by the RNA from the nucleus.

Other combinations of simple substances gave rise to chlorophyll, the pigment that absorbs light. In the presence of chlorophyll, the cells became rudimentary plants, using the energy of sunlight to convert carbon dioxide and water into sugars and releasing oxygen in the process known as photosynthesis. As this process went on, the composition of the atmosphere began to change to that of the air we breathe today. Ozone filtered out most of the sun's ultraviolet radiation, which had been necessary in the formation of compounds essential to life on earth; but as living matter became more complex, ultraviolet radiation became harmful to it.

We cannot be certain that the events leading to the emergence of life took place in exactly this way. But scientists have been able to make some simple amino acids and proteins in the laboratory by duplicating the ingredients and conditions that probably existed on the primitive earth.

Organisms having characteristics of both plants and animals

The smallest cells capable of independent existence are called mycoplasmas, and they include the organism that causes pleuropneumonia in cattle. They have an outer membrane and the minimum complement of molecules to give them attributes of life.

Other disease-causing organisms include viruses and bacteria. A virus can live only as a parasite within a living cell, unlike a bacterium, which can reproduce itself outside a living body. A bacterium consists of a single cell, and its DNA is often concentrated in a region called a nucleoid, but is not enclosed in a true nuclear membrane.

The basic difference between plants and animals is that plants obtain energy for growth by photosynthesis, whereas animals live by consuming other forms of life. Some life forms do not fit neatly into either the plant or the animal kingdom, but possess characteristics of both. The simplest animals, each consisting of only a single cell, are the hordes of Protozoa, or "first animals." There are four groups: Mastigophora, Sarcodina, Sporozoa, and Ciliata.

The mastigophorans move by lashing whiplike flagella—hence their alternate name of flagellates. Some, such as *Euglena*, contain chlorophyll and manufacture food by photosynthesis. Others, such as the trypanosomes, which cause sleeping sickness, are parasites. Best known of the sarcodines, and of all living protozoans, is the amoeba. The third group, the sporozoans, are parasites and include the malaria-causing *Plasmodium*. Ciliates are named after their thousands of hairlike cilia, which they beat rhythmically to move or to trap food particles.

Some flagellates, such as *Volvox*, live in colonies. *Volvox* colonies may represent an intermediate step between the flagellates and the multicelled sponges.

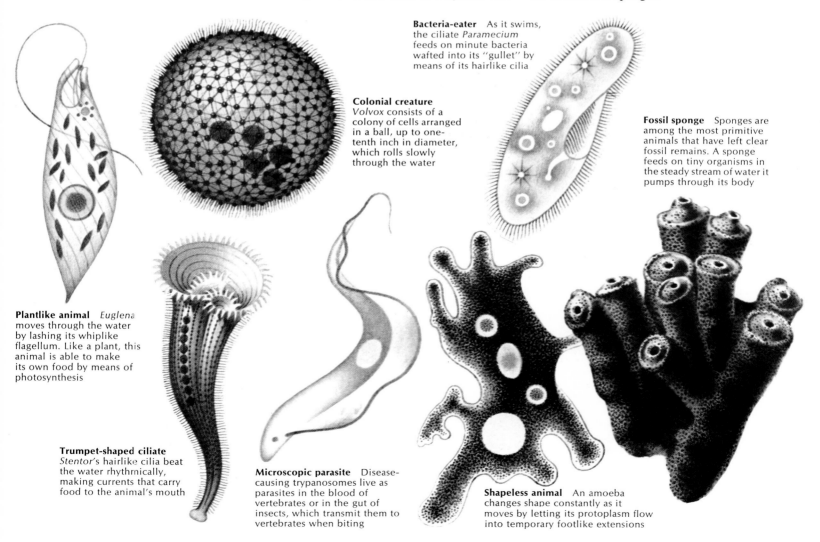

Bacteria-eater As it swims, the ciliate *Paramecium* feeds on minute bacteria wafted into its "gullet" by means of its hairlike cilia

Colonial creature *Volvox* consists of a colony of cells arranged in a ball, up to one-tenth inch in diameter, which rolls slowly through the water

Fossil sponge Sponges are among the most primitive animals that have left clear fossil remains. A sponge feeds on tiny organisms in the steady stream of water it pumps through its body

Plantlike animal *Euglena* moves through the water by lashing its whiplike flagellum. Like a plant, this animal is able to make its own food by means of photosynthesis

Trumpet-shaped ciliate *Stentor*'s hairlike cilia beat the water rhythmically, making currents that carry food to the animal's mouth

Microscopic parasite Disease-causing trypanosomes live as parasites in the blood of vertebrates or in the gut of insects, which transmit them to vertebrates when biting

Shapeless animal An amoeba changes shape constantly as it moves by letting its protoplasm flow into temporary footlike extensions

327

One cell to billions

The story of evolution is one of ever-increasing complexity: from a world populated by single-celled creatures to the emergence of the billion-celled squid

How single-celled Protozoa, which evolved possibly some two billion years ago, gave rise to multicelled Metazoa is one of the fundamental mysteries of evolution. The problem is complicated by the fact that the earliest metazoans, like most invertebrates, were soft-bodied and left few fossils.

Many researchers now hold to the view that coelenterates and comb jellies, sometimes considered a halfway stage between the Protozoa and Metazoa, are degenerate offshoots of primitive flatworms, which in turn evolved from ciliates. The straight-line descent produced modern-type flatworms, leading eventually to the higher animals. The most modern view is to treat no acellular or unicellular organisms as animals. Some scientists exclude even the sponges, putting them in some separate kingdom from higher plants and animals. The simplest metazoans alive today have bodies composed of two layers of cells, one surrounding the other, generally fringed by stinging cells. They include hydras, sea anemones, corals, and jellyfish.

The next evolutionary stage was the appearance of a third layer of cells sandwiched between the existing two. From the cells of this central layer there evolved muscles and various organs. Movement became more efficient and the body, instead of being radially symmetrical (and thus equally sensitive to stimuli from any direction), evolved right and left sides, a front, and a rear. The simplest living examples of such three-layered animals are all wormlike—the planarians and parasitic flukes and tapeworms.

A body cavity evolves

The appearance of a body cavity allowed the muscles of the body wall and the gut to operate independently. This cavity evolved in two different ways. One led to the pseudocoelomates, like nematode worms. The other led to the coelomates, in which the body cavity, or coelom, generally evolved from a split in the middle layer of cells. The earliest segmented annelid worms probably had a complete set of organs in each segment.

The most important group of invertebrate segmented coelomates is the arthropods, a group that includes insects, crabs, scorpions, and spiders. Mollusks are also coelomates, but only one primitive form has a segmented body. There is a bewildering array of mollusk forms, including snails, mussels, and octopuses.

In all these coelomates, the mouth forms in the embryo from a pore called the blastopore. In four other groups it arises elsewhere, and many zoologists consider this difference important because the evolutionary starting point for higher animals probably occurred among these animals.

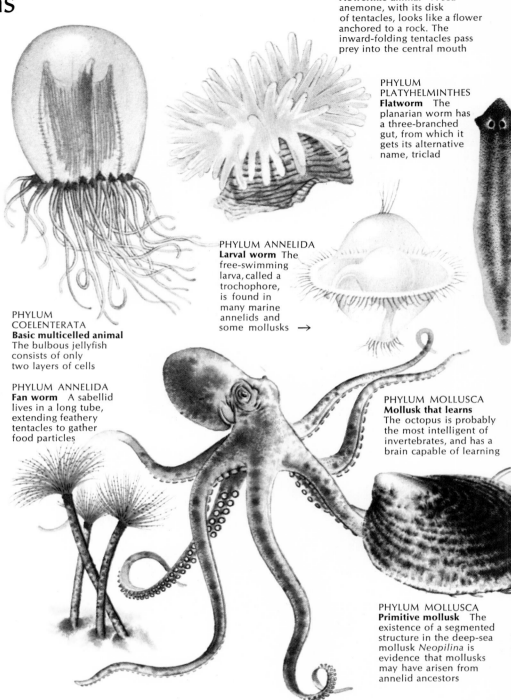

PHYLUM COELENTERATA
Flowerlike animal A sea anemone, with its disk of tentacles, looks like a flower anchored to a rock. The inward-folding tentacles pass prey into the central mouth

PHYLUM PLATYHELMINTHES
Flatworm The planarian worm has a three-branched gut, from which it gets its alternative name, triclad

PHYLUM ANNELIDA
Larval worm The free-swimming larva, called a trochophore, is found in many marine annelids and some mollusks →

PHYLUM COELENTERATA
Basic multicelled animal The bulbous jellyfish consists of only two layers of cells

PHYLUM ANNELIDA
Fan worm A sabellid lives in a long tube, extending feathery tentacles to gather food particles

PHYLUM MOLLUSCA
Mollusk that learns The octopus is probably the most intelligent of invertebrates, and has a brain capable of learning

PHYLUM MOLLUSCA
Primitive mollusk The existence of a segmented structure in the deep-sea mollusk *Neopilina* is evidence that mollusks may have arisen from annelid ancestors

ARCHEOZOIC E

◄2000 million years ago   1500

Phylum Protozoa: single-celled animals

Broken line = No fossil evidence; lines of ancestry are assumed from physical similarities
Solid line = Fossil remains have been found

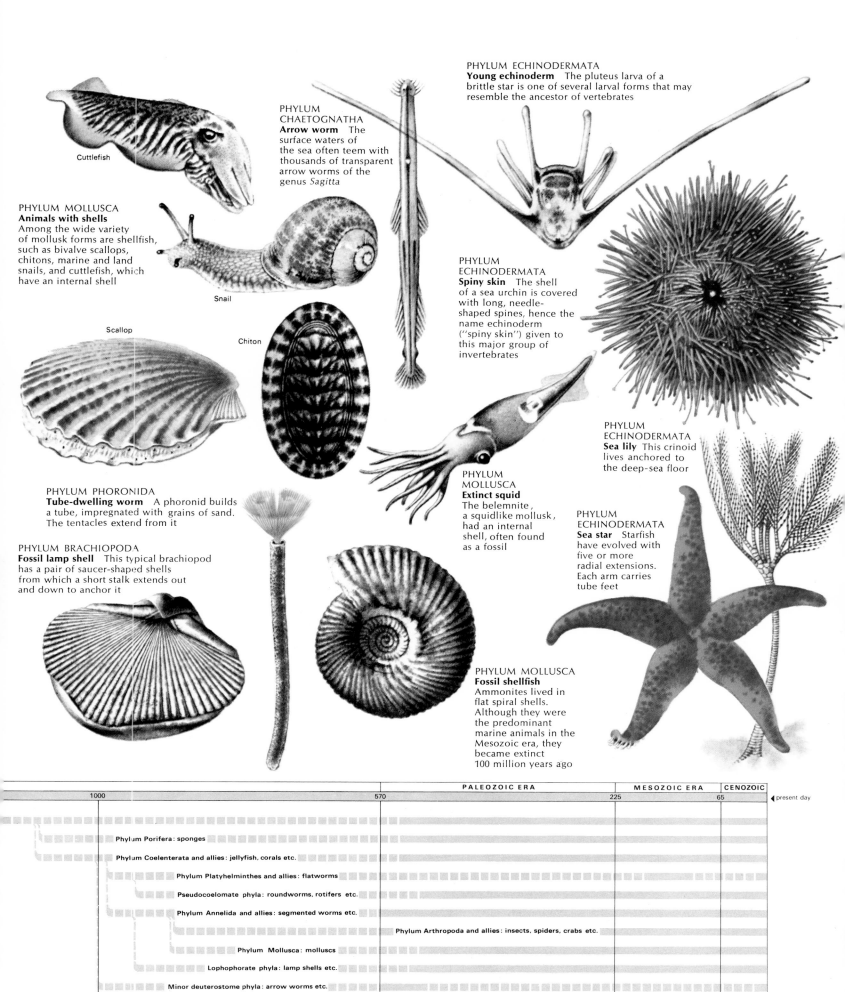

Cuttlefish

PHYLUM CHAETOGNATHA
Arrow worm The surface waters of the sea often teem with thousands of transparent arrow worms of the genus *Sagitta*

PHYLUM ECHINODERMATA
Young echinoderm The pluteus larva of a brittle star is one of several larval forms that may resemble the ancestor of vertebrates

PHYLUM MOLLUSCA
Animals with shells
Among the wide variety of mollusk forms are shellfish, such as bivalve scallops, chitons, marine and land snails, and cuttlefish, which have an internal shell

Snail

PHYLUM ECHINODERMATA
Spiny skin The shell of a sea urchin is covered with long, needle-shaped spines, hence the name echinoderm ("spiny skin") given to this major group of invertebrates

Scallop

Chiton

PHYLUM ECHINODERMATA
Sea lily This crinoid lives anchored to the deep-sea floor

PHYLUM PHORONIDA
Tube-dwelling worm A phoronid builds a tube, impregnated with grains of sand. The tentacles extend from it

PHYLUM MOLLUSCA
Extinct squid
The belemnite, a squidlike mollusk, had an internal shell, often found as a fossil

PHYLUM ECHINODERMATA
Sea star Starfish have evolved with five or more radial extensions. Each arm carries tube feet

PHYLUM BRACHIOPODA
Fossil lamp shell This typical brachiopod has a pair of saucer-shaped shells from which a short stalk extends out and down to anchor it

PHYLUM MOLLUSCA
Fossil shellfish
Ammonites lived in flat spiral shells. Although they were the predominant marine animals in the Mesozoic era, they became extinct 100 million years ago

			PALEOZOIC ERA		MESOZOIC ERA	CENOZOIC
1000		570		225		65	present day

Phylum Porifera: sponges
Phylum Coelenterata and allies: jellyfish, corals etc.
Phylum Platyhelminthes and allies: flatworms
Pseudocoelomate phyla: roundworms, rotifers etc.
Phylum Annelida and allies: segmented worms etc.
Phylum Arthropoda and allies: insects, spiders, crabs etc.
Phylum Mollusca: molluscs
Lophophorate phyla: lamp shells etc.
Minor deuterostome phyla: arrow worms etc.
Phylum Echinodermata: sea urchins etc.
Phylum Chordata: vertebrates and their ancestors

Arthropods

Out of more than a million known species of living animals, three quarters are arthropods—among the most adaptable and successful animals on earth

Millions of years before the land became habitable, the seas were teeming with arthropods—active creatures whose jointed legs and bodies were partially encased in a shell of jointed armor. They probably evolved from segmented worms like annelids. With their flexible bodies, usually carrying a pair of limbs on each segment, and equipped with eyes and mouths, the early arthropods were the most advanced creatures that had yet existed on earth.

From the crustaceans that scuttle along the bottom of the deepest sea to the spiders that live more than four miles up on Mount Everest, arthropods have become adapted to nearly every habitat on earth.

Modern arthropods (the name means "jointed feet") range in size from tiny mites of the genus *Demodex,* less than ¹⁄₂₀₀ of an inch long, to sea giants such as the Japanese spider crab, with a claw span of 11 feet.

The earliest fossil arthropods, the trilobites, date from the beginning of the Cambrian period, about 570 million years ago. They may have lived as scavengers. After flourishing for over 300 million years they were replaced by more efficient forms of life.

The successful crustaceans

A more fruitful line of development was that of the crustaceans—a class whose earliest fossils date from more than 500 million years ago—including lobsters, prawns, crabs, and water fleas. Most crustaceans have a single shell protecting their heads and part of their bodies, two pairs of antennae, and legs specialized for walking, swimming, or respiration.

The protective shell of "armor," or cuticle, which made arthropods so successful in the sea, also protected them on land.

Plants began to spread over the land in the Silurian period (about 435 to 395 million years ago). The first known land-living arthropods date from that time. The fossil record suggests that ancestors of modern scorpions were in the vanguard. Along with spiders, ticks, and mites, scorpions belong to the Arachnida class.

After the arachnids came the insects, teeming both in numbers and in variety of species as they radiated to fill the new environments. The great species explosion came after some winged arthropods, or insects, evolved in the Carboniferous period (345 to 280 million years ago). With land plants available to feed on, the first dragonflies, cockroaches, and grasshoppers appeared. The earliest known beetles date from the Permian period (280 to 225 million years ago). And after flowers had appeared on earth, in the Cretaceous period (136 to 65 million years ago) there evolved early forms of bees, butterflies, and moths, along with the world's first flies and mosquitoes.

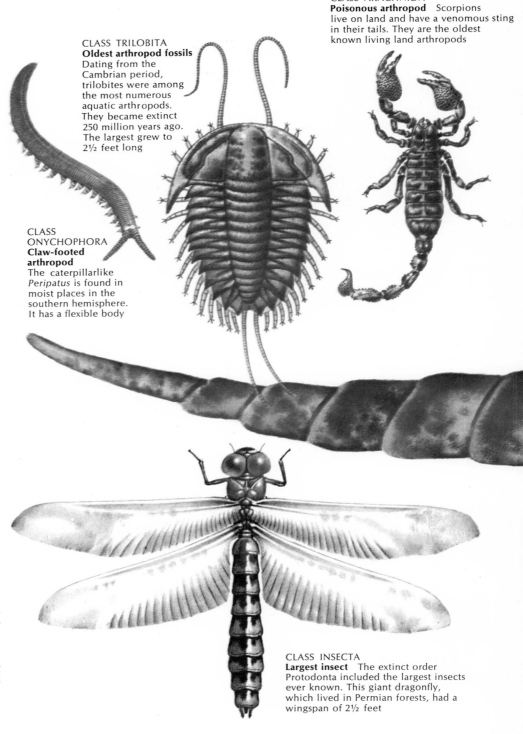

CLASS TRILOBITA
Oldest arthropod fossils
Dating from the Cambrian period, trilobites were among the most numerous aquatic arthropods. They became extinct 250 million years ago. The largest grew to 2½ feet long

CLASS ARACHNIDA
Poisonous arthropod Scorpions live on land and have a venomous sting in their tails. They are the oldest known living land arthropods

CLASS ONYCHOPHORA
Claw-footed arthropod
The caterpillarlike *Peripatus* is found in moist places in the southern hemisphere. It has a flexible body

CLASS INSECTA
Largest insect The extinct order Protodonta included the largest insects ever known. This giant dragonfly, which lived in Permian forests, had a wingspan of 2½ feet

	PALEOZOIC ERA				
◀570 million years ago.	500	440-430	395	345	
CAMBRIAN PERIOD	ORDOVICIAN PERIOD	SILURIAN PERIOD	DEVONIAN PERIOD		MISSISS
	Class Trilobita: arthropods with three-lobed body segments				
	Class Merostomata: king crabs etc.				
	Class Arachnida: spiders, scorpions etc.				
	Class Crustacea: crustaceans				
	Class Onychophora: velvet worms				
	Class Pauropoda: minute soft-bodied arthropods				
	Class Diplopoda: millipedes				
	Class Chilopoda: centipedes				
Annelid worms with lobed appendages	Class Symphyla: centipede-like arthropods				
	Class Insecta: insects				
	Class Thysanura: silverfish etc.				
	Class Diplura: two-pronged bristletails				
	Class Collembola: springtails				
	Class Protura: arthropods without antennae				
	Modern annelid worms				

Broken line = No fossil evidence; lines of ancestry are assumed from physical similarities
Solid line = Fossil remains have been found

CLASS PAUROPODA
Tiny scavengers Pauropods are minute animals 0.01 to 0.02 inches long. They have nine pairs of legs and feed on decaying plant material

CLASS SYMPHYLA
Tiny arthropod
A symphylan is a small, centipedelike arthropod. It has a flexible body, enabling it to wriggle into narrow crevices

CLASS CRUSTACEA
Legs for grasping Many crustaceans have five pairs of legs, some of which are modified into powerful, grasping claws. Crustaceans are the most abundant aquatic arthropods

CLASS THYSANURA
Three-pronged bristletail *Petrobius* is in the same class as the firebrat and silverfish, which live in houses and emerge to feed at night on starchy food scraps

CLASS CHILOPODA
Two legs per segment Centipedes have a single pair of legs on each body segment. A few species have 100 pairs, but 15 to 30 pairs are more usual

CLASS DIPLURA
Two-pronged bristletail
Campodea lives in the soil and in moist areas under logs and stones. Its thorax bears three pairs of legs, like that of springtails and proturans

CLASS MEROSTOMATA
Giant arthropod of the sea Eurypterids, some 5½ feet long, lived in the sea, where they probably fed on invertebrates and may also have preyed on ostracoderms, the first vertebrates

CLASS COLLEMBOLA
Springtail Arthropods of the class Collembola are wingless; most have forked organs on their tails with which they spring upward. Fossil forms are known from the mid-Devonian period

CLASS PROTURA
Arthropods without eyes Tiny arthropods of the genus *Acerentomon* have no eyes or antennae. Some use their front legs as feelers

CLASS DIPLOPODA
Four legs per segment Millipedes have two pairs of legs on many body segments and burrow into leaf litter. Despite their name they do not have 1000 legs, although some species have more than 200 pairs

			MESOZOIC ERA			CENOZOIC ERA	
280		225	195-190	136		65	3 ◀ present day
.VANIAN PERIOD	PERMIAN PERIOD	TRIASSIC PERIOD	JURASSIC PERIOD	CRETACEOUS PERIOD		TERTIARY PERIOD	Q

Q=QUATERNARY PERIOD

Fish and amphibians

For 440 million years fish have been among the world's dominant life forms. One group became amphibians, the first land invertebrates

Although vertebrates, the animals with backbones, form only one twentieth of all animal species, they include most of the world's large, active animals—fish, amphibians, reptiles, birds, and mammals. Good fossil records of vertebrates date back about 440 million years, to the beginning of the Silurian period.

Living in freshwaters at that time, sucking food through jawless mouths, was a class of small, fishlike animals with bony gill supports and a bone protecting the brain. A bony shell surrounded a soft body that contained a notochord—the rod of flexible tissue that was the forerunner of a backbone. These were ostracoderms, or "shell-skinned" animals, the remote ancestors of all the vertebrates, including man.

Like their nearest living relatives, the parasitic lampreys and scavenging hagfish, ostracoderms could not become active predators because they lacked jaws and could not grasp large prey.

It took another 40 million years before the next great advance—the evolution of jaws from gill-supporting bones. The first jawed fish, the placoderms, are now extinct. Their descendants, the cartilaginous fish, include the sharks, rays, and chimaeras.

Modern sharks evolved at the beginning of the Jurassic period, 195 million years ago, and have been among the major predators in the sea ever since.

About half of the 40,000 or so living species of vertebrates are bony fish of the class Osteichthyes. This class appeared during the Devonian period, 395 to 345 million years ago. They are split into two groups: the ray-finned fish and the fleshy-finned fish. Most modern fish are ray fins.

Invading the land

The earliest ray fins, the chondrosteans, had bony skeletons and originally lived in freshwaters. They evolved into holosteans, and these in turn gave rise to the teleosteans, which make up the majority of modern fish.

The keys to the invasion of the land by fleshy-finned fish were the improvement of the lungs, the development of internal nostrils leading to the mouth, the strengthening of the skeleton to bear the animal's weight on land, and the evolution of fins into walking limbs. These adaptations allowed the animals to move from dried-up pools to find water.

The first amphibians may have overlapped with the last of the ostracoderms. They crawled out of the water late in the Devonian period, some 350 million years ago. Like their modern descendants, frogs and toads, newts and salamanders, and caecilians, they had to return to water to lay their eggs. Their skin was probably not completely waterproof, so they lost moisture easily.

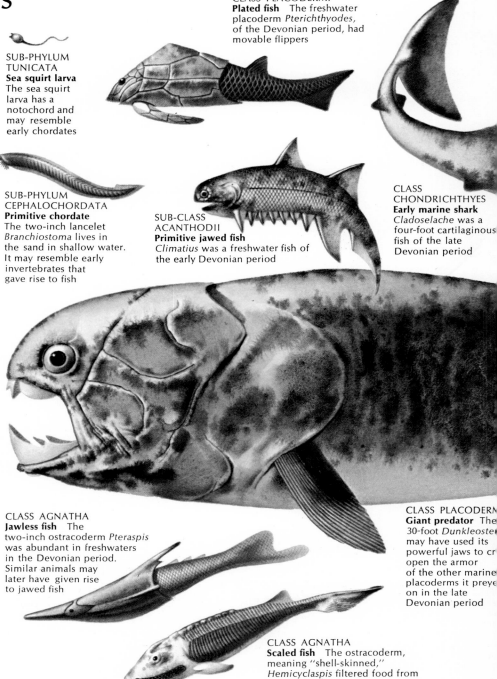

SUB-PHYLUM TUNICATA
Sea squirt larva The sea squirt larva has a notochord and may resemble early chordates

CLASS PLACODERMI
Plated fish The freshwater placoderm *Pterichthyodes*, of the Devonian period, had movable flippers

SUB-PHYLUM CEPHALOCHORDATA
Primitive chordate The two-inch lancelet *Branchiostoma* lives in the sand in shallow water. It may resemble early invertebrates that gave rise to fish

SUB-CLASS ACANTHODII
Primitive jawed fish *Climatius* was a freshwater fish of the early Devonian period

CLASS CHONDRICHTHYES
Early marine shark *Cladoselache* was a four-foot cartilaginous fish of the late Devonian period

CLASS AGNATHA
Jawless fish The two-inch ostracoderm *Pteraspis* was abundant in freshwaters in the Devonian period. Similar animals may later have given rise to jawed fish

CLASS PLACODERM
Giant predator The 30-foot *Dunkleoste*[r] may have used its powerful jaws to cr[ack] open the armor of the other marine placoderms it preye[d] on in the late Devonian period

CLASS AGNATHA
Scaled fish The ostracoderm, meaning "shell-skinned," *Hemicyclaspis* filtered food from the mud in freshwaters during the Devonian period

PALEOZOIC ERA					
◀ about 500 million years ago	440-430	395		345	325
ORDOVICIAN PERIOD	SILURIAN PERIOD		DEVONIAN PERIOD	MISSISSIPPIAN	PENNS
Class Placodermi: 'plate-skinned' fish					
		Sub-class Acanthodii: first jawed fish			
		Order Dipnoi: lungfish			
					To class R

Broken line = No fossil evidence; lines of ancestry are assumed from physical similarities
Solid line = Fossil remains have been found

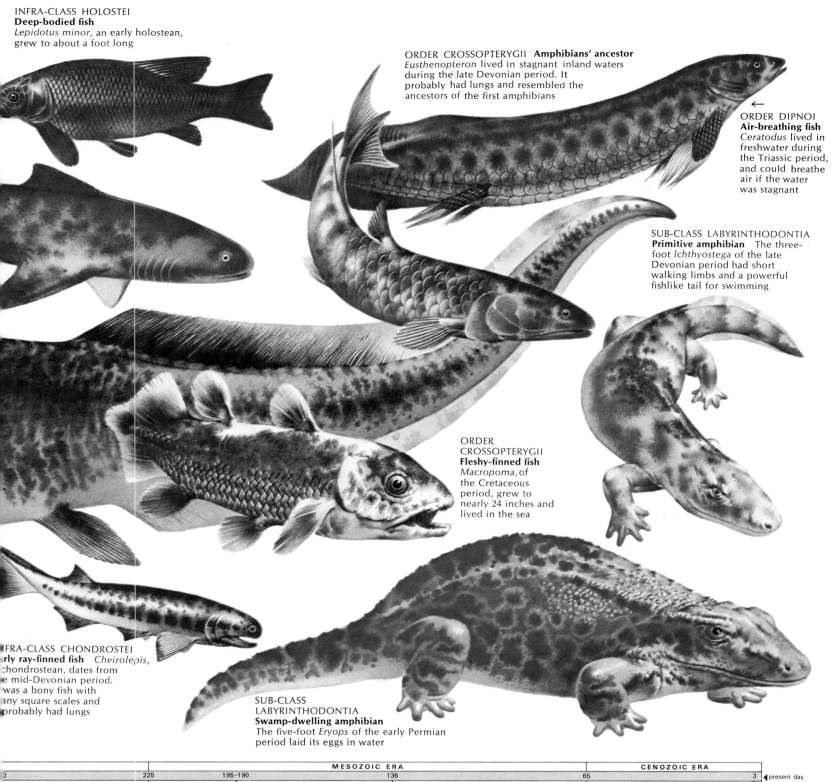

INFRA-CLASS HOLOSTEI
Deep-bodied fish
Lepidotus minor, an early holostean, grew to about a foot long

ORDER CROSSOPTERYGII Amphibians' ancestor
Eusthenopteron lived in stagnant inland waters during the late Devonian period. It probably had lungs and resembled the ancestors of the first amphibians

← **ORDER DIPNOI**
Air-breathing fish
Ceratodus lived in freshwater during the Triassic period, and could breathe air if the water was stagnant

SUB-CLASS LABYRINTHODONTIA
Primitive amphibian The three-foot *Ichthyostega* of the late Devonian period had short walking limbs and a powerful fishlike tail for swimming

ORDER CROSSOPTERYGII
Fleshy-finned fish
Macropoma, of the Cretaceous period, grew to nearly 24 inches and lived in the sea

INFRA-CLASS CHONDROSTEI
Early ray-finned fish *Cheirolepis,* a chondrostean, dates from the mid-Devonian period. It was a bony fish with many square scales and probably had lungs

SUB-CLASS LABYRINTHODONTIA
Swamp-dwelling amphibian
The five-foot *Eryops* of the early Permian period laid its eggs in water

		MESOZOIC ERA			CENOZOIC ERA	
0	225	195–190		136	65	3 ◀ present day
PERMIAN PERIOD	TRIASSIC PERIOD	JURASSIC PERIOD		CRETACEOUS PERIOD	TERTIARY PERIOD	Q
Class Agnatha : jawless fish						
		Class Chondrichthyes: sharks, rays etc.				
				Infra-class Chondrostei: sturgeons, bichirs and their ancestors		
				Infra-class Holostei: garpikes and bowfins and their ancestors		
		Infra-class Teleostei: modern bony fish				
				Order Crossopterygii: fleshy-finned fish		
Class Labyrinthodontia: primitive amphibians ancestral to reptiles						
	Sub-class Lepospondyli: ancestral to modern amphibians					
				Sub-class Lissamphibia: frogs, salamanders and caecilians		

Q = QUATERNARY PERIOD

Reptiles

By developing waterproof skins and the ability to lay shelled eggs, some amphibians evolved into reptiles and were able to invade the dry land

For some 50 million years, amphibians were by far the largest animals able to move on land with reasonable efficiency. But they were still dependent on freshwaters, where they laid their eggs and fed. At first the dry land, which had little suitable food, remained unoccupied by the vertebrates. Then insects began to colonize the land. About 325 million years ago wet-land amphibians evolved into dry-land reptiles. The most significant factor in this evolutionary development was the ability to lay a shelled egg. As a result, the animals could lay their eggs on land and remain near the food supply, instead of having to return to water to spawn. A reptile's egg contains its own water supply in which the embryo develops, protected by the shell from extremes of climate and from predators. Mechanisms for internal fertilization also evolved.

Another great advance was the evolution of a dry, horny skin through which internal water could not be lost. At the same time, lungs became larger and more efficient, since reptiles could no longer "breathe" through their skins. Associated with this development in breathing was an improvement in blood circulation that enabled two separate streams of blood to pass through the heart.

Adaptations to moving on land

The advantage in being able to move farther and faster in search of food and living space led to a third major change—the development of the breastbone and heavier pelvic and shoulder girdles to carry more powerful muscles. A longer neck allowed the head, carried clear of the ground, freer movement. Despite all these changes, modern reptiles still retain many amphibian features. They are cold-blooded (cannot maintain a steady body temperature); all their teeth are similar; and their skeletons broadly follow the amphibian pattern.

Reptiles are "improved amphibians" just as amphibians are "improved fish"; and there must have been intermediate forms of life—neither totally reptilian nor totally amphibian. For this reason it is difficult to say when reptiles first appeared. The oldest known fossil reptile is an animal called *Hylonomus,* found in coal deposits laid down 300 million years ago in Nova Scotia.

Once the basic reptile plan was established, there was an evolutionary explosion as reptiles began to invade new habitats. Fossils show a sudden variety of reptile types beginning to radiate into new environments in the Permian period (280 to 225 million years ago). There were reptiles that walked, ones that swam, running reptiles, flying reptiles, plant-eaters and flesh-eaters, giant reptiles, and midget reptiles. The scene was set for a period of evolution that was to last 150 million years—the age of the dinosaurs.

ORDER PELICOSAURIA
Fin-backed reptile
The ten-foot-long *Dimetrodon* of the Permian period had a huge sail along its back, which may have helped it regulate body temperature

ORDER THERAPSIDA
Mammallike reptile
The flesh-eating *Cynognathus* of the early Triassic period was about a modern pig's size and had several skeletal features like mammals', which may have evolved from this order

ORDER THECODONTIA
Forerunner of birds
The three-foot-long *Euparkeria* of the early Triassic period belonged to a group of reptiles that gave rise to dinosaurs and birds

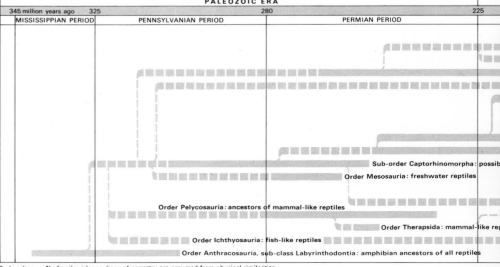

PALEOZOIC ERA			
345 million years ago 325		280	225
MISSISSIPPIAN PERIOD	PENNSYLVANIAN PERIOD	PERMIAN PERIOD	

Sub-order Captorhinomorpha: possib

Order Mesosauria: freshwater reptiles

Order Pelycosauria: ancestors of mammal-like reptiles

Order Therapsida: mammal-like rep

Order Ichthyosauria: fish-like reptiles

Order Anthracosauria, sub-class Labyrinthodontia: amphibian ancestors of all reptiles

Broken line = No fossil evidence; lines of ancestry are assumed from physical similarities
Solid line = Fossil remains have been found

SUB-ORDER LACERTILIA
Gliding reptile
Kuehneosaurus had "wings" of membrane-covered ribs that it may have used for gliding among the trees

ORDER CROCODILIA
Sea crocodile *Geosaurus* grew to 15 feet long and lived in the early Cretaceous period. It swam by thrashing its fishlike tail. It had strong, toothed jaws

ORDER MESOSAURIA
Swimming reptile
Mesosaurus had webbed feet and a streamlined body— adaptations for swimming in freshwaters

SUB-ORDER SERPENTES
Burrowing snake
The small, wormlike *Typhlops* burrowed beneath the ground of the Mesozoic forests, and similar forms still exist

ORDER CHELONIA
Ancestor of turtles
Proganochelys had a heavy, armored shell, like the modern turtles. It lived during the late Triassic period. It had no teeth, but crushed its food in a horny beak

↑ **ORDER ICHTHYOSAURIA**
Toothless sea reptile *Ophthalmosaurus* looked like a combination of shark and seal, and had large eyes and flexible paddles

ORDER RHYNCHOCEPHALIA
Primitive reptile The tuatara *Sphenodon punctatus* of New Zealand is the only survivor of a primitive group. It has a vestigial third eye on the top of its head

SUB-ORDER PLESIOSAURIA
The "snake turtle" Looking like a snake threaded through a turtle's shell, *Macroplata* of the late Jurassic period darted out its long neck to snatch prey

MESOZOIC ERA			CENOZOIC ERA	
195–190	136		65	3
JURASSIC PERIOD	CRETACEOUS PERIOD		TERTIARY PERIOD	Q

Sub-order Plesiosauria: sea reptiles
Sub-order Nothosauria: semi-aquatic reptiles
Order Placodontia: mollusc-eating reptiles
Order Araeoscelidia: primitive lizard-like reptiles
Order Chelonia: turtles and tortoises
Order Rhynchocephalia: tuatara and its ancestors
Sub-order Serpentes: snakes and their ancestors
Sub-order Lacertilia: lizards and their ancestors
Order Eosuchia: ancestors of snakes and lizards
Sub-order Procolophonia: remote ancestors of snakes and lizards
reptiles
ders Ornithischia, Saurischia, Pterosauria and class Aves
Order Crocodilia: crocodiles, alligators and gavial
Order Thecodontia: ancestors of crocodiles, dinosaurs and birds
ass Mammalia

Q = QUATERNARY PERIOD

Dinosaurs and birds

**For 150 million years giant reptiles ruled
the earth; 50-ton brontosaurs
wallowed in swamps and 50-foot-long
tyrannosaurs stalked the land for prey**

During the Mesozoic era, which extended
from about 225 to 65 million years ago, reptiles dominated life on land. Most successful
of these were the archosaurs, especially dinosaurs and the flying reptiles, pterosaurs.
From the same stock evolved the modern
crocodiles and birds.

There were two orders of dinosaurs ("terrible reptiles"): the "lizard-hipped" Saurischia and the "bird-hipped" Ornithischia.
The groups differed in pelvic structure; also,
most saurischians had a full set of teeth and
the order included flesh-eaters and plant-
eaters. Many ornithischians—all probably
plant-eaters—lacked front teeth.

"Lizard-hipped" dinosaurs developed in
the Triassic period about 200 million years
ago. Some, the carnivorous theropods,
walked on their hind legs and had massive
tails to counterbalance the weight of their
heads and bodies. One of this group, the 50-
foot-long *Tyrannosaurus*, was the largest
flesh-eater that ever lived. Most of the other
"lizard-hipped" dinosaurs walked on all
fours, ate plants, and had heavy bodies with
long necks as well as long tails.

A "brain" in the rump

"Bird-hipped" dinosaurs, some of which had
heavy defensive armor, also arose during
the Triassic period. Among them was the
20-foot-long *Stegosaurus*, which had two
pairs of spikes on its tail. Like most other
giant dinosaurs, this huge animal had extra
"brains" in its rump and shoulder region—
nerve centers larger than the brain in its
skull that directed movement of tail and
limbs.

The heavily armored ankylosaurians were
squat animals with bony plates on the back
and clublike tails. The duck-billed dinosaurs,
on the other hand, belonged to a group that
had no armor and walked upright.

Ceratopsians, or horned dinosaurs, which
existed late in the Cretaceous period, about
90 to 65 million years ago, also belonged to
the "bird-hipped" order. They included the
20-foot-long *Triceratops*, which had a brain
the size of a kitten's in its six-foot-long skull.

The ancestors of birds are believed to have
been a group of reptiles called pseudo-
suchians, flesh-eaters of the Triassic period.
At some stage their scales evolved into
feathers, probably as a means of temperature control. The evolution of feathers led
to flight. The first known bird, *Archaeopteryx*, was a weak flyer about the size of a
crow. It lived 150 million years ago.

The unrelated pterodactyls, flying reptiles,
had membranous wings connecting their
hind and fore limbs. They became extinct
about 75 million years ago—victims, along
with the dinosaurs, of some as yet unknown
set of conditions that wiped out many gigantic forms of animal life.

**SUB-ORDER
THEROPODA
Early dinosaur**
Coelophysis was a
small reptile of the
Triassic period. It
was only one-tenth
the length of later
giant dinosaurs

**SUB-ORDER SAUROPODOMORPHA
Heaviest dinosaur** *Brachiosaurus*
lived during the late Jurassic
period and weighed up to 50 tons.
It probably lived in shallow water

**SUB-ORDER
STEGOSAURIA
Plated dinosaur**
Stegosaurus had
upright bony
plates on its
back and tail
for defense.
It ate only
plants

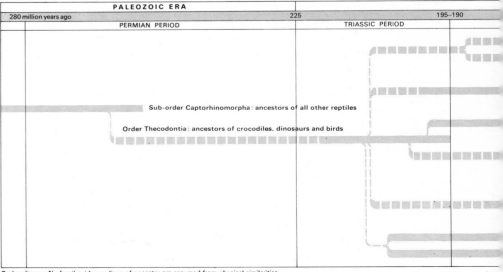

PALEOZOIC ERA		
280 million years ago	225	195–190
PERMIAN PERIOD		TRIASSIC PERIOD

Sub-order Captorhinomorpha: ancestors of all other reptiles

Order Thecodontia: ancestors of crocodiles, dinosaurs and birds

Broken line = No fossil evidence; lines of ancestry are assumed from physical similarities
Solid line = Fossil remains have been found

SUB-ORDER SAUROPODOMORPHA
Longest dinosaur *Diplodocus* was over 85 feet long, including a 45-foot tail. It fed on plants during the late Jurassic period

SUB-ORDER ORNITHOPODA
Bird-hipped dinosaur Walking upright on its clawed hind legs, *Camptosaurus* ate plants with its powerful jaws

SUB-ORDER PTERODACTYLOIDEA
Giant pterosaur It is possible that *Pteranodon* had a hairlike covering. The weight of its huge, toothless beak was balanced by a backward projection of bone

SUB-ORDER ANKYLOSAURIA
Armored dinosaur *Ankylosaurus* lived during the Cretaceous period. Its 15-foot-long body was almost completely covered by a mosaic of bony plates, fringed by spikes

SUB-ORDER ORNITHOPODA
Swimming dinosaur *Hadrosaurus* may have spent part of its time in swamps. It lived during the late Cretaceous period

SUB-ORDER RHAMPHORHYNCHOIDEA
Flying reptile *Rhamphorhynchus* of the late Jurassic period, a primitive pterosaur, had a three-foot wingspan and toothed jaws

SUB-ORDER THEROPODA
Largest carnivore About 50 feet long and standing nearly 20 feet tall, *Tyrannosaurus* lived in the late Cretaceous period

CLASS AVES
Earliest bird *Archaeopteryx* had hair on its body, wings, and lizardlike tail. The feathers probably evolved as a form of insulation, and the bird was not a good flier

CLASS AVES
Flightless diving bird Although *Hesperornis* could not fly, it was a true bird. It lived during the late Cretaceous period and fed on fish

MESOZOIC ERA		CENOZOIC ERA	
136		65	3
CRETACEOUS PERIOD		TERTIARY PERIOD	Q ◄Present day
Sub-order Stegosauria: armoured dinosaurs			
		Sub-order Ankylosauria: armoured dinosaurs	
		Sub-order Ceratopsia: armoured dinosaurs	
		Sub-order Ornithopoda: plant-eating reptiles that walked on hind legs only	
		Sub-order Pterodactyloidea: pterodactyls	
Sub-order Rhamphorhynchoidea: long-tailed flying reptiles			
Class Aves: birds and their immediate ancestors			
Sub-order Sebecosuchia: primitive crocodiles			
		Sub-order Eusuchia: advanced crocodiles	
		Sub-order Mesosuchia: primitive crocodiles	
Sub-order Thalattosuchia: sea crocodiles			
		Sub-order Theropoda: flesh-eating dinosaurs	
		Sub-order Sauropodomorpha: giant plant-eating dinosaurs	

Q = QUATERNARY PERIOD

Mammals

Reptiles, the first vertebrates to conquer the land completely, could not adapt to all environments, and they are less widespread than warm-blooded creatures

Mammals succeeded where reptiles failed by evolving a temperature-control mechanism in the brain, and insulating hair on the surface of the body. In addition, a mammal's diaphragm increases ventilation of the lungs, and a secondary palate allows the animal to breathe through its nose while its mouth is used for chewing. The legs do not stick out sideways but are underneath the body, giving improved locomotion.

From the start, mammals were more versatile than reptiles, and they became adapted to most environments. At the same time, they needed the ability to learn how to respond to changing conditions. This requirement was met by a larger brain and a prolonged period of parental care. Female mammals have mammary glands, which are modifications of certain sweat glands, and suckle their young on milk.

The earliest mammals probably carried their young in pouches, like modern monotremes and marsupials, allowing them a further period of development after they were born.

During Jurassic times, about 190 to 136 million years ago, there were five well-established orders of mammals, all now extinct. Three of these orders were evolutionary "dead ends," but the other two, docodonts and pantotherians, are thought to have given rise to all modern mammals. Living monotremes—the platypus and the spiny anteaters—possibly evolved from the docodonts. Marsupials and placental mammals (the large group, including man, whose young mature in the womb before birth) are probably all descended from the pantotherians.

The isolation of South America from the rest of the American continent during the Tertiary period resulted in the development of several groups of mammals: Edentata, such as anteaters, armadillos, sloths, and the extinct glyptodonts; the extinct Litopterna, which resembled the hooved animals of the Old World; the New World monkeys; and the marsupial opossums.

Outside South America, mammals diversified into various forms, many of which have survived until now. Large carnivores include the dogs, bears, and cats. Hooved planteaters also evolved, together with elephants. The first primates, a group that today includes monkeys, apes, and man, appeared about 80 million years ago.

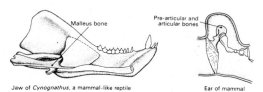

Jaw of *Cynognathus*, a mammal-like reptile   Ear of mammal

Malleus bone   Pre-articular and articular bones

From jaw to ear As certain reptile species became more mammal-like, two hinging bones in the lower jaw (indicated in color) evolved to form a small bone in the mammalian ear

ORDER EMBRITHOPODA
Large herbivore With paired horns, the 11-foot-long *Arsinoitherium* looked like a rhinoceros. It lived in northeast Africa in the Oligocene epoch

ORDER CREODONTA
Prehistoric carnivore *Oxyaena*, a large predator, resembled the modern wolverine. It lived during the Eocene period

ORDER PERISSODACTYLA
Ancestral horse A European and North American plant-eater, *Hyracotherium* was about the size of a fox terrier

ORDER PERISSODACTYLA
Giant rhinoceros *Paraceratherium* grew to 25 feet long and 18 feet tall

ORDER CONDYLARTHRA
Primitive hooved mammal *Phenacodus*, a hooved animal of the early Eocene epoch, was probably a plant-eater

ORDER AMBLYPODA
Large American herbivore The 12-foot-long *Uintatherium* was built like a modern rhinoceros and lived during the Eocene epoch. It had three pairs of horny swellings on its skull and the males had two tusklike canine teeth

	MESOZOIC ERA
◄195–190 million years ago	136
JURASSIC PERIOD	

Order Pantotheria: ancestors of all mammals except for monotremes

Order Symmetrodonta: early flesh-eating mammals

Order Multituberculata: first plant-eating mammals

Order Triconodonta: early flesh-eating mammals

Order Docodonta: possible ancestors of platypus, etc.

Broken line = No fossil evidence; lines of ancestry are assumed from physical similarities
Solid line = Fossil remains have been found

ORDER PROBOSCIDEA
Tusked lower jaw An early European elephant of the Pleistocene epoch, *Deinotherium* had downward-curving tusks in its lower jaw

ORDER ARTIODACTYLA
Prehistoric ruminant A plant-eater with a remarkable forked horn on its nose, *Synthetoceras* probably chewed the cud

ORDER LITOPTERNA
South American hooved mammal *Macrauchenia* of the Pleistocene epoch looked like a camel

ORDER CARNIVORA
Saber-toothed cat *Smilodon* had six-inch-long upper canine teeth, probably used in penetrating elephants' skin

ORDER NOTOUNGULATA
Giant browser The nine-foot-long *Toxodon* was built like a short-legged rhinoceros. It lived during the Pleistocene epoch

ORDER EDENTATA
Giant ground sloth *Megatherium* weighed several tons and was nearly 20 feet long. It lived in South America during the Pleistocene epoch and may have become extinct when man invaded its habitat

ORDER EDENTATA
Cousin of the armadillo The body armor of *Glyptodon*, which lived during the Pleistocene epoch, was fused into a single carapace

	CENOZOIC ERA						
	65	54–53	38–37	26		7	3
CRETACEOUS PERIOD			TERTIARY PERIOD				Q
	Paleocene epoch	Eocene epoch	Oligocene epoch	Miocene epoch		Pliocene	P

Order Primates: primates
Order Taeniodontia: primitive plant-eating mammals
Order Edentata: anteaters, armadillos, sloths etc. and their ancestors
Order Pholidota: scaly anteaters
Order Lagomorpha: rabbits and hares
Order Tillodontia: primitive mammals
Order Rodentia: rodents
Order Chiroptera: bats and their ancestors
Order Insectivora: insect-eaters
Order Dermoptera: colugos and their ancestors
Order Cetacea: whales, dolphins etc.
Order Creodonta: early flesh-eating mammals
Order Pinnipedia: seals, sea lions and walrus
Order Carnivora: flesh-eaters
Order Artiodactyla: pigs, camels, cattle, sheep etc. and their ancestors
Order Tubulidentata: aardvark and its ancestors
Order Condylarthra: primitive hoofed mammals
Order Perissodactyla: horses, tapirs, rhinos and their ancestors
Order Litopterna: early hoofed mammals
Order Notoungulata: early hoofed mammals
Order Astrapotheria: early hoofed mammals
Order Amblypoda: early hoofed mammals
Order Hyracoidea: hyraxes and their ancestors
Order Embrithopoda: early hoofed mammals
Order Proboscidea: elephants and their ancestors
Order Sirenia: sea cows and their ancestors
Order Desmostylia: shore-living tusked mammals
Order Marsupialia: pouched mammals
Order Monotremata: platypus, echidnas and their ancestors

Q = QUATERNARY PERIOD   P = Pleistocene epoch

◀ present day

339

Primates

Beginning 65 million years ago, a group of mammals evolved with large brains and dexterous hands. These early primates have given rise to monkeys, apes, and man

Primates are relatively unspecialized animals that have developed large brains, the ability to grasp with their hands, and acute senses of sight and touch. The eyes have become sited at the front of the face, giving stereoscopic frontal vision. Sensitive finger-pads are generally strengthened by flat nails instead of claws, and the thumb and big toe are generally separated from the other digits, giving grasping hands and feet.

Few of these features, however, are preserved as fossils, and scientists have to deduce the appearance and habits of an early animal from perhaps only a few teeth. The teeth of early primates were adapted for fruit-eating. The earliest fossil primate teeth date from the late Cretaceous period.

During the Eocene epoch, about 54 to 38 million years ago, there was a great expansion of mammals, and several families of primates were established. The three most important were the Adapidae, Tarsiidae, and Omomyidae. The adapids had fairly long snouts and were possibly ancestral to lemurs and lorises. The tarsiids were ancestors of the modern tarsier. And the omomyids probably gave rise to the higher primates.

The distribution of fossils shows that a tropical bridge between Eurasia and North America ceased to exist by the end of the Eocene epoch.

Primates of two worlds

Old World anthropoids became immediately successful and crowded out the adapids and tarsiids. But in North America primates died out entirely, leaving only omomyids to survive in South America—cut off from the north—where they evolved into the South American monkeys (platyrrhines).

Early Old World anthropoids (catarrhines) included apelike animals that walked on all fours. The earliest fossil apes, represented by *Aegyptopithecus*, date from the late Oligocene of Egypt (30 million years ago). By the mid-Miocene epoch, 20 to 15 million years ago, there were four types of primates in East Africa: *Proconsul*, the probable ancestor of the gorilla and chimpanzee; *Pliopithecus*, a more lightly built ape; *Victoriapithecus*, which may have given rise to the Old World monkeys; and a group of lorisids, ancestors of the modern bush-babies and pottos.

Viewed against the immensity of biological time, man has been on earth only a brief span. Fragmentary remains of a creature called *Ramapithecus*, from about 14 million years ago, may represent a link between the fossil apes and the ape-man *Australopithecus*. The first true man, *Homo erectus*, emerged about 1 million years ago. A mere 40,000 years ago, *Homo erectus* evolved into modern man, *Homo sapiens sapiens*.

FAMILY ADAPIDAE
Possible early lemur
Smilodectes was a typical adapid primate of the early Eocene epoch. It had sideways-facing eyes, and hands that could grab branches

FAMILY TARSIIDAE
Ancestral tarsier
Necrolemur had stereoscopic vision which enabled it to judge distances as it jumped from branch to branch

FAMILY PLESIADAPIDAE
Early primate
Plesiadapis had rodentlike teeth and a long muzzle

FAMILY CERCOPITHECIDAE
Ancestor of the langur The 15-inch-long *Mesopithecus* lived during the Pliocene epoch

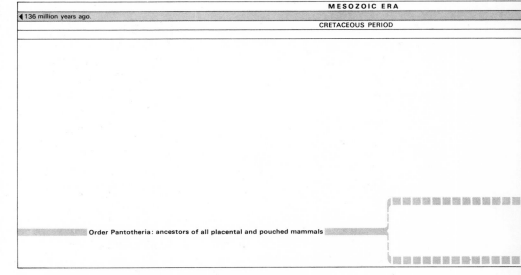

MESOZOIC ERA	
◀ 136 million years ago.	
CRETACEOUS PERIOD	

Order Pantotheria: ancestors of all placental and pouched mammals

Broken line = No fossil evidence; lines of ancestry are assumed from physical similarities
Solid line = Fossil remains have been found

FAMILY CEBIDAE
Spider monkey At the end of the Eocene epoch, monkeys from South America were isolated from primates of the Old World. Since that time, they have evolved independently

FAMILY PONGIDAE
Agile jumper *Pliopithecus* had teeth like a gibbon's, but its long legs and tail indicate that it was a runner and jumper, unlike modern gibbons

FAMILY HOMINIDAE
First true man *Homo erectus* lived in eastern Asia and Europe between 1 million and 300,000 years ago. He walked upright and probably lived by hunting and gathering

FAMILY HOMINIDAE
Modern man Cro-Magnon man appeared in Europe about the middle of the last ice age about 40,000 years ago. He was the first modern man, *Homo sapiens sapiens*

FAMILY HOMINIDAE
Early hominid *Ramapithecus,* known only from fragments of its teeth and jaws, lived 14 million years ago and probably more closely resembled early man than an ape

FAMILY PONGIDAE
Ancestral ape *Proconsul,* one of the early Miocene apes of Africa, was probably ancestral to all the modern apes

FAMILY HOMINIDAE
African ape-man *Australopithecus* lived in southern Africa 3½ million years ago. Early forms were about four feet tall, but they probably walked erect and some may have used crude tools

CENOZOIC ERA						
65	54–53	38–37	26	7	3	present day
		TERTIARY PERIOD				Q
Paleocene epoch	Eocene epoch	Oligocene epoch	Miocene epoch	Pliocene	Pleistocene	R

Family Hominidae: man and his ancestors
Family Oreopithecidae: man-like ape
Family Pongidae: apes and their ancestors
Family Parapithecidae: primitive monkey
Family Cercopithecidae: Old World monkeys
Family Callitrichidae: marmosets and their ancestors
Family Cebidae: New World monkeys
Family Omomyidae: ancestors of monkeys
Family Tarsiidae: tarsiers
Family Anaptomorphidae: ancestors of tarsiers
Family Adapidae: ancestors of lemurs and lorises etc.
Family Lemuridae: lemurs
Family Indriidae: indri and its ancestors
Family Paromomyidae: earliest primates
Family Daubentoniidae: aye-aye and its ancestors
Family Lorisidae: lorises
Family Carpolestidae: primitive primates
Family Plesiadapidae: primitive primates
Family Microsyopsidae: primitive primates
Family Tupaiidae: tree shrews
Other placental mammals
Order Marsupialia: pouched mammals

Q = QUATERNARY PERIOD R=Recent

341

Behavior and the senses

Everything an animal does in response to its environment is part of its behavior repertoire. This repertoire is dominated by staying alive and reproducing

Every animal species is adapted to tolerate a range of physical conditions, such as temperature and humidity. Whenever these conditions change, an animal must rediscover the conditions that enable it to survive, or it will perish. For example, wood lice placed in the open immediately crawl to a cool, damp place. In doing so, they perform behavior that ensures their survival.

A behavior pattern does not happen by chance, any more than does the physical shape of an animal; both evolved by natural selection and matched the animal with its environment. Swifts have the swept-back wings and wide-gaping mouths of animals that spend almost their entire lives flying and must catch their food on the wing. They catch pieces of grass, feathers, and straw on the wing, and cement them together with saliva to make nests; and they sometimes mate, and may even snatch short spells of sleep, on the wing.

Similar behavior, different species

Different species have evolved similar behavior as adaptations to similar ways of life. Jackals, wild dogs, and wolves, hunting in packs, can catch prey larger than themselves. During the summer many rodents and some birds store food which is eaten in winter when food is scarce.

Much behavior is stimulated by hormones—chemicals passed into the bloodstream by glands in the animal's body. In vertebrates, the hormone adrenaline prepares the body for emergencies; in some mammals it makes the hair stand on end, which may form part of their threat posture. Sex hormones initiate the elaborate courtship displays and nest-building behavior of many birds and other animals.

The complexity of an animal's behavior is largely determined by the size and complexity of its brain and the degree of sophistication of its senses. The squid's complex, centralized nervous system allows rapid, well-coordinated movements that are impossible for a jellyfish, with its diffuse and simple network of nerve cells. The extent to which particular behavior patterns can be modified by learning also depends on the brain and nervous system, and most behavior involves some kind of experience-structuring during its development in the individual.

Information from the senses

An animal can react to its surroundings only if it has sufficient information about them, and it relies for this information on its senses. Light, sounds, chemicals, and electrical fields are some of the things that provide animals with information. A falcon sees a pigeon and swoops to kill it; a mole senses a worm by its vibrations and digs toward it. An echo-locating bat lives in a world of sounds, but a long-nosed shrew lives in an incredibly complex world of smells. Some fish generate electrical fields as navigation aids.

The sense most important to an animal's way of life tends to be more highly developed than the others. Birds, spending much of their time on the wing, find their food by sight, and have acute vision; but their senses of taste and smell are poorly developed. A pigeon has only 50 to 60 taste buds, compared with 17,000 taste buds on the tongue of a rabbit.

Most animals have light-sensitive organs, ranging from the simple light-detectors of flatworms to the complex eyes of insects, squid, and vertebrates. The eyes of vertebrates are similar in construction to a camera. Light collected by the cornea and lens forms an image on the retina. The way this image is perceived depends on how it is analyzed by the retina and the brain; a frog, snake, bird, and mammal looking at the same scene may each see it differently. An insect's compound eye works in a different way from that of a vertebrate and may be sensitive to a different range of colors. Bees, for instance, can see ultraviolet light, which is invisible to man.

Sounds may indicate food, danger, or the arrival of a mate. Any moving object produces vibrations in its surroundings; and sense organs, such as the ears of vertebrates, the lateral lines of fish, and the tympanal organs of insects, can pick up the vibrations and produce a sensation of sound. In the ear of a land vertebrate, such as a frog or a man, sound waves in the air cause an eardrum to vibrate. Its vibrations are transmitted by bones to the inner ear, where they stimulate nerve impulses which the brain interprets as sounds. Other parts of the inner ear sense the attitude of the head and help in balance.

The senses of smell and taste, which enable animals to detect airborne or dissolved chemicals, are important to most animals living on or near the ground. Receptors in the feet of insects detect chemicals indicating the presence of food; and Jacobson's organ in the roof of a reptile's mouth serves the same purpose. The sense of smell is important to many mammals in helping them to hunt and identify food, and in detecting a mate or an enemy. Some mammals have glands that manufacture scent for marking trails or territories, attracting mates, or repelling predators.

In most animals the sense of touch is simple compared with vision or hearing, but it is equally important. A scorpion will not lay its eggs in the sand until a pair of "combs" beneath its body relay the information that the sand is of the correct consistency. Touch plays an important part in the social lives of higher primates, which spend a great deal of time fondling and grooming each other with their highly sensitive fingers.

Sensitive to infrared Some snakes have heat-sensitive facial cells, contained in a large pit on each side of the face in pit vipers and in rows of pits along the jaws in boas. These allow them to locate and strike unerringly at prey in pitch darkness. This emerald tree boa can detect objects that are as little as one degree warmer than their surroundings

Detecting smells The male luna moth (left) can find a female five miles away at night because the highly developed sensors on its comblike antennae can detect her scent in the air

Detecting ultrasonic sounds The long-eared bat, like other insectivorous bats, navigates and finds its prey by echo-location. It emits pulses of ultrasonic sounds and picks up any echoes

A gadfly's eye Many insects have large, bulging, compound eyes. These consist of a mosaic of tiny visual elements, each with its own lens. Some dragonflies have nearly 30,000 such units in each eye

Sensitive to touch Surrounding the mouth of the dahlia sea anemone is a ring of stinging tentacles. The outer ends of the tentacles curl around any passing prey that touches them. The prey is then seized and paralyzed before being slowly consumed by the nearly stationary animal

Defense against predators

**Animals that do not fly, run, or swim
away from predators, and are not equipped
to stand and fight, have evolved
special defensive behavior for survival**

One of the most widespread methods of animal defense is camouflage. Many species of small fish and crustaceans are almost transparent, but most camouflaged animals are made unobtrusive by their color—which generally blends with their surroundings—and by their habit of adopting the correct posture and "freezing" motionless when threatened. Many predators will not feed on an animal they have not killed themselves. This is especially true of cats. So some prey animals, such as the Virginia opossum, may play dead and thus deter predators from attempting to eat them.

Normally the shadow on the underside of an animal gives away its position. But countershading, a transition from a dark shade on top to a light shade beneath, cancels the effect of shadow. It is part of the camouflage of many animals, from impalas to mackerel. Patterns of strong contrasts, like the black bars on angelfish and the dark markings on a ringed plover, break up the outline of an animal and make it difficult to see against its surroundings. And some animals, such as chameleons and flatfish, can change color to match the background, and thus be concealed from predators.

Another kind of camouflage is the imitation of inanimate objects. Predators usually ignore seaweed, thorns, or bird droppings, and many animals escape attention because they resemble such commonplace objects. A species of sea horse, *Phyllopteryx eques*, is covered with outgrowths that look remarkably like pieces of seaweed, and several insects and spiders closely resemble bird droppings.

The way in which some insects have evolved resemblances to leaves, petals, bark, thorns, or twigs demonstrates the effectiveness of natural selection—only those with perfect mimicry survive. One of the most remarkable examples is that of flatid bugs *Hancenia glauca*, which may be green or pink. These bugs cluster around a plant stem, the green ones at the top and the pink below, so that they look like a hanging spike of flowers.

Advertising danger

For some animals, being conspicuous is as effective a means of protection as camouflage can be. Many of the animals with offensive weapons—poison glands or powerful teeth and claws—are conspicuously colored. This association has probably been favored by natural selection, because potential predators quickly learn which animals to avoid. Monarch butterflies contain poisons from the milkweed plants they feed on, and the brilliantly colored caterpillars and adults are both relatively immune from attack.

Skunks and various venomous snakes also advertise themselves by their conspicuous markings. Ants of the Dolichoderinae subfamily squirt a noxious fluid that quickly solidifies into a hard resin and incapacitates their enemies. Formicine ants squirt formic acid. The black-necked cobra spits its venom as far as eight feet.

Sometimes bright coloration is a second line of defense. Inconspicuously patterned fore wings overlie the bright hind wings of some moths, such as the sphinx moth, when they are at rest. But when the moth is pecked by a bird, the hind wings suddenly display two startling patterns like large eyes.

Warning colors confer immunity from attack on inedible species. Some edible animals mimic unpalatable ones. A number of forms of the African swallowtail butterfly mimic various distasteful butterflies. And the drone fly and bumblebee moth, both of them stingless, evade the attentions of birds because they look like bees.

In a second kind of mimicry a group of more or less unrelated but poisonous animals shows a tendency to resemble one another. This kind of mimicry is found among many bees, hornets, and wasps. Each species gains added protection by "advertising" itself as belonging to a group that is best left alone. This mimicking ensures that predators must "remember" only one warning coloration instead of a great number.

Confusing the attacker

Unpredictable behavior is an important part of defense. A predator must be able to anticipate the actions of its prey if it is to make a kill. Sand hoppers jump wildly in all directions when uncovered, and day-flying butterflies make interception difficult by flying erratically.

Many animals have special distraction displays which confuse predators. The wriggling tail of a lizard is an extreme example. If the tail is grasped, the lizard can leave all or part of it behind while darting away from its attacker.

Some birds feign injury to distract a predator when their brood is threatened. The ringed plover fans and drags its tail along the ground and flaps helplessly, as if a wing were broken. The predator then follows the apparently injured adult instead of attacking the brood.

Other animals frighten aggressors with sounds. Many mammals scream or hiss at a predator in an intimidating manner. The few moments when the predator is off guard give the prey animal time to escape. The clicks of click beetles and their erratic springing movements seem to frighten off enemies; and some moths produce ultrasonic clicks that may have an anti-predator function against bats.

Some relatively defenseless species protect themselves by forming associations with other animals. Black-throated warblers of Africa nest near hornet and wasp nests, and some weaverbirds of the African savanna seek out acacia trees where bees and wasps have already built their nests.

Imitating a flower The nymph of the mantis *Pseudocrebotra wahlbergii*, like many colored species, lies in wait for its prey, mimicking the African flowers on which it lives

Playing possum Lying on its back with its mouth open, a grass snake appears to be dead. Ignored by its predators, it resumes its daily activity when danger has passed

Living with danger Damselfish avoid predators by living among the stinging tentacles of a sea anemone. They are protected from any stings by a slimy film which covers their bodies

Warning signal from ears A bull African elephant warns a potential enemy by making a mock charge, rushing at its adversary but pulling up at the last minute. The position of an elephant's head, trunk, and ears indicate threat and fear expressions. Raising its tusked head slightly and holding its trunk to one side, the animal makes itself look even larger by fanning out its huge ears. Sometimes this charge is accompanied by a series of trumpeting calls. Only if such a sham attack fails does the elephant go completely over to the offensive and make a real charge

345

Living in groups

Living in groups is a matter of life or death for some animals. It protects them from predators, helps them find food and mates, and increases chances of survival

Most of the world's million and more species of animals cooperate with others of their own kind only to mate, leaving their numerous offspring to survive or not according to chance. When flies or wood lice, for instance, assemble in large numbers, they are simply a collection of individuals, with no social organization based on family group or rank order holding them together.

Among the mammals, however, the antelopes are an example of animals whose survival may depend on their forming and maintaining the correct type of society. Many antelopes roam in large herds. Animals such as lions and leopards, which prey on them, will not ordinarily attack the group. The predator generally snatches a solitary animal that has fallen behind because it is sick or injured, or too old or too young to keep up with the rest. When a predator does pursue its quarry into the group, it often becomes confused by the sheer number of animals, and gives up the chase without making any attempt at an attack.

Types of animal societies

Any natural grouping of higher animals is usually orderly. Each animal has its place within the community structure, and when food, nesting places, or mates become scarce, the strongest and healthiest take precedence. In this way, fighting is kept to a minimum.

If there are comparatively few animals in a group, such as in a pack of wolves, they tend to arrange themselves into a hierarchy often called a peck order—because it was first studied in domestic chickens. The most powerful and confident animal has the highest rank; it dominates the others and has the right to nip or peck the subordinate animals, which do not fight back, and so on throughout the group.

There is, however, a tremendous range of social organization in the animal world, and societies are rarely simple peck orders. In addition to specialized breeding societies, many animal communities are based on the family group. Gibbons, which are monogamous, move around in family groups, typically consisting of a pair of adults and their immature offspring. Families of geese and swans gather into large flocks in winter but still retain their small family units within the flock.

Although the male animal is generally dominant, in some species the female appears to be the leader of the society. Outside the breeding season, male red deer form their own herds, splitting up at the onset of the rut to attract hinds out of the all-female herds; but a female may retain leadership when the herd is threatened.

The most highly organized insect societies, those of ants, bees, and wasps, consist of one or more fertile females and their offspring. The work of the colony is shared by the various castes, which consist of the queen, workers, and males, or drones. A queen bee controls her family by means of chemicals secreted by glands on her head. She suppresses the production of new queens, fertile daughters who would be competitors, and stimulates the production of sterile females, the workers.

The influence of habitat

The type of society in which an animal lives may be determined by its habitat. Gibbons live in tropical rain forests and, since they spend most of their lives in the treetops, they are not usually worried by predators. By swinging through the trees at great speed, they can escape fairly easily from the leopard, their most dangerous attacker.

Baboons, on the other hand, find most of their food on the ground and so they are more vulnerable to attack. They live in more tightly organized troops, generally of 25 to 30 animals, although troops of up to 200 have been seen. Baboons cooperate, and individuals in the troops have a better chance of survival than does a solitary animal. The males defend the females against predators while the slow-maturing young are being reared.

Breeding societies

Many species of animals form groups only in order to reproduce; outside the breeding season, they lead a more solitary existence. Forming a large colony in the breeding season allows the animals a mixing of the breeding population, increases the chances of finding a mate, and possibly arouses the mating instinct.

Breeding animals tend to choose protected sites to lessen the danger from predators. Some of the largest breeding colonies are found among seabirds. Half a million royal penguins occupy 16½ acres of coastal terraces on Macquarie Island, and the average number of birds in a North Atlantic gannetry is 8000 to 10,000 pairs.

Challenges for living space rarely lead to bloodshed. Killing among members of the same species is biologically wasteful, and animal weapons and fighting methods have evolved in such a way that a less powerful animal of the same species usually has a chance to escape without serious harm.

Special weapons may be used for fighting among vertebrates of the same species, but damage rarely results. The sharp, rapierlike horns of oryxes or the branched antlers of deer lock together when two of these animals fight, so that the encounter develops into a harmless test of strength. But when used against an animal of another species, the same weapons can be lethal.

Elephant herd Large groups of African elephants generally consist entirely of females and their young. Males join the herd only at mating time

Seabird colony Gannets form huge cliff-top nesting colonies, which sometimes contain around 20,000 birds. Each gannet makes a nest just outside the pecking range of its neighbor. Returning birds unerringly land on the correct nest

How bees give directions

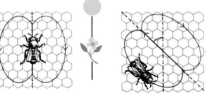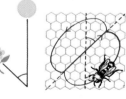

A worker bee, returning to the hive, dances on the honeycomb to indicate where food can be found. The angle between the center of the figure and the vertical shows the angle between the food and the sun. If the food is near the hive, the bee circles on the comb. If the food is to be found more than about 100 yards from the hive, the bee dances in a figure-of-eight, waggling its body (right)

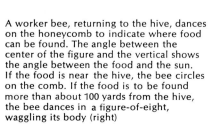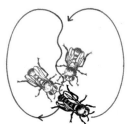

Finding a mate

Courtship, the behavior that precedes mating, is often a complex ritual in which animals recognize others of their species and select partners

Courtship is a time of stress for both the male and the female. They mate in response to powerful urges, and at mating the female tends to be frightened, the male aggressive. These conflicting moods or attitudes must be overcome. The displays that precede mating in many species are a series of signals, the main function of which is to suppress moods of fear and aggression and to synchronize and intensify the partners' desire to mate. Among insects and spiders, for example, courtship behavior often reduces the female's feeding urge, which might otherwise result in the courting male being treated as prey. Courtship is also concerned with mutual recognition; it ensures that the mating animals are of the same species.

Complicated courtship rituals have probably evolved from ordinary behavior such as cleaning, feeding, and nest building. But in most cases these original activities have become ritualized almost beyond recognition. One part of a bird's ritual, for example, may have evolved from feeding the young, but all that survives is the forward movement of the head, repeated many times, perhaps interspersed with other gestures.

The mandarin duck performs drinking and preening actions in its courtship display, as do several other species of ducks. Both actions are made more dramatic by the male's long, colorful head plumage and enlarged wing feathers, which are symbolically touched in a mock preening gesture.

Courtship habits within a group of animals vary greatly. Fish with simple life cycles, which normally swim in schools—such as whitefish of the genus *Coregonus*—fertilize eggs outside the female's body and exercise no parental care. The mating fish simply swim together and release sperm and eggs into the water. On the other hand, fish such as cichlids set up territories, often have internal fertilization, and care for their newborn young.

Song, dance, and color display

Most birds have a poor sense of smell, and they generally use song and visual signals to establish contact. Courtship display is more highly developed and spectacular in birds than in any other group of animals. With a few exceptions, the male bird has the more colorful plumage and performs the display, which is adapted to its habitat. Reed warblers, living in dense reed beds where the range of vision is limited, advertise their presence mainly by their songs. Species living in open country have visual displays, such as the high-stepping dance of the ostrich.

Bright colors, or special breeding plumage, add impact to the courtship signals of birds. The male blue bird of paradise is only medium-sized, but appears much larger when it raises its azure blue wings and long black tail feathers. Alternating movements of approach by the male and retreat by the female have evolved into dances in which these movements are often exaggerated and rhythmically repeated.

Correct species recognition is particularly important where many closely related species live near to one another. In such situations, each species has evolved displays that are strikingly different from those of neighboring species. Male fireflies produce a "language" of coded flashing lights. Where several species share a habitat the codes differ markedly from one species to another.

Reducing aggression

The courtship displays of many animals involve actions similar to threats. The male, having claimed a territory, is naturally aggressive toward any intruder, and the female is liable to be attacked unless she lessens his hostility by her submissiveness. Male and female black-headed gulls are alike in color and display. When they pair, each partner first adopts a head-down threatening attitude. Then each reduces the implication of threat in the posture by standing beside its mate and tilting up its bill. Finally, each bird turns away its threatening face mask as a gesture of appeasement.

Some displays counteract aggression by substituting another mood that conflicts with it. A female robin adopts the begging posture of a young bird, apparently arousing the male's parental instinct and thus reducing its aggression. Male owls, which are smaller and less powerful than the females, often offer the females a gift of food and thus avoid being attacked. In the elaborate courtship dance of the great crested grebe, which takes place on water, both the male and the female dive to collect a symbolic present of weed for each other.

Male spiders and mantises, which are in danger of being eaten by their mates, also behave in a way that reduces the female's hunting drive. One spider, *Pisaura mirabilis*, courts the female by offering her a fly wrapped in silk. Another species, *Xysticus cistatus*, takes the precaution of grasping one of the female's legs and sticking her to the ground with silk before mating; later she struggles free. Sometimes the female praying mantis's aggressiveness is not sufficiently subdued by the male's ritual wooing and she bites off his head.

The importance of scent

Female moths that are ready to mate attract males with a potent scent called a pheromone. The feathery antennae of the males are especially sensitive to pheromones, which they can detect three miles away downwind.

Most mammals have a good sense of smell, and scent often plays an important role in their courting behavior. Female mammals become sexually receptive at about the time they ovulate, and this condition is often indicated by their smell.

Courting aggressively

Preparing to mate, the male Siamese fighting fish builds a nest of mucus-covered air bubbles that stick together and float as a raft on the surface. If the female does not respond, he bumps and bites her until she does. Then he wraps himself around her, turning her upside-down

In this position, the male discharges his milt, or sperm. The female lays her eggs into the milt

The male leaves the female, swimming below her, and catches the falling eggs in his mouth

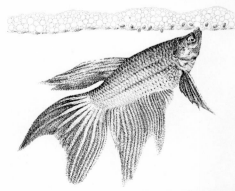

He sticks the eggs, coated with mucus, to the bubble nest, which he then guards for three or four days until the young fry hatch

Presenting a gift The male great egret, like male birds of several other species, brings small "gifts" of nest material to present to the female

Mating mantises (left) The male mantis *Sphodromantis gastrica* of southern Africa is in constant danger of being treated as prey by the more aggressive female. The male ritually identifies himself to the female. Occasionally this is not enough, and during the act of mating, she may turn on the male and devour him

Testing for mating readiness Like most four-footed mammals, waterbucks are alerted by their sense of smell that courtship can commence

349

Caring for the young

Animals that produce only one or a few offspring usually give them a great deal of care. But species that lay numerous eggs give their offspring no care

Having produced their young, many species of animals have nothing more to do with them. Many water-living animals, such as sea urchins, discharge their eggs and sperm into the water, and the fertilized eggs develop among the plankton before settling on the sea bottom. The young fend for themselves from birth, and many die before reaching maturity. But they are produced in such large numbers that the survival of the species is ensured.

Female insects often seek out and lay their eggs on the correct food plants for the larvae to feed on when they hatch, but after this the relationship between the adults and their young ends.

Spiders take more care of their young. Some spin egg nests, and some guard their eggs, although the young leave after they hatch. Wolf spiders of the Lycosidae family carry their eggs and young around with them, attached by a silk thread to their spinnerets, or spinning organs.

Some animals ensure care for their young by foisting them on other animals—a habit known as brood parasitism. Beetles of the genus *Lomechusa* crawl into ants' nests and lay eggs among the ant grubs; after hatching, the beetle larvae are fed by worker ants.

Birds of the duck, weaver, cowbird, and cuckoo families include species whose young are fostered by other birds. Brood parasitism is possible only if the host is not rare and if it builds a nest that is easy to enter. Host and parasite must have similar incubation periods and eat similar food.

The egg producers

The social lives of many ants, bees, and wasps are focused around one or more egg-producing females, or queens. Parental care in these species is indirect because it is the workers, sterile daughters of the queen, who look after the larvae.

The parental behavior of fish follows the general rule that the fewer eggs laid, the greater care they receive. Those fish that produce vast quantities of eggs simply lay the eggs, then abandon them to the mercy of the environment. One, the turbot, lays several million eggs at once. But such fish living near the shore, amid strong currents, do tend to produce heavy eggs that stick to the bottom.

Fish that produce smaller numbers of eggs have evolved various types of guarding behavior. Many gobies, blennies, and lump suckers deposit their eggs in empty shells and the male mounts guard over them. The male lump sucker guards the eggs—about 100,000 of them—against predators, and fans the egg mass with his fins to circulate oxygen-carrying water through it.

Mouth brooding, in which one of the parents keeps the eggs and sometimes the newly hatched young in its mouth, is found among both marine and freshwater fish. Many female cichlids protect their brood in this way. The male Australian cardinal fish carries about 150 young in its mouth.

The young of some birds, such as waterfowl, are hatched at an advanced stage of development. But most birds produce helpless young, which must be kept warm, fed, and cleaned.

Both parents usually take turns incubating the eggs. Since a brooding bird is reluctant to leave its eggs, birds have evolved elaborate nest-relieving ceremonies, which help to ensure that the correct bird takes over the task. Gentoo penguins, for example, bow to each other before changing places.

Some species go even further in cooperative care. Second broods of moorhens are raised both by parents and by any young from the first brood that are still nearby.

A young animal has special signals that tell its parents when it needs food, warmth, or protection. A hungry fledgling gapes, and the parent bird responds by filling the open mouth with food. In some birds the mouth-opening is a response to the movement of the nest when a parent lands or, later, to the sight of the parents.

Litter size and life style

Animals with different ways of life often have different numbers of offspring. Many rodents bear large litters of helpless young in the shelter of a nest, while hooved mammals usually bear well-developed young that can walk soon after birth. Most primates have single offspring that can cling to the mother's fur as she moves about.

A long period of parental care is typical of most mammals. A young mammal is utterly dependent on its mother for milk, and she cares for it almost exclusively. Most newborn mammals are licked clean by the mother. In many cases a female mammal that has been prevented from licking her newborn does not recognize it as her own, nor will she care for it.

How long to maturity

How long a young mammal is cared for by its parents depends on its maturity at birth and its rate of development. This period is shortest among small insectivores, such as the house shrew, which is weaned at 17 days and is sexually mature about two weeks later. It is longest among carnivores and primates. A lion cub, for example, cannot kill its own prey until it is about two years old; and in the higher primates parental care continues even longer.

In carnivores and primates, play is an important method of learning about the outside world. In playing with parents, brothers, and sisters, the young animal learns more efficient ways of moving about and catching prey, or escaping from enemies, and it also learns how to respond correctly to members of its own species.

Infant travelers The young of many species of herd animals, such as the hartebeest, can stand and walk almost immediately after birth. This means they can keep up with the herd, thus gaining protection from predators

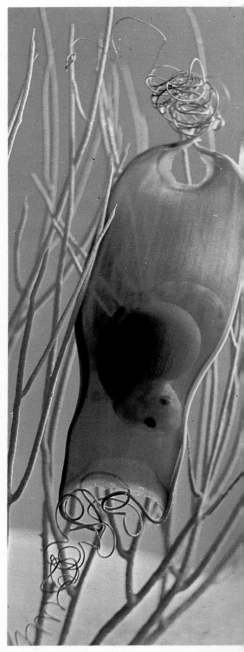

Abandoned yet protected The eggs of the swell shark, enclosed in horny capsules known as mermaid's purses, are attached to an underwater plant and left to develop and hatch without any form of parental care

Dependent on the mother The young Japanese macaque remains with its mother for two to three years. Such a prolonged period of parental care is common among primates, such as monkeys, apes, and man. The future rank of a young animal is dependent on the status of its mother. The infant of a dominant female macaque is likely to assume a similar role in adult life. An important part of the relationship between parents and offspring in macaques—and in baboons, apes, and man—involves play. Through playing, the young animal learns how to communicate with other members of the same species. This and other forms of interaction establish its position in the hierarchy of the group in which it lives

Migrating to feed and breed

Every year Arctic terns make a round-trip journey of 24,000 miles over the featureless ocean. They and other migratory birds are expert navigators

True migration is the two-way seasonal journey animals make from one area to another. These regular annual movements are different from the irregular irruptions of many northern birds, such as waxwings and snowy owls, and of mammals such as lemmings. Irruption is a little-understood phenomenon in which some species periodically break out of their usual habitat in the northern coniferous forest. These irruptions tend to occur at three- or four-year intervals, and may be caused by high population levels, poor food crops, or a combination of both. The nomadic habits of other animals, especially desert animals such as locusts, also differ from true annual migrations.

Migrating mammals

Many mammals migrate. Some North American caribou travel about 700 miles along regular routes between their tundra breeding grounds and their winter home, in the more sheltered coniferous forests to the south.

Migration is common among mammals that live in the sea. During the southern summer, from November to April, humpback whales feed in the southern ocean, which is rich in krill, but in winter they swim thousands of miles northward into the Atlantic, Pacific, and Indian oceans to breed in tropical waters.

Fish migrations

Fish, too, migrate to spawn or feed. Tuna, or tunny, spawn in the Mediterranean Sea and disperse as far north as Norway in the summer. An albacore was caught 550 miles southeast of Tokyo 11 months after it had been tagged off Los Angeles, almost 5000 miles away.

Ocean species that breed in freshwaters, such as the Atlantic salmon, migrate nearly 2000 miles to spawn. Atlantic freshwater eels spawn in the Sargasso Sea, and the young migrate to European and North American rivers, where they mature.

Aerial migrations

Some butterflies make seasonal journeys. One of the best known is the North American monarch, which travels each year from Canada and the northern United States to Florida and Mexico to breed. Monarchs can travel as much as 80 miles a day without stopping. South of the Sahara there are several species of migratory butterflies, such as *Libythea labdaca* of West Africa, which moves southward in the rainy season between February and May and returns between October and December.

Regular annual migrations are made mainly by birds of the northern temperate zone, which fly south in autumn to new feeding grounds and return to the north in spring to breed.

Migration probably originated when birds from warmer climates moved north or south to higher latitudes where food was plentiful, but were forced to withdraw when winter came.

The urge to fly in a particular direction is often stimulated by the decreasing length of daylight in autumn and increasing light in the spring. These external factors cause internal hormonal changes, increasing restlessness, and the accumulation of reserves of fat—up to half the body weight of the bird—which act as fuel for the long journey.

One of the most spectacular of all European migrants, the white stork, takes either a southwesterly path from the Netherlands to Spain, Gibraltar, and over the sea to Africa, or a southeasterly course from east of the Elbe River through Asia Minor and then south into Africa—a journey of up to 8000 miles.

How migrant birds navigate

Daytime migrants, such as ducks and geese, tend to travel in flocks, and geese are thought to make use of traditional routes taken in previous years by some members of the flock. For example, Ross's goose, which breeds in the Canadian Arctic, migrates south, then turns west in Montana and crosses the Rocky Mountains in order to reach its wintering grounds in California.

Hundreds of experiments with ringed birds have been carried out to test the homing abilities of birds over unknown territory. Groups of Manx shearwaters that had nested on the island of Skokholm, off the Welsh coast, were sent in closed boxes to the Swiss Alps, Venice, Boston, and a ship near the Faeroe Islands in the North Atlantic. Almost all of the birds, on being released under a clear sky, oriented themselves precisely and flew in direct lines back to Skokholm.

Experiments have also shown that birds traveling by day use the sun as a compass, and those traveling by night navigate by the stars. Caged starlings that can see the sun try to fly in the direction they would take if migrating. But if the sun is reflected into the cage at a different angle, they immediately realign themselves to its apparently new position. Night-flying buntings placed in a planetarium use the stars for guidance, but become disoriented when the stars are blacked out.

On nonstop flights lasting several days, birds must change from solar to stellar navigation. Experiments seem to prove that birds possess a sense, comparable to a built-in clock, by which they are able to compensate for changes in the angle of the sun at various times of day and in the position of the stars.

Radar can be used to plot the paths of migrating birds. It is now fairly certain that most birds do not fly low in the sky; some birds fly at a height of 2000 feet, and climb even higher to avoid clouds.

Migrating to breed Snow geese take off in a mass from a lake in California. These geese winter in the southern United States along the coasts of the Gulf of Mexico and the Pacific. They migrate in a high, broad V-formation to their breeding grounds above the timberline in northern Canada

Migrant butterflies In winter monarch butterflies migrate from the northern United States and Canada and congregate in vast numbers to breed along the Gulf of Mexico in Florida and Mexico. Their breeding grounds must contain the plant milkweed, for the larvae feed on its leaves. They fly north again in the spring

Migrating to new pasture Toward the end of the rainy season in Tanzania, huge herds of wildebeests in the Serengeti National Park join together and migrate westward in search of new grazing lands in which to spend the dry season. The animals mate during this migration and the young are born on the return trip to the grasslands

Inheritance and learning

The genes of an animal, inherited from its parents, and the environment in which it grows up, interact to structure behavior

If an animal is to survive, certain behavior patterns must function from birth. For example, a baby chimpanzee sucks its mother's milk and a newborn hedgehog erects its bristles when danger threatens. Sometimes such immediately functional behavior patterns are termed instincts, but that word has so many meanings and connotations that many scientists no longer use it.

Other kinds of behavior obviously require practice or some other form of learning to be perfected and integrated into a functional whole. Birds denied any practice in flying from the time of hatching can maintain themselves in the air when they are tossed into it for the first time, but they must learn how to land and take off, and must practice to acquire the art of flying in wind and using air currents for lift.

The physiological structures underlying behavior are structured both by genetic endowment and by environmental conditions in interaction. Learning is thought to be a special kind of modification of the nervous system due to experience with particular environmental conditions. Because every member of a species behaves in the same way does not mean that the behavior has not been influenced by learning: if the immediate environment is the same for all individuals in the species, each may learn in the same fashion.

The genetic control of behavior

In the development of some behavior, the inherited genes allow for great latitude in environmental conditions, so that all members of a species, no matter where they live, look and behave quite similarly. Ants, bees, wasps, and many other invertebrates have behavior that is little modified by individual experience.

Comparison of the behavior of crossbred animals with that of their parents shows the degree of genetic control. If Fischer's lovebird, which carries nesting material in its bill, is crossed with the closely related peach-faced lovebird, which tucks twigs into its rump feathers at nesting time, the resulting offspring does not know which method of carrying to adopt. Only after about three years does it learn to carry nesting material in its beak.

Early experience and imprinting

Young birds such as ducks, geese, and game birds, which leave the nest and run about as soon as they hatch, often attach themselves to whatever happens to be acting as parent during their first few days of life; such special learning is called imprinting.

In most cases it is the true parent that is imprinted on the young birds. But substitute parents can easily be imprinted. Goslings readily follow a man in preference to their own mother provided the man is the first moving thing the newly hatched birds see.

The ability to differentiate between the sexes must be specifically learned in some animals. Young cock zebra finches learn to tell the difference between cocks and hens when they are 35 or 40 days old. If they are isolated before this time, they later court cocks and hens indiscriminately.

Some birds produce their correct songs during the breeding season without having heard other members of the species sing. But in other birds learning and experience play an important part. When cock chaffinches are about 11 months old they compete with one another in developing their songs. A young cock chaffinch reared out of earshot of other chaffinches produces a song of normal length but without the usual phrases and elaborations. It appears that it has to hear other mature chaffinches singing in order to produce the correct song.

Most mammals depend on smell in their social responses, and it seems likely that the smell of their parents becomes imprinted on the young. Even such factors as texture—the "feel" of the mother—can influence the behavior of a young mammal. A young rhesus monkey offered a choice between two artificial "mothers," one covered with cloth and one made from wire, returns to the softer cloth parent when startled, even if it has been fed on the wire "mother."

Reactions to key stimuli

Animals respond to certain key stimuli. The color red is such a powerful stimulus to a cock robin during the breeding season that it will attack a stuffed robin or even a bunch of red feathers as a territorial rival. Similarly, herring gulls recognize their own eggs by a combination of stimuli, including size and shape, and when given a choice prefer round eggs to angular ones and large eggs to small.

It is possible to exaggerate a stimulus artificially until an animal finds it irresistible. If presented with an artificial egg, many times larger than its normal egg, a herring gull attempts to incubate the larger egg in preference to its own.

No behavior is completely new, because an animal can adapt only existing abilities. Blue tits and other birds have learned to peck open milk bottle tops, but their movements are similar to those they use in peeling bark from trees with their bills.

Trained animals also use basic movements, postures, or skills that they employ in the wild. Some wild chimpanzees use sticks as weapons or for extracting insects from holes. Zoo chimpanzees probably use these natural skills when they push one stick into another to make a single pole that is long enough to retrieve food placed outside their cage.

"Talking" birds, such as the Indian hill mynah, appear to learn sounds they would never normally utter, but their ability to mimic comes naturally.

Evoking a pecking response The herring gull chick pecks at the red spot near the tip of its parent's bill. Stimulated by the pecking action, the parent regurgitates food Even a cardboard model of a bird's head, if it has the red spot, will produce this pecking response in the chick

Learning to sing

Zoologists, studying animal behavior, record bird songs in the form of a sound spectrogram. This spectrogram shows the song of a mature wild male chaffinch. It has a complex, varying pattern, corresponding to the elaborate warbling, trills, and flourishes of the song with which the bird proclaims its territory

A male chaffinch reared in the laboratory out of earshot of other chaffinches has a much simpler song than the wild chaffinch's, as shown by its less elaborate sound spectrogram. It has the ability to sing, but cannot manage the subtle variations that are characteristic of the wild bird's song

Spinning different webs Many spiders, such as the orb spider (left), spin geometrical webs, but others make flat webs (right) with the strands randomly arranged. Radiating throughout the orb web is a sticky and elastic thread that ensnares the spider's prey

Providing food for future offspring After building a mud nest, the mason wasp stocks it with a paralyzed moth caterpillar, which is dragged to the nest. Then an egg is laid on top of it and the nest is sealed. When the egg hatches, the wasp grub eats the food supply provided by its parent

355

Man's place in the animal world

Man competes with some animals for food and space, exploits and preys on others, domesticates still others, and is host to parasitic animals on and within his body

Man, the animal species *Homo sapiens,* has been on the earth for about 400,000 years. He is classified in the order of primates, with apes, monkeys, bush-babies, and lemurs. His nearest living relatives are probably the chimpanzee and the gorilla.

Man is inextricably involved with almost every other animal community on earth. He may be a host to parasites, a competitor with other animals, a predator on some, the master of others, and sometimes he may even be prey.

Human activities, such as agriculture and urbanization, have destroyed many habitats of wild animals. At the same time, however, these activities have created new habitats. Fields and hedges provide homes for both agricultural pests and their natural predators. Buildings provide new hunting grounds for spiders, nesting sites for swallows and house martins, and roosts for bats. City gardens and parks provide sanctuary for a great variety of birds.

Many animals help man. Spiders eat harmful insects and bees pollinate flowers. Flies and maggots break down dead organic matter. People often welcome pest-destroying animals into their homes—not only domesticated animals such as cats but also wild animals. Geckos, for example, are welcomed in parts of Asia—in Bengal, southern China, and Indonesia—because they catch insects and mice. They are even said to prey occasionally on small snakes.

Parasites and disease carriers

Man's animal enemies include parasites and vectors—the animals that carry diseases. Parasites that live temporarily or permanently on the skin, such as fleas and lice, are called ectoparasites. Some of these, such as the body louse, merely cause skin irritations; others, like the chigger of the tropics, burrow deep into the skin, causing painful inflammation. Various blowflies and screwworm flies lay eggs that hatch into flesh-eating maggots, resulting in open sores. Some animals, such as the bedbug, mosquitoes, and leeches, may feed on human blood. The adult females of most species of mosquitoes must feed on human or animal blood or their eggs will not ripen.

Internal parasites, called endoparasites, take up residence inside the body. They include tapeworms, which live in the intestine and may grow to 40 feet long, and the African eye worm, which penetrates the eye.

Disease-causing parasites include protozoans of the genus *Plasmodium,* single-celled animals which every year cause more than a million human deaths from malaria. Another protozoan, *Trypanosoma gambiense,* causes sleeping sickness, and those of the genus *Leishmania* cause the debilitating disease known as leishmaniasis, common in Africa and Asia. In parts of Africa many people are infected with wormlike blood flukes that cause the disease bilharzia.

Most of these diseases and many others are transmitted to man by animal vectors. There are 175 species of mosquitoes in the genus *Anopheles,* all of which can carry malaria. Another mosquito, *Aedes aegypti,* transmits yellow fever; tsetse flies carry sleeping sickness; and sand flies pass on the organism causing leishmaniasis. Water snails are carriers of bilharzia, and various mammals, including bats, dogs, and foxes, can transmit rabies. Bubonic plague can be caught from fleas of rats; typhus from body lice; and typhoid, dysentery, and cholera from houseflies. Parrots and pigeons carry the respiratory disease psittacosis.

Drugs, such as quinine and its modern synthetic counterparts used against malaria, attack the parasites directly; insecticides and other poisons combat the vectors. Mosquito nets and insect repellents form physical barriers between man and the vectors, and vaccines confer immunity against some of the diseases.

Competitors for food

Some animals compete with man by attacking his food supplies and property. Animal pests destroy 10 to 25 percent of man's annual food and fiber production. Such pests are controlled directly, by trapping, shooting, or poisoning, or indirectly, by agricultural techniques such as crop rotation. More recently, scientists have exercised biological control by introducing predators, parasites, or diseases of the pests.

Biological control has also been used to reverse disasters caused by man's interference with the balance of nature. Prickly pear cactus was introduced into Australia during the last century as a food plant for cochineal insects, which produce a red dye. When the cochineal industry failed after the development of synthetic dyes, the cactus was left to spread over millions of acres. This plague was finally controlled by the introduction of a South American moth, the caterpillars of which feed on the cactus.

Control by radiation

A modern technique for controlling populations of insect pests involves releasing thousands of male insects that have been sterilized by exposure to nuclear radiation; this technique results in unsuccessful insect matings and therefore fewer offspring are produced.

No animal species relies entirely on man as prey, although several are occasional man-eaters. These include the large cats, bears, wolves, hyenas, killer whales, pythons, and sharks. Animals also kill man by accident or through fear of him. More than 300 species are man-killers in this sense. Every year, about 40,000 people die from snake bites, and, in Europe alone, some 800 people are killed by domestic animals.

Habitat created by man The equivalent to cliffs in man-made environments is buildings

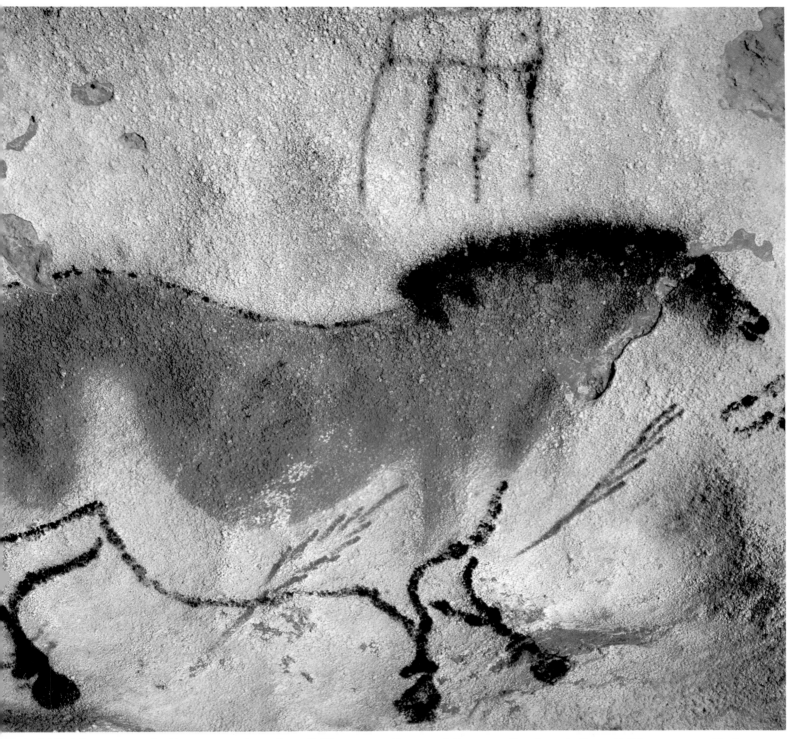

Animal killed by caveman Cro-Magnon man, the earliest representative of modern man, first appeared about 40,000 years ago. He covered his cave walls with paintings and carvings of the animals he hunted. Some 20,000 years ago, this horse was painted in a cave at Lascaux in southwest France

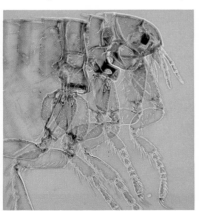

A parasite This flea causes itching and swelling on the human body

Pests Locusts periodically swarm, destroying crops over vast areas of Africa and Asia

Man as prey This eighth century B.C. Assyrian ivory panel shows a lioness devouring a slave

357

Man the hunter

The evolution of man accelerated when he began to cooperate with his fellows in hunting and to master the use of tools and primitive weapons

No one knows precisely when true men first appeared. Ape-men, such as *Australopithecus,* who existed between 3½ million and 1 million years ago, used tools and probably gradually discovered the advantages of co-operative hunting. But the transition from ape-man to human took thousands of generations, leading to the emergence of the species *Homo erectus* about a million years ago. *Homo erectus* made tools and weapons of stone and wood and used fire. He preyed mainly on large animals such as bears, elephants, and wild oxen.

About 400,000 years ago *Homo erectus* was succeeded by *Homo sapiens.* The earliest members of this species were succeeded by men of the Neanderthal type, *Homo sapiens neanderthalensis,* who lived on for a time as contemporaries of Cro-Magnon men, who were the first representatives of modern man, *Homo sapiens sapiens.* Men of the Cro-Magnon type appeared in western Eurasia about 40,000 years ago, possibly having developed from a Neanderthal stock.

Early men hunted creatures larger, stronger, and often swifter than themselves. But they compensated for their lack of strength by using weapons and hunting in groups. In this way men could ambush prey, encircle it, trap it in pits, stampede it over cliffs, or chase it in relays. This ability to work together stimulated changes in man himself, affecting his ways of thinking and behaving.

Hunting for food and to protect stock

The most successful early hunters were the Cro-Magnon men, who recorded their exploits in cave paintings. They invented the bow and arrow, colonized the New World, and domesticated the dog.

Somewhere in southwest Asia, about 12,000 years ago, Cro-Magnon men discovered the principles of herding and agriculture. These discoveries offered alternate means of obtaining food, and so freed mankind forever from being totally dependent on hunting for food.

Even today, however, communities exist which obtain all their food by hunting and gathering. They are found mainly in Southeast Asia, Australia, central Africa, and South America, where people use methods that have changed little in thousands of years. Moreover, all communities, including the most advanced, still catch fish by hunting, though fish farming is becoming more common.

Even when hunting ceased to be a necessity, men continued to hunt for other reasons: to protect their domestic animals and crops, to supplement their home-grown diets, to get meat and pelts for trading, to increase self-esteem or prestige, or for sport.

Once man had domesticated animals and started cultivating crops, his attitude toward wildlife changed. Any animal that preyed on his stock, or ate or damaged his crops, was ruthlessly hunted. In this way bears, lynxes, and wolves were eliminated from most of Europe by the eighteenth century, and from much of North America by the twentieth.

In other parts of the world many predators have been nearly wiped out. Animals that have been hunted to extinction in the last 200 years, either as game or as pests, include the South African blue buck, the quagga, and the Japanese race of the wolf.

Hunting and capturing animals for profit

Animal products, such as meat, skins, fur, feathers, oil, and ivory, have long been objects of trade for use as food, clothing, ornaments, and ingredients in drugs and perfumes. Trade in live animals for pets, circuses, and zoos is also of long standing. Today, with the added demands of scientific research, this traffic is bigger than ever before. Sponges, pearls, and shellac and cochineal from insects are other animal products collected for trade.

Firearms made the killing of birds and large mammals easy and profitable. The most extreme examples of trade hunting took place in North America during the nineteenth century. The passenger pigeon, which once numbered in the billions, was wiped out, and the buffalo, whose numbers were reduced from about 60 million to 541 by 1889, narrowly missed a similar fate. There are now about 30,000 buffalo in national parks in the United States and Canada. Animals in danger of extinction today from trade hunting include orang-utans, which are still collected for zoos although only about 5000 remain in the wild, and blue whales, which probably number about 1500.

In recent years several nations have established game reserves to conserve various species of animals, especially large animals that were in danger of extinction through overexploitation by hunters. Some protected species, however, are selectively hunted, or culled, so that the animal population does not outpace the available food supply.

Hunting for sport

Recreational hunting was long the prerogative of rulers and nobles, who zealously protected their hunting preserves. They hunted bears, bison, deer, and wild oxen, measuring their success solely in the number of animals killed. Today, recreational hunting centers on the skill required in such pursuits as big-game hunting, bird shooting, fox hunting, and angling. In addition to hunting animals in these sports, men now "hunt" animals in the wild simply to study, draw, and photograph them. Wildlife photography is becoming an increasingly popular activity. Sophisticated techniques and equipment, plus skill and great patience on the part of the photographer, produce gratifying results.

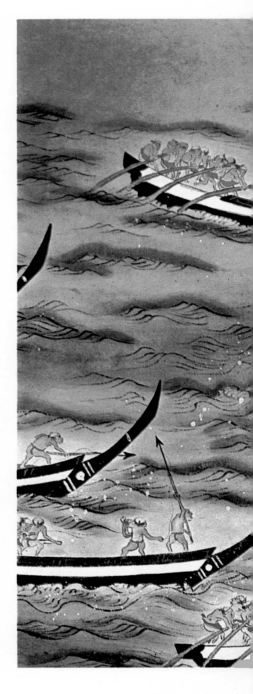

Primitive hunter This Australian aborigine has killed a wallaby with a stone-tipped spear, a weapon used thousands of years ago

Netting a whale The fishermen of Japan at one time caught whales by driving them into nets. As many as 20 small boats, with beaters drumming sticks on the sides to confuse the animal, chased it into a coarse net. Then the boats closed in and the fishermen harpooned the entangled whale

The evolution of man's hunting skills

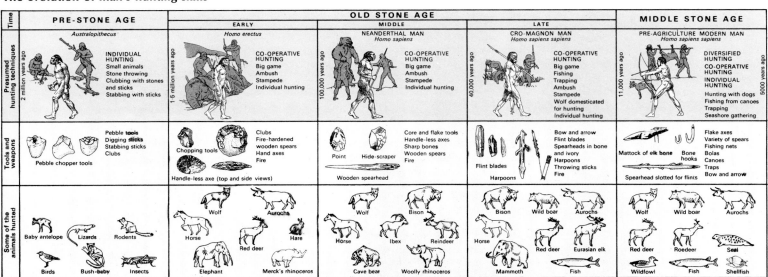

Time	PRE-STONE AGE	OLD STONE AGE			MIDDLE STONE AGE
		EARLY	MIDDLE	LATE	
Presumed hunting techniques	*Australopithecus* 2 million years ago INDIVIDUAL HUNTING Small animals Stone throwing Clubbing with stones and sticks Stabbing with sticks	*Homo erectus* 1.5 million years ago CO-OPERATIVE HUNTING Big game Ambush Stampede Individual hunting	NEANDERTHAL MAN *Homo sapiens* 100,000 years ago CO-OPERATIVE HUNTING Big game Ambush Stampede Individual hunting	CRO-MAGNON MAN *Homo sapiens sapiens* 40,000 years ago CO-OPERATIVE HUNTING Big game Fishing Trapping Ambush Stampede Wolf domesticated for hunting Individual hunting	PRE-AGRICULTURE MODERN MAN *Homo sapiens sapiens* 11,000 years ago DIVERSIFIED HUNTING CO-OPERATIVE HUNTING INDIVIDUAL HUNTING 5000 years ago Hunting with dogs Fishing from canoes Trapping Seashore gathering
Tools and weapons	Pebble chopper tools Pebble tools Digging sticks Stabbing sticks Clubs	Chopping tools Handle-less axe (top and side views) Clubs Fire-hardened wooden spears Hand axes Fire	Point Hide-scraper Wooden spearhead Core and flake tools Handle-less axes Sharp bones Wooden spears Fire	Flint blades Harpoons Bow and arrow Flint blades Spearheads in bone and ivory Harpoons Throwing sticks Fire	Mattock of elk bone Bone hooks Spearhead slotted for flints Flake axes Variety of spears Fishing nets Canoes Traps Bow and arrow
Some of the animals hunted	Baby antelope Lizards Rodents Birds Bush-baby Insects	Wolf Aurochs Horse Hare Red deer Elephant Merck's rhinoceros	Wolf Bison Horse Ibex Reindeer Cave bear Woolly rhinoceros	Bison Wild boar Aurochs Horse Red deer Eurasian elk Mammoth Fish	Wolf Wild boar Aurochs Red deer Roedeer Seal Wildfowl Fish Shellfish

Early hunters preyed singly on small or weak animals. Later, as weapons were improved and cooperative hunting methods were developed, men were able to hunt bigger animals, although they continued to hunt small animals with the old weapons and techniques throughout the entire period covered by the chart. Today, some primitive peoples that live mainly by hunting still use weapons similar to some illustrated here

The domestication of animals /1

Every domesticated animal, whether farm animal or pet, has a wild ancestor. But thousands of years of selective breeding make the line of descent hard to trace

The domestication of animals probably began in a gradual way more than 10,000 years ago, while Stone Age men were still nomadic hunters. Among the animals they hunted were wolves, which, like men, traveled in family groups. In those times wolves roamed widely and existed as many separate geographical races. Everywhere they were a menace around man's encampments, a competitor for the same prey, and a scavenger on man's leavings.

Some cubs were probably spared when their mothers were killed. They were friendly, easily tamed, and useful as decoys, and for these very reasons they gradually became domesticated.

While men were still moving from one hunting ground to another they had few opportunities to tame other species of mammals. But toward the end of the last ice age, about 10,000 years ago, men learned to cultivate wild grains such as wheat and barley, and this led to the beginnings of human settlements. The earliest settlement sites have been found in western Asia; and it is there that wild sheep and goats may first have been separated from their herds and kept to be killed when needed.

From these beginnings the domestication of animals progressed, as early farmers, recognizing that physical characteristics are inherited, started to cross selected animals to obtain a combination of valued characteristics in their offspring.

Effects of selective breeding

Selective breeding accounts for the great differences in appearance between many domestic animals and their wild ancestors. It has enabled man to reduce certain characteristics—such as male aggressiveness toward other males of the same species—which, although vital to the animal's survival in the wild, cause problems in domestication. The physical and behavioral changes that resulted make many domesticated animals dependent upon man for their existence.

The degree to which animals can be domesticated varies widely. The most successfully domesticated species—those most susceptible to selective breeding—are those whose wild ancestors lived in family groups, packs, or herds. They seem to transfer a dependence on the leader of the group into a dependence on their human owner.

How cats and dogs differ

A comparison between the cat and dog illustrates the difference between animals whose ancestors were solitary, and those descended from animals with a social instinct. All domestic cats are probably descended from one or more species of small African cats, and, although cats have been

kept by man since early Egyptian times and have lost much of the savagery of their ancestors, they remain solitary and aloof. Because cats will not become as dependent on man as dogs, they are less likely to work for him, so man has not developed a large range of breeds for special tasks. Dogs, in contrast, have been bred to perform a variety of tasks in widely differing environments.

Dogs are probably descended from the small southern races of wolf. They are sociable, dependent on man, and still ready to run in packs when the opportunity arises. The earliest dogs probably resembled dingos, which are directly descended from the dogs that Stone Age men took with them from Asia to Australia about 8000 years ago.

Some species that are difficult to breed in captivity usually have to be caught and then tamed. These include exotic pets and a large number of animals which have been kept since the time of the ancient Egyptians, such as falcons, cheetahs, and mongooses. Other animals can be raised more easily. They include the ferret—the domesticated form of the steppe polecat—which many peoples keep for hunting rabbits and rats.

But although such animals were first tamed by man thousands of years ago, they differ little from their wild forms, and if released they rapidly readjust to life in the wild. They are also solitary animals.

Dogs bred for work and show

Many modern breeds of dogs differ greatly in appearance, although all dogs belong to the same species. This is the result of many centuries of selective breeding. As long ago as 2000 B.C. the Egyptians had developed hunting breeds, such as the greyhound; working breeds, such as sheepdogs; and more ornamental breeds resembling the modern Welsh corgi and the Pomeranian. The more recent dictates of sport and of the show-ring have led to an increasing number of breeds, such as gundogs and decorative "toy" dogs.

A few of the domesticated herd animals —the camel, the reindeer, and the yak, for example—have not been greatly altered, because their value to man is based on their ability to perform tasks and to survive in a harsh environment.

But most domesticated herd animals have been specifically bred, either to provide a product such as meat or skins, or to act as draft animals or beasts of burden. Generally animals that are eaten have been bred to mature faster, fatten more easily, and reproduce at a greater rate than draft animals.

Many breeds of pigs are the result of long selective breeding. They are all descended from the wild boar, a fierce forest animal. But they differ strikingly from their ancestor in appearance. They are shorter-legged, fatter animals, with curly instead of straight tails; their bodies are less hairy; and they are often piebald. They also have quite different heads; their jaws are shorter, their teeth are smaller, and their eyes look forward rather than sideways.

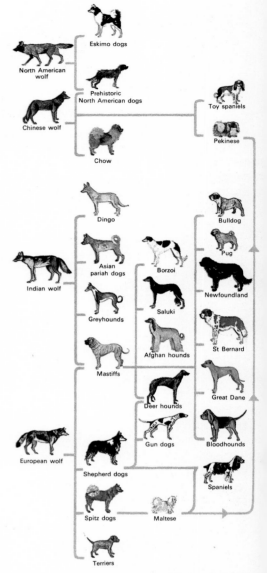

The ancestry of domestic dogs All dogs, even breeds as different as the Pekinese and the St. Bernard, belong to the same species, and the wolf is their common ancestor. All dogs, unless differences in size make mating impossible, can breed both with one another and with wolves, producing fertile offspring. This family tree is only a rough guide to the line of descent of any modern breed because so much interbreeding went on from the time the wolf was first domesticated until distinct breeds were established. The dingo is probably the only purebred dog in the world today

Contrasts in pigs The wild boar (top) is smaller and lighter and has a longer snout than domestic pigs, which are descended from it. It is also much hairier than the domestic species

Gathering honey in the Middle Ages Keeping honeybees in man-made hives was a widespread craft in Europe during the Middle Ages. Honey was eaten and was also fermented to make drinks, such as mead. Until the sixteenth century honey was man's main source of sugar

The domestication of animals / 2

Wild goats and sheep were probably the first animals to be herded by New Stone Age man. Both the wild goat, or bezoar, and the wild sheep of western Asia are impressive-looking creatures, with red-brown coats and great, curving horns. Domesticated sheep and goats tend to be shorter-legged, with white fleece and short or sometimes non-existent horns.

Sheep have been bred to increase the quantity and quality of their wool, meat, and fat. The invention of artificial fibers has undermined the wool trade in recent years, however, and sheep are now often regarded primarily as a source of meat.

Although cattle were domesticated somewhat later than either sheep or goats, they are probably the most important of all domesticated animals. They are exploited for their meat, hides, milk, fat, bones, and horns. Even cattle dung is used—not only as a fertilizer, but in some countries as fuel and in building primitive dwellings.

The European domestic breeds of cattle are all descended from the aurochs, or wild ox, specimens of which existed, in Poland, until as recently as the first decades of the seventeenth century.

Animals bred for work, food, and war

In some parts of the world the domesticated ox is still used primarily as a beast of burden or a draft animal. But in North America and Western Europe many breeds of cattle have been developed, most being used exclusively for either beef, as with the Hereford breed, or for dairying, as with the Holstein-Friesian and the Jersey. Dual-purpose cattle are now produced by mating dairy cows with beef bulls.

In Asia the chief breed is the zebu. Zebus are Indian humped cattle first developed thousands of years ago. They have not been specifically bred for beef or milk. In many places they are used as draft animals, although near rivers and in marshy areas water buffalo fill this role. Recent studies show that the water buffalo, besides being a stronger draft animal than the zebu, is a potentially superior beef and milk producer.

Between 3000 and 2000 B.C. man domesticated the horse. Three geographically separate species were probably domesticated about the same time. In North Africa the African wild ass was domesticated by the peoples of the Nile Valley as a beast of burden. Farther east the Asiatic wild ass, a larger animal, was trained by the Sumerians to pull their war chariots. True domestic horses, however, were developed from races of the Eurasian wild horse, of which the only surviving race is Przewalski's horse. It once roamed in herds across the Eurasian steppes but is now restricted in the wild to a few isolated corners of Mongolia. There are probably less than 50 of these small, big-headed horses left.

The nomadic peoples of the steppes domesticated the wild horse because it was stronger and faster. But it was not until the fifth century, when the Chinese invented the stirrup, that heavy cavalry became truly feasible and breeders turned their attention to producing horses strong enough to bear the weight of heavily armored men. These cavalry horses were huge, heavy animals, such as the old English Black Horse, the original Shire horse, which was similar in appearance to heavy working horses such as the Clydesdale. Working horses are dying out, but the number of horses and ponies used for riding is increasing.

Three Arab stallions

The comparatively light modern riding horses and racehorses owe their origin to the influence of three Arab stallions—Darley Arabian, Godolphin Arabian, and Byerley Turk—which were imported into England at the beginning of the eighteenth century and crossed with some heavier British breeds.

Three members of the camel family have been domesticated as beasts of burden, and a fourth for its wool. The dromedary, or Arabian camel, which is found from northern India westward to North Africa, and the two-humped Bactrian camel of the colder, mountainous regions of central Asia, can withstand harsh desert conditions. They are primarily beasts of burden, but they also provide milk, meat, hides, and hair. In the Andes Mountains of South America, the smaller llama plays a similar role. But its close relative, the alpaca, has been exploited by man purely for its wool.

Several species of wild fowl have been domesticated. Some, notably guinea fowl, quail, geese, and ducks, are usually kept out of doors in small flocks. This is also true of some breeds of domestic fowl, such as the Wyandotte, Rhode Island Red, and Plymouth Rock, which were developed from the Indian jungle fowl.

Giant turkeys bred by man

Intensive selective breeding has also been devoted to turkey rearing. Domestic turkeys are sometimes more than three times the size of their wild North American ancestor, and may weigh over 60 pounds.

The earliest records of bee-keeping date back about 4500 years, when the Egyptians encouraged bees to nest in hollowed-out logs, and then smoked them out to get the honey and wax, which was used for lighting and for making writing tablets. The beehive and the less aggressive nature of specially bred bees make it easier to collect honey today.

The existence of so many domesticated animals has tended to blind man to the possibilities of domesticating other wild species. In the last few years, however, animal breeders have been trying to domesticate the Eurasian moose, the North American musk-ox, and some species of African antelopes, notably the eland. These animals could form an important source of food, and domestication could ensure their survival.

Using animals for farming Four thousand years ago, Egyptian farmers harnessed oxen to their plows. By the use of animal power, larger areas could be cultivated. Domestic animals made an essential contribution to the growth of communities that obtained their food by growing crops

Lapland reindeer Reindeer are herded in Scandinavia in much the same way semiwild cattle and horses are rounded up elsewhere. They provide milk, meat, and hides, and carry packs

The horse in sport (left) As can be seen in this fifteenth century painting, the people of Florence celebrated the midsummer Feast of St. John by holding horse races through the narrow streets of the city. Because the jockeys rode bareback, falls, resulting in injuries, were common

Animals in human culture

**Man's attitude toward other animals
has been marked by curiosity, reverence,
and fear; these emotions have
been expressed in art and literature**

The earliest known evidence of man treating animals in a special way dates from about 100,000 years ago, when hunters enclosed a number of cave bears' skulls in stone chests and buried them in the innermost recesses of a cave dwelling at Drachenloch, in the Swiss Alps. Some of the skulls were arranged in patterns with other bones.

Only speculation is possible about the reason for this ritual, but perhaps it was inspired by a reverential fear of the cave bear. This bear, long extinct, could rear up nearly nine feet, and must have been a terrible adversary to a hunter armed only with stone implements.

Hunting was still man's chief occupation 70,000 years later. This is apparent in the paintings left behind by the people who sheltered from the bitter weather of successive ice ages in the limestone caverns of Lascaux in southwest France, Altamira in Spain, and many other sites. The walls of the caves are covered with thousands of paintings of animals, many of which are depicted as trapped, wounded, or dying.

All the paintings show an acute observation of animal movement and anatomy on the part of the artists. This was natural in a people whose livelihood depended on a profound understanding of animals. To them, as to all hunters, a detailed knowledge of animal behavior was a matter of life or death.

Animals worshiped as gods

Totemism is still practiced by primitive societies in many parts of the world. Members of such a society feel themselves to be related to a particular animal and possessed by its spirit. Different tribes of Australian aborigines accord great reverence to the emu, snakes, or various insect grubs; and the Asmat tribe of New Guinea considers itself to be related to a mantis.

Animal worship in one form or another was common to all primitive peoples. Long before the pharaohs, Egypt was peopled by wandering hunters who regarded wild animals such as the crocodile and the snake as sacred. Later, when a more settled existence led men to domesticate certain animals, the ram, the aurochs, and others were also given divine status.

As centuries passed, man made his gods less like animals and more like men. But for a long time man-animal combinations were held in reverence. The Egyptians worshiped Khnum, the ram-headed god of creation, and the Sphinx, part pharaoh and part lion. Man-animal hybrids such as centaurs (a man's torso and a horse's body) and satyrs (a man's torso and a goat's legs) abound in Greek mythology, in which gods frequently assumed the forms of animals.

Just as often, however, animals were represented as the darker side of creation. In one Greek legend Zeus, regulator of the universe, overcomes Typhon, who represents chaos. Typhon was a monster who terrified even the gods; his body was feathered, a hundred dragon heads sprang from his shoulders, and in his loins was a nest of vipers. The bull-headed Minotaur of Crete was another monster against whom ordinary men were powerless. His death at the hands of Theseus, like many other legends, became a subject for painters, sculptors, and poets.

Animals in books and in zoos

Animals have always figured prominently in literature. A favorite literary device is one in which animals are given human attributes, including speech, and are used to point up human folly or wickedness. This device, which has been used at least since Aesop wrote his *Fables* in about 500 B.C., has been employed in modern times by writers such as George Orwell and cartoonists such as Walt Disney.

Man's fascination with wild animals has led to the development of zoos and circuses. Menageries existed in ancient Mesopotamia, Egypt, and China, and large stocks of wild animals were kept for the arena in imperial Rome. At one point in his reign, Emperor Octavius Augustus (29 B.C. to 14 A.D.) kept 420 tigers, 260 lions, 600 other African carnivores, one rhinoceros, and a large snake.

The practice of caging animals seems to have been universal. The Aztecs of Mexico had been keeping large menageries for centuries before the Spanish conqueror Hernando Cortez saw them in 1520; and during the thirteenth century royal collections were maintained by Kubla Khan in China, and by English monarchs.

Man's emotional reactions to animals are not always rational. Most people, for instance, fear snakes, and think of them as cold, slimy creatures. In fact, relatively few species of snakes are deadly to man, and all are dry and often warm to the touch. On the other hand, almost all young mammals, which are furred, arouse feelings of affection and protectiveness in man.

Animals in medical research

Animals have played an important role in the history and practice of medicine, whether in the bizarre remedies of the Middle Ages or in modern research. Many important discoveries would have been impossible without them; and medical research depends on them in its search for future discoveries, using hamsters and mice in the study of cancer, and other rodents in tests of new drugs and food additives.

The insulin treatment of diabetes arose from the discovery that a dog suffered from diabetes when its pancreas was removed. In 1921 insulin, which is now made synthetically, was first extracted from the pancreases of dogs. Dogs were also used in the development of modern anesthetics.

Circuses In the second half of the nineteenth century circuses gained popularity and big cats, such as leopards, lions, and tigers, provided the highlights of the show. In this American circus poster of 1874, a woman lion tamer holds at bay three species of big cats

Man against animal Throughout the ages, man has pitted his intelligence and skill against the superior physical powers of animals for sport. The chief surviving example today is the bullfight, a popular spectacle in Spain, Portugal, and some Latin American countries

Leeching In the Middle Ages, and later, a favorite method of treating sickness was bloodletting, which was often carried out, as shown in this Dutch engraving of 1642, by using leeches. It was thought that diseases were caused by "influences" residing in body fluids which could be lessened by letting blood

Mythology In a Hindu legend the god Vishnu, portrayed in this eleventh-century bronze, became a man-lion with four arms, to kill the demon king

Upsetting the balance of nature

The delicate balance between the resources of a habitat and the number and variety of animals it will support can be upset by sudden changes caused by man

The balance of nature is constantly being adjusted by natural phenomena, such as changes in climate caused by the ebb and flow of the northern polar ice cap during the ice ages, the gradual drifting of the continents, the arrival of new predators or competitors, and disease. All have forced animals to adapt and over long periods of time have led to the extinction of various animal species. But the recent activities of man, especially the disruption of habitats, can and have suddenly and irreversibly upset the balance of nature.

Early men apparently killed off some of the large mammals of the northern hemisphere, such as the mammoth and the woolly rhinoceros. But since the rise of agriculture and industrialized societies, man's assaults on animals and their environments have increased at a tremendous rate, endangering many species.

Destruction of habitats

Agriculture has greatly changed large areas of vegetation and altered forever the habitats of countless forms of wildlife. The clearing of forests, the cultivation of crops, the spread of grassland, and topsoil erosion have transformed the land. Hunting and the poisoning of pests have disturbed complex natural food chains.

The building of railways, roads, and cities has completely obliterated some natural habitats. The waste products from homes and factories have poisoned the air, soil, and water on which all life depends.

Man's activities have been changing habitats for a long time. In northern Africa, the clearing of trees for farming, first by early men and later by the Romans, probably contributed to the enlargement of the Sahara Desert. The colonization of North America by Europeans and the gradual westward expansion destroyed many habitats.

Recently, expanses of eastern Africa have been turned into semidesert because of overgrazing by cattle. The island of Madagascar was once completely covered by forest; but during the last 1000 years, four fifths of the trees have been destroyed to create farmland. Indigenous Madagascan forest animals such as lemurs are now in great danger of extinction.

Animals introduced by man

Man has taken various animals with him on his travels, sometimes on purpose and sometimes by accident, and introduced them to new regions. The best-known species spread accidentally is the brown rat, which originated in Asia and spread throughout the world. It has become a major pest to man and his crops, a carrier of disease, and a predator that has contributed to the extinc-

tion of at least nine species of flightless birds.

Among the deliberately introduced species are dogs, cats, rabbits, squirrels, various birds, and most other domestic animals. The aborigines took dingos with them to Australia as hunting companions, but the dogs soon reverted to the wild and probably accounted for the decline or extinction of several species of marsupials on the mainland, such as the Tasmanian wolf.

The Javan mongoose was introduced to the West Indies in an attempt to keep down rats. But instead it preyed on indigenous animals, exterminating them, and allowing the rats to flourish.

Domestic animals have been introduced to many parts of the world. Goats, among the most destructive, have completely changed the habitats of the Mediterranean shores and several oceanic islands by eating most of the vegetation, leaving only bare soil or scrub. Goldfish, dropped into Madagascan rivers to beautify them, reverted to their original carplike form and killed off all the other edible freshwater fish.

Pollution of the environment

Man, particularly industrialized man, is the greatest polluter of the earth. The planet has neither the space nor the resources to continue to absorb the explosive growth of human populations. Our poisonous industrial wastes, toxic pesticides, and ever-accumulating garbage are making irreversible changes in the environment.

The pollution of the atmosphere began with man's discovery of fire. Every year countless tons of coal, oil, and gasoline are burned, producing smoke, sulfur dioxide, and what engineers call particulate matter: dust and dirt. Smog, a mixture of smoke, gases, and fog, can cause lung diseases and kill men and domestic animals. Car exhausts contain lead, which builds up in the body. Lead has been detected even in samples of snow taken from the North Pole.

Rivers and waterways become polluted by sewage, industrial effluents, detergents, and fertilizers and pesticides washed off farmland. In polluted rivers the natural plants are killed off, the water contains little or no oxygen, and fish and other aquatic animals die.

Oil discharged into the sea damages much wildlife, especially birds. Hot water discharged into temperate seas from coastal power stations can cause a temperature change that permits warm-water creatures to flourish and naturally occuring species to disappear.

Insecticides have controlled pests and improved the lives of whole communities of people. But some insecticides, such as DDT, persist in the environment and pass through the food chains, accumulating in the tissues of men and other animals. DDT may make birds of prey such as the peregrine falcon infertile, and so threatens their survival. The poison has even been found in the body fat of Antarctic penguins.

Overgrazing Cattle owned by Masai tribesmen have grazed so heavily in East African grassland that some areas have become deserts

Hunted to extinction The dodo, once common on the island of Mauritius in the Indian Ocean, became extinct about 1680 after having been hunted extensively by sailors visiting the island. It was also hunted by pigs and other animals that were introduced to Mauritius by man

Water pollution Foaming agents in detergents pass through sewers to rivers, where they may form clouds of suds. These shut off oxygen from aquatic creatures, and may carry the eggs of harmful organisms

Atmospheric pollution In industrial areas smoke and fumes from factory chimneys, domestic fires, and engine exhausts pollute the air with soot and poisonous gases. One of these gases, sulfur dioxide, can cause and aggravate often fatal lung diseases

Conserving the world's wildlife

Conservation aims at ensuring man's survival by preserving the environment. One aspect of conservation is the saving of wild animals from extinction

Man, like all other animals, depends on the natural resources of his environment. But he manages and changes the environment so drastically by farming and by building towns and cities that there is some danger that it will not support him indefinitely. The human species may become extinct unless environmental changes are controlled in an organized and long-term way.

The environment includes everything around us: land, air, water, climate, and all living organisms. Living organisms interact with the nonliving aspects of the environment to form a complex, dynamic, but fairly stable system.

Nearly all the earth's energy comes from the sun. Plants use the energy of sunlight in photosynthesis, converting simple food substances into a form that animals can use. Plant-eating animals are eaten by the flesh-eaters, and the excrement and carcasses of both groups contribute to the vital natural cycle of circulating nutrients. Interference with this cycle can upset the flow of energy and the basic life-sustaining mechanisms of the world that have evolved over millions of years. For example, faulty management of the environment in many Mediterranean lands, including the cutting down of forests and overgrazing, especially by goats, has resulted in near-desert conditions.

Reasons for conservation

For millions of years, natural changes of climate and geography have caused gradual changes in environments, and living things have adapted to these changes. But man-made changes are sudden. There is no time for living things to become adapted, and the whole balance of nature is upset. Under these circumstances, many species may become extinct.

Economically, many species of wild animals are valuable as sources of food and marketable products, or as tourist attractions. And there are still some wild animals, such as various African antelopes, which could be domesticated to the economic benefit of people in underdeveloped countries.

Books, films, television, and travel have made the enjoyable spectacle of animals in the wild available to more and more people. Most people find beauty and elegance in animals, and these aesthetic values have inspired artists and writers over the centuries. But if wild animals are not protected now, future generations will be deprived of such pleasures forever.

For many people, conservation is a question of moral responsibility. They feel that man has a duty to preserve the biological integrity of the earth, and that if he fails to do so he is neglecting a basic human responsibility.

There are several approaches to conservation: conserving resources such as vegetation, soil, and water, which provide animal habitats; limiting the growth of human populations; educating everyone to the need and reasons for conservation; and managing animal populations in a scientific way.

Conservation is based on the scientific principles of ecology, with biologists conducting field experiments when necessary to collect new scientific information. By proper management of habitats, the natural cycle of nutrients is maintained. This approach to conservation attempts to stabilize the balance between living things and their environment, between plants and animals, and between the plant-eating and flesh-eating animals.

Legal protection and rescue operations

Modern conservation also involves restoring disrupted habitats, by replanting forests and by depolluting rivers or creating new ones. The damming and reforestation of the Tennessee River Valley has restored habitats for many forest-living animals.

Today, many animals and wild places are protected by law, and the reserves are fenced and patrolled by wardens. An example is Spain's Coto Doñana, a reserve established by The World Wildlife Fund for the protection of the lynx.

Conservation must also ensure that the animal populations in reserves do not get too large for their habitats. This may involve selective killing, either by the wardens or by the holders of limited hunting licenses. Excess animals such as antelopes, deer, elephants, hippopotamuses, and seabirds may be killed to provide food for the species under protection.

Where populations of animals are faced with extermination, or individual species with extinction, conservationists carry out rescue operations. Britain's Fauna Preservation Society's "Operation Oryx," launched in 1961, formed a captive breeding colony of Arabian oryxes, from which it is hoped eventually to restock natural habitats.

Game wardens sometimes capture large wild animals on one reserve, by shooting them with tranquilizing darts, and then move them to another protected area. Animals conserved in this way include the white rhinoceros, 150 of which have been removed from an overgrazed reserve in Zululand to other parks in South Africa. Accidental conservation by the movement of protected animals saved Père David's deer, a Chinese species that was taken to Britain in 1900 from the last remaining captive populations in China. The deer later became extinct in China, and was reintroduced, in 1960, from the British stock.

Wildlife management may even make commercial exploitation of a protected species possible. This occurs when the populations of such animals grow sufficiently large. The sea otter and saiga, once in danger of extinction, are now numerous enough to be selectively hunted, the otter for its pelt and the saiga for its meat.

Rounding up gemsboks Wardens in the Namib Desert of southwestern Africa catch gemsboks by grabbing their tails. The animals are then tranquilized and trucked to a reserve, where they are released. Such techniques save animals from local hunters and help ensure their survival

Species under observation Zoologists are studying the polar bear to find ways to protect the species. Here a scientist is taking a blood sample

Head count Wardens of the Serengeti National Park in Tanzania fly over vast herds of migrating wildebeests to count the animals and ensure that they can all be supported by the resources of the reserve

Animals in danger of extinction

Over millions of years animals have become extinct by the process of natural selection. But man's activities have hastened the death of many species

Animals that become extinct because of the actions of man are not replaced by new, better-adapted forms, as are animals that become extinct in the process of natural selection. Many animals in peril today were well adapted to the environment into which they were born; but that environment has been changed or polluted or destroyed by man, or the animals have been hunted to the point of extinction.

During the last 2000 years, about 200 kinds of mammals and birds have become extinct, a third of these within the last 50 years—and the rate is increasing, as man drives off or exterminates animals and destroys their habitats.

At the same time, some animals previously believed to have been extinct have recently been rediscovered. The coelacanth, a fish of a group thought to have been extinct for 60 million years, was discovered in 1938. Ten years later, the takahe, a New Zealand flightless bird of the rail family, was found after it had been presumed extinct. The dibbler, a small Australian marsupial believed to have become extinct in 1884, was rediscovered in 1967.

It is difficult to take an accurate census of animals that live in many of the world's more remote habitats, such as polar seas, barren mountainous areas, or jungles. Scientists may feel that they have under observation the last remaining members of a particular species, when, unknown to them, one or more animals, including perhaps a pregnant female, may be hidden away. This may be one reason why members of a species pop up alive decades or even centuries after the species has officially been declared extinct.

The species whose habitats are indicated on the map below are those in greatest danger of extinction. In each case the total population is very small or believed to be decreasing. The white areas on the map show regions where the activities of man have altered habitats so greatly that the natural life zones have been destroyed or remain only as scattered pockets.

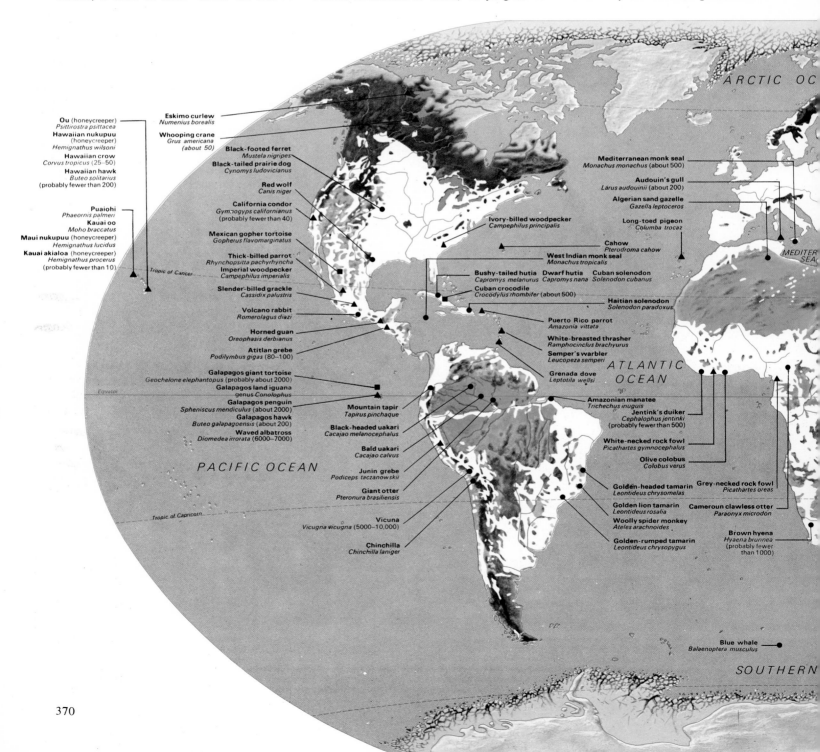

Distribution of human beings

Man is the most adaptable and successful species of animal, mainly because of his ability to modify environments to suit his needs. There are now more than 3.5 billion people in the world, and the population is increasing by about 60 million per year. People are not evenly distributed throughout the land areas. Europe is the most densely populated region, with an average of 150 people per square mile. In inhospitable areas, such as Greenland, there are few people. As the population increases, man either inhabits new areas or industrializes the old. The consumption of the world's natural resources is speeding up, and the by-products of their uses, rubbish and other wastes, are polluting the land, waterways, and atmosphere. First to suffer from the activities of man are animals. Many are doomed to extinction

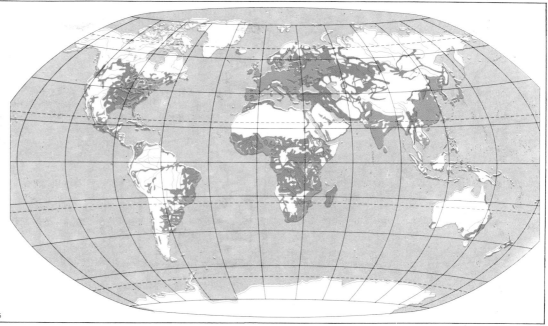

People per square mile:

| More than 50 | 5–50 | Fewer than 5 |

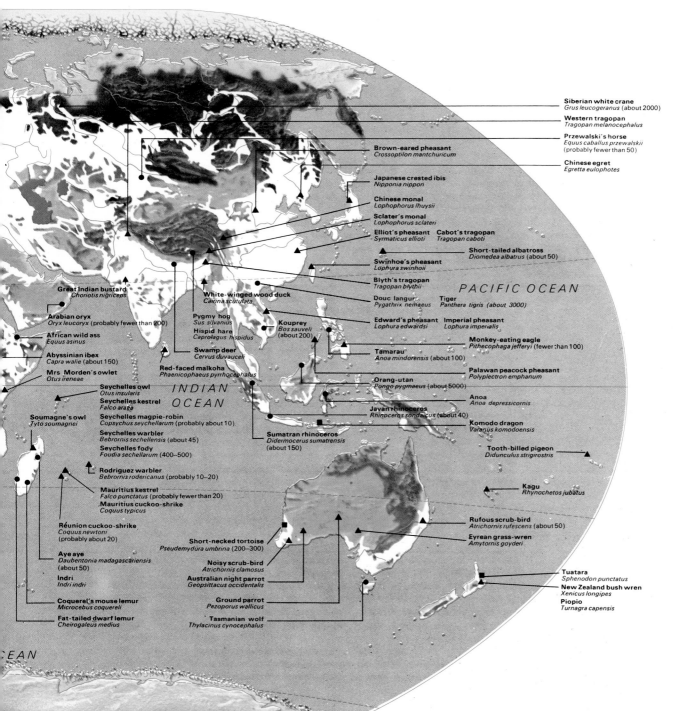

Siberian white crane
Grus leucogeranus (about 2000)

Western tragopan
Tragopan melanocephalus

Brown-eared pheasant
Crossoptilon mantchuricum

Przewalski's horse
Equus caballus przewalskii
(probably fewer than 50)

Chinese egret
Egretta eulophotes

Japanese crested ibis
Nipponia nippon

Chinese monal
Lophophorus lhuysii

Sclater's monal
Lophophorus sclateri

Elliot's pheasant   Cabot's tragopan
Syrmaticus ellioti   *Tragopan caboti*

Short-tailed albatross
Diomedea albatrus (about 50)

Swinhoe's pheasant
Lophura swinhoii

Blyth's tragopan
Tragopan blythii

Great Indian bustard
Choriotis nigriceps

White-winged wood duck
Cairina scutulata

Douc langur   Tiger
Pygathrix nemaeus   *Panthera tigris* (about 3000)

Arabian oryx
Oryx leucoryx (probably fewer than 200)

Pygmy hog
Sus silvanius

Edward's pheasant   Imperial pheasant
Lophura edwardsi   *Lophura imperialis*

African wild ass
Equus asinus

Hispid hare
Caprolagus hispidus

Kouprey
Bos sauveli
(about 200)

Tamarau
Anoa mindorensis (about 100)

Monkey-eating eagle
Pithecophaga jefferyi (fewer than 100)

Abyssinian ibex
Capra walie (about 150)

Swamp deer
Cervus duvauceli

Mrs Morden's owlet
Otus ireneae

Red-faced malkoha
Phaenicophaeus pyrrhocephalus

Palawan peacock pheasant
Polyplectron emphanum

Orang-utan
Pongo pygmaeus (about 5000)

Seychelles owl
Otus insularis

Anoa
Anoa depressicornis

Seychelles kestrel
Falco araea

Javan rhinoceros
Rhinoceros sondaicus (about 40)

Komodo dragon
Varanus komodoensis

Seychelles magpie-robin
Copsychus seychellarum (probably about 10)

Soumagne's owl
Tyto soumagnei

Seychelles warbler
Bebrornis sechellensis (about 45)

Sumatran rhinoceros
Didermocerus sumatrensis
(about 150)

Seychelles fody
Foudia sechellarum (400–500)

Tooth-billed pigeon
Didunculus strigirostris

Rodriguez warbler
Bebrornis rodericanus (probably 10–20)

Mauritius kestrel
Falco punctatus (probably fewer than 20)

Kagu
Rhynochetos jubatus

Mauritius cuckoo-shrike
Coquus typicus

Réunion cuckoo-shrike
Coquus newtoni
(probably about 20)

Rufous scrub-bird
Atrichornis rufescens (about 50)

Short-necked tortoise
Pseudemydura umbrina (200–300)

Eyrean grass-wren
Amytornis goyderi

Aye aye
Daubentonia madagascariensis
(about 50)

Noisy scrub-bird
Atrichornis clamosus

Australian night parrot
Geopsittacus occidentalis

Tuatara
Sphenodon punctatus

New Zealand bush wren
Xenicus longipes

Indri
Indri indri

Ground parrot
Pezoporus wallicus

Piopio
Turnagra capensis

Coquerel's mouse lemur
Microcebus coquereli

Fat-tailed dwarf lemur
Cheirogaleus medius

Tasmanian wolf
Thylacinus cynocephalus

INDIAN OCEAN

PACIFIC OCEAN

Polar regions
Top: permanent ice
Bottom: tundra

Coniferous forest

Temperate forests
Top: deciduous
Bottom: evergreen

Grasslands
Top: temperate
Bottom: savanna

Deserts

Tropical forests
Top: rain forest
Bottom: mountain forest

Mountains

Oceanic islands

Inland waters

Oceans

Areas where man has
disrupted natural conditions

● Mammals

▲ Birds

■ Reptiles

Figures in brackets are
latest population estimates,
where available

PART THREE

THE ANIMAL KINGDOM

Animal types in everyday terms

Invertebrates

Most of the living species of animals are invertebrates—animals without backbones. They entirely fill 25 of the 26 phyla into which the animal kingdom is divided

Fish

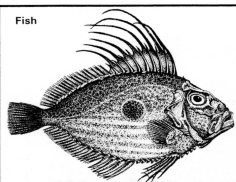

Together with amphibians, reptiles, birds and mammals, fish belong in the sub-phylum Vertebrata—animals with backbones. There are three classes of fish, each as distinct from the others as mammals are from birds, reptiles and amphibians

Amphibians

Amphibians, the most primitive class of land-living vertebrates, usually begin their lives in water and most of the adults return to it to breed. There are three orders of amphibians—newts and salamanders; frogs and toads; and caecilians

Reptiles

There are four orders in the reptile class—turtles and tortoises; lizards and snakes; crocodiles; and the tuatara, a lizard-like animal which is the sole survivor of its group. Other species in the tuatara order have been extinct for 100 million years

Birds

There are 27 orders of birds, grouped in the class Aves. They differ from reptiles, from which they have evolved, by having feathers and wings and being warm-blooded

Mammals

There are three types of mammals—monotremes, which lay eggs; marsupials, which give birth to poorly developed young and usually raise them in a pouch; and placentals, whose young are more advanced at birth

---

Animals are classified by giving them scientific names, which precisely identify them, and by placing them in groups which summarize evolutionary relationships

There are more than a million species of animals in the world, many of them with names which vary confusingly from place to place. The world's largest deer, for instance, which occurs in both Europe and North America, is called the elk by English-speaking Europeans but in North America it is known as the moose, and the name elk is reserved for another deer. This deer in turn is called the wapiti in other parts of North America, and the red deer in Europe. Some animals have an even longer list of alternative names: the puma, cougar, mountain lion, painter and catamount are one and the same animal.

With a proper system of classification, this kind of confusion does not arise. To a zoologist the moose or European elk is *Alces alces*, the red deer, wapiti or North American elk is *Cervus elephus*, and the puma, cougar, mountain lion, painter or catamount is *Felis concolor*.

Naming and grouping

Taxonomy, the science of classifying forms of life, does two things: it names every animal and plant, and it arranges them in groups according to how people believe they are related. The work of taxonomists is never ended, for just as a living language constantly breaks the man-made rules of grammar, so life in all its variety cannot be expected to fit neatly into man-made patterns of organization. Even the basic division of life-forms, into the animal kingdom and the plant kingdom, is not clear-cut; for there are some single-celled organisms which resemble plants in some ways and animals in others, or neither.

The only natural grouping in the animal kingdom is the species, a group which is easier to recognize than to define precisely. It is generally taken to mean a group of animals which can interbreed in the wild and produce fertile off-spring. The lion, the polar bear and the orang-utan are obviously separate species, but the distinctions are not always so clear-cut. Most zoologists, for instance, agree that there is only one species of gorilla, but some regard the mountain gorilla as a separate species. Similarly, it is not universally agreed whether there is one species of chimpanzee or two.

With new facts about animals constantly coming to light, the classification system needs constant up-dating, and zoologists sometimes disagree about its details. Some species have more than one scientific name, and different biologists may, in all good faith, quote different numbers for the total of species.

The 'father' of classification

Despite these difficulties, the definition of a species as an interbreeding population producing fertile offspring is basically accepted—even to the point that populations of animals which never meet in the wild may belong to the same species. The North American wolf and the European wolf, separated by the Atlantic Ocean, are generally regarded as belonging to the same species, *Canis lupus*, because zoologists believe that if they did meet in the wild they would breed and their offspring would be fertile.

Closely related species are grouped into a single genus. For example the lion *Panthera leo*, the leopard *Panthera pardus* and the tiger *Panthera tigris* are all the same genus, *Panthera*. The animal classification system continues by grouping related genera into a family, related families into an order, related orders into a class, related classes into a phylum and related phyla into the animal kingdom. Every animal can be placed in such a classification scheme.

In addition to the seven major classification divisions most taxonomists create intermediate divisions, such as sub-kingdoms, sub-phyla, infra-orders and sub-families. Fish, amphibians, reptiles, birds and mammals, for example, are all included in the phylum Chordata because they have a supporting rod of cells, called a notochord, at some time in their development. But they also have backbones, so they are grouped in the sub-phylum Vertebrata—animals with backbones.

The modern system of classification stems from the work of the 18th-century Swedish naturalist Karl von Linné (1707–78), who gave every known plant and animal a Latinized name, and grouped together what appeared to be similar forms of life according to their physical resemblances. Latin was chosen because it was then the international language of science. Von Linné, whose system gained widespread acceptance after the publication of the 1758 edition of his book *Systema Naturae*, even Latinized his own name, to Carolus Linnaeus.

What the scientific name means

The principles of naming he devised are still in use today. The two-part scientific name of an animal or plant is always printed in italics, and gives first the genus, with an initial capital letter, then the species. The information immediately conveyed by the name *Canis lupus* is that this is an animal of the species *lupus* (Latin for 'wolf'), of the genus *Canis* (Latin for 'dog'). The name of a family, always ending in *-idae*, is based on the name of one of the genera in it. The name of a super-family always ends in *-oidea*, and of a sub-family in *-inae*. So the wolf belongs to the family Canidae, to the super-family Canoidea and to the sub-family Caninae.

The Latinized name of a species may be derived from many sources, according to the choice of the discovering biologist. Often, the name describes the animal: the ptarmigan, a northern bird which has feathers on its toes and changes its plumage to white in winter, is *Lagopus mutus* (*Lagopus* is Latinized Greek for hare-foot, and *mutus* is from *mutare*, the Latin verb 'to change').

Sometimes the name may indicate the origin of a species: the New Guinea crocodile is *Crocodylus novaeguineae*. Or rarely it reflects the name of the animal's discoverer: the Hawaiian monk seal is *Monachus schauinslandi* (*Monachus* is from the Greek for monk, referring to the cowl-like appearance of rolls of fat on the neck; Dr. H. Schauinsland discovered the species). The name may even owe something to a language as unusual as Malagasy, as in the case of the tenrec: *Tenrec ecaudatus* (*ecaudatus* is Latin for 'tail-less' and *Tenrec* is taken straight from the Malagasy). But many names do not have translatable meanings, and whatever the origin of a name, its function is simply to act as a codeword identifying the category.

Groups based on evolution

The Linnaean system was devised merely to catalogue animals and plants according to their physical similarities. But in 1859, just over 100 years after *Systema Naturae*, another book was published that was to bring about a profound change in mankind's ways of thinking about the world. *On the Origin of Species*, by the English naturalist Charles Darwin (1809–82), provided the theory of natural selection, which explains how all living species have evolved from forms of life which existed previously. It became possible to devise a classification system which would not simply group animals according to their physical features but would arrange them in a way that showed how they had evolved.

In fact, much of the system devised by Linnaeus was not altered. But sometimes evolutionary pressures result in groups of unrelated animals having a similar appearance. Linnaeus had put the giant anteater of South America and the whalebone whales in the same major group because they both lack teeth; but in evolutionary terms these animals are far apart.

Since Darwin's time, classification has become more than merely a tool by means of which animals and plants can be named; it has become a summary of their relationships, with animals grouped together when they are believed to have evolved from a common ancestor. The entire classification system is, in turn, a summary of the story of evolution. So far as possible, it begins with the most primitive forms of life and leads on to those that are believed to be the most advanced.

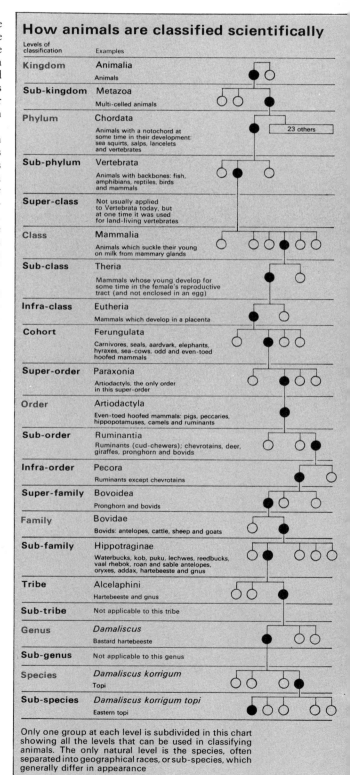

How animals are classified scientifically

Levels of classification	Examples
Kingdom	Animalia
	Animals
Sub-kingdom	Metazoa
	Multi-celled animals
Phylum	Chordata
	Animals with a notochord at some time in their development: sea squirts, salps, lancelets and vertebrates
Sub-phylum	Vertebrata
	Animals with backbones: fish, amphibians, reptiles, birds and mammals
Super-class	Not usually applied to Vertebrata today, but at one time it was used for land-living vertebrates
Class	Mammalia
	Animals which suckle their young on milk from mammary glands
Sub-class	Theria
	Mammals whose young develop for some time in the female's reproductive tract (and not enclosed in an egg)
Infra-class	Eutheria
	Mammals which develop in a placenta
Cohort	Ferungulata
	Carnivores, seals, aardvark, elephants, hyraxes, sea-cows, odd and even-toed hoofed mammals
Super-order	Paraxonia
	Artiodactyls, the only order in this super-order
Order	Artiodactyla
	Even-toed hoofed mammals: pigs, peccaries, hippopotamuses, camels and ruminants
Sub-order	Ruminantia
	Ruminants (cud-chewers); chevrotains, deer, giraffes, pronghorn and bovids
Infra-order	Pecora
	Ruminants except chevrotains
Super-family	Bovoidea
	Pronghorn and bovids
Family	Bovidae
	Bovids: antelopes, cattle, sheep and goats
Sub-family	Hippotraginae
	Waterbucks, kob, puku, lechwes, reedbucks, vaal rhebok, roan and sable antelopes, oryxes, addax, hartebeeste and gnus
Tribe	Alcelaphini
	Hartebeeste and gnus
Sub-tribe	Not applicable to this tribe
Genus	*Damaliscus*
	Bastard hartebeeste
Sub-genus	Not applicable to this genus
Species	*Damaliscus korrigum*
	Topi
Sub-species	*Damaliscus korrigum topi*
	Eastern topi

Only one group at each level is subdivided in this chart showing all the levels that can be used in classifying animals. The only natural level is the species, often separated into geographical races, or sub-species, which generally differ in appearance

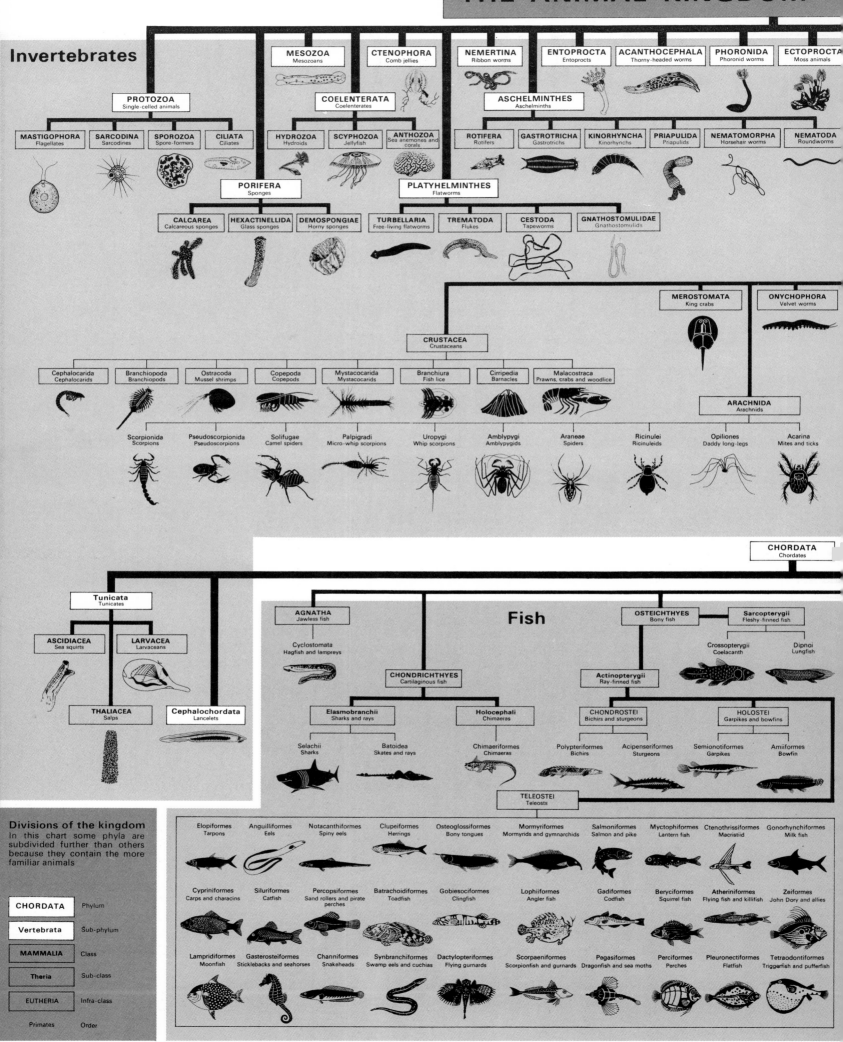

THE ANIMAL KINGDOM

Invertebrates

| MESOZOA Mesozoans | CTENOPHORA Comb jellies | NEMERTINA Ribbon worms | ENTOPROCTA Entoprocts | ACANTHOCEPHALA Thorny-headed worms | PHORONIDA Phoronid worms | ECTOPROCTA Moss animals |

PROTOZOA Single-celled animals

COELENTERATA Coelenterates

ASCHELMINTHES Aschelminths

| MASTIGOPHORA Flagellates | SARCODINA Sarcodines | SPOROZOA Spore-formers | CILIATA Ciliates | HYDROZOA Hydroids | SCYPHOZOA Jellyfish | ANTHOZOA Sea anemones and corals | ROTIFERA Rotifers | GASTROTRICHA Gastrotrichs | KINORHYNCHA Kinorhynchs | PRIAPULIDA Priapulids | NEMATOMORPHA Horsehair worms | NEMATODA Roundworms |

PORIFERA Sponges

PLATYHELMINTHES Flatworms

| CALCAREA Calcareous sponges | HEXACTINELLIDA Glass sponges | DEMOSPONGIAE Horny sponges | TURBELLARIA Free-living flatworms | TREMATODA Flukes | CESTODA Tapeworms | GNATHOSTOMULIDAE Gnathostomulids |

| MEROSTOMATA King crabs | ONYCHOPHORA Velvet worms |

CRUSTACEA Crustaceans

| Cephalocarida Cephalocarids | Branchiopoda Branchiopods | Ostracoda Mussel shrimps | Copepoda Copepods | Mystacocarida Mystacocarids | Branchiura Fish lice | Cirripedia Barnacles | Malacostraca Prawns, crabs and woodlice |

ARACHNIDA Arachnids

| Scorpionida Scorpions | Pseudoscorpionida Pseudoscorpions | Solifugae Camel spiders | Palpigradi Micro-whip scorpions | Uropygi Whip scorpions | Amblypygi Amblypygids | Araneae Spiders | Ricinulei Ricinuleids | Opiliones Daddy long-legs | Acarina Mites and ticks |

CHORDATA Chordates

| Tunicata Tunicates |

Fish

| ASCIDIACEA Sea squirts | LARVACEA Larvaceans | AGNATHA Jawless fish | OSTEICHTHYES Bony fish | Sarcopterygii Fleshy-finned fish |

Cyclostomata Hagfish and lampreys

Crossopterygii Coelacanth

Dipnoi Lungfish

CHONDRICHTHYES Cartilaginous fish

Actinopterygii Ray-finned fish

| THALIACEA Salps | Cephalochordata Lancelets |

| Elasmobranchii Sharks and rays | Holocephali Chimaeras | CHONDROSTEI Bichirs and sturgeons | HOLOSTEI Garpikes and bowfins |

| Selachii Sharks | Batoidea Skates and rays | Chimaeriformes Chimaeras | Polypteriformes Bichirs | Acipenseriformes Sturgeons | Semionotiformes Garpikes | Amiiformes Bowfin |

TELEOSTEI Teleosts

Divisions of the kingdom
In this chart some phyla are subdivided further than others because they contain the more familiar animals

| Elopiformes Tarpons | Anguilliformes Eels | Notacanthiformes Spiny eels | Clupeiformes Herrings | Osteoglossiformes Bony tongues | Mormyriformes Mormyrids and gymnarchids | Salmoniformes Salmon and pike | Myctophiformes Lantern fish | Ctenothrissiformes Macristiid | Gonorhynchiformes Milk fish |

CHORDATA	Phylum
Vertebrata	Sub-phylum
MAMMALIA	Class
Theria	Sub-class
EUTHERIA	Infra-class
Primates	Order

| Cypriniformes Carps and characins | Siluriformes Catfish | Percopsiformes Sand rollers and pirate perches | Batrachoidiformes Toadfish | Gobiesociformes Clingfish | Lophiiformes Angler fish | Gadiformes Codfish | Beryciformes Squirrel fish | Atheriniformes Flying fish and killifish | Zeiformes John Dory and allies |

| Lampridiformes Moonfish | Gasterosteiformes Sticklebacks and seahorses | Channiformes Snakeheads | Synbranchiformes Swamp eels and cuchias | Dactylopteriformes Flying gurnards | Scorpaeniformes Scorpionfish and gurnards | Pegasiformes Dragonfish and sea moths | Perciformes Perches | Pleuronectiformes Flatfish | Tetraodontiformes Triggerfish and pufferfish |

The simplest division of the living world is into the plant and animal kingdoms, though some simple organisms, such as viruses, do not fit conveniently into either. Animals are broadly distinguished from plants by being capable of independent movement and by needing to feed on other living matter, either plant or animal

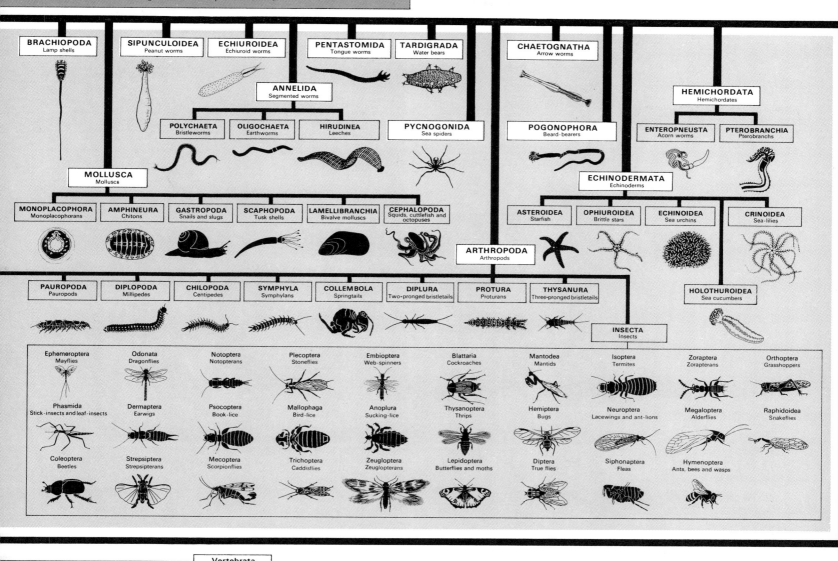

Amphibians

AMPHIBIA
Amphibians

Apoda
Legless amphibians

Urodela
Newts and salamanders

Anura
Frogs and toads

Reptiles

REPTILIA
Reptiles

Chelonia
Turtles and tortoises

Rhynchocephalia
Tuatara

Squamata
Lizards and snakes

Crocodilia
Crocodiles

Vertebrata
Vertebrates

Birds

AVES Birds

Apterygiformes Kiwis
Struthioniformes Ostrich
Rheiformes Rheas
Casuariiformes Cassowaries and emus
Tinamiformes Tinamous
Podicipediformes Grebes
Gaviiformes Loons
Sphenisciformes Penguins
Procellariiformes Albatrosses, shearwaters and petrels

Pelecaniformes Pelicans and allies
Ciconiiformes Herons, storks and flamingoes
Anseriformes Screamers and ducks
Falconiformes Eagles, hawks and vultures
Galliformes Game birds and hoatzin
Gruiformes Cranes and allies
Charadriiformes Waders, gulls and auks
Columbiformes Pigeons
Psittaciformes Parrots

Cuculiformes Cuckoos and turacos
Strigiformes Owls
Caprimulgiformes Frogmouths and nightjars
Apodiformes Swifts and hummingbirds
Trogoniformes Trogons
Coliiformes Colies
Coraciiformes Kingfishers, hornbills and allies
Piciformes Woodpeckers, barbets and toucans
Passeriformes Passerines

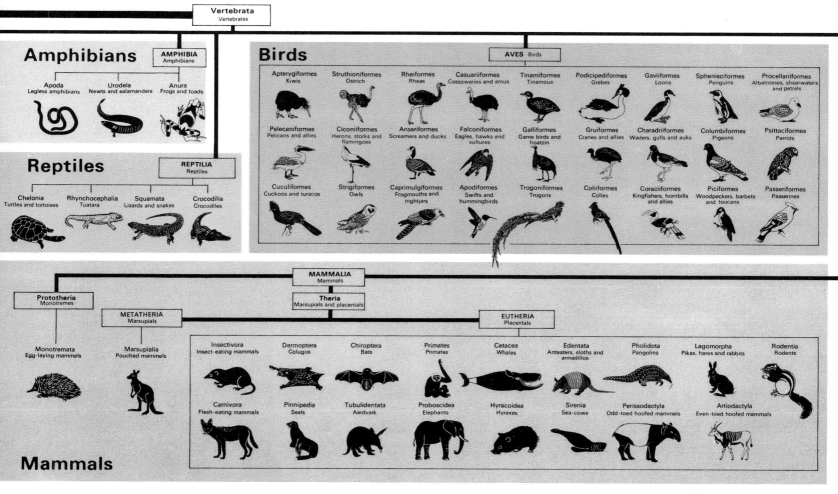

Mammals

MAMMALIA
Mammals

Prototheria
Monotremes

Theria
Marsupials and placentals

METATHERIA
Marsupials

EUTHERIA
Placentals

Monotremata
Egg-laying mammals

Marsupialia
Pouched mammals

Insectivora
Insect-eating mammals

Dermoptera
Colugos

Chiroptera
Bats

Primates
Primates

Cetacea
Whales

Edentata
Anteaters, sloths and armadillos

Pholidota
Pangolins

Lagomorpha
Pikas, hares and rabbits

Rodentia
Rodents

Carnivora
Flesh-eating mammals

Pinnipedia
Seals

Tubulidentata
Aardvark

Proboscidea
Elephants

Hyracoidea
Hyraxes

Sirenia
Sea-cows

Perissodactyla
Odd-toed hoofed mammals

Artiodactyla
Even-toed hoofed mammals

CLASSIFICATION

Invertebrates

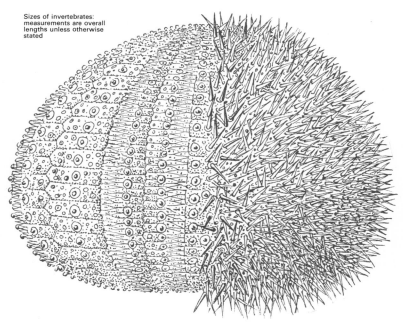

Sizes of invertebrates: measurements are overall lengths unless otherwise stated

The word invertebrates, meaning animals without backbones, is used to describe 95 per cent of the species in the animal kingdom in order to differentiate them from the remaining 5 per cent—the vertebrates, or animals with backbones. Man gives this importance to vertebrates mainly because he is a vertebrate himself. But the invertebrates vastly outnumber the vertebrates, both in species and individuals, and they show a greater variety of forms.

PHYLUM PROTOZOA

Single-celled animals; more than 30,000 species

Protozoans are animals of the simplest type, consisting of only one complex and often specialized cell. In some cases the distinction between the plant and animal kingdoms is difficult to define, and some biologists put unicellular organisms in a kingdom separate from plants and animals. Most of the thousands of species are microscopic, but some are $\frac{1}{4}$ in. long. There are four classes:

CLASS MASTIGOPHORA
Flagellates
The free-living or parasitic organisms in this class have at least one flagellum—a long, whip-like fibre which beats in such a way that the animal is pushed forward. In some species cells are grouped together to form a colony. Reproduction is usually by binary fission—the division of the animal into two or more daughter cells of equal size; in some species a sexual process involving the fusion of reproductive cells occurs. Example:
Chlamydomonas angulosa: found world-wide in fresh waters. It has plant-like cell walls and produces its food by photosynthesis—the process by which carbon dioxide and water are combined into carbohydrates, using the energy of sunlight

CLASS SARCODINA
Sarcodines
These protozoans have mobile extensions of the body called pseudopodia, which are used for capturing prey. Members of the group that move about actively also use them for locomotion. Sarcodines are either parasitic or free-living in water or damp soil. They reproduce by binary fission or by a sexual process involving the fusion of reproductive cells. Some forms bear flagella at certain stages of their lives. Examples:

Amoeba proteus (diameter 0·02 in.): found in fresh waters everywhere, it is the most widely known protozoan. It varies in shape as new pseudopodia are formed, and the cell contains a nucleus and tiny membrane packages called vacuoles, one for food and one which fills with water and then expels it to regulate the body's water content

Actinophrys sol: one of the heliozoans, or 'sun animalcules', it is found everywhere in fresh waters. It has pseudopodia stiffened with silica—a mineral present in many types of stone—projecting all round the cell. Some members of this group secrete a shell of silica, and the ooze covering the bed of warm, deep oceans often consists of a multitude of these shells deposited over millions of years

CLASS SPOROZOA
Spore-formers
These parasitic organisms are simple in structure and, like many parasites, have complex life cycles with several distinct generations and often more than one host. At some stages they increase very rapidly by multiple division of the cell. Example:
Plasmodium vivax: formerly widespread but now uncommon in civilized areas. It is spread by mosquitoes of the genus *Anopheles* and causes benign tertian malaria in man; the malaria parasites attack the red blood corpuscles, and produce fever and weakness as side-effects. The victim suffers a paroxysm (chills and fever) every 48 hours. The fevers usually occur every other day for several weeks, slowly decreasing in severity, and may start anew several weeks afterwards

CLASS CILIATA
Ciliates
These protozoans, some of which are parasitic, have many tiny, short, lash-like extensions called cilia and at least two nuclei, one large and one or more smaller. They reproduce asexually by binary fission and sexually by conjugation, which involves the temporary joining together of two individuals to exchange nuclear material. Example:
Paramecium caudatum: common in fresh waters everywhere, it moves by means of its cilia and feeds on small particles of organic matter taken in at a special receptive point

PHYLUM PORIFERA

Sponges; about 5000 species
Sponges are metazoans (multicellular) that some biologists place in a new kingdom, neither plant nor animal. The cells, grouped together so as to produce a network of chambers connected both to one another and to the exterior, are of different types. They include some irregularly shaped cells which move in amoeba-like fashion and secrete mineral fibres called spicules which strengthen the sponges, and others called collar-cells, which bear a flagellum. Oxygen and small particles of food are drawn into the sponge through the pores by the beating of the flagella. Most sponges are marine but some inhabit fresh water. Reproduction is either sexual or asexual. In the case of asexual reproduction, small groups of cells enclosed in a horny coat are budded off. There are three classes:

CLASS CALCAREA
Calcareous sponges
These sponges have no jelly-like substance between the cells, and their supporting skeleton is composed of chalk (calcium carbonate) spicules. These are either single and straight or have three or four branches. Example:
Leucosolenia botryoides: inhabits shallow coastal waters of the Atlantic

CLASS HEXACTINELLIDA
Glass sponges
These sponges also have no jelly-like substance between the cells, but their skeleton is composed of spicules of silica. In this case, each of the spicules has six branches. Some spicules are often fused to form a lattice structure, giving the sponge a glass-like appearance when dried. Example:
Venus's flower basket *Euplectella aspergillum*: lives in deep seas. It has a white filmy skeleton and a tuft of long spicules holding its body away from the mud of the sea floor

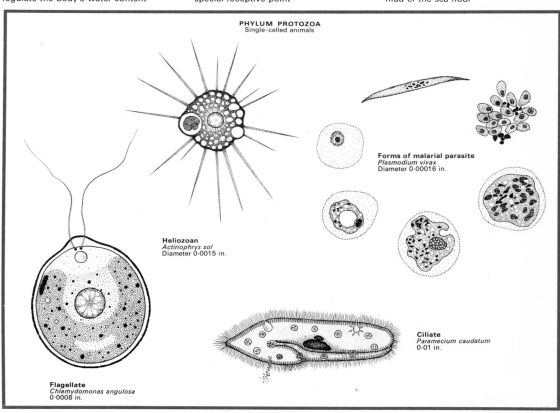

PHYLUM PROTOZOA
Single-celled animals

Heliozoan
Actinophrys sol
Diameter 0·0015 in.

Forms of malarial parasite
Plasmodium vivax
Diameter 0·00016 in.

Ciliate
Paramecium caudatum
0·01 in.

Flagellate
Chlamydomonas angulosa
0·0008 in.

CLASS DEMOSPONGIAE
Horny sponges

All members of this class have a jelly-like substance between the cells, and a skeleton consisting of spicules of silica, or of a horny substance called spongin, or of a combination of silica spicules and spongin. They vary greatly in shape and size. Those with spicules have straight or four-branched ones. Example:

Bath sponge *Euspongia mollissima*: inhabits warm seas, including the Mediterranean and the Caribbean. The dead skeleton, rich in spongin, forms the bathroom sponge

PHYLUM PORIFERA
Sponges

Calcareous sponge
Leucosolenia botryoides
Diameter less than 4 in.

Venus's flower basket
Euplectella aspergillum
Diameter 10 in.

Bath sponge
Euspongia mollissima
Diameter 6 in.

PHYLUM MESOZOA

Mesozoans; 50 species

This is a small and obscure group of parasites whose slender bodies consist of more than one cell, although the total number is small. Unlike most other multi-cellular animals, they lack distinct layers of cells and may not be related to them. They are simple in structure, but have a complex life cycle which includes a single-celled amoeba-like phase. Example:

Pseudicyema truncatum: a micro-scopic parasite in cuttlefish

Mesozoan
Pseudicyema truncatum
Microscopic

PHYLUM COELENTERATA

Hydroids, jellyfish, sea anemones and corals

The members of this purely aquatic group, one primitive form of the true multi-celled animals, have radially symmetrical bodies with two layers of cells surrounding a body cavity which opens to the outside at one end to form a mouth. The mouth is fringed by tentacles bearing cells which can seize, sting and paralyze prey. There are two different structural types: the slender cylindrical polyps attached to rocks or other stationary objects, and the umbrella-shaped, free-swimming medusae. Some coelenterates pass through both forms during their life cycle. Polyps typically reproduce asexually by budding, in which a new animal is formed as an outgrowth of the parent polyp and the division of the animal into two is unequal. Medusae always reproduce sexually. There are three classes:

CLASS HYDROZOA
Hydroids; 2700 species

Typical hydroids pass through both polyp and medusa phases in their life cycle, but some species live only as polyps. Singly, hydroids are inconspicuous creatures, measuring a fraction of an inch, and much of the marine growth on rocks and shells is produced by hydroid polyps. Example:
Obelia geniculata: a colonial hydroid found in seas all over the world. Each colony consists of branching polyps protected by an external covering made of a skeletal material called chitin

CLASS SCYPHOZOA
Jellyfish; 200 species

The medusa phase is the dominant part of the life cycle of jellyfish, although there is also a smaller, stationary polyp stage. Most jellyfish are found in coastal waters. Example:
Common jellyfish *Aurelia aurita*: found in all parts of the world

CLASS ANTHOZOA
Sea anemones and corals; 6500 species

Anthozoans are either solitary or colonial animals in which there is no medusa phase. The digestive cavity of the polyp is divided by sheets of tissue bearing sting-ing cells on their edges. Corals are polyps protected by a hard external skeleton composed of calcium carbonate, which forms the material normally thought of as coral. Accumulations of coral in warm shallow seas form coral reefs. Example:
Brain coral *Meandrina cerebriformis*: its shape suggests the cerebral hemi-spheres of the human brain—a zigzag pattern of troughs separated by skeletal ridges. A colony of brain coral can measure up to 4 ft in diameter

PHYLUM CTENOPHORA

Comb jellies or sea walnuts; about 100 species

Like hydroids, comb jellies have two layers of cells, but they do not exist as either polyps or medusae. Most of them are round, and they live in surface waters, swimming by means of cilia. Some have a pair of tentacles bearing adhesive cells which produce a sticky secretion used in catching the small floating animals on which the comb jellies feed. Example:
Sea gooseberry *Pleurobrachia pileus*: common in the Atlantic Ocean. It is phosphorescent

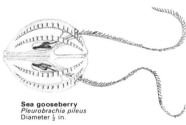

Sea gooseberry
Pleurobrachia pileus
Diameter ½ in.

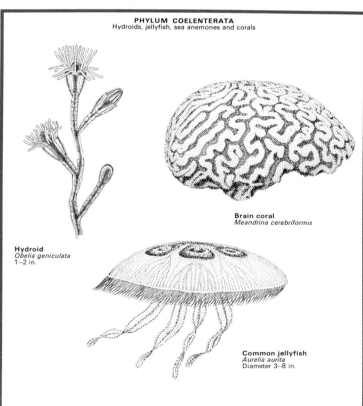

PHYLUM COELENTERATA
Hydroids, jellyfish, sea anemones and corals

Hydroid
Obelia geniculata
1–2 in.

Brain coral
Meandrina cerebriformis

Common jellyfish
Aurelia aurita
Diameter 3–8 in.

PHYLUM PLATYHELMINTHES

Flatworms

These flattened, worm-like animals are unsegmented and have no true body cavity. Both male and female reproductive organs occur in one individual and they reproduce both sexually and asexually. Some are free-living and others are parasites. In free-living forms the cell-layer called the ectoderm is ciliated. There are four classes:

CLASS TURBELLARIA
Free-living flatworms; 1600 species

Most of these flatworms are aquatic and live at the bottom of the sea or fresh waters in sand or mud, under stones and shells or on seaweed. They are usually less than 1 in. long. Example:
Planaria lugubris: a carnivorous form common in fresh water. Like many of this group, it has remarkable powers of regeneration of lost parts of the body

CLASS TREMATODA
Flukes; 2400 species

These parasitic worms are oval to elongated in shape and vary in length from 0·04 in. to 23 ft. Fish are their main hosts. They reproduce sexually.

CLASS CESTODA
Tapeworms; 1500 species

Tapeworms are parasites living in the gut of vertebrates. They are usually long, some reaching 40 ft. Example:
Taenia solium: a tapeworm which is parasitic in man. A hooked front end enables the worm to attach itself to the wall of the intestine and absorb digested food through its surface. It appears to be segmented, but each section is a com-plete individual, with its own reproductive system. Under-cooked pork is a source of infection

CLASS GNATHOSTOMULIDAE
Gnathostomulids; perhaps 80 species

Gnathostomulids are microscopic organ-isms that were not discovered until the late 1960s. They appear to live between grains of sand on ocean beaches through-out the world. Example:
Pterognathia: a recently described genus of gnathostomulids that lives on North Carolina beaches

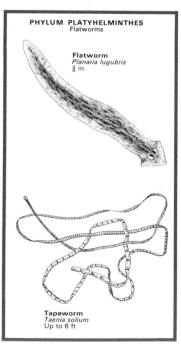

PHYLUM PLATYHELMINTHES
Flatworms

Flatworm
Planaria lugubris
¾ in.

Tapeworm
Taenia solium
Up to 6 ft

Invertebrates

PHYLUM NEMERTINA	Ribbon worms	PHYLUM ECTOPROCTA	Moss animals
PHYLUM ASCHELMINTHES	Aschelminths	PHYLUM PHORONIDA	Phoronids
PHYLUM ENTOPROCTA	Entoprocts	PHYLUM BRACHIOPODA	Lamp shells
PHYLUM ACANTHOCEPHALA	Thorny-headed worms	PHYLUM MOLLUSCA	Molluscs

PHYLUM NEMERTINA

Ribbon worms; 750 species

Like flatworms, the ribbon worms are long and flattened. They lack a body cavity, are unsegmented and have an outer layer covered with cilia. Unlike flatworms, they have an alimentary canal opening to the outside at the mouth and the anus. The sexes are always separate. Some species of ribbon worms are more than 60 ft long. Most inhabit shallow seas and coastal waters. Example:
Tubulanus annulatus: frequently dredged from shallow waters around European coasts

Ribbon worm
Tubulanus annulatus
Up to 20 in.

PHYLUM ASCHELMINTHES

Aschelminths

This group resembles ribbon worms. All taxonomists are not in agreement that the animals listed below actually belong in this phylum; some may belong to another phylum or classes or to as yet unrecognized phyla or classes.

CLASS ROTIFERA

Rotifers; 1500 species
All rotifers are microscopic—few exceed 0·02 in. in length—and live in fresh water. Their bodies are usually transparent, but some, appear to be delicately colored. Some elongated forms live in mud at the bottom of ponds; other more rounded forms are free-swimming; and others are stationary. A ring of thread-like cilia round the mouth provides the propulsion for the swimmers and creates water currents that convey food to the animals. Reproduction is sexual and asexual; the sexes are separate. In most cases, male rotifers are very much smaller than the females. Example:
Hydatina senta: found world wide. The male measures 0·005 in.; the female 0·01 in.

CLASS GASTROTRICHA

Gastrotrichs; 175 species
These are marine and freshwater animals similar to rotifers. Example:
Chaetonotus brevispinosus: found on the bottoms of lakes, ponds and streams

CLASS KINORHYNCHA

Kinorhynchs; 100 species
The kinorhynchs resemble the gastrotrichs but are exclusively marine. Example:
Echinoderes dujardiniis: lives in the muddy bottoms of coastal waters

CLASS PRIAPULIDA

Priapulids; 8 species
These cucumber-shaped animals live in muddy bottoms of coastal waters of the colder parts of the oceans. Example:
Priapulus bicaudatus: found in mud in cold coastal waters

CLASS NEMATOMORPHA

Horsehair worms; 225 species
These long slender worms are parasitic in insects and crustaceans when juvenile, but inhabit damp soil or water when adult. Example:
Gordius aquaticus: lives in fresh water when adult

CLASS NEMATODA

Roundworms; over 10,000 species
All roundworms are similar in appearance, with long bodies, pointed at each end, covered by a thick horny layer, or cuticle. There are parasitic species and species which live in soil, fresh water and the sea. The smallest are microscopic and the largest is about 40 in. long. The sexes are usually separate. Example:
Ascaris lumbricoides: found world wide, it is a common parasite of mammals such as pigs, and sometimes of man

PHYLUM ENTOPROCTA

Entoprocts; 60 species

Entoprocts are rather similar in appearance to hydroid polyps, but possess an alimentary canal with both the mouth and the anus situated within a ring of stingless tentacles. A chalky external skeleton supports and protects the body. Most of the species inhabit the seashore or shallow seas. Example:
Loxosoma saltans: widely distributed on European, American and Asian coasts

Entoproct
Loxosoma saltans
Microscopic

PHYLUM ACANTHOCEPHALA

Thorny-headed worms; 300 species
These are parasitic worms which attach themselves to the host by means of a proboscis with curved spines. Otherwise they are very like nematode worms; they range from less than 1 in. long to about 20 in. Typical hosts are waterfowl which become infected by eating freshwater shrimps which harbor the larvae. Example:
Neoechinorhynchus rutili: a widespread species. The larva attaches itself to the intestines of a vertebrate which has eaten a crustacean harboring it.

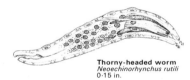

Thorny-headed worm
Neoechinorhynchus rutili
0·15 in.

PHYLUM ECTOPROCTA

Moss animals; about 4000 species
The horny or chalky external cases of these small, colonial, mainly marine animals are branching and are often mistaken for small seaweeds. They possess a lophophore, a horseshoe-shaped fold of the body wall encircling the mouth. Ciliated tentacles round the mouth carry food particles through the gut. Ectoprocts are hermaphrodites and reproduction is both asexual and sexual. Example:
Lophopus crystallinus: a freshwater species with a horny case

Moss animal
Lophopus crystallinus

PHYLUM PHORONIDA

Phoronids; about 15 species
These marine, tube-dwelling animals, like the moss animals, have ciliated tentacles situated on a lophophore. The cilia on the tentacles drive a current of water through the lophophore and plankton is collected in the process. Example:
Phoronis architecta: lives buried in sand near the low water mark

Phoronid
Phoronis architecta
Up to 8 in.

PHYLUM BRACHIOPODA

Lamp shells; about 260 species
These exclusively marine animals are enclosed in a shell and bear a superficial resemblance to molluscs such as clams. Molluscs' shells, however, are placed one on each side of the body, while those of brachiopods cover the upper and lower surfaces of the animals. Typically, lamp shells have ciliated tentacles borne on a lophophore, a true body cavity and, in some forms, a muscular stalk. Reproduction is sexual, and the sexes are usually separate. Example:
Lingula unguis: found in the Pacific from Japan to Queensland, living in vertical burrows in sand and mud. This species belongs to a genus which appears to be very ancient—living forms exactly resemble fossil forms of 500 million years ago

Lamp shell
Lingula unguis
Diameter 4–5 in.

PHYLUM MOLLUSCA

Molluscs
These unsegmented animals, with body cavities and highly developed blood and nervous systems, live on land, in fresh water and in the sea. The body is divided into a head, a muscular foot and a humped back covered by a mantle of skin which is folded to form a cavity used as a lung in some forms. This mantle usually secretes the animal's chalky shell. Molluscs do not have a standard shape, and in an evolutionary sense they are plastic material. The outlines of the body are freely altered as new habits are acquired and new structures are needed. Most molluscs are slow-moving. Reproduction is sexual; the sexes are separate in some species, and others are hermaphroditic. There are six classes:

PHYLUM ASCHELMINTHES
Aschelminths

Gastrotrich
Chaetonotus brevispinosus
Microscopic

Kinorhynch
Echinoderes dujardiniis
0·025 in.

Rotifer
Hydatina senta
Up to 0·01 in.

Roundworm
Ascaris lumbricoides
14 in.

Priapulid
Priapulus bicaudatus
2 in.

Horsehair worm
Gordius aquaticus
Up to 6 in.

CLASS MONOPLACOPHORA
Monoplacophs; 2 species
This class contains the most primitive surviving molluscs. They are superficially like limpets, but differ in that the two sides of the body are symmetrical and in having more organs such as kidneys and gills. This indicates that molluscs might have been originally derived from segmented animals. Example:
Neopilina galatheae: the first surviving member of this group to be discovered, it was dredged up from the depths of the Pacific in 1952. It has a flat, saucer-shaped shell, with a ventral foot, a mouth in front and anus behind. Five pairs of gills lie in shallow grooves between the mantle skirt and the foot

CLASS AMPHINEURA
Chitons; 1150 species
The elongated and bilaterally symmetrical chitons are primitive molluscs, lacking both tentacles and eyes. A broad, flat foot enables them to adhere to rocks and shells. Example:
Chiton tuberculatus : found on West Indian coasts

CLASS GASTROPODA
Slugs, snails and limpets; more than 35,000 species
The members of this large group have both tentacles and eyes. The visceral mass is horizontally twisted through 180°, so that the body is not symmetrical. There is a single shell, but in some forms the shell is very small or absent altogether. A typical shell is a conical spire composed of tubular whorls. All the land molluscs belong to this group, as well as many aquatic gastropods. Example:
Edible or **Roman snail** *Helix pomatia*: a plant-eating land snail of continental Europe

CLASS SCAPHOPODA
Tusk shells; about 200 species
These small marine animals live in sand under deep water. They have tubular shells, and feet adapted for burrowing and long, thin projections growing from the head which bear suckers used to seize food. Example:
Dentalium entalis: lives on sandy North Atlantic coasts

CLASS LAMELLIBRANCHIA
Bivalve molluscs; 8000 species
Members of this large group of flattened molluscs have rounded, oval or elongated shells, and a mantle divided into two lobes, each secreting half of the shell, which is hinged over the animal's back. The large gills strain small food particles from water swept in by movement of the thread-like cilia. There are sedentary and slow-moving forms, many of which are adapted for burrowing. Example:
Common mussel *Mytilus edulis*: clamps itself to rocks by means of sticky threads

CLASS CEPHALOPODA
Squids, cuttlefish and octopuses; about 700 species
These are the most highly evolved of the molluscs, some possessing a very efficient nervous system and eyes. The two sides of the body are symmetrical, and the well-developed head is surrounded by a circle of sucker-bearing arms. Water enters and leaves the mantle cavity through a muscular tubular organ called a siphon, derived from the foot. The shell is often almost invisible or entirely absent. The only surviving genus with a complete external shell is *Nautilus*. Example:
Common octopus *Octopus vulgaris*: lives at the bottom of shallow, warm seas and feeds largely on crabs

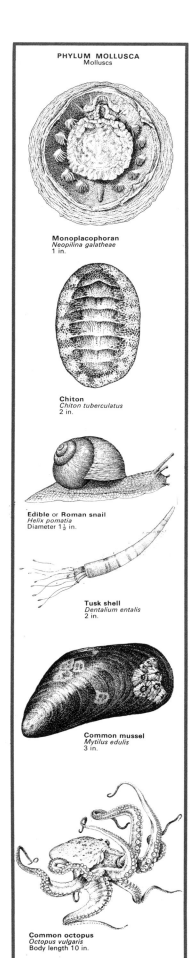

PHYLUM MOLLUSCA
Molluscs

Monoplacophoran
Neopilina galatheae
1 in.

Chiton
Chiton tuberculatus
2 in.

Edible or Roman snail
Helix pomatia
Diameter 1½ in.

Tusk shell
Dentalium entalis
2 in.

Common mussel
Mytilus edulis
3 in.

Common octopus
Octopus vulgaris
Body length 10 in.

Peanut worms; about 250 species
The exclusively marine peanut worms have a well-developed body cavity, but are apparently unsegmented. The forepart of the body can be tucked into the plumper part immediately behind. The animals of this phylum are generally sedentary, living in burrows in sand. Reproduction is sexual and the sexes are separate. Example:
Dendrostomum pyroides : burrows in sand and mud on the west coast of North America

Peanut worm
Dendrostomum pyroides
3–4 in.

Echiuroid worms; about 60 species
These unsegmented marine worms have one or more pairs of bristles similar to those of annelid worms, to which they may be related. The characteristic mobile proboscis cannot be introduced into the mouth. Most echiuroid worms live in sand or rock crevices, intertidally or in shallow water. Example:
Genus *Echiurus* : live in U-shaped, mucus-lined burrows. The mobile proboscis traps particles of food from the sand surface which are brought to the mouth by thread-like cilia

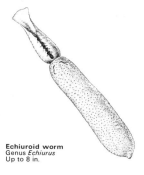

Echiuroid worm
Genus *Echiurus*
Up to 8 in.

Segmented worms
The worms in this group have bodies divided into similar parts, or segments, and the muscular body of each segment is covered with a thin cuticle from which segmentally arranged bristles, or chaetae, protrude. The head contains the brain; the body cavity surrounds the alimentary canal; and the nerve cord runs along the underside of the body. There are three classes:

CLASS POLYCHAETA
Bristle worms; over 4000 species
These marine annelid worms have numerous bristles growing from muscular, fleshy, paddle-like appendages called parapodia. They are either free-moving or sedentary, and vary greatly in structure and way of life. The sexes are usually separate. Example:
Green ragworm *Nereis virens*: an Atlantic species. It is an active burrower, swimmer and predator

CLASS OLIGOCHAETA
Earthworms; over 2500 species
These worms have fewer bristles than the bristle worms and they lack parapodia. All are hermaphrodites, but they usually have a complex reproductive system which eliminates the possibility of self-fertilization. They range in length from a few inches to more than 10 ft. Example:
Common earthworm *Lumbricus terrestris*: found in the Northern Hemisphere. It feeds by swallowing soil and digesting particles of organic matter contained in it

CLASS HIRUDINEA
Leeches; more than 300 species
These parasitic annelids have relatively few segments, a greatly reduced body cavity, and neither bristles nor parapodia. They have suckers at both ends of the body with which they cling to their hosts, plants or animals, feeding on sap or blood. They breed in a similar complex way to earthworms and most species are found in water. Example:
European medicinal leech *Hirudo medicinalis*: formerly used in medicine to suck blood

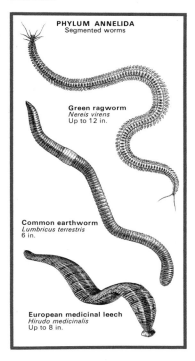

PHYLUM ANNELIDA
Segmented worms

Green ragworm
Nereis virens
Up to 12 in.

Common earthworm
Lumbricus terrestris
6 in.

European medicinal leech
Hirudo medicinalis
Up to 8 in.

Tongue worms; about 70 species
These worms, found in the lungs and nasal passages of vertebrates, are covered by a thick cuticle which is shed periodically. They have no circulatory or respiratory systems. Tongue worms occur mostly in the tropics. Example:
Cephalobaena tetrapoda : found in the lungs of tropical snakes

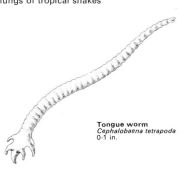

Tongue worm
Cephalobaena tetrapoda
0.1 in.

PHYLUM TARDIGRADA	Water bears
PHYLUM PYCNOGONIDA	Sea spiders
PHYLUM ARTHROPODA	Arthropods

Invertebrates

PHYLUM TARDIGRADA

Water bears; about 180 species
These small, usually microscopic animals are found in fresh waters and on the seashore. They have flattened bodies and four pairs of short legs. They move clumsily and feed by sucking the sap from plant cells. Example:
Macrobiotus hufelandi: a widespread species in the Northern Hemisphere, living in small pockets of fresh water among mosses and similar habitats

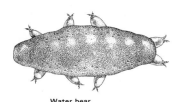

Water bear
Macrobiotus hufelandi
0·0025 in.

PHYLUM PYCNOGONIDA

Sea spiders; about 500 species
This is a small group of marine animals with long narrow bodies and four to seven pairs of legs. The head and thorax are joined and have five segments, and the abdomen is minute. They have no respiratory or excretory organs. Sea spiders are found in all oceans. Example:
Nymphon hirsites: found among algae low in the intertidal zone

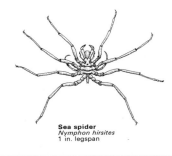

Sea spider
Nymphon hirsites
1 in. legspan

PHYLUM ARTHROPODA

Arthropods
The arthropods form the largest phylum in the animal kingdom. Their bodies, divided into a series of similar segments (like those of annelids, or segmented worms), are encased in a horny layer, or cuticle, which may be flexible, stiff or rigid, and forms an outer skeleton. Some of the body segments bear appendages such as legs or wings, and there is a head or head-like structure bearing sense organs and paired mouth-parts. In the earliest arthropods all the body segments carried appendages. There are 13 classes:

CLASS CRUSTACEA

Crustaceans
Crustaceans, which are primarily aquatic and breathe through gills, have two pairs of antennae, and a body divided into head, thorax and abdomen, although the head and thorax are usually fused. The head part bears three pairs of feeding appendages or mouth-parts. The appendages of crustaceans are usually two-branched. Many crustaceans have oval, unsegmented larvae known as nauplius larvae, with three pairs of appendages. There are eight sub-classes:

SUB-CLASS CEPHALOCARIDA

Cephalocarids; 4 species
These tiny primitive crustaceans were not discovered until 1955. They are shrimp-like, with two-branched appendages on the thorax and abdomen. Example:
Hutchinsoniella macracantha: lives in soft marine sediments and feeds on organic debris. It is found from the intertidal zone to depths of 1000 ft

SUB-CLASS BRANCHIOPODA

Branchiopods; about 1200 species
Branchiopods have flattened, gill-carrying appendages on the trunk; these give them their name—branchiopod means 'gill-foot'. Example:
Brine shrimp *Artemia salina*: found in salty lakes and pools

SUB-CLASS OSTRACODA

Mussel shrimps; 20,000 species
These minute crustaceans range in length from microscopic to over 1 in. The carapace forms two valves which completely enclose the body, like a shellfish. They have only one or two pairs of appendages on their trunks. Example:
Macrocypridina castanea: a fairly widespread marine species

SUB-CLASS COPEPODA

Copepods; 4500 species
This large group of tiny animals—they are only 0·04 in. to ⅛ in. long—forms an important part of the plankton community of the oceans. Example:
Calanus finmarchicus: lives in northern seas; eaten by herrings

SUB-CLASS MYSTACOCARIDA

Mystacocarids; 3 species
This is a little-known group with only one genus, related to the copepods. Example:
Derocheilocaris ramanei: lives between grains of sand

SUB-CLASS BRANCHIURA

Fish lice; 75 species
All fish lice are parasites, living mainly on the skin and in the gill cavities of fish. They have flattened bodies, sucking mouth-parts and no gills. Example:
Argulus trilineatus: has strong claws and swims strongly with four pairs of swimming legs

SUB-CLASS CIRRIPEDIA

Barnacles; 800 species
Most adults attach themselves by the head, sometimes with long stalks, to rocks, driftwood and marine animals. Chalky plates usually protect the body. Barnacles feed by protruding the legs through the plates and using them to filter plankton from the water and pass it to the mouth. Example:
Balanus tintinnabulum: found mainly in tropical waters, often attached to the bottoms of boats

SUB-CLASS MALACOSTRACA

Shrimps, prawns, lobsters, crabs and woodlice; about 18,000 species
Crustaceans of this large group are found in many habitats and are very varied in appearance. The body is usually divided into a trunk composed of eight segments and an abdomen of six, each segment bearing appendages. Some species are only 0·02 in. long, while the Japanese spider crab *Macrocheira kaempferi* has an 11 ft limb span and is the largest living arthropod. Examples:

Pill woodlouse *Armadillidium vulgare* (up to ¾ in.): common around human habitation. Its back has a smooth, hard surface and it can contract into a ball if danger threatens
Freshwater shrimp *Gammarus lacustris* (⅓ in.): found in rivers and lakes and on the seashore. It has seven pairs of walking legs and the female carries her young in a brood pouch between her legs
European lobster *Homarus vulgaris*: lives in shallows round rocky shores

CLASS MEROSTOMATA

King crabs or horseshoe crabs; 5 species
This group, more common in Paleozoic times 570—225 million years ago, is today found mainly in warm seas. These crabs have bodies divided into two sections, both encased in heavy protective plates. The head/thorax carries five pairs of walking legs and a pair of pincers. The other section, the abdomen, terminates in a long spine. The king crab breathes through book-gills on the abdomen, which resemble thin plates arranged like the leaves of a book. Example:
King crab *Limulus polyphemus*: lives on the muddy sea bottom and sandbanks of the north-western Atlantic coast and the Gulf of Mexico

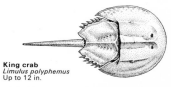

King crab
Limulus polyphemus
Up to 12 in.

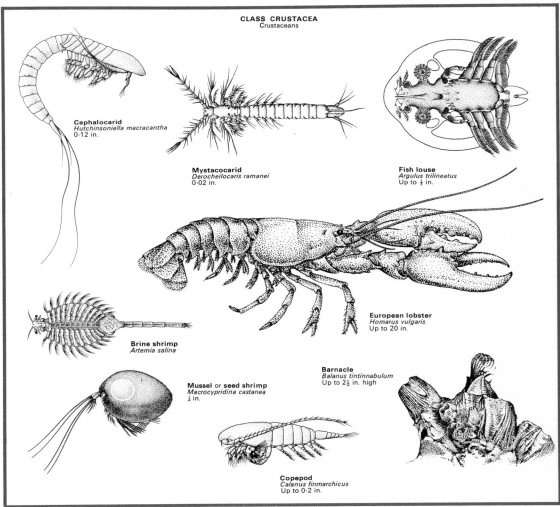

CLASS CRUSTACEA
Crustaceans

Cephalocarid
Hutchinsoniella macracantha
0·12 in.

Mystacocarid
Derocheilocaris ramanei
0·02 in.

Fish louse
Argulus trilineatus
(up to ⅛ in.)

European lobster
Homarus vulgaris
Up to 20 in.

Brine shrimp
Artemia salina

Mussel or **seed shrimp**
Macrocypridina castanea
⅓ in.

Barnacle
Balanus tintinnabulum
Up to 2½ in. high

Copepod
Calanus finmarchicus
Up to 0·2 in.

CLASS ARACHNIDA
Arachnids

These are almost all land animals which normally breathe through gill-like structures called book-lungs. Their bodies are divided into two main parts. The first part is the prosoma, bearing two pairs of appendages (the chelicerae and the pedipalps) which are often pincer-like, and four pairs of legs; the second part is an abdomen which lacks limbs. Arachnids are generally aggressive, predatory creatures, preying on small arthropods. There are ten orders:

ORDER SCORPIONIDA
Scorpions; 600 species

These secretive, nocturnal animals are abundant in tropical regions. Their pedipalps are large pincers, but their chelicerae are small. The scorpion's body, which may be $\frac{1}{2}$—7 in. long, has a sting on its last segment. Example:
Androctonus aeneas: found mainly in North Africa, under stones and logs and in burrows. Its venom, produced in two glands at the base of the sting, causes paralysis of the heart and respiratory muscles in mammals

ORDER PSEUDOSCORPIONIDA
Pseudoscorpions; 1100 species

Found throughout the world, these small arachnids live in leaf litter and damp nooks and crannies. They lack stings but have two pairs of pincers: large pedipalps bearing poison glands and small chelicerae containing silk glands. Example:
Chelifer cancroides: found in houses all over the world

ORDER SOLIFUGAE
Camel spiders or sun spiders; 570 species

These large, swift-moving, tropical and sub-tropical animals prefer arid environments. They have large, pincer-like chelicerae and leg-like pedipalps with sensitive adhesive organs. Example:
Galeodes arabs: lives in North Africa, hiding under stones and in crevices

ORDER PALPIGRADI
Micro-whip scorpions; 21 species

These tiny, soil-dwelling arachnids are found in the warmer parts of the world. They have a pair of well-developed pincer-like chelicerae and leg-like pedipalps. The trunk is segmented and ends in a long flagellum, or tail. Example:
Koenenia mirabilis: lives in the Mediterranean region

ORDER UROPYGI
Whip scorpions; 105 species

These small to medium-sized arachnids are named after the very long, narrow, bristle-like structure borne by the last segment of the abdomen. The chelicerae are large and hooked, the pedipalps are short, stout and often pincer-like, and the first pair of legs is very long. Example:
Mastigoproctus giganteus: found in the southern U.S.A. Hides under leaves, rocks and debris during the day

ORDER AMBLYPYGI
Amblypygids; 50 species

These medium-sized arachnids, ranging in length from 0·16 in. to $1\frac{3}{4}$ in., are found in warm countries, usually in damp, dark habitats. The chelicerae and pedipalps are similar to those of whip scorpions, and the first pair of legs, which are long and thin, is held out in front like antennae Example:
Charinus milloti: found in Africa in dark, damp habitats

ORDER ARANEAE
Spiders; 20,000 species

With mites and ticks, spiders are the most widespread and abundant arachnids. Spiders, which range in length from less than 0·03 in. to 10 in., have chelicerae bearing poisonous fangs and have silk glands in the abdomen. The pedipalps, leg-like in the female, are modified into copulatory organs in the male. Many species have excellent vision. Example:
Garden spider *Araneus diadematus*: one of the most common species in Europe. The male is smaller than the female, and is often eaten by her after mating

ORDER RICINULEI
Ricinuleids; about 15 species

These small, compact, little-known arachnids, from Africa and the warmer parts of America, live in leaf mold. Both the chelicerae and the pedipalps are small and pincer-like. Example:
Ricinoides afzeli: lives in Africa

ORDER OPILIONES
Daddy long-legs or harvestmen; 2400 species

Long legs and short compact bodies distinguish these arachnids, which are normally found in moist environments. Their chelicerae are small with pincers, and their pedipalps are leg-like. They are called harvestmen in Britain and daddy long-legs in North America. Example:
Phalangium opilio: one of the most common European species, it is active by night

ORDER ACARINA
Mites and ticks; 10,000 species

Most of this abundant and widespread group of animals are tiny. Many are parasites, and most of the free-living species inhabit leaf-litter. They are arachnids with a false head, or capitulum, set apart from the rest of the body, and carrying mouth-parts. External segmentation is reduced or absent. Larval stages normally have three pairs of legs; nymphal and adult stages four pairs. The chelicerae and pedipalps are pincer-like, leg-like or needle-like, depending on their function. Example:
Harvest mite *Trombicula autumnalis*: common in Europe

CLASS ONYCHOPHORA
Velvet worms; about 120 species

These animals live under logs and stones in the tropics and southern temperate regions. They have a soft outer covering, a pair of short legs on each trunk segment and a pair of long antennae. They range from $\frac{1}{2}$ in. to 6 in. in length. Example:
Peripatopsis capensis: lives in South Africa

Velvet worm
Peripatopsis capensis
2 in.

CLASS PAUROPODA
Pauropods; 60 species

These tiny arthropods—they are 0·02–0·08 in. long—have a 12-segment body with two pairs of mouth-parts, branched antennae and nine or ten pairs of legs. The plates on the back are alternately large and small. Example:
Pauropus silvaticus: lives in forest humus and soil in north-western Europe

Pauropod
Pauropus silvaticus
0·04 in.

CLASS DIPLOPODA
Millipedes; 8000 species

The millipede's horny outer layer forms a hard armor which is used in head-on burrowing. There are two pairs of mouth-parts, and simple seven-segment antennae. The body segments are cylindrical and joined together in pairs, each bearing two pairs of legs. The longest millipede has no more than 200 legs. Millipedes are usually vegetarian, and are found all over the world. Example:
Cylindroiulus londinensis: a typical burrowing species, which sometimes eats the sprouts of seed grain. The females construct a nest for their eggs. Found in the Northern Hemisphere

Millipede
Cylindroiulus londinensis
$1\frac{1}{2}$ in.

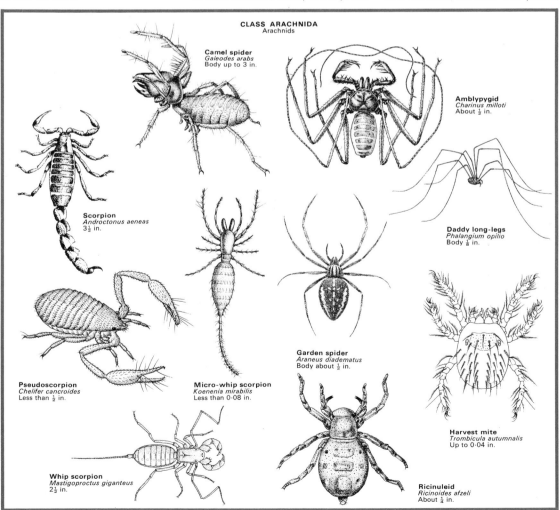

CLASS ARACHNIDA
Arachnids

Camel spider
Galeodes arabs
Body up to 3 in.

Amblypygid
Charinus milloti
About $\frac{1}{2}$ in.

Scorpion
Androctonus aeneas
$3\frac{1}{2}$ in.

Daddy long-legs
Phalangium opilio
Body $\frac{3}{8}$ in.

Garden spider
Araneus diadematus
Body about $\frac{1}{2}$ in.

Pseudoscorpion
Chelifer cancroides
Less than $\frac{1}{4}$ in.

Micro-whip scorpion
Koenenia mirabilis
Less than 0·08 in.

Harvest mite
Trombicula autumnalis
Up to 0·04 in.

Whip scorpion
Mastigoproctus giganteus
$2\frac{1}{2}$ in.

Ricinuleid
Ricinoides afzeli
About $\frac{1}{4}$ in.

381

CLASSIFICATION

Invertebrates

CLASS CHILOPODA
Centipedes; 2000 species
Centipedes are carnivorous, land-dwelling animals ranging in length from ⅓ in. to 12 in. They have 15–177 pairs of legs, one on each segment. The first pair of legs is modified into poison fangs, and there are three pairs of mouth-parts. Example:
Scolopendra morsitans: found mainly in the tropics

Centipede
Scolopendra morsitans
6–8 in.

CLASS SYMPHYLA
Symphylans; 120 species
These small animals—the longest does not exceed ⅓ in.—have a trunk of 14 segments protected by overlapping dorsal plates. The head bears a pair of long segmented antennae and three pairs of mouth-parts. Example:
Scutigerella immaculata: found in most parts of the world, under stones, logs and in leaf litter. It causes damage to vegetable and fruit crops

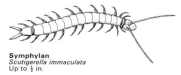

Symphylan
Scutigerella immaculata
Up to ⅓ in.

CLASS COLLEMBOLA
Springtails; 1100 species
Like all the succeeding groups of arthropods, springtails have three pairs of mouth-parts and one pair of antennae on the head, a three-segmented thorax with three pairs of legs, and an abdomen, usually lacking legs. Springtails have six abdominal segments. A forked organ on the end of the abdomen enables the springtail to spring upwards when the fork is suddenly released. They are important animals of the leaf litter, and up to 250 million may live in 1 acre of meadow. Example:
Sminthuroides aquaticus: common all over the world in soil or decaying matter. It feeds mainly on fungi, spores and grains of pollen

Springtail
Sminthuroides aquaticus
0·1–0·3 in.

CLASS DIPLURA
Two-pronged bristletails; 400 species
Bristletails have a ten-segmented abdomen, at the end of which are two filaments. They live under stones or logs, or in buried decaying leaves. Example:
Campodea folsomi: widely distributed in more northerly regions

Two-pronged bristletail
Campodea folsomi
0·2–0·3 in.

CLASS PROTURA
Proturans; 45 species
These tiny creatures have a 12-segmented abdomen with tiny appendages on the first three segments. They use their forelegs as feelers, holding them in front of their heads. Example:
Acerentomon doderoi: found in Europe in woodland litter

Proturan
Acerentomon doderoi
0·1 in.

CLASS THYSANURA
Three-pronged bristletails; 350 species
The Thysanura have smooth, tapering bodies with long antennae and three long, slender filaments on the abdomen. As they grow, they cast off the outer skeleton which is replaced by a larger one underneath. This occurs throughout life in Thysanura, unlike most arthropods, whose outer skeleton is not shed once maturity is reached. Example:
Silverfish *Lepisma saccharina*: prefers damp, cool situations and is often found in kitchens and bathrooms

Silverfish
Lepisma saccharina
½ in.

CLASS INSECTA
Insects
Insects have a head with one pair of antennae and three pairs of mouth-parts; a three-segmented thorax with a pair of legs on each segment and usually a pair of wings on each of the two rear segments; and a legless abdomen of 11 segments. There are 29 orders:

ORDER EPHEMEROPTERA
Mayflies; 1300 species
Mayflies are fragile insects, usually with four membranous wings, held vertically over the body when at rest; the hind wings are small and may be absent. The aquatic larval stage with gills may last three years before the first adult stage is reached. Then, after a few hours, the skin is shed and the fully functional adult with stronger wings and more lustrous color appears—only to die after one day. Example:
Ephemera danica: always found near water. It is the largest British mayfly

ORDER ODONATA
Dragonflies and damselflies; 4500 species
The members of this order are strong fliers with a long narrow abdomen, very short antennae, huge eyes and legs set well forward to catch the smaller insects they prey on. The well-developed lower lip of the aquatic larva covers the face like a mask, and can be unfolded rapidly to seize small aquatic animals. There are two main sub-orders—the Anisoptera, the dragonflies, which rest with their wings spread out; and the Zygoptera, the more delicate damselflies, which rest with their wings folded back. Example:
Hawker dragonfly *Aeschna juncea*: found in North America, Europe and Asia as far south as Kashmir

ORDER NOTOPTERA
Notopterans; 6 species
These wingless insects, living in the cold mountains of North America, Japan and Siberia, show a combination of features found in other orders. The insects with which they share characteristics include crickets and earwigs. Example:
Grylloblatta campodeiformis: found at high latitudes under stones and debris. It was the first known species of this order, and was discovered in 1914 in North America

ORDER PLECOPTERA
Stoneflies; 1300 species
The weak-flying stoneflies, like the mayflies and dragonflies, have aquatic larvae. They are soft-bodied, rather flat insects with a broad head, long antennae and clear wings. Example:
Isoperla confusa: found in North America

ORDER EMBIOPTERA
Web-spinners; 150 species
These fragile insects live in silken tunnels under stones, especially in the tropics. The first segments of the forelimbs are expanded and carry silk glands. The female is wingless. Example:
Embia major: found in northern India

ORDER BLATTARIA
Cockroaches; 3500 species
Cockroaches have long antennae, short cigar-shaped bodies, and thick leathery forewings which protect the hind wings. When at rest, the wings are folded back and lie on the abdomen. Example:
Oriental cockroach *Blatta orientalis*: a domestic species found all over the world. It is dark brown, with small wings and is sometimes called the black beetle

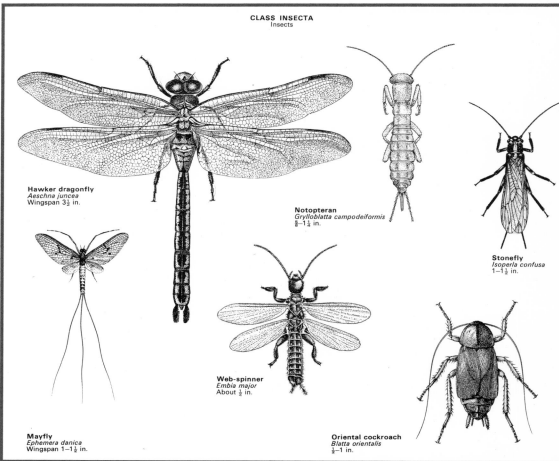

CLASS INSECTA
Insects

Hawker dragonfly
Aeschna juncea
Wingspan 3½ in.

Notopteran
Grylloblatta campodeiformis
⅝–1¼ in.

Stonefly
Isoperla confusa
1–1½ in.

Web-spinner
Embia major
About ⅓ in.

Mayfly
Ephemera danica
Wingspan 1–1½ in.

Oriental cockroach
Blatta orientalis
¾–1 in.

ORDER MANTODEA
Mantids; 1800 species

These insects sit motionless as if praying, then quickly grasp an insect, impaling it on the sharp spines of their front legs. The female eats the male after mating has taken place. Example:
Praying mantis *Mantis religiosa*: found in western Europe and introduced into eastern America. It is pale green

ORDER ISOPTERA
Termites; 1900 species

Termites are near-relatives of cockroaches but differ from them in having two small pairs of fragile wings which are shed after a brief courtship flight, and before mating. The mated pairs found colonies, which may vary in numbers from a hundred to hundreds of thousands of termites living in large elaborate nests, or in galleries built in wood or soil. Termites have a highly developed social organization based on many castes. The female, or queen, fertilized at intervals by the king, becomes distended, like a soft white sausage. The workers—small, wingless, sterile offspring—construct the nest, care for the eggs and find food. Sterile and wingless soldiers, often with big heads and jaws, defend the colony. Colonies may last up to 100 years. Example:
Reticulitermes flavipes: a destructive subterranean species found in North America

ORDER ZORAPTERA
Zorapterans; 16 species

These minute insects, less than $\frac{1}{8}$ in. long, are related to the book-lice. They live under bark in decaying wood and in humus in West Africa, Ceylon, Java, Texas, Florida and Bolivia. Example:
Zorotypus guineensis: found in Africa

ORDER ORTHOPTERA
Grasshoppers, crickets and allies; 10,000 species

Most of the Orthoptera have long hind legs with powerful thighs enabling them to make long jumps. They make noises by rubbing hard parts of the body together and they have hearing organs. Leathery forewings protect the fan-like hind wings. Locusts, which swarm in huge numbers and destroy vegetation, are members of this family. Example:
Desert locust *Schistocerca gregaria*: found in northern Africa, Arabia and the Near East, through India to Assam

ORDER PHASMIDA
Stick-insects and leaf-insects; 2000 species

The bodies of these predominantly tropical insects are either thin and twig-like, or flattened like leaves. They remain motionless by day, disguised by their resemblance to plants, and feed and move at night. Their eggs, which are large and hard-shelled, resemble seeds. Example:
Didymuria violescens: lives in Australia, where it defoliates alpine ash

ORDER DERMAPTERA
Earwigs; 900 species

These insects have horny forceps, used in defense. Short leathery forewings protect the delicate semicircular hind wings, which are pleated like a fan. Example:
Common European earwig *Forficula auricularia*: native to Europe and introduced into North and South America, South Africa and Australasia. It is omnivorous and nocturnal

ORDER PSOCOPTERA
Book-lice; 1000 species

These tiny, soft-bodied insects with long antennae are found on trees or under bark and stones. Some are wingless. Example:
Liposcelis divinatorius: found in temperate regions of the Northern Hemisphere. It feeds on fragments of both animal and vegetable matter, including the paste of book bindings

ORDER MALLOPHAGA
Bird-lice; 2600 species

These tiny, wingless, rather flat insects with small eyes live as parasites on birds and some mammals. They feed on feathers and skin, and some drink blood. Example:
Chicken louse *Menacanthus stramineus*: a pest of domestic poultry in all parts of the world

ORDER ANOPLURA
Sucking-lice; 250 species

These parasites on mammals have mouth-parts which are adapted for biting or piercing the skin for blood. Example:
Human louse *Pediculus humanus*: found world wide on man, and responsible for typhus

ORDER THYSANOPTERA
Thrips; 5000 species

These small, slender-bodied insects, common on flower-heads, especially dandelions, have piercing mouth-parts and tiny narrow wings fringed with hairs. Example:
Red-banded thrips *Heliothrips rubrocinctus*: widespread in North America. It sucks plant juices and may transmit plant viruses

ORDER HEMIPTERA
Bugs; 55,000 species

All the members of this diverse order have mouth-parts in the form of a beak, with the jaws transformed into thread-like stylets capable of piercing and sucking. The forewings have a thickened membranous section which overlaps the abdomen when the wings are at rest. The sub-order Heteroptera includes bed-bugs, waterboatmen and water scorpions. The sub-order Homoptera includes cicadas and aphids. Example:
Apple aphid *Aphis pomi*: occurs on plants and trees in the Northern Hemisphere. It attacks leaves, shoots and blossoms

ORDER NEUROPTERA
Lacewings and ant-lions; 4000 species

These insects, which vary greatly in size, are usually predatory. The adults have biting mouth-parts and gauzy, net-like wings which form a roof over the abdomen when at rest. Their larvae are predatory. Example:
Green lacewing *Chrysopa flava*: widely distributed in Europe

ORDER MEGALOPTERA
Alderflies; 500 species

These insects are commonly found on vegetation near water. Their larvae are aquatic, with gills on the abdominal segments. Example:
Alderfly *Sialis lutaria*: common in Britain and throughout Europe

ORDER RAPHIDIODEA
Snakeflies; 80 species

This group is found in all continents except Australia. Most species have unusual neck-like extensions of the thorax and the female lays eggs under bark, particularly of conifers, through a long needle-like ovipositor. Example:
Snakefly *Raphidia notata*: found in woods, shrubs and rank vegetation

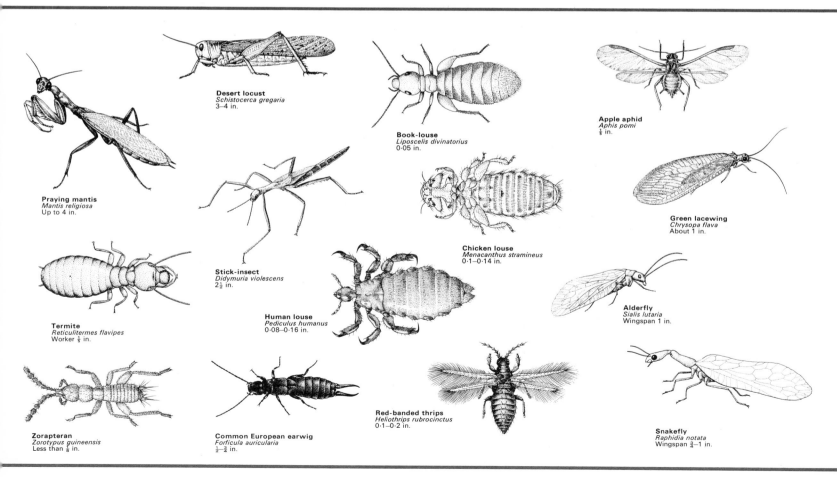

Desert locust
Schistocerca gregaria
3–4 in.

Book-louse
Liposcelis divinatorius
0·05 in.

Apple aphid
Aphis pomi
$\frac{1}{8}$ in.

Praying mantis
Mantis religiosa
Up to 4 in.

Green lacewing
Chrysopa flava
About 1 in.

Stick-insect
Didymuria violescens
2½ in.

Chicken louse
Menacanthus stramineus
0·1–0·14 in.

Termite
Reticulitermes flavipes
Worker $\frac{1}{8}$ in.

Human louse
Pediculus humanus
0·08–0·16 in.

Alderfly
Sialis lutaria
Wingspan 1 in.

Zorapteran
Zorotypus guineensis
Less than $\frac{1}{8}$ in.

Common European earwig
Forficula auricularia
½–¾ in.

Red-banded thrips
Heliothrips rubrocinctus
0·1–0·2 in.

Snakefly
Raphidia notata
Wingspan ¾–1 in.

Invertebrates

PHYLUM ARTHROPODA	Arthropods
PHYLUM CHAETOGNATHA	Arrow worms
PHYLUM POGONOPHORA	Beard-bearers
PHYLUM ECHINODERMATA	Echinoderms

ORDER COLEOPTERA
Beetles; 300,000 species
About 30–40 per cent of all insects are beetles. They vary greatly in size and structure, but can be easily recognized because their forewings are modified into horny sheaths completely concealing the hind wings when the insect is not flying. Their sizes range from 0·03 in. to 6 in. long, and the heavily built Goliath beetle *Goliathus giganteus* is 8 million times heavier than the smallest species. Beetles live in water or on land, and some burrow in the soil. Their larvae vary from legless grubs to caterpillar-like forms preying on other insects. Example:
Common dor beetle *Geotrupes stercorarius*: found in burrows under cattle or horse dung throughout Europe and northern Asia

ORDER STREPSIPTERA
Strepsipterans; 300 species
The larvae of these insects are parasites in bugs, ants, bees and wasps. The adult female, which is little more than a sac of eggs, never leaves the host. The male is winged and free-living, but has only hind wings, the forewings being represented by balancing organs which are important in regulating stable flight. Example:
Stylops shannoni found in North America, where it is parasitic on solitary species of bees

ORDER MECOPTERA
Scorpionflies; 300 species
The elongated heads of these insects point vertically downwards. The male has prominent reproductive organs contained in the last segment of the abdomen, which curl up over the back like a scorpion's tail. Example:
Common scorpionfly *Panorpa com-*

munis: inhabits sunny hedgerows in Europe, from Britain to Scandinavia. It feeds mainly on dead or dying insects

ORDER TRICHOPTERA
Caddisflies; 3500 species
These weak-flying flies are moth-like in appearance, but their wings are hairy, not scaly. Their mouth-parts are adapted for licking fluids but probably many do not feed at all as adults. The aquatic larvae, sometimes called caddis worms, build and live in protective cases made of secreted silk, stones, leaves or shells. Example:
Rhyacophila fenestra: found in North America

ORDER ZEUGLOPTERA
Zeuglopterans; 100 species
These small moth-like insects are found in large numbers on flowers such as buttercups in spring. They feed on pollen. Example:
Micropterix calthella: common throughout Europe

ORDER LEPIDOPTERA
Butterflies and moths; 120,000 species
Six of the 80 families of this large group consist of brightly colored, day-active butterflies, most of which fold their wings vertically; the rest are moths, which fold their wings horizontally and are mostly nocturnal. All members of the order have two pairs of wings covered with powdery scales and a long sucking proboscis formed from one pair of mouth-parts. This is coiled when not in use. Example:
Peacock butterfly *Nymphalis io*: found in Europe, and from northern Asia to Japan. It passes the winter in adult form, sleeping in hollow trees, and emerges in early spring to breed

ORDER DIPTERA
True flies; 75,000 species
The true flies have only one pair of functional wings, the hind pair being reduced to a pair of knobs used to maintain balance. One group includes the slender-bodied midges, craneflies (known as daddy long-legs in Britain) and mosquitoes. Another contains the blood-sucking horse-flies and clegs, and a third, the compactly built houseflies, bluebottles, hoverflies and fruit flies with mouths adapted for sucking fluids. The soft, plump-bodied larvae, called maggots, usually feed on decaying matter or dung. Example:
Housefly *Musca domestica*: found wherever man lives. The larvae develop in rotten plant or animal matter and adults transmit diseases

ORDER SIPHONAPTERA
Fleas; 1800 species
Adult fleas are parasites on birds and mammals. They are brown, wingless insects with bristly, vertically compressed bodies. The mouth-parts are modified for piercing and sucking, and in many species the well-developed hind legs are used for jumping. Example:
Common rat flea *Nosopsyllus fasciatus*: widely distributed, particularly in the Northern Hemisphere. It feeds on man as well as on its rodent hosts

ORDER HYMENOPTERA
Ants, bees and wasps; 100,000 species
Members of this group have two pairs of glossy, membranous wings, and the forewings are linked to the hind wings. The mouth-parts are primarily adapted for biting, and often for lapping and sucking as well. There are two sub-orders. The

Symphyta includes the saw-flies and the wood wasps, which insert their eggs into plants and have no obvious 'wasp waist' between the thorax and the abdomen. The Apocrita includes the parasitic gall wasps, which lay their eggs in plants; ichneumon flies, which lay their eggs in the larvae or eggs of other insects; and the free-living bees, wasps and ants, which have a noticeable waist and seek food for their larvae. Many of these live in complex societies. Example:
Honey bee *Apis mellifera*: originated in northern Europe. It nests in the wild in caves or hollow trees, or more often in artificially housed colonies, with a queen and a number of males (drones), which are fed by the workers (sterile females). Workers are slightly smaller than drones

PHYLUM CHAETOGNATHA
Arrow worms; about 50 species
These worms are abundant in marine plankton and feed on microscopic single-celled plants and small planktonic animals. They have a well-developed body cavity, and the elongated body is divided into a head with eyes and horny teeth, a trunk and a tail. There are fins on the side and tail. One genus is not planktonic, but lives on the sea floor. Most species are tropical. Example:
Sagitta elegans: inhabits coastal North Atlantic waters

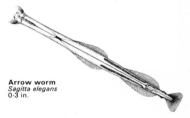

Arrow worm
Sagitta elegans
0·3 in.

PHYLUM POGONOPHORA
Beard-bearers; 80 species
These small, tube-dwelling animals are found in the sea at depths of 6000–30,000 ft, and may be related to the starfish and the most primitive chordates. Their bodies are in three parts: the proboscis, bearing the tentacles, the main body, and a segmented and bristly region. They have a well-developed blood system, but no gut. The food is probably trapped inside the tentacles and digested there. The sexes are separate, although externally males and females look alike. The first specimen ever found was dredged from Indonesian waters in 1900. Example:
Spirobrachia grandis: this species has more tentacles than average

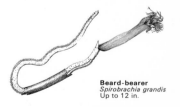

Beard-bearer
Spirobrachia grandis
Up to 12 in.

PHYLUM ECHINODERMATA
Echinoderms
Of the higher invertebrates with a body cavity, only echinoderms are symmetrically radial in form. Most echinoderms can move, though slowly. They have no head and no true brain for overall co-ordination of the body. Externally, they are covered by chalky plates just under the skin and, sometimes, by spines. The mouth is usually on the lower surface of the body. There are five classes:

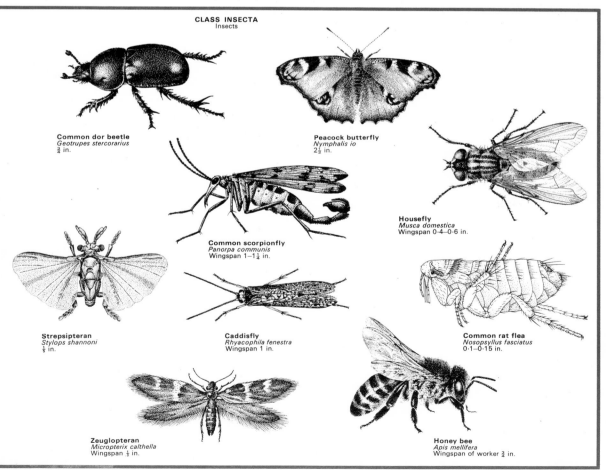

CLASS INSECTA
Insects

Common dor beetle
Geotrupes stercorarius
¾ in.

Peacock butterfly
Nymphalis io
2½ in.

Common scorpionfly
Panorpa communis
Wingspan 1–1¼ in.

Housefly
Musca domestica
Wingspan 0·4–0·6 in.

Strepsipteran
Stylops shannoni
½ in.

Caddisfly
Rhyacophila fenestra
Wingspan 1 in.

Common rat flea
Nosopsyllus fasciatus
0·1–0·15 in.

Zeuglopteran
Micropterix calthella
Wingspan ¼ in.

Honey bee
Apis mellifera
Wingspan of worker ¾ in.

CLASS ASTEROIDEA
Starfish; 1600 species

Most starfish have five arms radiating from a central disc, though some have as many as 40. They move by means of very small tube-feet bearing suckers which run down the underside of each arm; they have chalky plates buried in the skin, though these do not form a shell. Starfish are usually carnivorous; some feed on small organisms swallowed whole, others on microscopic morsels conveyed to the mouth by cilia. They have remarkable

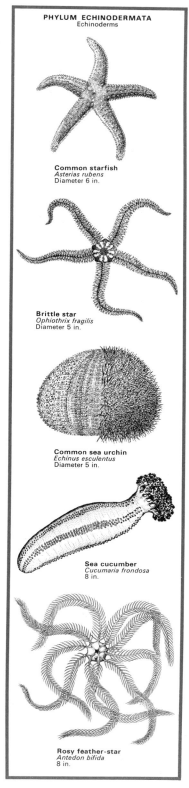

PHYLUM ECHINODERMATA
Echinoderms

Common starfish
Asterias rubens
Diameter 6 in.

Brittle star
Ophiothrix fragilis
Diameter 5 in.

Common sea urchin
Echinus esculentus
Diameter 5 in.

Sea cucumber
Cucumaria frondosa
8 in.

Rosy feather-star
Antedon bifida
8 in.

powers of regeneration; provided one-fifth of the central disc is attached to an arm, the entire starfish will grow again. The sexes are separate. Example:
Common starfish *Asterias rubens*: often found just below low tide mark on North Atlantic coasts. It feeds on mussels

CLASS OPHIUROIDEA
Brittle stars; about 2000 species

The members of this class are star-shaped, with arms which are much more slender than the central disc of the body. They move by means of their arms, and the tube-feet, which play little part in loco-motion, lack suckers. Brittle stars feed on plankton and decaying matter. Example:
Ophiothrix fragilis: common off the coasts of north-western Europe

CLASS ECHINOIDEA
Sea urchins; about 800 species

The echinoids, found on the seabed or buried in sand, are circular or oval in shape and do not have arms. The chalky plates in the skin form a complete shell, and the bodies are covered with spines. They feed on both animal and plant matter, and move by means of tube-feet bearing suckers. Example:
Common sea urchin *Echinus esculentus*: common in both the Atlantic and the Mediterranean

CLASS HOLOTHUROIDEA
Sea cucumbers or cotton-spinners; about 900 species

These elongated animals have no arms. Some of the tube-feet near the mouth are adapted as tentacles; the rest have suckers and are used in locomotion. Sea cucumbers feed on decaying matter, swallowed with sand from the seabed, or on small floating organisms. Example:
Cucumaria frondosa: a sea cucumber of the North Atlantic

CLASS CRINOIDEA
Sea-lilies; about 80 species

This is an ancient group and little is known about their way of life. Surviving forms living on the beds of deep seas are permanently attached to a stalk; those in shallower water become detached from the stalk when adult and swim by waving their branched arms. They are the only echinoderms with the mouth on the upper surface of the body. Example:
Rosy feather-star *Antedon bifida*: found on the European continental shelf. It feeds on small particles conveyed to the mouth by ciliary action

PHYLUM HEMICHORDATA

Hemichordates

These marine animals were once classified with the chordates but are now thought to be unrelated. What was thought to be a notochord in them has been shown to be merely an extension of the gut. Their bodies are divided into three regions, the proboscis, collar and trunk, each containing part of the body cavity, or coelom. There are two classes:

CLASS ENTEROPNEUSTA
Acorn worms; 70 species

These worm-shaped animals inhabit sand and mud on the shore and in shallow waters. The sexes are separate. Example:
Atlantic acorn worm *Saccoglossus kowalevskii*: is common in Europe and the Atlantic coast of North America

CLASS PTEROBRANCHIA
Pterobranchs; 20 species

Most of these small animals live on the seabed in tubes secreted by themselves. The collar bears a number of branched arms, carrying cilia which collect plank-tonic food. Some pterobranchs live in colonies. Example:
Rhabdopleura normani : found near European coasts. It lives in colonies in which the individuals are connected to one another inside a system of tubes

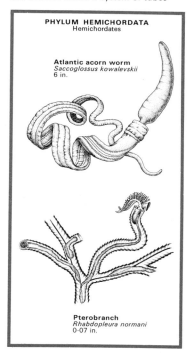

PHYLUM HEMICHORDATA
Hemichordates

Atlantic acorn worm
Saccoglossus kowalevskii
6 in.

Pterobranch
Rhabdopleura normani
0·07 in.

PHYLUM CHORDATA

Chordates

This is a large, varied and highly successful group of complex multi-cellular animals which at some stage in their life history have a supporting skeletal rod or noto-chord, a hollow dorsal nerve cord, and gills. This phylum includes the vertebrates. It also includes two other sub-phyla of animals which lack backbones, but resemble vertebrates in certain important respects. These are:

SUB-PHYLUM TUNICATA

Tunicates

These unsegmented marine chordates, with no body cavity, are protected by a tough outer tunic usually consisting of a cellulose-type substance called tunicin. The tadpole-like larvae have a notochord in the tail, but the adults, apart from their gills, bear little resemblance to other chordates. They feed by filtering sea water. Enormous quantities are involved: a tunicate an inch or so long may filter 300 pints a day. There are three classes:

CLASS ASCIDIACEA
Sea squirts; 1200 species

Most of these sedentary tunicates live near the seashore, attached to rocks, shells and the bottoms of ships. They range from pea-size to the size of a large potato. Like most tunicates, they are usually hermaphrodites. Some are colonial and reproduce asexually. Example:
Ciona intestinalis : found in European coastal waters

CLASS THALIACEA
Salps; 30 species

Salps are free-floating, sometimes colonial, tunicates, much resembling sea squirts in structure and mode of life. They reproduce sexually, and also asexually, by budding. Most species live in tropical and sub-tropical waters. Example:
Pyrosoma: Salps of this genus live in phosphorescent, cylindrical colonies which vary in length from a few inches to several feet. Some giant colonies recently discovered in Australian waters measure up to 30 ft long

CLASS LARVACEA
Larvaceans; 30 species

These tiny, transparent, free-floating animals feed on tiny planktonic organisms which are caught on filters of a house that the animal builds. Example:
Oikopleura albicans : is common in North Atlantic waters

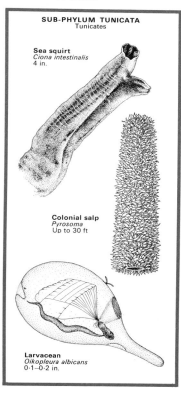

SUB-PHYLUM TUNICATA
Tunicates

Sea squirt
Ciona intestinalis
4 in.

Colonial salp
Pyrosoma
Up to 30 ft

Larvacean
Oikopleura albicans
0·1–0·2 in.

SUB-PHYLUM CEPHALOCHORDATA

Lancelets; 20 species

These are small segmented animals found close to the shore on sandy bottoms. They are the most fish-like of the non-verte-brate chordates and bury themselves in sand, leaving only the head visible. They have a notochord and dorsal nerve cord, and feed on particles taken in at the mouth and filtered through the gill-slits. Reproduction is sexual, and the sexes are separate. Example:
Amphioxus lanceolatus : found in European coastal waters. It is covered by a transparent, iridescent cuticle. It swims and burrows by rapidly flexing its body, waves of contractions passing through it

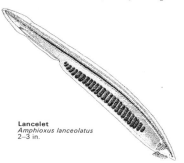

Lancelet
Amphioxus lanceolatus
2–3 in.

Fish

PHYLUM CHORDATA	Animals with notochords
SUB-PHYLUM VERTEBRATA	Animals with backbones

All vertebrates are chordates. What distinguishes them from the lower chordates, such as seasquirts and lancelets, is that in vertebrates the notochord, a rod of cells along the back, is strengthened or replaced by a backbone (either of bone or cartilage), and the brain is protected by a cranium

CLASS AGNATHA	Jawless fish
CLASS CHONDRICHTHYES	Cartilaginous fish
CLASS OSTEICHTHYES	Bony fish

CLASS AGNATHA

Jawless fish
The world's first vertebrates belonged to this class; the few living representatives belong to this single order:

ORDER CYCLOSTOMATA
Hagfish and lampreys; 45 species
Lampreys and hagfish are parasites and scavengers. They lack scales and jaws.

Hagfish remain buried in mud, sand or gravel during the day and emerge at night to scavenge on dead animals and organic waste, or to act as parasites on live prey. Their eyes are vestigial and sightless. They hunt by touch and smell; the tip of their snout bears fleshy, sensitive tentacles, called barbels.

Lampreys attach themselves by suckers to the flanks of fish, then rasp through their prey's flesh and drain it of blood. Adult lampreys die after egg-laying and fertilization; the eggs are laid in the gravel of stream beds and, although some species return to the sea as they mature, others remain in fresh water. Examples:
Glutinous Atlantic hag *Myxine glutinosa* (18 in.): found on both sides of the North Atlantic
Sea lamprey *Petromyzon marinus*: it has a similar range to the glutinous Atlantic hag

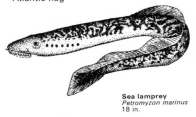

Sea lamprey
Petromyzon marinus
18 in.

CLASS CHONDRICHTHYES

Cartilaginous fish
These jawed fish have skeletons composed primarily of cartilage, with mosaics of small, bony plates as reinforcements.

They have paired stabilizing fins and their mouths are adapted for biting, with a band of teeth attached to each jaw. They have small, tooth-like scales, covered with an enamel-like substance. There is no swim-bladder; lift is provided by the flattened head, pectoral fins and tail.

The sense of smell is well developed and the lateral line system, the pressure-sensitive organs with which fish detect vibrations in the sea, is highly developed. The male fertilizes the eggs while they are still inside the female, by means of a pair of claspers on the inner edge of the pelvic fins. There are two sub-classes:

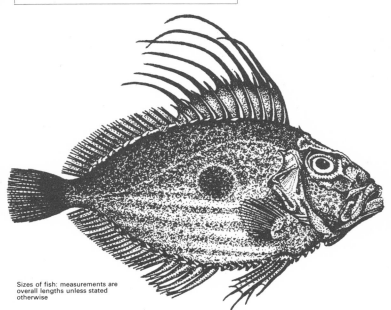

Sizes of fish: measurements are overall lengths unless stated otherwise

Fish, although they all live in water, are cold-blooded, have muscular, streamlined bodies and for the most part breathe through gills, do not form a single natural group. They fall into three classes as distinct from one another as are reptiles from mammals.

SUB-CLASS ELASMOBRANCHII
Sharks and rays
These have five to seven pairs of gills, numerous teeth, and an upper jaw which is not attached to the cranium. They lack swim-bladders. There are two orders:

ORDER SELACHII
Sharks; 200 species
All sharks are good swimmers, with cigar-shaped bodies and gill slits at the side of the head. Most are predators and some are dangerous to man. There are a few freshwater species. Dogfish are merely small sharks, 1–2 ft long. Example:
Basking shark *Cetorhinus maximus*: found in the North Atlantic; it is the second largest living fish—only the whale shark *Rhincodon typus* is larger, growing to 60 ft

ORDER BATOIDEA
Skates and rays; 350 species
Members of this order have flat bodies with wing-like pectoral fins attached to the sides of the head. Examples:
Atlantic manta *Manta birostris* (20 ft wide): moves through surface waters of the temperate and tropical Atlantic with leisurely flaps of its wing-like pectoral fins, scooping in plankton with the horns at the side of its mouth
Common sawfish *Pristis pectinatus* (18 ft): found in tropical and sub-tropical Atlantic waters. The sawfish uses its long, narrow snout with a series of teeth on each side to forage in the mud or to stun fish, slashing its saw from side to side
Thornback ray *Raja clavata*: found in the eastern North Atlantic and the Mediterranean Sea, where it preys upon bottom-living crustaceans

SUB-CLASS HOLOCEPHALI

There is one order:

ORDER CHIMAERIFORMES
Chimaeras; 25 species
These fish have an upper jaw immovably fixed to the cranium, four pairs of gills and six pairs of grinding teeth, which resemble small, flat plates. The males have a clasper in front of the eyes, probably used during courtship, and a pair in front of the pelvic fins. They live near the sea bottom. The spine in front of the dorsal fin is venomous in some species. Example:
Rat fish *Chimaera monstrosa*: found in the eastern Atlantic and the Mediterranean

CLASS OSTEICHTHYES

Bony fish
The bony fish, by far the most numerous of the three classes, have skeletons made of bone. Their teeth are fixed into the upper jaw and they have a lung opening into the gullet which may be converted into a swim-bladder. There are two sub-classes:

SUB-CLASS ACTINOPTERYGII
Ray-finned fish
The fins of these fish are strengthened by bony rays which are jointed. They have large eyes, no internal nostrils, and a lung which is usually converted into a swim-bladder. There are three infra-classes:

INFRA-CLASS CHONDROSTEI
These fish have scales with a thick layer of enamel-like ganoine, and an elongated mouth with the lower jaw hinged far back. There are two orders:

ORDER POLYPTERIFORMES
Bichirs; 12 species
These African fish, with five to 18 flag-like finlets instead of a dorsal fin, have air-breathing lungs. They are found in tropical African rivers and feed on worms, insect larvae and small fish. Example:
Weeks' bichir *Polypterus weeksi*: found in the Congo River. It is protected by rows of scales connected by fibres. It can survive out of water for hours

ORDER ACIPENSERIFORMES
Sturgeons; 22 species
Members of this order are found in temperate or Arctic rivers and coastal waters. Sturgeons have shark-like bodies with scales only along the sides, well-developed swim-bladders and often upturned tails. Examples:
Royal sturgeon *Huso huso* (up to 28 ft): found in the Caspian, Adriatic and Black Seas. This fish weighs about a ton, and caviar is made from its roe
Atlantic sturgeon *Acipenser oxyrhynchus*: found in the Atlantic coastal waters of North America and the Gulf of Mexico. It uses its long snout which bears sensitive barbels to forage through mud and sand for small invertebrates

INFRA-CLASS HOLOSTEI
Like the Chondrostei, from which they developed some 300 million years ago, holostean fish have scales with a layer of ganoine. Unlike them, however, they have jaws that hinge near the front of the head and are not rigidly connected to the skull. There are two orders:

ORDER SEMIONOTIFORMES
Garpikes; 7 species
These fish, which sometimes reach a length of 10 ft, are distinguished by their elongated snouts, air-breathing lungs, and the positions of their dorsal and anal fins, which are far back on the body, directly in front of the tail. They drift along sluggishly, taking their prey with sudden, sideways snaps. Example:
Long-nosed garpike *Lepisosteus osseus*: found in North American fresh waters from the Mississippi basin eastwards; it will imitate driftwood in order to get closer to fish it preys on

ORDER AMIIFORMES
There is one species:
Bowfin *Amia calva*: found in North American rivers and swamps. It has a long, arching, spineless dorsal fin. Males make nests of aquatic plants in which the eggs incubate. They guard the nests and the young fish after they hatch. Bowfins prey on fish and invertebrates

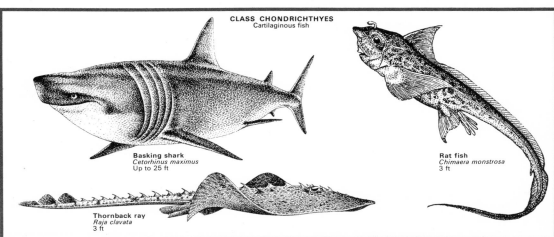

CLASS CHONDRICHTHYES
Cartilaginous fish

Basking shark
Cetorhinus maximus
Up to 25 ft

Thornback ray
Raja clavata
3 ft

Rat fish
Chimaera monstrosa
3 ft

PHYLUM CHORDATA	Animals with notochords
SUB-PHYLUM VERTEBRATA	Animals with backbones
CLASS OSTEICHTHYES	Bony fish

INFRA-CLASS TELEOSTEI

The teleosts are the most numerous group of living vertebrates. They evolved from the holosteans about 190 million years ago, and have no ganoine in their scales. The tail fin is symmetrical, its rays fanning out from enlarged bones at the end of the spines, and the upper jaw is attached to the skull only at the snout. The swim-bladder, which functions almost entirely as a buoyancy control, is lost in many species. These fish tend to be highly vocal and social. There are 30 orders:

ORDER ELOPIFORMES
Tarpons; 12 species
This is a primitive group, closely resembling holosteans. Like eels, they have colorless, flattened larvae. Example:
Atlantic tarpon *Tarpon atlanticus*: found in tropical and sub-tropical waters. It can leap to a height of 6–7 ft

ORDER ANGUILLIFORMES
Eels; 300 species
Most eels are marine, but one family, the Anguillidae, spend most of their time as adults in rivers. Eel larvae are transparent and ribbon-like. The adults return to the spawning grounds when they are fully grown, and then generally die. Example:
European eel *Anguilla anguilla*: unlike most fish, it can survive out of water for considerable periods, having the ability to breathe through its skin

ORDER NOTACANTHIFORMES
Spiny eels; 20 species
Members of this order are long-bodied, deep-sea fish with tail fins and larvae like those of eels. Example:
Spiny eel *Lipogenys gilli*: found in the deep waters of the North Atlantic

ORDER CLUPEIFORMES
Herrings; 350 species
Most herrings are found in shoals near the surface of the sea, but many live in fresh water. The dorsal fin is placed near the centre of the body and the tail fin is deeply forked; the swim-bladder and the inner ear are closely connected. Example:
Atlantic herring *Clupea harengus*: found in the North Atlantic. Shoals of herrings make unpredictable seasonal migrations, as well as migrating to and from their spawning grounds

ORDER OSTEOGLOSSIFORMES
Arapaima and bony tongues; 16 species
These large, pike-like fish, found in the rivers of the tropics, have thick, ornamented scales and tooth-like tongue bones used in biting. Examples:
Arapaima *Arapaima gigas* (15 ft): found in South America. One of the largest freshwater fish, it weighs about 400 lb.
Bony tongue *Osteoglossum bicirrhosum*: found in South American rivers only, although fossilized relatives have been

discovered in North America and Britain. It is believed to carry its eggs in its mouth until they hatch

ORDER MORMYRIFORMES
Mormyrids and gymnarchids; 150 species
These fish, closely related to the bony tongues and only found in Africa, also have toothed tongues. They are usually insect-eating and keep to fresh water. Many have a tube-like, down-curving snout, and all possess weak electric organs which enable them to locate anything within their electric field. Example:
Elephant snout fish *Mormyrus kanume*: found in the Nile and Lake Victoria. It uses its long, flexible snout to search between crevices for food

ORDER SALMONIFORMES
Salmon, pike and stomiatoids; 500 species
All salmon have a small, fleshy fin behind the dorsal fin, and deep-sea forms have light-producing organs. Examples:
Northern pike *Esox lucius* (3 ft 6 in.): found in fresh waters in Europe and North America
Stomiatoid *Stomias atriventer* (12 in.): found in deep waters in the Gulf of California and off the coast of Chile
Atlantic salmon *Salmo salar*: found in cold and temperate seas. It spends the first one to three years of its life in fresh

waters, then migrates to the sea. After several years in the Atlantic, it returns to the same river in which it hatched. There, a 20 lb. female lays an average of 14,000 eggs, and then generally dies

ORDER MYCTOPHIFORMES
Lantern fish; 300 species
These deep-sea fish have light-producing organs along their sides. They live at depths down to 3500 ft, but feed at the surface. Some species have a fatty dorsal fin. Example:
Myctophum punctatum : found in the Atlantic and Mediterranean; it has large, sensitive eyes and its luminous organs may be a means of identification between members of the species

ORDER CTENOTHRISSIFORMES
There is one species:
Macristium *Macristium chavesi*: the single surviving species of this order; found in deep waters of the South Atlantic. There are several fossil forms of these fish, which are related to the lantern fish

ORDER GONORHYNCHIFORMES
Milk fish; 15 species
These fish form a link between the macristiids and the carp. They have deeply forked tails and no teeth. Example:
Chanos chanos : found in the surface waters of the Indian Ocean. The female lays up to 9 million eggs at a time

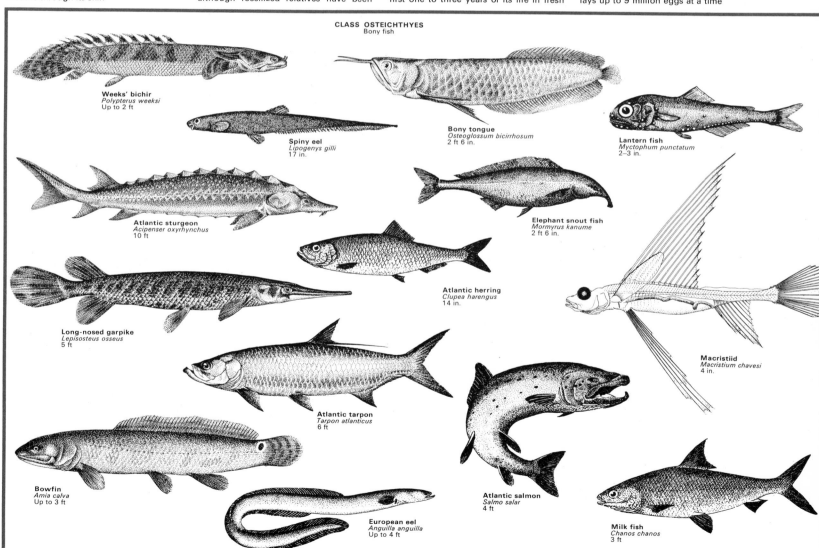

CLASS OSTEICHTHYES
Bony fish

Weeks' bichir
Polypterus weeksi
Up to 2 ft

Spiny eel
Lipogenys gilli
17 in.

Bony tongue
Osteoglossum bicirrhosum
2 ft 6 in.

Lantern fish
Myctophum punctatum
2–3 in.

Atlantic sturgeon
Acipenser oxyrhynchus
10 ft

Elephant snout fish
Mormyrus kanume
2 ft 6 in.

Atlantic herring
Clupea harengus
14 in.

Long-nosed garpike
Lepisosteus osseus
5 ft

Macristiid
Macristium chavesi
4 in.

Atlantic tarpon
Tarpon atlanticus
6 ft

Bowfin
Amia calva
Up to 3 ft

Atlantic salmon
Salmo salar
4 ft

European eel
Anguilla anguilla
Up to 4 ft

Milk fish
Chanos chanos
3 ft

387

CLASSIFICATION

Fish

PHYLUM CHORDATA	Animals with notochords
SUB-PHYLUM VERTEBRATA	Animals with backbones
CLASS OSTEICHTHYES	Bony fish

ORDER CYPRINIFORMES
Carp, characins and gymnotids; 350 species
All members of this order, which contains the majority of freshwater fish, possess a series of small bones connecting the swim-bladder with the inner ear—an arrangement which probably increases the acuteness of their hearing. Most have scales on their bodies. Examples:
Electric eel *Electrophorus electricus* (5 ft): South American freshwater fish
Common carp *Cyprinus carpio*: originally found from the Black Sea to Turkestan, it has been introduced to and domesticated in many countries

ORDER SILURIFORMES
Catfish; 200 species
Most catfish are found in African, Asian and South American fresh waters, but some are marine, and some occur in northern fresh waters. The majority have barbels or feelers on the lower jaw and some species have a fleshy fin on the back. The inner ear and swim-bladder are connected, but the body is naked or covered only with bony plates. Example:
Armored catfish *Corydoras aeneus*: South American freshwater fish

ORDER PERCOPSIFORMES
Sand rollers and pirate perches; 10 species
These minnow-like North American freshwater fish have spiny dorsal fins. Example:

Pirate perch *Aphredoderus sayanus*: found in fresh waters of the U.S.A.

ORDER BATRACHOIDIFORMES
Toadfish; 10 species
These predatory marine fish have large heads, strong teeth and long, tapering bodies. The front of the dorsal fin is spiny. Example:
Opsanus tau : found in shallow Atlantic waters. It has a special swim-bladder which it vibrates to make sounds

ORDER GOBIESOCIFORMES
Clingfish; 100 species
A large sucker, formed from pelvic fins, enables these small marine fish to cling to rocks in tide-pools. Example:
Tomicodon fasciatus : found in coastal waters of Brazil

ORDER LOPHIIFORMES
Anglers and frogfish; 150 species
Anglers have flat, squat bodies and huge heads with wide mouths. The first ray of the spiny dorsal fin has a flap of flesh at the end which acts as a fishing rod to lure prey. Some male angler fish are many times smaller than the females, to which they attach themselves. Although they still draw in water for respiration, they are completely dependent on their mates for nourishment. Example:
Whiskery angler *Antennarius scaber*: found in Atlantic waters. It has a well developed 'fishing rod'

ORDER GADIFORMES
Codfish and allies; 450 species
Codfish have long, tapering bodies. The dorsal and anal fins, which are usually without spines, may be divided into several parts. Example:
Atlantic cod *Gadus morhua*: found on both sides of the North Atlantic. Cod congregate in great shoals, especially at spawning time; about 400 million of them are caught each year

ORDER BERYCIFORMES
Squirrel fish and whalefish; 150 species
These deep-bodied fish have a series of spines in front of the dorsal and anal fins, and 18 or 19 rays on the tail fin. Example:
Striped squirrel fish *Holocentrus xantherythrus*: found near Pacific coral reefs

ORDER ATHERINIFORMES
Flying fish and killifish; 600 species
These small, slender, rather primitive teleosts with soft-rayed, spineless fins, are found in surface marine waters and fresh waters in the tropics. Example:
Flying fish *Oxyporhymphus micropterus*: found in the tropical Atlantic and Pacific. Its pectoral fins enable it to glide through the air for as much as 500 ft

ORDER ZEIFORMES
John Dory and allies; 60 species
These form a group of spiny-rayed, inshore, marine fish related to the squirrel fish; the tail fin has 11 to 14 rays. Example:
John Dory *Zeus faber*: found in the Atlantic. It has a thin body which enables it to approach prey undetected; when close enough it thrusts its jaws forward with a sudden snap

ORDER LAMPRIDIFORMES
Moonfish, earfish, ribbon-fish and mirrapinnids; 50 species
A group of deep-sea fish with protrusible jaws. The pelvic fins are placed at the front end of the scaleless body. Example:
Moonfish *Lampris guttatus*: widely distributed in the open seas. Its oval body is vertically flattened and weighs almost 600 lb. It eats squids and octopuses

ORDER GASTEROSTEIFORMES
Sticklebacks, seahorses and pipefish; 150 species
The fish in this group have elongated bodies encased in bony armor, and small mouths, often at the end of a tubular snout. Examples:
Three-spined stickleback *Gasterosteus aculeatus* (4 in.): found from the Arctic to temperate regions in both fresh and brackish water
Common American Atlantic seahorse *Hippocampus hudsonius*: found inshore. Female seahorses lay their eggs in brood pouches in the male's bodies, where they are incubated. Young seahorses also retreat to the pouch for the first few days following hatching

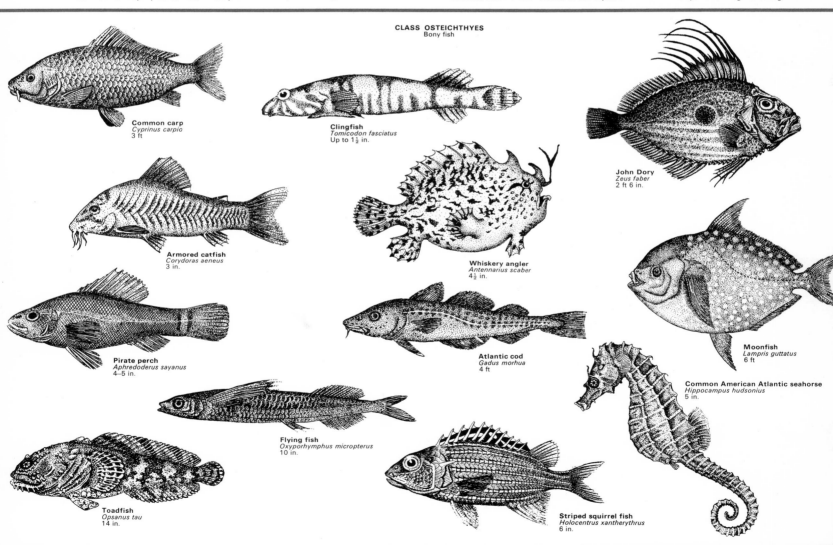

CLASS OSTEICHTHYES
Bony fish

Common carp
Cyprinus carpio
3 ft

Clingfish
Tomicodon fasciatus
Up to 1½ in.

John Dory
Zeus faber
2 ft 6 in.

Armored catfish
Corydoras aeneus
3 in.

Whiskery angler
Antennarius scaber
4½ in.

Pirate perch
Aphredoderus sayanus
4–5 in.

Atlantic cod
Gadus morhua
4 ft

Moonfish
Lampris guttatus
6 ft

Common American Atlantic seahorse
Hippocampus hudsonius
5 in.

Flying fish
Oxyporhymphus micropterus
10 in.

Toadfish
Opsanus tau
14 in.

Striped squirrel fish
Holocentrus xantherythrus
6 in.

PHYLUM CHORDATA	Animals with notochords
SUB-PHYLUM VERTEBRATA	Animals with backbones
CLASS OSTEICHTHYES	Bony fish

ORDER CHANNIFORMES
Snakeheads; 5 species

These freshwater fish possess an extra lung-like respiratory organ which enables them to survive out of water for long periods. Example:
Ophicephalus striatus : found in rivers, ponds and marshes in Asia. It can survive droughts by burying itself in mud and becoming torpid

ORDER SYNBRANCHIFORMES
Swamp eels and cuchias; 7 species

A small group of coastal fish from south Asia and Africa which are not closely related to true eels; they have no paired fins and no scales. Example:
Cuchia *Amphipnous cuchia*: found in fresh and brackish waters in India and Burma. It breathes air and spends much time out of water in grass near the edges of ponds. It has two lung-like air sacs connected to the gill cavity

ORDER SCORPAENIFORMES
Scorpionfish, gurnards and bull-heads; 700 species

Well-developed bony ridges and spines on the head are the main characteristics of this group, which are often known as mail-cheeked fish. Examples:
Scorpionfish *Scorpaena cirrhosa* (10 in.): a tropical species found in the Indian and Pacific Oceans
Yellow gurnard *Trigla hirundo*: found inshore in the Atlantic

ORDER DACTYLOPTERIFORMES
Flying gurnards; 6 species

Long, wing-like pectoral fins enable these fish to glide through the water. Their heads are covered with bony plates. Example:
Dactylopterus orientalis: found inshore in the Indo-Pacific region. The pectoral fins of this fish are even larger than those of the flying fish, although it cannot accomplish such long leaps

ORDER PEGASIFORMES
Dragonfish and sea moths; 4 species

This group of small, armored fish, from the tropical Indo-Pacific region, have large, wing-like pectoral fins and small mouths beneath long snouts. Example:
Dragonfish *Pegasus draconis*: found among coral in shallow seas

ORDER PERCIFORMES
Perch and allies; 6500 species

This is the largest order of ray-finned fish. Many of its members bear spines on their fins. The tail fin has 17 rays and the scales often have serrated edges. Examples:
Discus fish *Symphysodon discus*: found in South American fresh waters
Blue-spotted argus *Cephalopholis argus* (18 in.): found near coral reefs in the Indian and Pacific Oceans
Common perch *Perca fluviatilis* (24 in.): found in Eurasian lakes, rivers and ponds
Mackerel *Scomber scomber* (up to 24 in.): found in the surface waters on both sides of the Atlantic

Remora *Echeneis naucrates* (2 ft 6 in.): found in tropical oceans, always associated with sharks or turtles

ORDER PLEURONECTIFORMES
Flatfish; 500 species

These fish spend most of their lives lying on their sides on the ocean bottom. After the juvenile stage one eye starts to move to the other side of the head so that eventually the fish has two eyes on the same side; from that time on the fish lies on its blind side. Sole, plaice and turbots lie on the left side, flounders on the right. Flatfish are derived from perches, but do not have hard fin spines. Example:
European plaice *Pleuronectes platessa*: found near the coasts of north-west Europe. It has the ability to blend into its surroundings, and can also hide by rapidly burrowing into mud or sand

ORDER TETRAODONTIFORMES
Triggerfish and pufferfish; 250 species

All have tiny mouths armed with heavy teeth, and short, deep bodies often covered with spines. The dorsal fin is spiny and the pelvic fins are either small or absent. Example:
Pufferfish *Spheroides spengleri*: found near coral reefs in tropical and subtropical regions of the Atlantic. It has spines instead of scales, and when the fish inflates itself these spines form an impenetrable barrier

SUB-CLASS SARCOPTERYGII
Fleshy-finned fish

The second sub-class of bony fish—the fleshy-finned fish—is the one which gave rise to amphibians. The fins are supported by large, fleshy lobes containing bony skeletons. There are two orders:

ORDER CROSSOPTERYGII

There is one species:
Coelacanth *Latimeria chalumnae*: the first live coelacanth was caught off South Africa in 1938. Until then, only fossils had been found and it was believed that the order had been extinct for 60 million years. It uses its heavy pectoral and pelvic fins to stir up the mud of the sea floor in search of prey

ORDER DIPNOI
Lungfish; 5 species

These fish belong to two families: the Ceratodidae, with a single Australian species, with heavy bodies, large scales, rayed fins and a single air-breathing lung; and the Lepidosirenidae of Africa and South America, which have slimmer bodies, smaller scales, rayless fins and obtain 95 per cent of their oxygen from the air through paired lungs. Example:
Australian lungfish *Neoceratodus forsteri*: unlike the African and South American family, this species does not build mud burrows to survive droughts; it dies rapidly if its river dries out

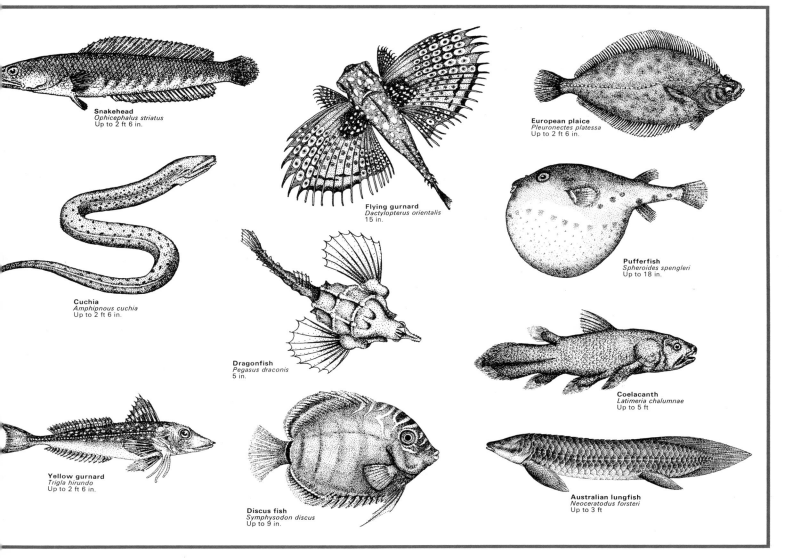

Snakehead
Ophicephalus striatus
Up to 2 ft 6 in.

Cuchia
Amphipnous cuchia
Up to 2 ft 6 in.

Yellow gurnard
Trigla hirundo
Up to 2 ft 6 in.

Flying gurnard
Dactylopterus orientalis
15 in.

Dragonfish
Pegasus draconis
5 in.

Discus fish
Symphysodon discus
Up to 9 in.

European plaice
Pleuronectes platessa
Up to 2 ft 6 in.

Pufferfish
Spheroides spengleri
Up to 18 in.

Coelacanth
Latimeria chalumnae
Up to 5 ft

Australian lungfish
Neoceratodus forsteri
Up to 3 ft

Amphibians

PHYLUM CHORDATA	Animals with notochords
SUB-PHYLUM VERTEBRATA	Animals with backbones
CLASS AMPHIBIA	Amphibians
ORDER APODA	Caecilians
ORDER URODELA	Newts and salamanders

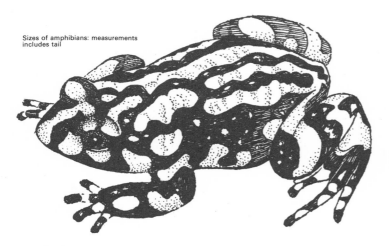

Sizes of amphibians: measurements includes tail

Amphibians The most primitive class of land-living vertebrates, amphibians were the first group of vertebrate animals to emerge from an aquatic environment and live on land for much of their adult lives. Although in most cases the gill-breathing and aquatic young gradually change into lung or skin-breathing terrestrial adults, few amphibians are entirely independent of water, most requiring it at least for breeding. Amphibians are usually scaleless or have only small scales, and their skin—used in respiration—is generally moist. Their body fluids are easily lost through the thin skin, so most must remain in a damp environment. Like fish, amphibian larvae and aquatic adults have a lateral line, a pressure-sensitive organ which is of great use in water.

Amphibians evolved from an extinct sub-order of fleshy-finned fish called Rhipidistia. The main evolutionary changes involved the development of efficient lungs, the evolution of legs, the development of salivary glands and eyelids, and the elaboration of a double circulation. There are three living orders.

ORDER APODA

There is one family:

FAMILY CAECILIIDAE
Caecilians; 167 species
This is a little-known group of legless amphibians living in South America, tropical Africa, the Seychelles and southeast Asia. Their resemblance to earthworms is enhanced by their grooved skin, which gives an appearance of segmentation. They have large mucous glands on the lower part of each ring, 75–273 vertebrae and a small tentacle on each side of the face near the eye. Caecilians are internally fertilized and some species bear live young; others lay eggs. They retain no traces of limb bones, or of pectoral or pelvic girdles. Example:
Panamanian caecilian *Caecilia ochrocephala*: lives in moist ground

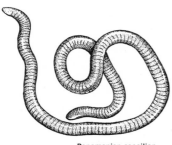

Panamanian caecilian
Caecilia ochrocephala
6½ in.

ORDER URODELA

Newts and salamanders
The skin of newts and salamanders is close-fitting, unlike that of frogs and toads. They possess limbs and have from 12 to more than 60 vertebrae; long, strong tails with muscles arranged in segments; and pectoral girdles made mainly of cartilage. The larvae have three pairs of external gills, and a few genera retain these throughout life. Some adult forms have neither gills nor lungs, but breathe only through the skin or the mouth. Fertilization may be external or internal; most lay eggs. There are eight families:

FAMILY HYNOBIIDAE
Asiatic land salamanders; 30 species
Members of this family, found in eastern and central Asia, have movable eyelids. Some species live entirely on land. They are among the most primitive of the Urodela, and their eggs are fertilized externally. Example:
Siberian salamander *Ranodon sibiricus*: found in mountain streams in southern parts of central Asia

FAMILY CRYPTOBRANCHIDAE
Giant salamanders; 3 species
This is an aquatic family, whose members do not have movable eyelids. One species is found in the eastern U.S.A., the other two in China and Japan. Example:
Japanese giant salamander *Andrias japonicus*: the largest living amphibian. It lives in mountain brooks and is carnivorous, feeding on crabs, fish and snails

FAMILY AMBYSTOMIDAE
Mole salamanders; 32 species
All members of this family are found in North and Central America. Fertilization is internal (as in all succeeding families of Urodela). Mole salamanders have rows of teeth across their palates. Examples:
Mexican axolotl *Ambystoma mexicanum* (female 8½ in., male 5¼ in.): lives in lakes. It usually retains its larval form for life, but can change to a salamander if its habitat dries up
Marbled salamander *Ambystoma opacum*: found in the U.S.A. from New England south to northern Florida and west to Texas. It lives on hillsides near ponds and streams

FAMILY SALAMANDRIDAE
Newts and salamanders; 42 species
Newts have long rows of teeth in the roof of the mouth, and the adults never have gills. Examples:
Fire salamander *Salamandra salamandra* (12½ in.): found in the lowlands of Europe, North Africa and Asia Minor, living under roots and moss in moist areas. It hibernates in soil and breeds in running water, bearing live young
Smooth newt *Triturus vulgaris*: found in Europe and western Asia. The male has a crest along the back in the mating season, and its tail is vertically flattened for swimming. This newt hibernates on land

FAMILY AMPHIUMIDAE
Congo or lamper eels; 3 species
These small, blackish-green salamanders, with eel-like bodies and minute limbs, are found in swampy, stagnant water in the eastern parts of the U.S.A. Example:
Three-toed amphiuma *Amphiuma means tridactylum*: the female lays its eggs in a long string and incubates them

FAMILY PLETHODONTIDAE
Lungless salamanders; 183 species
Most of these are aquatic, but the adults have no gills except in one genus. The land-living species are less active and consume less oxygen than those living in mountain brooks, whose well-aerated waters are suited to skin-breathing amphibians. Lungless salamanders are found in southern Europe, North and Central America and northern South America. Examples:
Texas blind salamander *Typhlomolge rathbuni* (3–4 in.): lives in water, 190 ft underground in San Marcos, Texas. It has permanent gills
Red-backed salamander *Plethodon cinereus*: lives in the eastern U.S.A. It is active at night and spends the day under logs and in crevices in rocks

FAMILY PROTEIDAE
Proteids; 6 species
Proteids are permanently larval in form, and lack eyelids. Example:
Mud-puppy *Necturus maculosus*: night-active in weedy North American streams. It eats a wide variety of aquatic animals

FAMILY SIRENIDAE
Sirens; 3 species
The members of this family, from southern U.S.A. and northern Mexico, have no hind limbs, teeth or eyelids. Their jaws are covered with horny plates and their gills persist throughout life. Example:
Greater siren *Siren lacertina*: found in south-eastern U.S.A. in shallow ponds and ditches. It swims like an eel, and burrows in soft mud

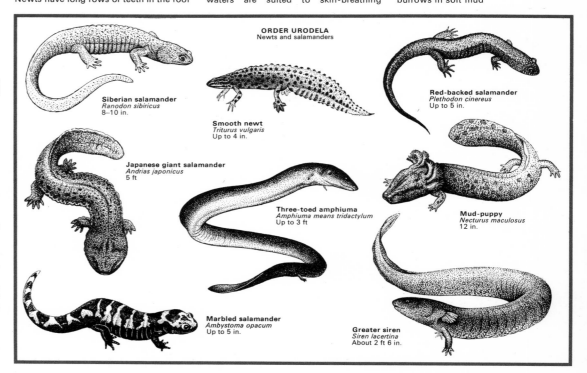

ORDER URODELA
Newts and salamanders

Siberian salamander
Ranodon sibiricus
8–10 in.

Smooth newt
Triturus vulgaris
Up to 4 in.

Red-backed salamander
Plethodon cinereus
Up to 5 in.

Japanese giant salamander
Andrias japonicus
5 ft

Three-toed amphiuma
Amphiuma means tridactylum
Up to 3 ft

Mud-puppy
Necturus maculosus
12 in.

Marbled salamander
Ambystoma opacum
Up to 5 in.

Greater siren
Siren lacertina
About 2 ft 6 in.

PHYLUM CHORDATA	Animals with notochords
SUB-PHYLUM VERTEBRATA	Animals with backbones
CLASS AMPHIBIA	Amphibians
ORDER ANURA	Frogs and toads

ORDER ANURA

Frogs and toads

The members of this group, the largest of the living orders of amphibians, have loosely fitting skins, no tails when adult, bony pectoral girdles, and usually no ribs. Fertilization is typically external, and no species remains larval for life. The anatomy is specialized for jumping: the vertebral column is short, with extensively fused vertebrae, the main bones of the limbs are fused, and the hind limbs are much longer than the forelimbs. Frogs and toads breathe by moving the floor of the mouth, first drawing air into the mouth and then forcing it into the lungs. The following 12 families are commonly recognized:

FAMILY ASCAPHIDAE
Ascaphids; 4 species
Members of this family have ribs and rudimentary tail-wagging muscles. There are two genera, one in New Zealand and one in North America. Example:
Hochstetter's frog *Leiopelma hochstetteri*: lives under stones on the Coromandel Peninsula of the North Island of New Zealand

FAMILY PIPIDAE
Pipid toads; 15 species
These toads are entirely aquatic. Only the larvae have ribs. Both jaws are usually toothless, and all species are tongueless. Eyelids are sometimes present. Examples:
Surinam toad *Pipa pipa* (6 in.): found in Trinidad and South America as far south as the Mato Grosso in Brazil. Spawning takes place while the female is clasped by the male; he catches and fertilizes the eggs, and then helps to squeeze them into the puffy skin on the female's back. The young emerge after about three months' incubation
African clawed toad *Xenopus laevis*: it has claws on three toes of its hind legs, some teeth in its upper jaw, and a tentacle under each eye. The female lays its eggs in still water and does not incubate them

FAMILY DISCOGLOSSIDAE
Discoglossids; 10 species
Discoglossids, found in Europe and Asia, have toothless lower jaws, and their ribs are present throughout life. Example:
Midwife toad *Alytes obstetricans*: found in Europe. The tadpoles hatch from spawn tangled round the male's thighs

FAMILY RHINOPHRYNIDAE
There is one species:
Mexican burrowing toad *Rhinophrynus dorsalis*: found among scrub and savanna on the coastal plains of Mexico and Guatemala

FAMILY PELOBATIDAE
Pelobatids; 54 species
These small toads with minute teeth are found in Eurasia, North Africa and North America. Example:
Iberian spadefoot toad *Pelobates cultripes*: found in south-western Europe and north-western Morocco

FAMILY BUFONIDAE
Toads; 300 species
The toads in this family have no upper teeth. There are several genera, the best known being *Bufo*, which contains 250 species and is found in all continents except Australia. These toads live on land and are active at dusk and before dawn. They are specialized for crawling and trap insects on their sticky tongues. Example:
Common toad *Bufo bufo*: found in Eurasia as far east as Lake Baikal; it lives a sedentary life under roots and logs. Its warty back secretes venom

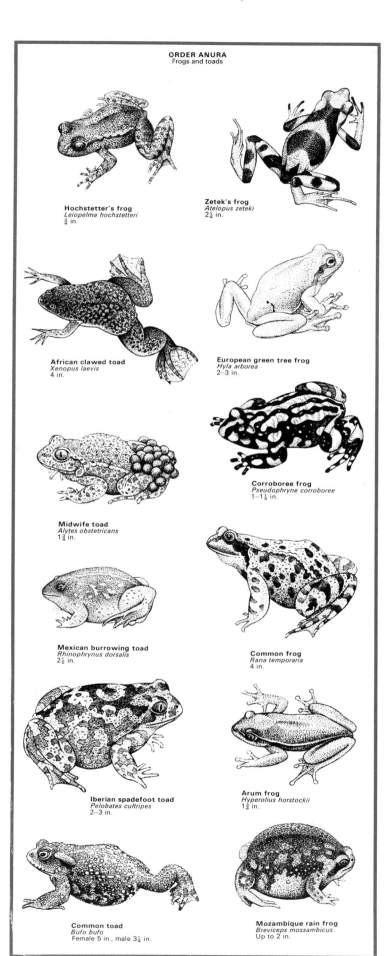

ORDER ANURA
Frogs and toads

Hochstetter's frog
Leiopelma hochstetteri
¾ in.

Zetek's frog
Atelopus zeteki
2¼ in.

African clawed toad
Xenopus laevis
4 in.

European green tree frog
Hyla arborea
2–3 in.

Corroboree frog
Pseudophryne corroboree
1–1¼ in.

Midwife toad
Alytes obstetricans
1¾ in.

Mexican burrowing toad
Rhinophrynus dorsalis
2½ in.

Common frog
Rana temporaria
4 in.

Iberian spadefoot toad
Pelobates cultripes
2–3 in.

Arum frog
Hyperolius horstockii
1¾ in.

Common toad
Bufo bufo
Female 5 in., male 3¼ in.

Mozambique rain frog
Breviceps mossambicus
Up to 2 in.

FAMILY ATELOPODIDAE
Atelopodids; 26 species
There are only two genera in this family of small, brightly colored frogs, which live near forest streams in Central and South America. Many species walk rather than hop. In one species, *Atelopus stelzneri* the tadpoles hatch within 24 hours of the eggs being laid. Example:
Zetek's frog *Atelopus zeteki*: lives near streams in Panama. It can neither swim nor jump very well, but its skin is poisonous and may deter predators

FAMILY HYLIDAE
Tree frogs; almost 600 species
Tree frogs are adapted for life in trees, and have an extra cartilage between the two end digits of the hands and feet, which gives them a better grip. The family, which also contains ground-living and aquatic forms, includes the large genus *Hyla*, containing 350 species, which is found throughout the world, except in Africa south of the Sahara and in eastern Polynesia. Example:
European green tree frog *Hyla arborea*: usually bright green but can rapidly change color to yellow or slate gray

FAMILY LEPTODACTYLIDAE
Leptodactylids; 650 species
Members of this family are found in South and Central America, Australia and southern Africa. Several genera are adapted to the more arid areas of Australia. During the dry season they retire deep into the ground. Some species lay their eggs in burrows and rely on rainfall for development; the tadpoles' metamorphosis is so rapid that they become adults before the water evaporates. Example:
Corroboree frog *Pseudophryne corroboree*: lives in New South Wales in burrows beneath sphagnum moss in boggy country above the snow line

FAMILY RANIDAE
Frogs: hundreds of species
This group, which occurs on all continents, is unspecialized except for jumping—the specialization common to all anurans. It includes the virtually world-wide genus *Rana*, containing 200–300 species, all of which have a notch on the end of the tongue. Some, such as the marsh frog *Rana ridibunda* and the edible frog *Rana esculenta*, are aquatic and have vocal sacs at the corner of the mouth; others have no vocal sacs. Example:
Common frog *Rana temporaria*: widespread in Eurasia, reaching the Arctic coast in places. The vocal sac is concealed under the skin of the throat

FAMILY RHACOPHORIDAE
Oar-legged frogs; hundreds of species
These frogs, found in the tropics of Africa, Madagascar and eastern Asia, resemble tree frogs in their adaptations to living in trees. They have webbed hind feet. Example:
Arum frog *Hyperolius horstockii*: found in southern Africa, where it often conceals itself within arum lilies

FAMILY MICROHYLIDAE
Microhylids; hundreds of species
This little-known family of burrowing and tree-living forms is found in the Old and New World tropics, except western Africa. The tadpoles hatch either at an advanced stage or completely metamorphosed. Example:
Mozambique rain frog *Breviceps mossambicus*: found in southern Africa. It burrows in open grassland and scrub at altitudes up to 4000 ft

Reptiles

PHYLUM CHORDATA	Animals with notochords
SUB-PHYLUM VERTEBRATA	Animals with backbones
CLASS REPTILIA	Reptiles
ORDER CHELONIA	Turtles and tortoises
ORDER RHYNCHOCEPHALIA	Tuatara

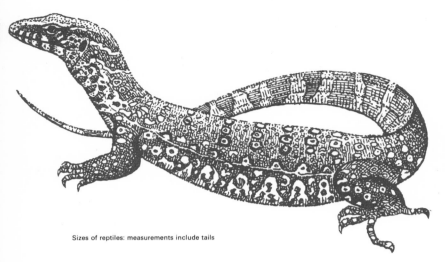

Sizes of reptiles: measurements include tails

Reptiles The first vertebrates to become truly adapted to a terrestrial life, reptiles can easily be distinguished from amphibians by their scaly skins, which prevent them from drying out.

Unlike amphibians, they have no aquatic larval stage and the new-born young are miniature versions of the adults. They always breathe by means of lungs, never with gills or through the skin. Reptiles are internally fertilized. Most lay eggs, but a few species produce live young.

Unlike mammals and birds, reptiles cannot regulate the body temperature by internal means, but they maintain a fairly constant temperature by moving between warm and cool surroundings. Reptiles have several bones in the lower jaw, while mammals have only one. In all reptiles, except crocodiles, some of the deoxygenated blood from the body mingles in the heart with reoxygenated blood from the lungs.

The reptile embryo, like those of mammals and birds, is enclosed in the egg by a fluid-containing sac called the amnion. A sac-like outgrowth from the gut, the allantois, absorbs oxygen from outside the shell and collects waste products.

ORDER CHELONIA

Turtles and tortoises
All the members of this primitive group, which has hardly changed in 200 million years, possess a shell of bony plates covered by horny scales. This forms an arched upper shell (the carapace) and an under-shell (the plastron). Their ribs, immobile and fused to the shell, cannot be used in breathing; the necessary pumping action is provided by the abdominal muscles. There are two sub-orders:

SUB-ORDER CRYPTODIRA
Hidden-necked turtles
The turtles in this group withdraw their heads into the shell by flexing the neck vertically. There are seven families:

FAMILY CHELYDRIDAE
Snapper, mud and musk turtles; 23 species
These turtles live on the bottom of ponds and rivers in warmer regions of the New World. Examples:
Eastern mud turtle *Kinosternon subrubrum* (4 in.): found in eastern North America. Its plastron is hinged
Common snapping turtle *Chelydra serpentina*: found in North America. It lies in wait for prey under water, and is also aggressive on land. It will eat anything it can catch

FAMILY DERMATEMYDIDAE
There is one species:
Central American river turtle *Dermatemys mawi*: little is known about this turtle, which lives in coastal rivers of Mexico and Guatemala

FAMILY TESTUDINIDAE
Tortoises and terrapins; 115 species
This family contains the most familiar land tortoises and freshwater turtles. Land tortoises are found in all the warmer parts of the world except Australia, and in all habitats from deserts to tropical forests and oceanic islands. Most species have blunt, heavily scaled feet and high-domed carapaces. Examples:
Painted terrapin *Chrysemys picta* (up to 7 in.): found in North America from southern Canada to the southern states of the U.S.A. It has a flat green shell, and a red streak near the ear. These terrapins, which are often kept as pets, are called 'turtles' in the U.S.A.
European pond tortoise *Emys orbicularis* (10 in.): lives mainly in southern Europe, but also occurs as far north as northern Germany
Leopard tortoise *Geochelone pardalis*: lives in southern and eastern Africa

FAMILY DERMOCHELYIDAE
There is one species:
Leathery turtle or **luth** *Dermochelys coriacea*: this 1200 lb. marine turtle lives in warm seas, but is rare. It feeds on jellyfish and tunicates, and breeds in the tropics. It has a smooth-backed appearance because its shell, unlike that of most turtles, consists of a mosaic of small bony plates embedded in skin. The shell is not joined to the ribs or the vertebrae

FAMILY CHELONIIDAE
Marine turtles; 5 species
These turtles live in the ocean and come ashore only to breed. The powerful front limbs are modified to form flippers, and the streamlined body narrows towards the back. The head cannot be withdrawn into the shell. Example:
Green turtle *Chelonia mydas*: lives in all warm oceans. Its Malaysian breeding grounds are protected. It weighs 1000 lb.

FAMILY TRIONYCHIDAE
Soft-shelled turtles; 22 species
These highly aquatic animals, from the fresh waters of North America, Asia and Africa, have no horny scales. They have partly webbed hind feet. Example:
Eastern soft-shelled turtle *Trionyx spiniferus*: found in eastern North America, it feeds on water insects and crayfish

FAMILY CARETTOCHELIDAE
There is one species:
New Guinea pitted-shelled turtle *Carettochelys insculpta*: this very rare turtle lives in rivers. It has a complete bony shell, but no covering of horny scales. It has paddle-shaped limbs

SUB-ORDER PLEURODIRA
Side-necked turtles
These turtles withdraw their heads into the shell by bending the neck sideways. There are two families:

FAMILY CHELIDAE
Snake-necked turtles; 31 species
This group is found in South America, Australia and New Guinea. Example:
Australian snake-necked turtle *Chelodina longicollis*: lives in eastern Australian rivers and feeds on fish

FAMILY PELOMEDUSIDAE
Pelomedusid turtles; 14 species
These turtles, from South America, Africa and Madagascar, bend their necks sideways like the snake-necks, but their necks are hidden by skin when they are withdrawn. Example:
Podocnemis unifilis: lives in South American rivers

SUB-ORDER PLEURODIRA
Side-necked turtles

Australian snake-necked turtle
Chelodina longicollis
12 in.

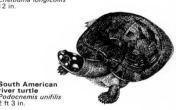

South American river turtle
Podocnemis unifilis
2 ft 3 in.

ORDER RHYNCHOCEPHALIA

There is only one surviving species in this order, the others having become extinct 100 million years ago. This species, which forms the family Sphenodontidae, is:
Tuatara *Sphenodon punctatus*: once found throughout New Zealand, now lives only on small islands off the coast of the North Island. This primitive, lizard-like reptile has teeth fused to the edges of the jaws (not set in sockets), a rudimentary third eye on top of the head and no copulatory organ

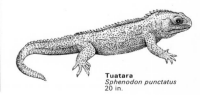

Tuatara
Sphenodon punctatus
20 in.

SUB-ORDER CRYPTODIRA
Hidden-necked turtles

Leathery turtle or luth
Dermochelys coriacea
Nearly 7 ft

Common snapping turtle
Chelydra serpentina
Up to 14 in.

Green turtle
Chelonia mydas
4 ft

Central American river turtle
Dermatemys mawi
12 in.

Eastern soft-shelled turtle
Trionyx spiniferus
Up to 16 in.

Leopard tortoise
Geochelone pardalis
23 in.

New Guinea pitted-shelled turtle
Carettochelys insculpta
Up to 20 in.

PHYLUM CHORDATA	Animals with notochords
SUB-PHYLUM VERTEBRATA	Animals with backbones
CLASS REPTILIA	Reptiles
ORDER SQUAMATA	Lizards and snakes

ORDER SQUAMATA

Lizards and snakes

Members of this order, the most successful group of modern reptiles, have bodies covered with small overlapping scales. There may be a single row of broad scales along the belly, and the head often has well-defined scales, sometimes containing bony plates fused to the skull. The tongue is notched or forked, the teeth are fused to the rims of the jaws. Some lizards are legless, like snakes.

The females usually lay eggs with parchment-like shells, but some hatch the eggs in their bodies. There are two sub-orders, whose members are not always easily distinguishable:

SUB-ORDER LACERTILIA

Lizards

Many lizards are snake-like in appearance with small limbs, or no limbs at all, and small eyes and ears. Some families consist entirely of limbless forms, and many others have some limbless members. A few lizards—some skinks, for example—give birth to live young. Some forms can shed the tail and regenerate it, but the new tail lacks the original pattern and has a cartilaginous rod instead of vertebrae. The skin is shed in pieces, and many lizards can change color, if only slightly. There are 20 families:

FAMILY GEKKONIDAE

Geckos; 400 species

These lizards are usually nocturnal and have big eyes, generally covered by a transparent membrane which is cleaned with the tongue. Their digits are short, usually with large, backward-curved claws, and most geckos have hair-like filaments on the undersides of their digits which can hook on to irregularities on vertical surfaces as smooth as glass. They are the only lizards with well-developed voices. Example:

Tokay gecko *Gekko gecko*: a south-east Asian gecko, named after its cry. It feeds on insects and mice

FAMILY PYGOPODIDAE

Flap-footed lizards; 13 species

These snake-like lizards from Australasia lack forelimbs and have flap-like hind limbs. Example:

Sharp-snouted snake-lizard *Lialis burtoni*: found in savanna in Australia and New Guinea

FAMILY XANTUSIIDAE

Night lizards; 11 species

These nocturnal lizards with gecko-like eye membranes hide by day in crevices in rocks and logs. They are found in Central America and south-western North America. Example:

Granite night lizard *Xantusia henshawi*: lives in California and Mexico, and feeds at night on insects, spiders, scorpions and centipedes. It bears live young

FAMILY IGUANIDAE

Iguanas; about 700 species

Iguanas have teeth on the inner sides of their jaws. There are long-legged, often swift-running forms, and some have a scaly crest on their backs. They occur mainly in the New World, but also in Madagascar, the Galapagos Islands, Fiji and Tonga. Examples:

Green anole *Anolis carolinensis* (9 in.): known as 'chameleon' in North America. It is brightly colored and swift-moving, and can change color rapidly, like the true chameleons

Common iguana *Iguana iguana*: lives in the trees of South American tropical forests

FAMILY AGAMIDAE

Agamid lizards; about 300 species

The agamid lizards are the counterparts in Europe, Africa, Asia and Australia of the iguanas, and closely resemble them, except that their teeth are borne on the rims of the jaws. Like iguanas, some forms have high crests supported by vertebral spines. Some species have throat sacs, some have spiny tails, some have spiny skins, and some have frills and run on their hind legs. Example:

Starred agama or **hardun** *Agama stellio*: lives in Greece, Asia Minor and Egypt in mountainous or rocky country

FAMILY CHAMAELEONTIDAE

Chameleons; 85 species

The feet of these tree-living lizards are adapted to grasping by having two toes opposed to the other three. Chameleons also have grasping tails. Their eyes move independently and their fused eyelids admit light through a small hole in the middle. The skull is crested, and the sticky tongue, which is half as long as the animal, shoots out to catch insects. Some members of the genus *Chamaeleo*, which contains 73 of the 85 species, have flamboyant horns. Example:

Common chameleon *Chamaeleo chamaeleon*: found in southern Spain, North Africa and Palestine

FAMILY DIBAMIDAE

Burrowing lizards; 4 species

Found in Indo-China and from the Philippines to New Guinea, and in Mexico, these short-tailed lizards are blind and earless, and are either limbless or have small limbs. Example:

Dibamus novae-guineae: lives in New Guinea, often in rotting logs

FAMILY SCINCIDAE

Skinks; about 700 species

The bodies of skinks tend to be elongated, and their limbs are small and sometimes absent, as are their ear apertures. They burrow in sand or live in leaf litter. The family includes the genus *Eumeces*, comprising 59 species, found in North and Central America, Asia and North Africa. These have longer legs than other skinks, and live in steppe and stony desert. About half the species lay eggs; the others bear live young. Example:

Australian blue-tongued skink *Tiliqua scincoides*: feeds on leaves, fruit and earthworms. It can withstand a wide range of temperatures

FAMILY FEYLINIIDAE

Limbless skinks; 4 species

These termite-eaters from equatorial Africa and Madagascar are entirely without legs. Example:

Feylinia currori: found in equatorial Africa, under decaying logs. It feeds almost exclusively on termites

FAMILY GERRHOSAURIDAE

Plated lizards; 25 species

Found in the dry areas of Africa and Madagascar, these lizards have armor-like scales. Example:

Sudan plated lizard *Gerrhosaurus major*: digs tunnels several feet long

FAMILY CORDYLIDAE

Girdle-tailed lizards; 23 species

These lizards are found in the grasslands of eastern and southern Africa. Members of the genus *Platysaurus* have flattened bodies, enabling them to shelter in rock crevices. Example:

Giant girdle-tailed lizard or **sungazer** *Cordylus giganteus*: a South African spiny lizard. It flattens itself to the ground in defense, protecting its underparts and exposing only its spiny upper surface

FAMILY LACERTIDAE

African and Eurasian lizards; about 150 species

These small, agile lizards have very long fragile tails and head shields which are fused to the bones of the skull. Examples:

Viviparous lizard *Lacerta vivipara* (6 in.): found in northern and central Eurasia; it is the only lizard to live within the Arctic circle. It produces live young

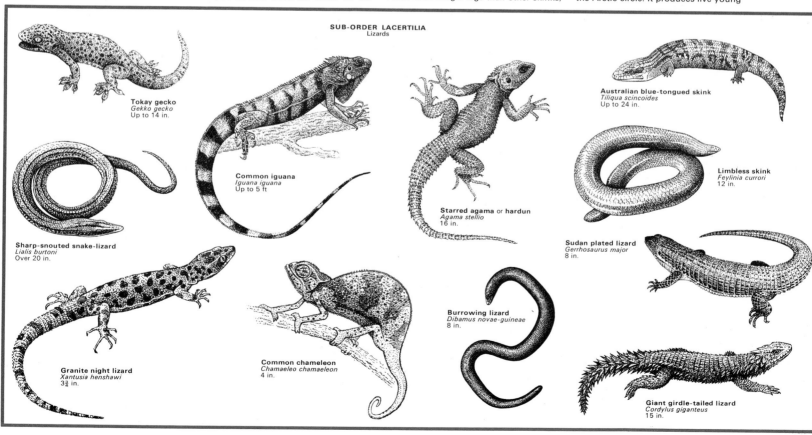

SUB-ORDER LACERTILIA
Lizards

Tokay gecko
Gekko gecko
Up to 14 in.

Sharp-snouted snake-lizard
Lialis burtoni
Over 20 in.

Granite night lizard
Xantusia henshawi
3¾ in.

Common iguana
Iguana iguana
Up to 5 ft

Common chameleon
Chamaeleo chamaeleon
4 in.

Starred agama or **hardun**
Agama stellio
16 in.

Burrowing lizard
Dibamus novae-guineae
8 in.

Australian blue-tongued skink
Tiliqua scincoides
Up to 24 in.

Limbless skink
Feylinia currori
12 in.

Sudan plated lizard
Gerrhosaurus major
8 in.

Giant girdle-tailed lizard
Cordylus giganteus
15 in.

Reptiles

PHYLUM CHORDATA	Animals with notochords
SUB-PHYLUM VERTEBRATA	Animals with backbones
CLASS REPTILIA	Reptiles
ORDER SQUAMATA	Lizards and snakes

Wall-lizard *Lacerta muralis* (8 in.): found from central Europe to northern Asia and Asia Minor. It is marked with lines and spots which harmonize with surroundings such as walls and debris where it spends much of its time

Eyed lizard *Lacerta lepida*: found in southern Europe and north-western Africa. It preys on mice, snakes and other lizards

FAMILY TEIIDAE
South American lizards or tegus; about 200 species
Tegus are the New World counterparts of the Lacertidae, but their head shields are separate from their skull bones. Example:
Common tegu *Tupinambus teguixin*: found in tropical America. It feeds on insects, worms and rodents

FAMILY ANGUIDAE
Slow worms; 40 species
These lizards are found in the New World, Europe and parts of Asia; they have fragile tails and forked tongues. Some species are completely legless. Example:
Slow worm *Anguis fragilis*: occurs from 60° N in Europe southwards to North Africa and in western Asia. It feeds on soft-bodied prey, such as slugs and earthworms

FAMILY ANNIELLIDAE
Legless lizards; 2 species
These Californian lizards are found in sandy ground, in which they catch their insect prey. They are small burrowers with no limbs or external ears, and small eyes. Example:
Californian legless lizard *Anniella pulchra*: a silvery or silver-black lizard which feeds on insects

FAMILY XENOSAURIDAE
Xenosaurid lizards; 4 species
This is a little-known group. All species have strong legs and robust bodies covered in a mixture of large and small scales. There are three species in Central America and one in China. Example:
Chinese crocodile-lizard *Shinisaurus crocodilurus*: lives near streams in China and feeds on tadpoles and fish

FAMILY HELODERMATIDAE
Venomous lizards; 2 species
These are the only poisonous lizards. The venom glands are in the lower jaw, not in the upper jaw as in snakes. Example:
Gila monster *Heloderma suspectum*: found in northern Mexico and south-western states of the U.S.A. A venomous lizard which preys mainly on small rodents; its bite is rarely fatal to man

FAMILY LANTHANOTIDAE
There is one species:
Earless monitor *Lanthanotus borneensis*: found in Borneo. It has short legs and its lower eyelids have a clear window

FAMILY VARANIDAE
Monitors; 24 species
All these large lizards belong to the genus *Varanus*, found throughout the warmer regions of the Old World. They are swift-moving predators. Examples:
Komodo dragon *Varanus komodoensis* (up to 12 ft): this, the largest lizard, was not discovered by Europeans until 1912. It lives only on some of the Lesser Sunda Islands of Indonesia
Nile monitor *Varanus niloticus*: lives near rivers in Africa. It feeds on frogs, birds, crocodiles' eggs and small lizards

FAMILY AMPHISBAENIDAE
Worm-lizards; 120 species
This is a family of burrowing, legless lizards with short, thick tails. The small head is not marked off from the body, so both ends look similar—hence the family's scientific name ('going both ways'). They are found in Florida, Mexico, South America, the Mediterranean and Africa. Example:

White-bellied worm-lizard *Amphisbaena alba*: lives in tropical America. Often found on manure heaps, it feeds on ants and termites

SUB-ORDER SERPENTES
Snakes
Most snakes, unlike lizards, are adapted to swallow prey larger than themselves; flexible ligaments and joints allow the two parts of the lower jaw to move apart during swallowing and give them some independence of movement. Snakes are always legless, and their skin is usually shed whole. The tail does not regenerate if lost; the eyelids are fused to form a transparent covering. The left lung is usually reduced in size, while the right lung is greatly enlarged and elongated. In many forms the forked tongue is protruded and retracted constantly through a notch in the snout, without the mouth being opened. Snakes probably evolved from burrowing lizards, and burrowing snakes, like lizards, appear to have evolved several times. Venomous snakes predominate only in Australia. There are 11 families:

FAMILY ANOMALEPIDAE
Anomalepid snakes; about 20 species
This is a small tropical South American group of blind snakes, with large head shields. Example:
Helminthophis bondensis: this snake burrows in South American forest floors

FAMILY TYPHLOPIDAE
Blind snakes; 150 species
This is the commonest burrowing family. The skull is rigid and the front of the head has a single plate for pushing through earth. The body is cylindrical, and the very short tail ends in a spine. There are no teeth in the lower jaw; and the eyes are tiny and often do not function. These snakes, which come to the surface after heavy rain, feed on earthworms and millipedes. They are found in southern Eurasia, Africa, Madagascar, tropical parts of the Americas and Australia. Example:
Spotted blind snake *Typhlops punctatus*: lives in African equatorial forests

FAMILY LEPTOTYPHLOPIDAE
Blind or thread snakes; 40 species
These blind snakes, with large teeth in the lower jaw and none in the upper, are found in Africa and tropical America. Example:
Western blind snake *Leptotyphlops humilis*: this burrowing snake is found in south-western U.S.A. and Mexico

FAMILY UROPELTIDAE
Shield-tailed snakes; 43 species
These small, primitive burrowers from India and Ceylon have a large shield-like scale at the end of the tail. They do not lay eggs, but give birth to about six live young. Example:
Uropeltis ocellatus: burrows in soft ground in the Indian forests

FAMILY ANILIIDAE
Pipe snakes; 10 species
Members of this small family of burrowers, from South America and south-east Asia, still have vestiges of hind limbs. They prey on other snakes. Example:
Flower-pot snake *Typhlops braminus* (4 in.): found in Mexico, Madagascar, south-east Asia and many Pacific islands. It lives among the roots of plants and feeds on insect larvae and other small soil-dwelling animals
Cylindrophis rufus: lives in south-east Asia. It is cylindrical, but flattens itself when disturbed

FAMILY XENOPELTIDAE
There is one species:
Sunbeam snake *Xenopeltis unicolor*: found in south-east Asia. A burrower with iridescent brown scales, it preys on other snakes. The teeth of its lower jaw are set in a loosely hinged bone

FAMILY BOIDAE
Constrictors; about 70 species
These large, non-poisonous snakes often have claws, which are vestigial hind limbs, and sometimes they have two

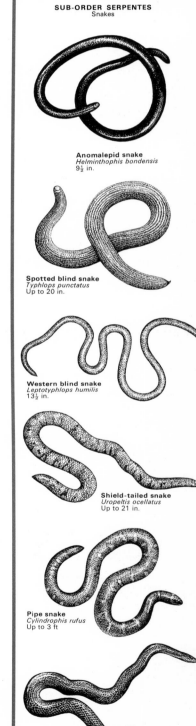

SUB-ORDER SERPENTES
Snakes

Anomalepid snake
Helminthophis bondensis
9½ in.

Spotted blind snake
Typhlops punctatus
Up to 20 in.

Western blind snake
Leptotyphlops humilis
13½ in.

Shield-tailed snake
Uropeltis ocellatus
Up to 21 in.

Pipe snake
Cylindrophis rufus
Up to 3 ft

Sunbeam snake
Xenopeltis unicolor
Up to 3 ft 4 in.

SUB-ORDER LACERTILIA
Lizards

Eyed lizard
Lacerta lepida
Over 24 in.

Chinese crocodile-lizard
Shinisaurus crocodilurus
10–15 in.

Gila monster
Heloderma suspectum
20 in.

Common tegu
Tupinambus teguixin
Up to 4 ft

Earless monitor
Lanthanotus borneensis
17 in.

Slow worm
Anguis fragilis
20 in.

Nile monitor
Varanus niloticus
6 ft

Californian legless lizard
Anniella pulchra
8–10 in.

White-bellied worm-lizard
Amphisbaena alba
24 in.

PHYLUM CHORDATA	Animals with notochords
SUB-PHYLUM VERTEBRATA	Animals with backbones
CLASS REPTILIA	Reptiles
ORDER SQUAMATA	Lizards and snakes
ORDER CROCODILIA	Crocodiles

fully developed lungs. They kill their prey by constriction: the snake coils its body round its victim and squeezes, causing suffocation. Nearly all constrictors are found in the tropics. The largest species, the reticulated python *Python reticulatus* occasionally grows to 33 ft. Examples:
Boa constrictor *Boa constrictor* (11 ft): found in dry forests and scrub in South America. It lives in tree-holes, among tree roots and in holes in the ground. It is rarely found in water, and it preys mainly on small mammals and rats

Anaconda *Eunectes murinus* (25 ft): lives in swamps and slow-moving rivers in the Amazon forests. It stays under water for long periods, and may burrow in mud when the water dries up. Peccaries, deer, caymans and fish are its main prey
Indian python *Python molurus*: found in India and south-east Asia. It has spearhead markings on the head and neck

FAMILY ACROCHORDIDAE
Oriental water snakes; 2 species
These snakes are well adapted to life in estuaries and coastal waters, with nostrils on top of the snout, and small eyes. They give birth to about 30 live young at a time. Example:
Elephant's trunk snake *Acrochordus javanicus*: found from India to northern Australia. The female is heavy-bodied, and much larger than the male

FAMILY VIPERIDAE
Vipers; 100 species
The viper has tubular fangs at the front of the mouth, folded back when the jaw is closed, but erect when it is open; they are so long that the viper need only strike, and not chew, its victim. The venom runs down a canal in each fang, and is more potent just after the snake sheds its skin. It primarily affects the circulatory system of the victim and causes swelling, inflammation and hemorrhage. There is only a vestige of a reduced lung, and often no trace of it at all. The family includes the rattlesnakes of the genera *Crotalus* and *Sistrurus* whose modified tail skin vibrates to produce a warning. Rattlesnakes are members of the group known as pit-vipers because they possess heat-sensitive organs located in pits between the eyes and the nostrils. Pit-vipers are found mainly in America, whereas true vipers, which lack facial pits, live in the Old World. Examples:
Common adder or **viper** *Vipera berus* (up to 30 in.) found in northern Eurasia in forests, tundra and heath. Its poison acts quickly on small rodents, but is too mild to cause many fatalities to man
Eastern diamond-back rattlesnake *Crotalus adamanteus* (8 ft): abundant in Florida in moist ground. It swims well
Puff adder *Bitis arietans*: found in Africa. Highly venomous, it is fat and sluggish and one of the longest vipers

FAMILY ELAPIDAE
Cobras, mambas, coral snakes and sea-snakes; about 200 species
All these snakes are highly poisonous. The grooved or tubular fangs at the front of the mouth are not very long, so the poison must be injected by chewing. The venom affects mainly the nervous system, and does not usually produce local effects. The sea-snakes usually give birth to live young, but the land forms usually lay eggs. Examples:
Black-and-yellow sea-snake *Pelamis platurus* (up to 3 ft): lives in tropical seas. It has a vertically flattened tail and a long flexible body
King cobra or **hamadryad** *Ophiophagus hannah*: lives in south-east Asia. It is one of the largest poisonous snakes, but is seldom aggressive to man. The female buries her eggs in leaves, then coils herself above them. It feeds mainly on monitor lizards and other snakes

FAMILY COLUBRIDAE
Colubrid snakes; about 1100 species
This family has the most species and its members are found throughout the world. Most are harmless; some have poison, but the small fangs at the back of

the jaw are rarely harmful to large mammals. There are no traces of hind limbs, and the left lung is small or absent. Examples:
Boomslang *Dispholidus typus* (up to 6 ft): a green snake found in African savanna. It is the only colubrid whose bite may be fatal to man
Grass snake *Natrix natrix*: found in Europe, parts of North Africa and eastwards to central Asia

ORDER CROCODILIA
Crocodiles
The closest living relatives of the dinosaurs, these large reptiles are adapted to an aquatic existence. A fold of skin closes the windpipe at the back, so that the animal can open its mouth under water and breathe with its nostrils above the surface. The nostrils, like the eyes and ears, are placed high on the head. When crocodiles are completely submerged, the ears and nostrils are closed by valves, and the eyes covered by membranes. Crocodiles have no salivary glands and usually eat under water. Some species sweep their prey from the land into the water with their powerful, vertically flattened tails. Crocodiles' scales are hard and square, and a few rows of raised scales down the back and tail contain knobs of bone. There are two families:

FAMILY GAVIALIDAE
There is one species:
Gavial or **gharial** *Gavialis gangeticus*: also known as the true or Indian gavial, it lives in the Indus, Ganges and Brahmaputra river systems, feeding on fish. It has very small nasal bones, 27–29 teeth on each side, and a long narrow snout that widens at the nostrils

FAMILY CROCODYLIDAE
Crocodiles; 120 species
Crocodiles live mainly in tropical rivers, though some forms swim out to sea. There are three sub-families. The Alligatorinae sub-family includes the alligators and caymans, which have 17–22 teeth on each side of each jaw; the fourth tooth of the lower jaw fits into a pit in the upper jaw and is invisible when the mouth is closed. In the Crocodylinae, the true crocodiles, with 14 or 15 teeth on each side, the fourth tooth fits into a pit in the upper jaw, but remains visible when the mouth is closed. This tooth is also visible in the Tomistominae, the false gavials; these have 20 or 21 teeth a side. Example:
Nile crocodile *Crocodylus niloticus*: found in southern and central Africa and Madagascar. It lives in lairs dug out of river banks and feeds mainly on fish, though it also eats land animals

SUB-ORDER SERPENTES
Snakes

Indian python
Python molurus
Up to 20 ft

Elephant's trunk snake
Acrochordus javanicus
Up to 6 ft

Puff adder
Bitis arietans
3–4 ft

King cobra or **hamadryad**
Ophiophagus hannah
18 ft

Grass snake
Natrix natrix
Female up to 6 ft

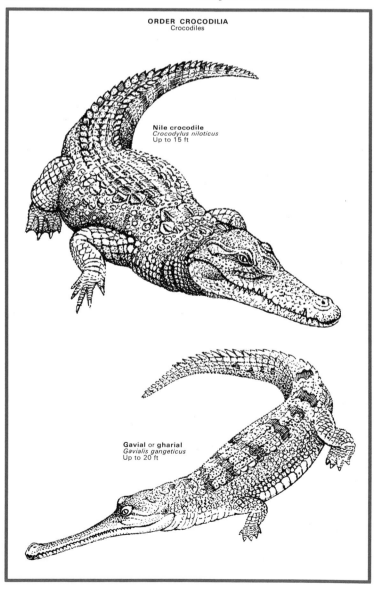

ORDER CROCODILIA
Crocodiles

Nile crocodile
Crocodylus niloticus
Up to 15 ft

Gavial or **gharial**
Gavialis gangeticus
Up to 20 ft

Birds

PHYLUM CHORDATA	Animals with notochords	ORDER RHEIFORMES	Rheas
SUB-PHYLUM VERTEBRATA	Animals with backbones	ORDER CASUARIIFORMES	Cassowaries and emus
CLASS AVES	Birds	ORDER TINAMIFORMES	Tinamous
ORDER APTERYGIFORMES	Kiwis	ORDER PODICIPEDIFORMES	Grebes
ORDER STRUTHIONIFORMES	Ostrich		

Sizes of birds: measurements are from beak to tail or beak to toe, whichever is the greater

runner. There are only two toes on each foot. Ostriches live in bands of 10–50, mainly in southern and eastern Africa, but are also found in the Sahara

for a blue spot on each side. It has brown and yellow stripes as a chick and deep brown plumage when adult

Ostrich
Struthio camelus
Up to 7 ft

ORDER CASUARIIFORMES
Cassowaries and emu

Australian cassowary
Casuarius casuarius
4 ft 6 in.–5 ft

Emu
Dromaius novaehollandiae
Over 6 ft

ORDER RHEIFORMES

There is one family:

FAMILY RHEIDAE
Rheas; 2 species
The largest birds in the New World, rheas live in flocks on the pampas. The head, neck and thighs are feathered, but they have no tail plumes. Example:
Common rhea or **South American ostrich** *Rhea americana*: feeds on vegetable matter or insects

ORDER TINAMIFORMES

There is one family:

FAMILY TINAMIDAE
Tinamous; 50 species
Tinamous, which are brown or grey birds (often barred and mottled), have short tails. They can fly. Example:
Little tinamou *Crypturellus soui*: found in forests and savanna from southern Mexico to southern Brazil

Studies of fossils and comparative anatomy show that birds are descended from reptiles. The earliest bird—still almost a reptile in its general construction—probably appeared about 140 million years ago. Birds' feathers are derived from reptilian scales, their forelimbs are modified into wings, and their light, delicate bones with air-filled cavities are well adapted to flight. Like mammals, birds have a constant body temperature—averaging 3°C more than that of mammals—and a four-chambered heart. In most birds the breastbone has a keel-like projection of bone to which the powerful wing muscles are attached; there are no teeth in the horny beak.

The class Aves was formerly divided into two sub-classes—the ratites (running birds, with very small wings and an unkeeled breastbone) and the flying birds. Now, however, it is divided only into 27 orders of equal status, of which one—Passeriformes—contains more than half of the known bird species.

ORDER APTERYGIFORMES

There is one family:

FAMILY APTERYGIDAE
Kiwis; 3 species
These flightless New Zealand birds—surviving relatives of the extinct New Zealand moas—have short, muscular legs and strong claws. Their hair-like feathers hide their stubby wings and they lack tails. They inhabit forested areas, remaining hidden by day. At night they probe for invertebrates with their long bills. The females are larger than males. Example:
Large gray kiwi *Apteryx haasti*: found only in the South Island. Like the other two species it is a slow breeder, usually laying only one egg. Incubation, which takes about 11 weeks, is often carried out by the male

Large gray kiwi
Apteryx haasti
2 ft 4 in.

ORDER STRUTHIONIFORMES

There is one family:

FAMILY STRUTHIONIDAE
There is one species:
Ostrich *Struthio camelus*: the ostrich is the largest living bird. Its weight, small wings and inadequate wing muscles combine to make it flightless. It is a swift

Common rhea or **South American ostrich**
Rhea americana
Up to 5 ft 6 in.

ORDER CASUARIIFORMES

Cassowaries and emu
These heavily built, flightless birds have coarse plumage, but the head and neck are virtually featherless. The young are longitudinally striped. There are two families:

FAMILY CASUARIIDAE
Cassowaries; 3 species
Found in forests from New Guinea to northern Australia, the cassowaries have a large bony crest on the forehead, possibly used to fend off obstructions as they run through the undergrowth, and a spike-like inner toe. The skin of the head and the neck is blue or purple. Example:
Australian cassowary *Casuarius casuarius*: lives in Australia

FAMILY DROMAIIDAE
There is one species:
Emu *Dromaius novaehollandiae*: found on the Australian plains. It has no crest, and the head and neck are feathered except

Little tinamou
Crypturellus soui
11 in.

ORDER PODICIPEDIFORMES

There is one family:

FAMILY PODICIPEDIDAE
Grebes; 21 species
The weak-flying grebes have long, thin necks and pointed bills. The feet, set far back on the body, have stiff horny flaps on the toes which increase the surface area for swimming. Example:
Great crested grebe *Podiceps cristatus*: found in fresh waters in the Old World. It has two stiff tufts of black feathers on its head

Great crested grebe
Podiceps cristatus
19 in.

PHYLUM CHORDATA	Animals with notochords	ORDER SPHENISCIFORMES	Penguins
SUB-PHYLUM VERTEBRATA	Animals with backbones	ORDER PROCELLARIIFORMES	Albatrosses, shearwaters and petrels
CLASS AVES	Birds	ORDER PELECANIFORMES	Pelicans and allies
ORDER GAVIIFORMES	Loons		

ORDER GAVIIFORMES

There is one family:

FAMILY GAVIIDAE
Loons or divers; 5 species
These Arctic birds have legs encased in body skin down to the ankles, and webbed feet which are used for swimming. Their bodies are streamlined for diving. Example:
Common loon or **great northern diver** *Gavia immer*: it swims on fresh water in summer but seeks unfrozen salt water in winter

Common loon or great northern diver
Gavia immer
2–3 ft

ORDER SPHENISCIFORMES

There is one family:

FAMILY SPHENISCIDAE
Penguins; 18 species
These Southern Hemisphere birds have feet far back on the body and body skin covering the legs down to the ankles. They swim with their wings. Example:
Jackass or **black-footed penguin** *Spheniscus demersus*: breeds on South African shores. It is called 'jackass' because it brays rather like a donkey

Jackass or black-footed penguin
Spheniscus demersus
18 in.

ORDER PROCELLARIIFORMES

Albatrosses, shearwaters and petrels
The oceanic birds of this order, characterized by long tubular nostrils opening out of their hooked bills, seldom come ashore except to breed. They discharge a clear yellow stomach oil when disturbed. This oil is also used to feed the young. These birds usually nest in a burrow in the ground. There are four families:

FAMILY DIOMEDEIDAE
Albatrosses; 13 species
These large, stout-bodied birds with long, narrow wings are superb gliders. Example:
Wandering albatross *Diomedea exulans*: lives in the southern oceans

FAMILY PROCELLARIIDAE
Shearwaters and fulmars; 53 species
This is a marine and highly migratory family of birds with slender bodies and webbed feet. They skim low over the water. Example:
Fulmar *Fulmarus glacialis*: found in the Northern Hemisphere

FAMILY HYDROBATIDAE
Storm petrels; 20 species
These small dark birds are named petrels after St. Peter, because they lower their feet as they skim over the surface of the sea and appear to walk on it. They have short, broad wings, which they use to support their top-heavy bodies when running on land. Example:
Storm petrel *Hydrobates pelagicus*: breeds in dense colonies on islands off the coast of Europe and in the western Mediterranean

FAMILY PELECANOIDIDAE
Diving petrels; 5 species
These stout, short-billed birds dive for crustaceans and fish instead of taking them from the surface like storm petrels. Example:
Peruvian diving petrel *Pelecanoides garnotii*: found off the western coast of South America

ORDER PELECANIFORMES

Pelicans and allies
These are the only birds with all four toes webbed, but only the pelicans have a large pouch suspended from the bill. There are six families:

FAMILY PHAETHONTIDAE
Tropic birds; 3 species
The black-and-white tropic birds are found only in tropical seas, often hundreds of miles from land. Example:
White-tailed or **yellow-billed tropic bird** *Phaethon lepturus*: lives in the Atlantic, Indian and Pacific Oceans

FAMILY PELECANIDAE
Pelicans; 8 species
The pelican's large beak-pouch holds two or three times as much as its stomach, and is used as a scoop to catch fish. Pelicans breed on big lakes, and some go to the coast in winter. Example:
White pelican *Pelecanus onocrotalus*: found in Eurasia and Africa

FAMILY PHALACROCORACIDAE
Cormorants and shags; 30 species
These coastal birds, which have long bodies, necks and hooked beaks, hunt by diving for their underwater prey. They cannot fly long distances because, like the loons, their wings are short. Example:
Common cormorant *Phalacrocorax carbo*: found on coasts of northern Europe, Iceland, western Greenland, Africa, Asia, Australia and New Zealand

FAMILY ANHINGIDAE
Darters; 4 species
Darters, found in warm waters throughout the world, are like cormorants but have long, straight, pointed bills. They often swim partly submerged, with only their heads out of water. Example:
American anhinga *Anhinga anhinga*: found from southern U.S.A. to Argentina

FAMILY SULIDAE
Gannets and boobies; 9 species
These birds, which inhabit coastal waters and islands in tropical and temperate seas, have long, pointed wings, straight, sharp bills, long tails, and short, stout legs. They dive from a great height and chase fish under water. Example:
Masked booby *Sula dactylatra*: nests in colonies on cliffs in the tropics

FAMILY FREGATIDAE
Frigate-birds; 5 species
Their big wingspan enables frigate-birds to soar effortlessly for hours. They rarely enter the sea, and usually feed by making other birds disgorge their food. Example:
Magnificent frigate-bird *Fregata magnificens*: commonly found in the tropical waters of the south Atlantic, Pacific and Indian Oceans

ORDER PROCELLARIIFORMES
Albatrosses, shearwaters and petrels

Wandering albatross
Diomedea exulans
Wingspan 10 ft or more

Fulmar
Fulmarus glacialis
20 in.

Storm petrel
Hydrobates pelagicus
6 in.

Peruvian diving petrel
Pelecanoides garnotii
9 in.

ORDER PELECANIFORMES
Pelicans and allies

White-tailed or yellow-billed tropic bird
Phaethon lepturus
2 ft 8 in.

American anhinga
Anhinga anhinga
3 ft

White pelican
Pelecanus onocrotalus
5 ft 6 in.

Masked booby
Sula dactylatra
2 ft 3 in.

Common cormorant
Phalacrocorax carbo
3 ft 4 in.

Magnificent frigate bird
Fregata magnificens
Wingspan 7 ft

Birds

PHYLUM CHORDATA	Animals with notochords
SUB-PHYLUM VERTEBRATA	Animals with backbones
CLASS AVES	Birds
ORDER CICONIIFORMES	Herons, storks and flamingoes
ORDER ANSERIFORMES	Screamers and ducks
ORDER FALCONIFORMES	Eagles, hawks and vultures

ORDER CICONIIFORMES

Herons, storks and flamingoes
Most birds in this group have long, featherless legs adapted for wading, a long bill, broad, rounded wings, short tails and four long, spreading toes on each foot. They feed on fish, aquatic animals and insects. There are seven families:

FAMILY ARDEIDAE
Herons; 64 species
The heron's neck is permanently S-shaped because the development of the vertebrae is uneven. The middle toe has a serrated claw. Example:
Purple heron *Ardea purpurea*: found in freshwater marshes and on river banks in the Old World. It nests in colonies

FAMILY COCHLEARIIDAE
There is one species:
Boat-billed heron *Cochlearius cochlearius*: lives in the mangroves of Central and South America. It has a broad, scoop-like bill and a combed claw

FAMILY BALAENICIPITIDAE
There is one species:
Shoebill or **whale-headed stork** *Balaeniceps rex*: lives in the papyrus swamps of the White Nile. It has a combed middle claw and a wide, 8 in. long beak. It flies with its neck folded

FAMILY SCOPIDAE
There is one species:
Hammerkop *Scopus umbretta*: flies with neck extended like a stork, but possesses heron-like vocal organs. It has serrated claws and a fourth toe level with the other toes. It lives in Africa

FAMILY CICONIIDAE
Storks; 17 species
Storks do not have a serrated middle claw. Their short toes are partly webbed at the base, and the hind toe is elevated above the other three. Example:
White stork *Ciconia ciconia*: nests in Europe and eastern Asia; the European population winters in South Africa and the Middle East

FAMILY THRESKIORNITHIDAE
Ibises and spoonbills; 32 species
These birds are like storks, but the hind toe is only slightly elevated, and the middle claw only slightly serrated. Example:
Sacred ibis *Threskiornis aethiopica*: widespread in Africa, it has a large body, short legs and a thin, down-curved bill

FAMILY PHOENICOPTERIDAE
Flamingoes; 4 species
Flamingoes fly with their necks straight, their legs trailing behind, and honk like geese during flight. The hind toe is elevated or absent, and the others are webbed. These birds breed in tropical brackish waters. Example:
Greater flamingo *Phoenicopterus ruber*: found in the Americas, Africa, Europe and western Asia

ORDER ANSERIFORMES

Screamers and ducks
These full-bodied waterfowl have a long neck and a feathered oil gland situated near the base of the tail. The oil, transferred to the feathers by the bill, waterproofs the body. There are two families:

FAMILY ANHIMIDAE
Screamers; 3 species
These are rather long-legged South American waders with a short, curved bill, little webbing on the toes, and two sharp spurs on the front edge of each wing. They have a harsh, resounding cry. Example:
Horned screamer *Anhima cornuta*: lives in the flooded forests and marshes of tropical South America

FAMILY ANATIDAE
Swans, geese, ducks; 145 species
These are gregarious water birds, with short legs, webbed front toes and broad bills. Most of them dive for their food. Example:
Canada goose *Branta canadensis*: breeds on lake shores and marshes in Canada and Alaska and migrates in winter to coastal and southern states of the U.S.A.

ORDER CICONIIFORMES
Herons, storks and flamingoes

Shoebill or **whale-headed stork**
Balaeniceps rex
4 ft

Sacred ibis
Threskiornis aethiopica
18 in.

Purple heron
Ardea purpurea
2 ft 6 in.

Hammerkop
Scopus umbretta
20 in.

Boat-billed heron
Cochlearius cochlearius
20 in.

Greater flamingo
Phoenicopterus ruber
Up to 5 ft

White stork
Ciconia ciconia
4 ft; wingspan nearly 7 ft

ORDER ANSERIFORMES
Screamers and ducks

Horned screamer
Anhima cornuta
2 ft 9 in.

Canada goose
Branta canadensis
Up to 2 ft 1 in.

ORDER FALCONIFORMES

Eagles, hawks and vultures
These birds of prey, which are active during the day, have sharp, down-hooked bills with a waxy membrane across the base, through which the nostrils open. They lay small clutches of eggs and incubation is lengthy. There are five families:

FAMILY CATHARTIDAE
American vultures and condors; 6 species
The toes of these birds are weak and adapted for walking and running, not clutching; the three front toes have rudimentary webbing. Their bills are also weak and unable to tear most flesh until it is partly decayed. Example:
King vulture *Sarcorhamphus papa*: found from southern Mexico to the tropical forests of northern Argentina. It has a bare neck and a wattle on its beak

PHYLUM CHORDATA	Animals with notochords
SUB-PHYLUM VERTEBRATA	Animals with backbones
CLASS AVES	Birds
ORDER FALCONIFORMES	Eagles, hawks and vultures
ORDER GALLIFORMES	Game birds and hoatzin

ORDER FALCONIFORMES
Eagles, hawks and vultures

King vulture
Sarcorhamphus papa
Wingspan 6 ft

Osprey
Pandion haliaetus
Up to 24 in.

Secretary bird
Sagittarius serpentarius
4 ft

Peregrine falcon
Falco peregrinus
Up to 20 in.

African fish eagle
Haliaeëtus vocifer
2 ft 6 in.

FAMILY SAGITTARIIDAE
There is one species:
Secretary bird *Sagittarius serpentarius*: found in sparsely wooded grasslands or veldts in Africa. It has a long crest and long legs. It can fly, but usually runs. It eats snakes and other reptiles

FAMILY ACCIPITRIDAE
Eagles, hawks and Old World vultures; 205 species
These birds have broad wings, usually rounded at the tip, and strong claws. Unlike falcons, they have no notch or 'tooth' on the bill. Examples:
Griffon vulture *Gyps fulvus* (up to 3 ft 5 in.): a carrion-eater, found in the mountains of southern Europe, south-west Asia and Africa. It can draw its neck into its neck ruff
Goshawk *Accipiter gentilis* (24 in.): found in Eurasia and North America, nesting in clefts of branches. It strikes and

pursues its victim, whereas most hawks disable prey in passing and return for it
African fish eagle *Haliaeëus vocifer*: common on the banks of African rivers and lakes. It has a powerful bill and legs

FAMILY PANDIONIDAE
There is one species:
Osprey *Pandion haliaetus*: widely distributed near water, where it catches fish. It has broad, pointed wings and four toes of equal length, the outer one being reversible

FAMILY FALCONIDAE
Falcons; 58 species
These birds have long pointed wings, bare ankles and feet, and a notch or 'tooth' on the upper part of the bill. They do not make nests but breed on the ground, on ledges or in deserted nests. Example:
Peregrine falcon *Falco peregrinus*: practically worldwide in coastal areas

Game birds and hoatzin
Most of this group are ground-living birds with short, turned-down bills and long, heavy feet, with a short fourth toe behind and short, rounded wings. There are seven families:

FAMILY MEGAPODIDAE
Megapodes; 12 species
Found from Australia to Malaya, the megapodes (from the Greek for 'large feet') rarely fly. They build enormous nests in which their eggs are incubated by the heat of rotting vegetation, stored warmth from the sun or volcanic heat. The fourth toe is almost level with the others. Example:
Mallee fowl *Leipoa ocellata*: found in inland southern Australia. It lays its eggs in large mounds of leaf mold and covers them with sand. The male regulates the temperature of the mound by adding or removing sand

FAMILY CRACIDAE
Curassows; 43 species
Curassows nest in trees but feed mainly on the ground. The fourth toe is level with the others. Curassows have shaggy, permanently erect crests and the male has a brightly colored bill. Example:
Great curassow *Crax rubra*: found in tropical forests from Mexico to Central America

FAMILY TETRAONIDAE
Grouse; 18 species
The ankles of these birds are at least partly feathered, and most grouse grow fringes on their toes in winter. The fourth toe is elevated. The nostrils are feathered and there is often a bright, bare eye-patch. Example:
Capercaillie *Tetrao urogallus*: found in Eurasian coniferous forests. The male displays its tail in the breeding season

FAMILY PHASIANIDAE
Fowl; 165 species
Most fowl are heavily built ground-living birds, with feathered nostrils, naked feet and spurs on the back of the legs. They cannot fly for long. Examples:
Partridge *Perdix perdix* (12–18 in.): lives in dunes, heaths and grassland in Europe and western Asia. It nests in a straw-lined hollow in the ground
Common or **ringed pheasant** *Phasianus colchicus*: a native of central Asia, introduced to Europe by the Romans
Indian jungle fowl *Gallus gallus*: lives in Asian tropical forests, from sea level to 5000 ft. It is the ancestor of all domestic breeds and was domesticated in India by 3200 BC

FAMILY NUMIDIDAE
Guinea fowl; 10 species
These African game birds are generally found in flocks in bushy grasslands and open forests. They have a bare head and neck, dark feathers spangled with white, and rudimentary spurs. Example:
Vulturine or **long-tailed guinea fowl** *Acryllium vulturinum*: lives in East Africa

FAMILY MELEAGRIDIDAE
Turkeys; 2 species
Found throughout the world as domestic birds and occasionally in the wild in North and Central America, turkeys have spurs, and rudimentary webs between the toes. Their heads and necks are naked; the males have long throat pouches and both sexes have nose pouches. Example:
Common turkey *Meleagris gallopavo*: lives in open woodland and forest clearings in southern North America

ORDER GALLIFORMES
Game birds and hoatzin

Mallee fowl
Leipoa ocellata
2 ft 3 in.

Great curassow
Crax rubra
Up to 3 ft

Capercaillie
Tetrao urogallus
Up to 3 ft

Indian jungle fowl
Gallus gallus
2 ft 6 in.

Vulturine or **long-tailed guinea fowl**
Acryllium vulturinum
24 in.

Common turkey
Meleagris gallopavo
Up to 4 ft

Hoatzin
Opisthocomus hoazin
24 in.

FAMILY OPISTHOCOMIDAE
There is one species:
Hoatzin *Opisthocomus hoazin*: lives beside rivers in South American tropical forest. It is a brown, pheasant-like bird with a long loose crest and a huge crop. The chicks have two well-developed claws at the tip of each wing with which they creep along branches

399

Birds

PHYLUM CHORDATA	Animals with notochords
SUB-PHYLUM VERTEBRATA	Animals with backbones
CLASS AVES	Birds
ORDER GRUIFORMES	Cranes and allies
ORDER CHARADRIIFORMES	Waders, gulls and auks

ORDER GRUIFORMES

Cranes and allies
Members of this order have long necks, lack webs on their feet, and usually have long legs. There are 11 families:

FAMILY MESITORNITHIDAE
Mesites; 3 species
These are rather thrush-like birds from Madagascar which have functional wings but do not fly. They have five pairs of powder-down feather patches—disintegrating feather material used for cleaning the feathers. Example:
Brown mesite *Mesoenas unicolor*: common in the rain forest of eastern Madagascar. It nests in a platform of sticks about 3 ft above the ground

FAMILY TURNICIDAE
Button or bustard quails; 14 species
Button quails are secretive, ground-living birds found in Old World grasslands. Example:
Barred bustard quail *Turnix suscitator*: found in southern Asia. It seldom flies but can run fast

FAMILY GRUIDAE
Cranes; 15 species
Cranes are gregarious birds found in open marshy land in all continents except South America and Antarctica. They have a partly bare head and elevated hind toes. Their cry is resonant and they also clack their bills like storks. Cranes migrate in V-formation, flying with their necks straight out. They dance during courtship. Example:
Manchurian or **Japanese crane** *Grus japonensis*: found in marshes in Manchuria, Korea, eastern China and Japan

FAMILY ARAMIDAE
There is one species:
Limpkin *Aramus guarauna*: found in marshes from Florida to Argentina, it is related to both cranes and rails. It is a large, gray-brown bird whose long hind toes are level with the front ones

FAMILY PSOPHIDAE
Trumpeters; 3 species
Trumpeters have long legs and short bills. Example:
Gray-winged trumpeter *Psophia crepitans*: lives in humid tropical forest in north-eastern South America

FAMILY RALLIDAE
Rails, moorhens and coots; 132 species
These birds are often weak flyers, with vertically flattened bodies and long toes. Example:
Moorhen or **common gallinule** *Gallinula chloropus*: lives in marshes in temperate and tropical areas of the Americas, Africa and Eurasia

FAMILY HELIORNITHIDAE
Finfoots; 3 species
These are secretive, grebe-like birds with long bodies and bills. They are found in South America, Africa and south-east Asia. Example:
African finfoot *Podica senegalensis*: found in tropical streams. It hunts from low perches which are sometimes partly submerged

FAMILY RHYNOCHETIDAE
Kagu *Rhynochetos jubatus*: found in New Caledonia, it sleeps among rocks or under tree roots by day. It has a red bill and a big crest

FAMILY CARIAMIDAE
Seriamas; 2 species
These large South American birds have a crest, down-curved at the tip, at the base of the beak. Example:
Crested seriama *Cariama cristata*: found in open grasslands in Brazil and Paraguay

FAMILY EURYPYGIDAE
There is one species:
Sun bittern *Eurypyga helias*: a solitary wader with a long bill, which it uses to spear its prey. It is found in Central and South America

FAMILY OTIDIDAE
Bustards; 22 species
These powerful runners of the Old World grasslands can fly but usually do not; they are gray-brown, barred and spotted, and sometimes have a crest. They lay their eggs on the ground. Example:
Great bustard *Otis tarda*: lives on the plains of Eurasia and North Africa. It is one of the largest flying birds

ORDER CHARADRIIFORMES

Waders, auks and gulls
Most of this order are medium-sized waders or shore birds possessing a tufted oil gland. There are 16 families:

FAMILY JACANIDAE
Jacanas or lily trotters; 7 species
Found in the Old and New Worlds in tropical pools, jacanas have very long toes and claws which enable them to walk on water-lilies and other floating leaves. They have a frontal shield on the bill, and sharp, horny spurs on the wings. Example:
American jacana *Jacana spinosa*: found from Texas to Argentina

FAMILY ROSTRATULIDAE
Painted snipes; 2 species
These are long, straight-billed, green-brown birds found in southern Asia, Africa, South America and Australia. Example:
Painted snipe *Rostratula benghalensis*: lives in tropical and sub-tropical Africa, Madagascar, southern Asia and Australia

FAMILY HAEMATOPODIDAE
Oyster-catchers; 6 species
These noisy birds have long, blunt, flat bills which they use to open shellfish. Example:
European oyster-catcher *Haematopus ostralegus*: common along coasts

FAMILY CHARADRIIDAE
Plovers; 56 species
These plump birds have short bills, slightly swollen at the tip, and are found all over the world. They have bold black or brown markings on white. They migrate in flocks of thousands. Example:
Lapwing *Vanellus vanellus*: lives in temperate Eurasia and nests in the open. It is a noisy bird

FAMILY SCOLOPACIDAE
Sandpipers; 70 species
This is a group of drab-colored, ground-dwelling waders with thin, straight or down-curved bills. Examples:
Common snipe *Gallinago gallinago* (11 in.): lives in marshes and meadows in Europe, northern Asia, Africa, the Americas
Common sandpiper *Tringa hypoleucos*: found on the banks of rivers and streams in Eurasia and North America

FAMILY RECURVIROSTRIDAE
Avocets and stilts; 7 species
The members of this widely distributed family of long-legged waders have slender legs and very long thin bills. Only the avocets have up-curved bills. Example:
Eurasian avocet *Recurvirostra avosetta*: breeds in Eurasia and Africa. It walks along, skimming the surface of water or mud with its up-curved bill in search of small invertebrates

FAMILY PHALAROPODIDAE
Phalaropes; 3 species
All the phalaropes have lobe-webbed feet and toes like grebes, and thin, straight bills. They nest in the Arctic tundra and winter in the Southern Hemisphere, especially in Argentina. Example:
Grey or **red phalarope** *Phalaropus fulicarius*: found from the Arctic to the southern oceans. It feeds on plankton

FAMILY DROMADIDAE
There is one species:
Crab plover *Dromas ardeola*: found on the coasts of the Indian Ocean and the Red Sea. It has a long, straight, pointed bill and partly webbed toes

ORDER GRUIFORMES
Cranes and allies

Manchurian or Japanese crane
Grus japonensis
4 ft 6 in.

African finfoot
Podica senegalensis
Up to 24 in.

Brown mesite
Mesoenas unicolor
10 in.

Barred bustard quail
Turnix suscitator
5–8 in.

Kagu
Rhynochetos jubatus
21 in.

Limpkin
Aramus guarauna
3 ft

Crested seriama
Cariama cristata
3 ft

Sun bittern
Eurypyga helias
Up to 23 in.

Gray-winged trumpeter
Psophia crepitans
18 in.

Moorhen or common gallinule
Gallinula chloropus
14 in.

Great bustard
Otis tarda
3 ft 6 in.

PHYLUM CHORDATA	Animals with notochords
SUB-PHYLUM VERTEBRATA	Animals with backbones
CLASS AVES	Birds
ORDER CHARADRIIFORMES	Waders, gulls and auks
ORDER COLUMBIFORMES	Pigeons and sandgrouse
ORDER PSITTACIFORMES	Parrots

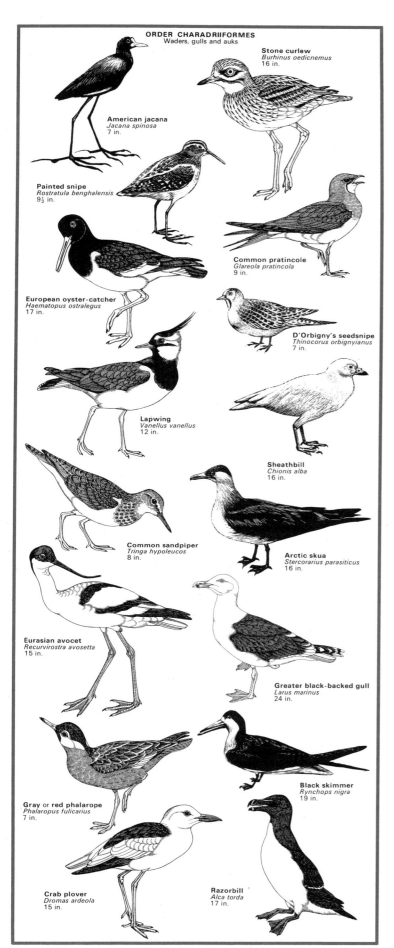

ORDER CHARADRIIFORMES
Waders, gulls and auks

American jacana
Jacana spinosa
7 in.

Stone curlew
Burhinus oedicnemus
16 in.

Painted snipe
Rostratula benghalensis
9½ in.

Common pratincole
Glareola pratincola
9 in.

European oyster-catcher
Haematopus ostralegus
17 in.

D'Orbigny's seedsnipe
Thinocorus orbignyianus
7 in.

Lapwing
Vanellus vanellus
12 in.

Sheathbill
Chionis alba
16 in.

Common sandpiper
Tringa hypoleucos
8 in.

Arctic skua
Stercorarius parasiticus
16 in.

Eurasian avocet
Recurvirostra avosetta
15 in.

Greater black-backed gull
Larus marinus
24 in.

Black skimmer
Rynchops nigra
19 in.

Gray or **red phalarope**
Phalaropus fulicarius
7 in.

Crab plover
Dromas ardeola
15 in.

Razorbill
Alca torda
17 in.

FAMILY BURHINIDAE
Stone curlews and thick knees; 9 species
All have swollen knee joints, short bills and large eyes. They are found in pebbly areas all over the world. Example:
Stone curlew *Burhinus oedicnemus*: found in Europe, south-west Asia and North Africa

FAMILY GLAREOLIDAE
Coursers and pratincoles; 16 species
These gregarious, insect-eating, running birds, with down-curved bills, are found in sandy areas of the Old World. They also feed on fish and seeds. Example:
Common pratincole *Glareola pratincola*: ranges over southern Europe, Africa and southern Asia

FAMILY THINOCORIDAE
Seedsnipes; 4 species
Seedsnipes are plump, short-legged birds, with stout, sparrow-like bills and long wings. They are found in tundra in southern South America and in the Andes northwards to the Equator. Example:
D'Orbigny's seedsnipe *Thinocorus orbignyianus*: feeds on seeds, tender shoots and leaves

FAMILY CHIONIDIDAE
Sheathbills or paddies; 2 species
These bold scavengers, found on islands near the Antarctic and some mainland coasts, have a horny, saddle-like sheath over the base of the upper bill. They feed on gulls' eggs and chicks. Example:
Sheathbill *Chionis alba*: lives on islands off Antarctic coasts

FAMILY STERCORARIIDAE
Skuas; 4 species
Skuas are strong flyers, living mainly in open waters. They breed in the Arctic and Antarctic, and winter in the middle latitudes. A horny protuberance on the base of the upper bill, through which the nostrils open, distinguishes them from gulls. They harass seabirds, forcing them to disgorge their food. Example:
Arctic skua *Stercorarius parasiticus*: found on coasts and islands through the Arctic and in Scandinavia, Nova Scotia and northern Scotland

FAMILY LARIDAE
Gulls and terns; 82 species
Gulls have no fleshy protuberance on their bills and do not migrate as far as the skuas. Terns are smaller and less plump than gulls, with narrower wings and thin, sharp bills. Example:
Greater black-backed gull *Larus marinus*: found on the Atlantic coasts of Europe and North America

FAMILY RYNCHOPIDAE
Skimmers; 3 species
Skimmers catch fish by flying with the longer, lower half of the bill just cutting the surface of the water. The sharp edge of the bill fits into a groove in the upper half of the bill. They are found on Atlantic coasts and by African and southern Asian rivers. Example:
Black skimmer *Rynchops nigra*: found from New Jersey to Argentina

FAMILY ALCIDAE
Auks; 22 species
Found in Europe, northern Asia and North America, these short-winged birds, with heavy bodies and legs placed far back, are the Northern Hemisphere's equivalent of penguins. They dive, swim with their wings, and fly. Example:
Razorbill *Alca torda*: found around North Atlantic coasts, it breeds in flocks on cliffs and islands

ORDER COLUMBIFORMES
Pigeons and sandgrouse
These are thickly feathered land birds, similar to the waders and gulls in palate and wing structure. They are vegetarian and, unlike other birds, they can swallow water without raising their heads. There are two families:

FAMILY PTEROCLIDAE
Sandgrouse; 16 species
Found in the tropics and sub-tropics of the Old World in open, sandy country; the sandgrouse have short, pointed bills without any protuberances, and legs which are feathered to the toes. Example:
Pallas's sandgrouse *Syrrhaptes paradoxus*: found in central Asia

FAMILY COLUMBIDAE
Pigeons; 289 species
The members of this worldwide family have short necks, small heads, and slender bills with a protuberance at the base. Two eggs are laid in a nest consisting of a flimsy stick platform; the male incubates by day, the female by night. The young are fed on 'pigeon's milk', a liquid from the lining of the crop. Example:
Rock dove *Columba livia*: the ancestor of the domestic pigeon, found in Europe, India, west and central Asia, and north and western Africa. It nests on cliffs on the coast or on mountains

ORDER COLUMBIFORMES
Pigeons and sandgrouse

Pallas's sandgrouse
Syrrhaptes paradoxus
12 in.

Rock dove
Columba livia
12 in.

ORDER PSITTACIFORMES
There is one family:

FAMILY PSITTACIDAE
Parrots, parakeets, cockatoos, macaws and lories; 315 species
These mainly tropical and Southern Hemisphere birds have big heads, short necks, strong, down-curved upper bills with a broad protuberance at the base, and feet with two toes in front and two behind. They are long-lived birds, some of them living 80 years. Examples:
African gray parrot *Psittacus erithacus*: found in African tropical forest. It is the finest talking bird when trained

African gray parrot
Psittacus erithacus
13 in.

PHYLUM CHORDATA	Animals with notochords	ORDER STRIGIFORMES	Owls
SUB-PHYLUM VERTEBRATA	Animals with backbones	ORDER CAPRIMULGIFORMES	Frogmouths and nightjars
CLASS AVES	Birds	ORDER APODIFORMES	Swifts and hummingbirds
ORDER CUCULIFORMES	Cuckoos and turacos		

ORDER CUCULIFORMES

Cuckoos and turacos
Members of this order are closely related to the parrots, with similar feet. They have no protuberance or hook on the upper bill. There are two families:

FAMILY MUSOPHAGIDAE
Turacos and plantain eaters; 20 species
These birds are often brilliantly colored with long tails, high crests and fourth toes that can be turned forwards. They feed on fruit and insects. Example:
Knysa turaco *Tauraco corythaix*: found in South African forests

FAMILY CUCULIDAE
Cuckoos; 127 species
Cuckoos are slender birds with long tails, down-curved bills and pointed wings, found in all the warmer regions of the world. Example:
Common cuckoo *Cuculus canorus*: found in Eurasia and Africa. Only the male cries 'cuckoo'

ORDER STRIGIFORMES

Owls
The members of this worldwide order—the owls—have short mobile necks, and commonly have soft, fluffy plumage which silences their flight. Most owls are nocturnal. There are two families:

FAMILY TYTONIDAE
Barn owls; 10 species
The barn owls have heart-shaped faces, fully feathered long legs, and a serrated comb on the middle claw. They nest in hollow trees and buildings and detect prey largely by sound. Example:
Common barn owl *Tyto alba*: has almost worldwide distribution

FAMILY STRIGIDAE
Typical owls; 120 species
These round-faced birds, with huge eyes, bare feet and no serrated comb, hunt by sight as well as by sound. They nest in hollow trees, on cliff edges and in ground burrows. Example:
Great eagle owl *Bubo bubo*: found in woods of Europe, Asia and North Africa

ORDER CAPRIMULGIFORMES

Frogmouths and nightjars
These birds, with long pointed wings, small feet and huge gaping mouths, are active at dusk or night, feeding mainly on insects, which are usually caught on the wing. There are five families:

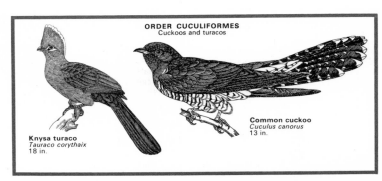

ORDER CUCULIFORMES
Cuckoos and turacos

Knysa turaco
Tauraco corythaix
18 in.

Common cuckoo
Cuculus canorus
13 in.

ORDER STRIGIFORMES
Owls

Common barn owl
Tyto alba
13 in.

Great eagle owl
Bubo bubo
24 in.; wingspan 5 ft 6 in.

FAMILY STEATORNITHIDAE
There is one species:
Oilbird *Steatornis caripenses*: found in caves in northern South America, this bird is a fruit-eater, with a stout, hooked bill. In the dark caves where it roosts, it navigates by echo-location, like bats, emitting sounds at pitches that are audible to humans

FAMILY PODARGIDAE
Frogmouths; 12 species
Found from Australia to Malaya, the frogmouths are nocturnal birds with large, flat, horny, triangular and sharply hooked bills. They prey on mice as well as on insects. They have short wings and silky plumage. Example:
Tawny frogmouth *Podargus strigoides*: lives in forests in Australia and Tasmania

FAMILY NYCTIBIIDAE
Potoos or wood-nightjars; 5 species
Found in Central and South America, the

potoos sit bolt upright on tree stumps, resembling a broken branch. Example:
Common potoo *Nyctibius griseus*: has very short legs and large eyes

FAMILY AEGOTHELIDAE
Owlet frogmouths; 6 species
These birds, which are like tiny, long-tailed owls, do not adopt the broken-branch camouflage of the potoos. They are found in Australia and New Guinea. Example:
Rufous owlet frogmouth *Aegotheles insignis*: found in New Guinea

FAMILY CAPRIMULGIDAE
Nightjars; 70 species
These birds have a loud monotonous call. They fly quietly with slow wingbeats, and are found all over the world except in the Arctic and Antarctic. Most species are active at dusk or night. Example:
Whip poor-will *Caprimulgus vociferus*: found in North and Central America

ORDER APODIFORMES

Swifts and humming birds
These are fast-flying, short-legged and weak-footed birds of the tropics and subtropics. There are three families:

FAMILY APODIDAE
Swifts; 65 species
Swifts, some flying between 150 and 200 mph, catch insects on the wing, high in the air. They fly faster, straighter and less erratically than the unrelated swallows. Their rapid wing-beats alternate with gliding, and they steer with their wings as their tails are too short. Example:
White-rumped swift *Apus caffer*: lives in Africa

FAMILY HEMIPROCNIDAE
Crested swifts; 3 species
These swifts, with their long, forked tails, softer plumage and erectile crests, are not as highly specialized for flight as other swifts. They perch on trees. Example:
Indian crested swift *Hemiprocne coronata*: lives near tropical forest verges

FAMILY TROCHILIDAE
Hummingbirds; 319 species
These are tiny American birds, with slender, pointed bills and tubular, fringe-tipped tongues projecting beyond their beaks. Their wings hum in flight; they never soar, but they can hover. Example:
Ruby-throated hummingbird *Archilochus colubris*: lives in jungles and tropical mountains in Central America and eastern North America

ORDER APODIFORMES
Swifts and hummingbirds

White-rumped swift
Apus caffer
6 in.

Indian crested swift
Hemiprocne coronata
8–9 in.

Ruby-throated hummingbird
Archilochus colubris
13 in.

ORDER CAPRIMULGIFORMES
Frogmouths and nightjars

Oilbird
Steatornis caripenses
13 in.

Common potoo
Nyctibius griseus
14 in.

Tawny frogmouth
Podargus strigoides
19 in.

Rufous owlet frogmouth
Aegotheles insignis
10 in.

Whip poor-will
Caprimulgus vociferus
9 in.

PHYLUM CHORDATA	Animals with notochords
SUB-PHYLUM VERTEBRATA	Animals with backbones
CLASS AVES	Birds
ORDER TROGONIFORMES	Trogons
ORDER COLIIFORMES	Colies
ORDER CORACIIFORMES	Kingfishers, hornbills and allies

ORDER TROGONIFORMES

There is one family:

FAMILY TROGONIDAE

Trogons; 35 species
These brightly colored, sedentary birds are found in all tropical forests. The first and second toes turn backwards, and they have weak legs, feathered ankles, short wings and a long square tail. Trogons nest in tree holes. Example:
Quetzal *Pharomachrus mocinno*: found in forests in Central America

Quetzal
Pharomachrus mocinno
4 ft

ORDER CORACIIFORMES

Kingfishers, hornbills and allies
These carnivorous birds are found all over the world. Two or three of their front toes are partly fused. There are eight families:

FAMILY ALCEDINIDAE

Kingfishers and kookaburras; 80 species
These are thick-set birds, with short, thick necks, short tails, big heads (often crested) and long sharp beaks. Example:
Common kingfisher *Alcedo atthis*: found by Old World streams and lakes, feeding on fish

FAMILY TODIDAE

Todies; 5 species
Todies are very small West Indian birds with finely serrated flattened bills, green backs and red breasts. They nest in horizontal burrows up to 12 in. long, which they excavate in earth or sand with their bills. They catch insects by swooping down suddenly like kingfishers. Example:
Jamaican tody *Todus todus*: found near forest verges and in bushy areas

FAMILY MOMOTIDAE

Motmots; 8 species
Quiet birds of Central and South American tropical forests, the motmots have soft, brightly colored feathers and long tails. They hop clumsily. Example:
Blue-crowned motmot *Momotus momota*: like the other species of motmots, it nests in burrows

FAMILY MEROPIDAE

Bee-eaters; 24 species
The Old World bee-eaters are colorful, slender birds with long, down-curved beaks and long, slender tail feathers. They eat bees and locusts. Example:
Common bee-eater *Merops apiaster*: found in Europe, Asia and Africa

FAMILY CORACIIDAE

Rollers; 11 species
These birds of the Old World tropics have stout bills, big heads and long tails. Some species display with acrobatic flights involving rolls, twists and dives. They eat insects, frogs, mice and small lizards. They hop clumsily. Example:
Abyssinian roller *Coracias abyssinica*:

found in dry areas from south-west Arabia westwards to Senegal

FAMILY UPUPIDAE

There is one species:
Hoopoe *Upupa epops*: found in open country in Eurasia and Africa. It has a long, curved, pointed bill and a crest. It feeds on the ground, nests in tree cavities—often unlined—and never removes feces or food from the nest. The female has a gland at the base of her tail which emits an offensive smell when she is brooding

FAMILY PHOENICULIDAE

Wood hoopoes; 16 species
These birds, which are found only in Africa, are slimmer in build than the hoopoe, and have no crest. They are tree-loving birds and are rarely seen on the ground. The female has a scent gland. Example:
Senegal wood hoopoe *Phoeniculus senegalensis*: found in Africa

FAMILY BUCEROTIDAE

Hornbills; 45 species
These short-legged, black-and-white birds of the Old World tropical forests have huge, down-curved, serrated bills, usually with a horny protuberance on top. The bill is often highly colored. When incubating her eggs, the female is walled into a tree-hole nest, leaving only a small opening through which the male can pass food to her. The female spends 30–50 days in the hole, and molts during this period. Example:
Great Indian hornbill *Buceros bicornis*: lives in India, Malaya and Indonesia

ORDER COLIIFORMES

There is one family:

FAMILY COLIIDAE

Colies or mousebirds; 6 species
These gregarious African birds are acrobatic and often hang upside-down. They have a slender, prominent crest, a long thin tail and reversible first toes. Example:
Bar-breasted coly or **speckled mousebird** *Colius striatus*: lives in Africa south of the Sahara

Bar-breasted coly
or speckled mousebird
Colius striatus
14 in.

ORDER CORACIIFORMES
Kingfishers, hornbills and allies

Common kingfisher
Alcedo atthis
6½ in.

Jamaican tody
Todus todus
4 in.

Hoopoe
Upupa epops
11 in.

Common bee-eater
Merops apiaster
11 in.

Blue-crowned motmot
Momotus momota
18 in.

Senegal wood hoopoe
Phoeniculus senegalensis
4 in.

Abyssinian roller
Coracias abyssinica
16 in.

Great Indian hornbill
Buceros bicornis
5 ft

403

Birds

PHYLUM CHORDATA	Animals with notochords
SUB-PHYLUM VERTEBRATA	Animals with backbones
CLASS AVES	Birds
ORDER PICIFORMES	Woodpeckers, barbets and toucans
ORDER PASSERIFORMES	Passerines

ORDER PICIFORMES
Woodpeckers, barbets and toucans

Black spotted barbet
Capito niger
6 in.

Collared puffbird
Bucco capensis
7 in.

Greater honey-guide
Indicator indicator
7½ in.

Toco toucan
Ramphastos toco
2 ft 1 in.

Paradise jacamar
Galbula dea
11 in.

Green woodpecker
Picus viridis
12 in.

ORDER PASSERIFORMES
Passerines

Dusky broadbill
Corydon sumatranus
5 in.

Black-faced ant-thrush
Formicarius analis
7 in.

Barred woodcreeper
Dendrocolaptes certhia
10–11 in.

Rufous ovenbird
Furnarius rufus
8 in.

Black-breasted gnat-eater
Conopophaga melanogaster
6 in.

Great-footed turco
Pteroptochus megapodius
9 in.

ORDER PICIFORMES

Woodpeckers, barbets and toucans
This is a group of tree-dwelling, usually solitary birds with two toes pointing forwards and two backwards. In some species the outer hind toe is lacking. There are six families:

FAMILY CAPITONIDAE
Barbets; 76 species
Found all over the world in tropical forests, these plump, gaudy birds have big, heavy bills and short wings. Example: **Black-spotted barbet** *Capito niger*: ranges from Panama to Brazil

FAMILY INDICATORIDAE
Honey-guides; 12 species
These dull-colored relatives of the barbets feed on the wax of honeycombs. They lead honey-eating animals to bees' nests, and after the nest has been plundered the birds eat the wax. Example: **Greater honey-guide** *Indicator indicator*: widely distributed in tropical and southern Africa

FAMILY GALBULIDAE
Jacamars; 15 species
A family of Central and South American forest birds with tapering bodies, long, thin bills, and gaudy, long tails. Example: **Paradise jacamar** *Galbula dea*: found in northern South America

FAMILY BUCCONIDAE
Puffbirds; 30 species
These Central and South American birds are heavily built with big heads, flattened bills, and dark plumage. Example: **Collared puffbird** *Bucco capensis*: an inhabitant of South America

FAMILY RAMPHASTIDAE
Toucans; 37 species
These fruit-eaters, with brightly colored, slightly down-curved bills, live in American tropical forests. Example: **Toco toucan** *Ramphastos toco*: found in South America

FAMILY PICIDAE
Woodpeckers; 230 species
The birds of this worldwide family have long, straight bills and tails, and strong front toes with sharp claws. They chip through the bark of trees with their bills to reach the insects underneath. Example: **Green woodpecker** *Picus viridis*: found in deciduous woodlands in Europe and western Asia

ORDER PASSERIFORMES

Passerines
This worldwide order of perching birds contains more than half of the known bird species. All have four, similar, un-webbed front toes and a hind toe which is highly developed but not reversible.

Their young are born naked and helpless. There are 56 families listed here. However, they have evolved comparatively recently and are not well defined. Some authorities would divide the order into fewer families and some into more

FAMILY EURYLAIMIDAE
Broadbills; 14 species
Broadbills are brightly colored forest birds of the Old World tropics. They have big heads and partly joined front toes. Example: **Dusky broadbill** *Corydon sumatranus*: found in Sumatra

FAMILY DENDROCOLAPTIDAE
Woodcreepers; 50 species
This is a family of New World tropical forest birds with partly joined front toes and vertically flattened bills. Example: **Barred woodcreeper** *Dendrocolaptes certhia*: found in the lower and middle layers of forests

FAMILY FURNARIIDAE
Ovenbirds; 221 species
These Central and South American birds are very similar to the woodcreepers. They build intricate, oven-shaped clay nests. Some species live on the ground and nest in burrows. Example: **Rufous ovenbird** *Furnarius rufus*: found in wooded areas of grasslands in South America

FAMILY FORMICARIIDAE
Antbirds; 223 species
Antbirds are similar to ovenbirds, but their beaks are hooked at the tip and they build simpler nests. They are confined to Central and South America. Example: **Scale-breasted ant pitta** *Grallaria excelsa* (9 in.): found in the high Andes of northern South America
Black-faced ant-thrush *Formicarius analis*: lives in South America in the undergrowth of forests and in scrub. It runs rather than flies when disturbed

FAMILY CONOPOPHAGIDAE
Ant pipits; 11 species
These small, stocky birds, with broad bills, are found on the floor of the Amazonian rain forests. Example:
Black-breasted gnat-eater *Cono-pophaga melanogaster*: found in Brazil and Bolivia. The male has a black crown and prominent white brows

FAMILY RHINOCRYPTIDAE
Tapaculos; 30 species
These are ground-living birds, and fly very little. They have erect tails, long, strong legs and weak wings. They live in scrub or mountain forests in Central and South America. Example:
Great-footed turco *Pteroptochus megapodius*: lives in northern and central Chile in hills and mountains at heights of up to 8000 ft

PHYLUM CHORDATA	Animals with notochords
SUB-PHYLUM VERTEBRATA	Animals with backbones
CLASS AVES	Birds
ORDER PASSERIFORMES	Passerines

Umbrella bird
Cephalopterus ornatus
16 in.

Reddish plantcutter
Phytotoma rutila
7 in.

Sharpbill
Oxyruncus cristatus
7 in.

Wattled philepitta or velvet asity
Philepitta castanea
6½ in.

Skylark
Alauda arvensis
7 in.

Barn swallow
Hirundo rustica
7 in.

Golden-headed manakin
Pipra erythrocephala
3½ in.

Superb lyrebird
Menura superba
3 ft

Gurney's pitta
Pitta gurneyi
8 in.

Eastern kingbird
Tyrannus tyrannus
8 in.

New Zealand bush wren
Xenicus longipes
4 in.

Rufous scrub-bird
Atrichornis rufescens
7 in.

Red-shouldered cuckoo-shrike
Campephaga phoenicea
8 in.

FAMILY COTINGIDAE
Cotingas; 90 species
These solitary birds have a wide range of ornamentation and many have bare patches or wattles on their heads. They are found in forests from Argentina to Texas. Example:
Umbrella bird *Cephalopterus ornatus*: found high in the forest trees in Costa Rica and Brazil. A large, tubular, fleshy appendage hangs from its chest

FAMILY PIPRIDAE
Manakins; 59 species
These are brightly colored, tiny birds that feed mainly on small fruits, plucked on the wing. The males perform elaborate courtship rites on special display grounds. Example:
Golden-headed manakin *Pipra erythrocephala*: like the rest of the family, it is confined to South American forests

FAMILY TYRANNIDAE
Tyrant flycatchers; 365 species
Related to the cotingas and manakins, tyrant flycatchers hunt in the open, capturing insects in short, speedy bursts of flight. Their crown feathers stand erect, and the birds are found throughout the Americas up to the timberline. Example:
Eastern kingbird *Tyrannus tyrannus*: found in North America, this bird has a dark-colored plumage on its upper parts and a white-tipped tail

FAMILY PHYTOTOMIDAE
Plantcutters; 3 species
These plump, finch-like birds with short, saw-toothed bills are found on the lower slopes of the Andes. Example:
Reddish plantcutter *Phytotoma rutila*: common in open forest and bush grasslands in Argentina

FAMILY OXYRUNCIDAE
There is one species:
Sharpbill *Oxyruncus cristatus*: this bird, which has a sharp beak with a feathery rim at the base, has no close relatives and is confined to the forests of Central and South America

FAMILY PITTIDAE
Pittas; 23 species
These plump birds have slightly down-curved bills, big heads, short tails and long legs. They are found in tropical forest undergrowth in the Old World. Example:
Gurney's pitta *Pitta gurneyi*: lives in lowland jungles in India. It eats snakes

FAMILY ACANTHISITTIDAE
New Zealand wrens; 3 species
This is a family of small, brown birds which rarely fly higher than about 100 ft; they often scurry along the ground with their tails erect. Example:
New Zealand bush wren *Xenicus longipes*: forages on tree trunks and on the forest floor

FAMILY PHILEPITTIDAE
Asitys; 4 species
These plump, tree-living birds are found only on Madagascar. Mainly fruit-eaters, they sometimes eat insects. They make a hanging nest. Example:
Wattled philepitta or **velvet asity** *Philepitta castanea*: found in humid forests on the eastern slopes of Madagascar up to 5000 ft

FAMILY MENURIDAE
Lyrebirds; 2 species
Brown above and ashen below, these solitary birds are long-tailed and they seldom fly. The male has a long tail with two feathers—up to 24 in. long—forming the frame of the lyre, six pairs of central plumes forming the 'strings' and a web-less central pair of feathers. The male has one of the most elaborate displays of any bird. Example:
Superb lyrebird *Menura superba*: lives in eastern Australia

FAMILY ATRICHORNITHIDAE
Scrub-birds; 2 species
Scrub-birds, which look like wrens with long tails, are related to lyrebirds. They are good mimics and are found only in Australia. The noisy scrub-bird *Atrichornis clamosus*, long feared extinct, was recently rediscovered. Example:
Rufous scrub-bird *Atrichornis rufescens*: lives in eastern Australia

FAMILY ALAUDIDAE
Larks; 70 species
These widely distributed birds have long, pointed wings, rounded, scaly ankles and long, straight hind claws. They always live in open country and nest on the ground. Example:
Skylark *Alauda arvensis*: common in open country in Eurasia and North Africa

FAMILY HIRUNDINIDAE
Swallows and martins; 74 species
This is a family of cosmopolitan birds which resemble swifts but fly more erratically. They have long, pointed wings, weak legs and relatively large mouths with a wide gape; several species have forked tails. They are not good perchers and spend most of their time on the wing. Example:
Barn swallow *Hirundo rustica*: found in North America, Europe, Asia and North Africa. It migrates over enormous distances

FAMILY CAMPEPHAGIDAE
Cuckoo-shrikes; 70 species
These are insect-eating birds from Africa, southern Asia and Australia. They have stout beaks, notched at the tip. Some are as big as pigeons, others as small as sparrows. Example:
Red-shouldered cuckoo-shrike *Campephaga phoenicea*: found in bushy savanna and forest in Africa

Birds

PHYLUM CHORDATA	Animals with notochords
SUB-PHYLUM VERTEBRATA	Animals with backbones
CLASS AVES	Birds
ORDER PASSERIFORMES	Passerines

ORDER PASSERIFORMES
Passerines

African drongo
Dicrurus adsimilis
9 in.

Kokako or wattled crow
Callaeus cinerea
Up to 18 in.

Regent bowerbird
Sericulus chrysocephalus
11 in.

Brown treecreeper
Certhia familiaris
5 in.

Golden oriole
Oriolus oriolus
9½ in.

Magpie-lark
Grallina cyanoleuca
11 in.

Lawes' six-wired bird of paradise
Parotia lawesi
10 in.

Red-browed treecreeper
Climacteris erythrops
5½ in.

Raven
Corvus corax
24 in.

Black-headed butcher-bird
Cracticus cassicus
10 in.

Great tit
Parus major
5½ in.

European nuthatch
Sitta europaea
5½ in.

FAMILY DICRURIDAE
Drongos; 20 species
Drongos are aggressive, insect-eating birds with stout, arched beaks and strong feet; they are found in the tropical forests of the Old World. Example:
African drongo *Dicrurus adsimilis*: found in woodland and savanna

FAMILY ORIOLIDAE
Orioles; 28 species
These birds are found in the forests of Europe and western Asia; they winter in Africa, southern Asia and Australia. The true orioles—different from the American orioles—are generally yellow and black, the males being brighter than the females. They have an undulating flight. Example:
Golden oriole *Oriolus oriolus*: found in woodlands of Eurasia, North Africa and India

FAMILY CORVIDAE
Crows, magpies and jays; 102 species
These aggressive, noisy and usually omnivorous birds are widely distributed. Their ankles are scaled in front and smooth at the back. Examples:
Nutcracker *Nucifraga caryocatactes* (12½ in.): found in coniferous forests of northern Europe and Asia. It is brown with white specks and feeds on pine seeds
Raven *Corvus corax*: lives in tundra, deciduous forests and sandy deserts in the Northern Hemisphere

FAMILY CALLAEIDAE
Wattlebirds; 3 species
These are New Zealand forest birds with large wattles at the corners of their jaws. They have weak wings. Example:
Kokako or **wattled crow** *Callaeus cinerea*: leaps from branch to branch in the forest trees

FAMILY GRALLINIDAE
Mudnest-builders; 4 species
The black-and-white Australian birds of this group build deep, open nests of mud on branches. Example:
Magpie-lark *Grallina cyanoleuca*: found near streams and waterways. It feeds on insects and small snails

FAMILY CRACTICIDAE
Song-shrikes; 10 species
Noisy and gregarious, the Australian song-shrikes are strong flyers which impale their prey—insects, lizards and small birds—on thorns to store them. Example:
Black-headed butcher-bird *Cracticus cassicus*: found in open forest and bushy grassland in New Guinea

FAMILY PTILONORHYNCHIDAE
Bowerbirds and catbirds; 18 species
The Australian bowerbirds build huge, often hut-shaped bowers or stages to attract females; they adorn the bowers with bright objects. Example:

Regent bowerbird *Sericulus chrysocephalus*: found in eastern Australian forests; it mixes saliva with plant juices or charcoal to make a 'paint' with which to decorate its bower

FAMILY PARADISAEIDAE
Birds of paradise; 42 species
Relatives of the bowerbirds and crows, these birds live in the northern Australian and New Guinea tropical forests. Most males are ornate and colorful and generally have long tail feathers and crests or ruffs. The females are usually plain. Example:
Lawes' six-wired bird of paradise *Parotia lawesi*: lives in eastern New Guinea high up in forest areas. The male performs his courting display on an area of cleared ground

FAMILY PARIDAE
Tits and chickadees; 59 species
The adaptable and intelligent tits are very small (3–8 in.), with soft, thick plumage which may be gray or black, with blue on the back and yellow on the breast. They have stout, pointed beaks, strong feet and rounded wings. They feed mostly on insects and are found throughout the world except in South America, Australia and Madagascar. Example:
Great tit *Parus major*: found in open woodland throughout Asia and Europe and in the north-west tip of Africa

FAMILY CERTHIIDAE
Tree creepers; 5 species
These slender, brown birds (streaked and spotted above, paler below) have thin, down-curved probing bills and long, stiff tails. They creep up and around the trunks of trees, foraging for the insects on which they feed. Example:
Brown treecreeper *Certhia familiaris*: common in coniferous woodland in North America, Europe and Asia

FAMILY CLIMACTERIDAE
Australian treecreepers; 6 species
The tail feathers of these birds, which live in wooded country in Australia and New Guinea, are not adapted for climbing trees. Some species feed on the ground. Example:
Red-browed treecreeper *Climacteris erythrops*: found in eastern Australia

FAMILY SITTIDAE
Nuthatches; 30 species
These birds are stocky and small, and have thin straight bills, long toes and sharp claws. They are found throughout the world, except in South America and New Zealand. They hunt face downwards on tree trunks for insects and spiders. Northern species also eat seeds, including nuts, in winter. Example:
European nuthatch *Sitta europaea*: common in woodland throughout most of Eurasia

PHYLUM CHORDATA	Animals with notochords
SUB-PHYLUM VERTEBRATA	Animals with backbones
CLASS AVES	Birds
ORDER PASSERIFORMES	Passerines

Red-whiskered bulbul
Pycnonotus jocosus
7 in.

Common mockingbird
Mimus polyglottos
10½ in.

Hedge sparrow
Prunella modularis
6 in.

Hook-billed vanga-shrike
Vanga curvirostris
8 in.

Blue-backed fairy bluebird
Irena puella
10 in.

Gray wagtail
Motacilla cinerea
7 in.

Great gray or northern shrike
Lanius excubitor
9½ in.

Spotted flycatcher
Muscicapa striata
5½ in.

Bohemian waxwing
Bombycilla garrulus
7 in.

Eurasian or white-breasted dipper
Cinclus cinclus
7 in.

Wren
Troglodytes troglodytes
4–5 in.

White-browed wood swallow
Artamus superciliosus
7–8 in.

Hill mynah
Gracula religiosa
13 in.

FAMILY PYCNONOTIDAE
Bulbuls; 120 species
Bulbuls are noisy, drab birds from Africa and southern Asia; they have slender beaks and hair-like feathers on the backs of their necks. Example:
Red-whiskered bulbul *Pycnonotus jocosus*: common in gardens, cities and in wooded countryside in India

FAMILY IRENIDAE
Leafbirds; 14 species
These forest-living, fruit-eating birds from south-east Asia are similar to bulbuls. Example:
Blue-backed fairy bluebird *Irena puella*: found in the upper layers of evergreen forests

FAMILY CINCLIDAE
Dippers; 4 species
Found in cool mountain streams in Eurasia and the Americas, these birds run in and out of the water, capturing small water invertebrates. Example:
Eurasian or **white-breasted dipper** *Cinclus cinclus*: found on mountains in Eurasia

FAMILY TROGLODYTIDAE
Wrens; 60 species
These small (3¾–9 in.), brown birds, most numerous in South America, have slender, sharp beaks, upright tails and a quick, strong flight. Example:

Wren *Troglodytes troglodytes*: insect-eating bird of Europe, northern Asia and North America

FAMILY MIMIDAE
Mockingbirds; 34 species
Found living near the ground from Canada to Chile, mockingbirds are good singers and mimics. They build open, cup-shaped nests 2–6 ft above the ground. Both sexes incubate the eggs. Example:
Common mockingbird *Mimus polyglottos*: found in the southern U.S.A. and Central America

FAMILY MUSCICAPIDAE
Flycatchers, babblers, thrushes and warblers; about 1200 species
Most members of this huge family are Old World, insect-eating birds characterized by ten primary wing feathers. Examples:
Nightingale *Luscinia megarhynchos* (6½ in.): found in woodland undergrowth in southern Europe, western Asia and north-west Africa
Blackcap *Sylvia atricapilla* (5½ in.): found in woodlands in western Asia, north-west Africa and Atlantic islands
Spotted flycatcher *Muscicapa striata*: lives in forests and wooded grasslands in western Eurasia and north-west Africa. It hunts flying insects from a perch
Gray-sided laughing thrush *Garrula caerulatus* (12 in.): lives in forests, ranging from the Himalayan area to Taiwan

FAMILY PRUNELLIDAE
Accentors; 12 species
Stout, drab birds with thin beaks and rounded wings, the accentors are found only in Eurasia and are typical of Arctic regions. Example:
Hedge sparrow *Prunella modularis*: widespread in Europe and western Asia

FAMILY MOTACILLIDAE
Wagtails and pipits; 48 species
These slender birds with thin, pointed beaks walk along the ground and are found throughout the world. Example:
Gray wagtail *Motacilla cinerea*: found near streams in Eurasia and the north-west corner of Africa

FAMILY BOMBYCILLIDAE
Waxwings and palmchats; 9 species
This is a family of fruit-eating birds of the Northern Hemisphere; they have broad beaks and silky plumage. Example:
Bohemian waxwing *Bombycilla garrulus*: lives in coniferous forests in Europe, Asia and North America

FAMILY ARTAMIDAE
Wood-swallows; 10 species
These small birds of south-east Asia and Australia have long, pointed wings; they catch insects in flight. Example:
White-browed wood-swallow *Artamus superciliosus*: nests in rock crevices or hollow trees in Australia

FAMILY VANGIDAE
Vanga-shrikes; 12 species
A Madagascar family of blue-and-white or black-and-white birds with rounded wings and short tails. The species vary in size from 5 to 12 in. Their beaks also vary considerably, though all are strongly made and hooked. Example:
Hook-billed vanga-shrike *Vanga curvirostris*: lives in forests and grasslands. It is an insect-eater which also takes small frogs and lizards

FAMILY LANIIDAE
Shrikes; 74 species
These miniature birds of prey, found in Europe, Asia, Africa and North America, kill insects and small vertebrates with their sharp, hooked beaks and often impale their prey on thorns. Example:
Great gray or **northern shrike** *Lanius excubitor*: breeds in Canada; winters in the United States

FAMILY STURNIDAE
Starlings; 110 species
This is an Old World, largely tropical family of active and highly gregarious birds with straight or slightly down-curved beaks. Their flight is strong and direct. Example:
Hill mynah *Gracula religiosa*: a fruit-eating bird from the forests of southern Asia. It is a close relative of the common starling

CLASSIFICATION

Birds

PHYLUM CHORDATA	Animals with notochords
SUB-PHYLUM VERTEBRATA	Animals with backbones
CLASS AVES	Birds
ORDER PASSERIFORMES	Passerines

ORDER PASSERIFORMES
Passerines

White-bearded honey-eater
Meliornis novaehollandiae
7 in.

Oriental white-eye
Zosterops palpebrosa
4 in.

Magnolia warbler
Dendroica magnolia
5 in.

Chaffinch
Fringilla coelebs
6 in.

Scarlet-chested sunbird
Chalcomitra senegalensis
6 in.

Yellow-throated vireo
Vireo flavifrons
5½ in.

Troupial
Icterus icterus
9½ in.

Gouldian finch
Poephila gouldiae
5½ in.

Yellow-tailed diamond bird
Pardalotus punctatus
3¼ in.

Hawaiian honeycreeper or iiwi
Vestiaria coccinea
6 in.

Cardinal
Richmondena cardinalis
7¾ in.

Red bishop
Euplectes orix
5½ in.

FAMILY MELIPHAGIDAE
Honey-eaters; 167 species
Honey-eaters are small, often patterned, birds from Australia, the Pacific islands and southern Africa. They have slender, down-curved beaks and tube-like, brush-tipped tongues adapted for feeding on nectar and insects. Example:
White-bearded honey-eater *Meliornis novaehollandiae*: found in scrubland, open forest and sometimes swampy areas, from southern Queensland to Tasmania

FAMILY NECTARINIIDAE
Sunbirds; 106 species
Sunbirds are the gaudy, Old World counterparts of the New World hummingbirds, but they usually perch on, rather than hover above, flowers; some are known as spider-hunters. Their nests are always suspended from leaves or branches of trees. Example:
Scarlet-chested sunbird *Chalcomitra senegalensis*: found in the savannas of Africa

FAMILY DICAEIDAE
Flowerpeckers; 55 species
These are plump, active birds from southeast Asia and Australia; they have tubular tongues and shorter beaks than the sunbirds. Example:
Yellow-tailed diamond bird *Pardalotus punctatus*: found only in the forests of south-eastern Australia

FAMILY ZOSTEROPIDAE
White-eyes; 85 species
These nectar-eaters, with brush-tipped tongues, narrow white rings round the eyes, and nine primary wing feathers, are found throughout the Old World tropics. Gregarious birds, they often travel in large flocks. Example:
Oriental white-eye *Zosterops palpebrosa*: found in woody country and evergreen forests up to 8000 ft from India to the Philippines

FAMILY VIREONIDAE
Vireos; 45 species
This family of small green birds, 4–6 in. long, live among trees in the New World. The North American species usually migrate to the tropics in winter. Example:
Yellow-throated vireo *Vireo flavifrons*: found in the deciduous forests of eastern North America

FAMILY DREPANIDIDAE
Hawaiian honeycreepers; 22 species
This recently evolved group has radiated from a single colonist species. The males are brightly colored in green, red, yellow, gray or black; the females are duller and gray-green. Honeycreepers have beaks and tongues of various shapes. Example:
Hawaiian honeycreeper or **iiwi** *Vestiaria coccinea*: found in flowering trees, where it feeds on nectar and insects for food

FAMILY PARULIDAE
Wood-warblers; 113 species
This group exhibits a wide range of social, feeding and breeding behavior. They also vary greatly in size—from 6½ to 21 in.—but all have conical beaks. They are found throughout the New World. Example:
Magnolia warbler *Dendroica magnolia*: breeds in Canadian coniferous forests

FAMILY ICTERIDAE
American blackbirds and orioles; 87 species
New World birds found from Alaska to Argentina. They are small, with slender, pointed beaks. The North American species are migratory, often travelling in huge, mixed flocks. The tropical species do not migrate. A number of species regularly interbreed in the wild. Example:
Troupial *Icterus icterus*: an outstanding songster of northern South America

FAMILY EMBERIZIDAE
Tanagers, cardinals, sugarbirds and buntings; 525 species
This is a diverse group of birds found in Europe, Asia and America; it includes many brightly colored species. Examples:
Paradise tanager *Tangara chilensis* (5½ in.): found in tropical South America east of the Andes
Cardinal *Richmondena cardinalis*: found in North America

FAMILY FRINGILLIDAE
Finches; 138 species
These tree-loving seed-eaters make open cup nests. They are found throughout the world, except in Australia; many are migratory. Examples:
Chaffinch *Fringilla coelebs*: found in forests and cultivated areas in Europe, North Africa and western Asia
Cactus ground finch *Geospiza scandens* (5 in.): one of Darwin's finches from the Galapagos Islands, where it feeds on cactus

FAMILY ESTRILDIDAE
Weaver-finches; 108 species
These small seed-eaters of the Old World tropics make solitary, untidy nests. Example:
Gouldian finch *Poephila gouldiae*: found in Australia

FAMILY PLOCEIDAE
Weavers and sparrows; 132 species
Members of this family, found in Europe, Asia and Africa, often live in large colonies. Examples:
House sparrow *Passer domesticus* (6 in.): found originally in Europe, Asia and Africa; has been introduced into Australia and North America, where it is now a pest. It eats seeds and insects
Red bishop *Euplectes orix*: found in southern and eastern Africa. The male has brilliant orange-red coloring

Mammals

PHYLUM CHORDATA	Animals with notochords	ORDER MONOTREMATA	Egg-laying mammals
SUB-PHYLUM VERTEBRATA	Animals with backbones	SUB-CLASS THERIA	Mammals that do not lay eggs
CLASS MAMMALIA	Mammals	INFRA-CLASS METATHERIA	Marsupials
SUB-CLASS PROTOTHERIA	Monotremes	ORDER MARSUPIALIA	Pouched mammals

Sizes of mammals: measurements are combined head and body lengths, unless otherwise stated. Tail lengths are given separately

A typical mammal is a warm-blooded, air breathing vertebrate. The heart is divided into four chambers. The body temperature is regulated by a mechanism in the brain, and maintained by the body hair. Young mammals are suckled on milk from the mother's mammary glands. The basic anatomical distinction between mammals and reptiles is the presence of only one bone in the lower jaw—reptiles have more than one. Bones inside the ears of mammals have evolved from the additional jaw bones of reptiles.

Living mammals are classified as monotremes, or egg-laying mammals; marsupials, whose offspring are born at an early stage of development and complete their development attached to a nipple, generally in the mother's pouch; and placentals, whose offspring are nourished throughout their embryonic stage by means of a placenta and are born at an advanced stage of development.

Nearly half the living species of mammals are rodents, and about another quarter are bats.

SUB-CLASS PROTOTHERIA

This group of primitive mammals has only one order:

ORDER MONOTREMATA

Egg-laying mammals

Monotremes, the most primitive living mammals, are the only ones that lay eggs. They do not have the bridge of nerve tissue that connects the hemispheres of the brain in more advanced mammals. Like reptiles, they have only one posterior opening to the body—the anal and urinogenital apertures open into a common chamber at the end of the gut. But the way in which they regulate their body temperatures is more like that of mammals than of reptiles. The control is fairly constant when the external temperature is between about 28 and 32°C (82 and 90°F), but outside these limits it tends to vary. They possess rudimentary bones typical of marsupials, such as those that support the pouch in kangaroos. After hatching, the young are nourished

on milk from teatless mammary glands. In living forms there are no functional teeth in the adult, and the male has a horny spur on each ankle, which in the platypus is grooved underneath and connects with a poison gland. There are two families:

FAMILY TACHYGLOSSIDAE

Spiny anteaters or echidnas; 5 species

Echidnas are burrowers with broad feet and small eyes. They are covered with short, barbless spines, except on the belly. The snout is long and tubular, and the long, sticky tongue, used to sweep up ants, has horny serrations which grind against ridges on the palate; there are no teeth. In the breeding season, the female develops a pouch into which she puts her egg (generally only one but sometimes two or three). Echidnas occur in New Guinea, Australia and Tasmania. Example: **Australian spiny anteater** *Tachyglossus aculeatus*: an echidna found throughout Australia

FAMILY ORNITHORHYNCHIDAE

There is one species:
Platypus *Ornithorhynchus anatinus*: found in rivers in eastern Australia and Tasmania. It is well adapted to life in water, with dense underfur, a flattened tail, webbed feet, no external ears and a sensitive bill covered with soft, rubbery skin

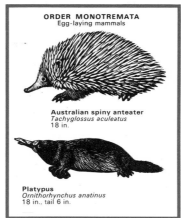

ORDER MONOTREMATA
Egg-laying mammals

Australian spiny anteater
Tachyglossus aculeatus
18 in.

Platypus
Ornithorhynchus anatinus
18 in., tail 6 in.

SUB-CLASS THERIA

This group contains the majority of living mammals, which do not lay eggs. There are two infra-classes:

INFRA-CLASS METATHERIA

There is one order:

ORDER MARSUPIALIA

Pouched mammals

These animals have bones to support a pouch, but not all have external pouches. The young are born at such an early stage of development that the short period of gestation in the womb is followed by a further development period. The mother licks a path in her fur from the base of the tail to the teats, which are in the pouch when there is one, and the offspring crawls along and attaches itself to a teat. Like monotremes, marsupials have no nerve tissue connecting the hemispheres of the brain. There are nine families:

FAMILY DIDELPHIDAE

Opossums; 65 species

These largely tree-dwelling animals,

ranging from south-eastern Canada to Argentina, have a large, clawless great toe, set like a thumb in opposition to the other four digits. Most species have no pouch, and their gestation period is the shortest of any mammal—only 12–13 days. Opossums have 50 teeth. Examples: **Water opossum** or **yapok** *Chironectes minimus*: found in South American streams and lakes
Virginian or **common opossum** *Didelphis marsupialis* (20 in., tail 9–20 in.): lives near lakes, streams and swamps from eastern U.S.A. to South America

FAMILY DASYURIDAE

Australian native cats and marsupial mice; 45 species

A family of mammals whose pouch, if there is one, is poorly developed or conspicuous only in the breeding season. Examples:
Fat-tailed marsupial mouse *Sminthopsis crassicaudata*: found in south-western and south-eastern Australia. It is mainly insect-eating
Eastern native cat *Dasyurus viverrinus* (17 in., tail 11 in.): common in forests and grasslands in Tasmania; also found in southern Australia. It is a gray-brown nocturnal animal with light spots

FAMILY MYRMECOBIIDAE

There is one species:
Numbat or **banded anteater** *Myrmecobius fasciatus*: found in western and southern Australia in open forest and scrub. A red-brown animal with six or seven white bands, a long tail and no pouch, it feeds on ants and termites

FAMILY NOTORYCTIDAE

Marsupial moles; 2 species

Australian burrowing mammals. Example: **Southern marsupial mole** *Notoryctes typhlops*: inhabits deserts in South Australia. This mole-like animal has a horny knob on its short tail, and a horny shield on its nose which protects it when it digs its shallow burrows

FAMILY PERAMELIDAE

Bandicoots; 19 species

Bandicoots, found in Ceram, New Guinea, Australia and Tasmania, have long, pointed flexible muzzles with which they root in the soil. Their ears are often large and their hind limbs are long. Example: **Long-nosed bandicoot** *Perameles nasuta*: found in eastern Australia

ORDER MARSUPIALIA
Pouched mammals

Water opossum or **yapok**
Chironectes minimus
13 in., tail 16 in.

Numbat or **banded anteater**
Myrmecobius fasciatus
10 in., tail 7 in.

Fat-tailed marsupial mouse
Sminthopsis crassicaudata
3½ in., tail 4 in.

Long-nosed bandicoot
Perameles nasuta
16 in., tail 5 in.

Southern marsupial mole
Notoryctes typhlops
5½ in., tail 1 in.

PHYLUM CHORDATA	Animals with notochords	ORDER MARSUPIALIA	Pouched mammals
SUB-PHYLUM VERTEBRATA	Animals with backbones	INFRA-CLASS EUTHERIA	Placental mammals
CLASS MAMMALIA	Mammals	ORDER INSECTIVORA	Insect-eating mammals
SUB-CLASS THERIA	Mammals that do not lay eggs	ORDER DERMOPTERA	Colugos
INFRA-CLASS METATHERIA	Marsupials		

FAMILY CAENOLESTIDAE
Rat opossums; 7 species
These shrew-like marsupials from the forests of South America are the only marsupials apart from the opossums outside Australasia. They have long heads and long sensory whiskers. Example:
Chilean rat opossum *Rhyncholestes raphanurus*: a rare species, found only in the dense forests in the province of Llanquihue and on Chiloe Island, Chile

FAMILY PHALANGERIDAE
Phalangers or possums; 45 species
These tree-dwelling, plant-eating mammals are found from Timor and Celebes to Tasmania. Examples:
Koala *Phascolarctos cinereus* (2 ft 8 in., rudimentary tail): confined to the eucalyptus forests of eastern Australia. It has woolly fur, large ears, a soft pad on the nose and the female has a rearward-opening pouch
Brush-tailed possum *Trichosurus vulpecula*: occurs widely in Australia, usually in forests, open woodland or trees growing in grassland

FAMILY VOMBATIDAE
Wombats; 2 species
Wombats are large, burrowing, tail-less mammals with rodent-like grinding teeth. Some of their burrows extend for as much as 100 ft. Example:
Hairy-nosed wombat *Lasiorhinus latifrons*: found in hilly regions of southeastern Queensland and in southern parts of South Australia. It sleeps during the day in long burrows

FAMILY MACROPODIDAE
Kangaroos; 52 species
Kangaroos, found in Australia, Tasmania and New Guinea, have small heads, large ears and long hind limbs and feet (the family name means 'large-footed' animals). The tail, usually thick at the base, is used as a prop or additional leg, and to balance the kangaroo when it leaps. Examples:
Brush-tailed rock wallaby *Petrogale penicillata* (2 ft 5 in., tail 23 in.): lives on boulder-strewn outcrops in dry forests of eastern Australia. It is a nocturnal animal with a long, slender tail, not thickened at the base
Red kangaroo *Megaleia rufa*: occurs in open grasslands throughout most of Australia. The males have red fur, whereas the females are blue-gray

INFRA-CLASS EUTHERIA
This group contains the placental mammals, which nourish their growing embryos for a comparatively long period of gestation through a complete placenta (as opposed to the incomplete placenta of marsupials) attached to the wall of the womb. There are 19 orders:

ORDER INSECTIVORA
Insect-eating mammals
Most members of this loosely knit group are small, primitive mammals with a long, sensitive snout, clawed toes, and the cheek teeth have sharp, conical cusps, enabling them to seize and crush insects. Most members of the order have five toes on each foot. There are eight families:

FAMILY SOLENODONTIDAE
Solenodons; 2 species
These are comparatively large, stoutly built nocturnal animals with long, nearly naked tails and very long snouts. Example:
Haitian solenodon *Solenodon paradoxus*: occurs in the forests and bush in Haiti. The other species lives in Cuba

FAMILY TENRECIDAE
Tenrecs; 20 species
Superficially like small solenodons, tenrecs have long, pointed snouts and live on Madagascar and the nearby Comoro Islands. Some species are spiny and some are burrowing. Example:
Long-tailed tenrec *Microgale longicaudata*: inhabits forests on Madagascar

FAMILY POTAMOGALIDAE
Otter shrews; 3 species
Externally resembling small otters, these mammals, found only in tropical Africa, have soft fur with a protective coat of coarse guard hairs. They eat small fish and crustaceans. Example:
Giant otter shrew *Potamogale velox*: found in the African forest rivers

FAMILY CHRYSOCHLORIDAE
Golden moles; 20 species
These mammals are the African equivalent of the true moles. They have thick fur with a metallic golden to violet luster, loose skin, a smooth leathery pad on the muzzle, used for burrowing into the soil, eyes covered with hairy skin, and small ears concealed by fur. They feed mainly on worms and insects. Example:

Cape golden mole *Chrysochloris asiatica*: found in southern Africa

FAMILY ERINACEIDAE
Hedgehogs; 15 species
Hedgehogs are covered with short, barbless spines, except on the belly, and when disturbed they can roll into a ball for protection. They range throughout Europe, Africa and Asia. Examples:
Desert hedgehog *Paraechinus aethiopicus*: found in northern Africa and the Middle East in desert areas
Gymnure or **Malayan moon-rat** *Echinosorex gymnurus* (12 in., tail 9 in.): found near streams in forests of southeastern Asia. It has a naked tail, flattened at the end for swimming, a narrow body, a long nose, and a harsh (not actually prickly) coat

FAMILY SORICIDAE
Shrews; more than 200 species
Shrews are small, short-legged mammals with a long, pointed nose, short dense fur, and small weak eyes. They are found throughout the world except in Australia and polar regions. Examples:
Lesser white-toothed shrew *Crocidura suaveolens* (3 in., tail 1 in.): ranges from Europe to eastern Asia. The tips of its teeth are white
Common shrew *Sorex araneus*: ranges through moist areas of Europe and Asia. It has sleek fur, and teeth with brown or purple tips

FAMILY TALPIDAE
Moles; 19 species
The short, thick, cylindrical body, minute eyes and ears, short neck and short, stout limbs of moles help make them highly efficient burrowers. The front feet, turned permanently outwards, move the earth aside with a breast-stroke action. The velvety fur will lie in any direction, and moles can move backwards as well as forwards in their tunnels. Example:
Common Eurasian mole *Talpa europaea*: found in Europe and Asia

FAMILY MACROSCELIDIDAE
Elephant shrews; 14 species
Elephant shrews, found only in Africa, are rat-sized animals with a long, scaly tail, a long, sensitive snout, and large eyes. Most are active during the day, taking refuge at night in burrows of other animals or in holes in the ground. The young are well developed at birth and

can walk almost immediately. Elephant-shrews eat insects, eggs and small mammals. Example:
Rufous elephant shrew *Elephantulus rufescens*: occurs in grasslands in eastern Africa. It runs along the ground, using its powerful, long hind limbs

ORDER DERMOPTERA
This order contains a single family, consisting of two species of colugos; both of them are found in the tropical forest of eastern Asia

FAMILY CYNOCEPHALIDAE
Colugos; 2 species
These slender-limbed mammals have a large, gliding membrane attached to the neck and sides of the body and extending to the tips of the fingers, the sharp-clawed toes, and the tail. Some of their lower teeth slope outwards and are comb-like in form; they are used for grooming and for straining food. Colugos spend the day hanging head-upwards from branches, and become active at night, when they feed on fruit, buds and leaves, often gliding as far as 70 yds from tree to tree. Example:
Philippines colugo or **flying lemur** *Cynocephalus volans*: confined to forests in the Philippines. The other species lives in parts of Indo-China, Indonesia and Malaysia

Philippines colugo
Cynocephalus volans
17 in., tail 11 in.

ORDER MARSUPIALIA
Pouched mammals

Chilean rat opossum
Rhyncholestes raphanurus
5 in., tail 3½ in.

Brush-tailed possum
Trichosurus vulpecula
18 in., tail 11 in.

Hairy-nosed wombat
Lasiorhinus latifrons
3 ft 6 in.

Red kangaroo
Megaleia rufa
5 ft, tail 3 ft 6 in.

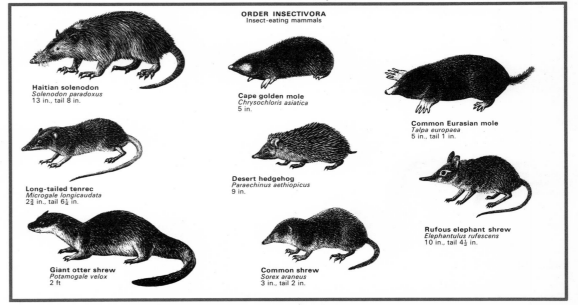

ORDER INSECTIVORA
Insect-eating mammals

Haitian solenodon
Solenodon paradoxus
13 in., tail 8 in.

Long-tailed tenrec
Microgale longicaudata
2¾ in., tail 6¼ in.

Giant otter shrew
Potamogale velox
2 ft

Cape golden mole
Chrysochloris asiatica
5 in.

Desert hedgehog
Paraechinus aethiopicus
9 in.

Common shrew
Sorex araneus
3 in., tail 2 in.

Common Eurasian mole
Talpa europaea
5 in., tail 1 in.

Rufous elephant shrew
Elephantulus rufescens
10 in., tail 4½ in.

PHYLUM CHORDATA	Animals with notochords
SUB-PHYLUM VERTEBRATA	Animals with backbones
CLASS MAMMALIA	Mammals
SUB-CLASS THERIA	Mammals that do not lay eggs
INFRA-CLASS EUTHERIA	Placental mammals
ORDER CHIROPTERA	Bats

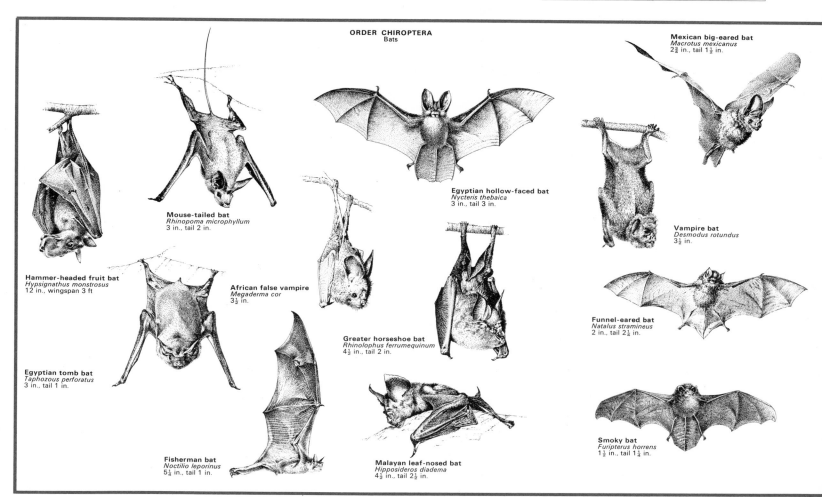

ORDER CHIROPTERA
Bats

Mexican big-eared bat
Macrotus mexicanus
2¾ in., tail 1½ in.

Mouse-tailed bat
Rhinopoma microphyllum
3 in., tail 2 in.

Egyptian hollow-faced bat
Nycteris thebaica
3 in., tail 3 in.

Vampire bat
Desmodus rotundus
3½ in.

Hammer-headed fruit bat
Hypsignathus monstrosus
12 in., wingspan 3 ft

African false vampire
Megaderma cor
3½ in.

Funnel-eared bat
Natalus stramineus
2 in., tail 2½ in.

Greater horseshoe bat
Rhinolophus ferrumequinum
4½ in., tail 2 in.

Egyptian tomb bat
Taphozous perforatus
3 in., tail 1 in.

Smoky bat
Furipterus horrens
1½ in., tail 1¼ in.

Fisherman bat
Noctilio leporinus
5¼ in., tail 1 in.

Malayan leaf-nosed bat
Hipposideros diadema
4½ in., tail 2½ in.

ORDER CHIROPTERA

Bats

Bats are the only flying mammals. The paper-thin, elastic membranes extending from the sides of the body, legs and tail are extensions of the skin on the belly and back; sometimes the tail is very loosely connected with the membrane which stretches from heel to heel. There are two sub-orders:

SUB-ORDER MEGACHIROPTERA

Fruit-eating bats

This sub-order contains a single family of bats that feed mainly on fruit and nectar

FAMILY PTEROPODIDAE

Old World fruit bats and flying foxes; 130 species

Members of this family, found in the tropics and sub-tropics, have short, rudimentary tails and generally a claw on the second as well as the first finger. By day they hang in trees, emerging at night to forage for food. Example:

Hammer-headed fruit bat *Hypsignathus monstrosus*: found in forests from Uganda to West Africa. The adult male has a large, square head, a thick muzzle, huge pendulous lips, ruffles round the nose, a warty snout, a hairless split chin and highly developed voice organs which produce a continual croaking and quacking, probably to attract the female

SUB-ORDER MICROCHIROPTERA

Members of this sub-order are small or medium-sized bats with small eyes, comparatively short snouts and no claw on the second finger. Most have flaps in front of their large ears, which are used for navigation and detecting flying prey by echo-location. There are 16 families:

FAMILY RHINOPOMATIDAE

Mouse-tailed bats; 4 species

The bats of the single genus in this family have a tail nearly as long as the head and body together. Example:

Rhinopoma microphyllum: found in the Old World tropics

FAMILY EMBALLONURIDAE

Sheath-tailed bats; 50 species

Many of these rather small tropical bats have glandular wing-sacs secreting a strong-smelling red substance; these are more developed in the male and may serve to attract the female. The tip of the tail is free of skin, so that in flight the tail membrane can be lengthened by stretching out the hind legs. Example:

Egyptian tomb bat *Taphozous perforatus*: found in north-east Africa and India, they begin feeding at dusk

FAMILY NOCTILIONIDAE

Bulldog bats; 2 species

Bats of this family have full, swollen-looking lips, the upper lip being divided by a fold of skin. They have long, narrow wings. Example:

Fisherman bat *Noctilio leporinus*: ranges from Mexico southwards to Brazil, patrolling the sea and fresh waters and catching fish in its claws

FAMILY NYCTERIDAE

Slit-faced bats; 10 species

These bats have long, loose fur, large ears and a furrow extending from the nostrils to between the eyes, ending in a deep pit in the forehead. The tail has a T-shaped tip, a unique feature among mammals. Example:

Egyptian hollow-faced bat *Nycteris thebaica*: found in Corfu, Africa and south-west Asia

FAMILY MEGADERMATIDAE

False vampires; 5 species

Once thought to be blood-suckers, these bats eat insects and small vertebrates. They have a divided lobe in front of the ear and the leaf-like appendage known as a nose-leaf, which the bats use in echo-location, is long and erect in this family. Example:

African false vampire *Megaderma cor*: roosts in large numbers in caves and trees from Ethiopia to Tanzania

FAMILY RHINOLOPHIDAE

Horseshoe bats; 50 species

These bats, found in the Old World as far eastwards as Australia, have a very complex nose-leaf extending over the upper lip, round the nostrils, and coming to a point above them. Example:

Greater horseshoe bat *Rhinolophus ferrumequinum*: occurs in the Mediterranean region and western Europe, including southern England

FAMILY HIPPOSIDERIDAE

Leaf-nosed bats; 100 species

This family is closely related to the horseshoe bats. Its members are found in Africa and southern Asia. Some species hibernate. Example:

Malayan leaf-nosed bat *Hipposideros diadema*: roosts in hollow trees, caves and buildings

FAMILY PHYLLOSTOMATIDAE

American leaf-nosed bats; about 100 species

The nose-leaf of these bats, which feed on insects, fruit and nectar, is sometimes absent. Some have a long nose and tongue with which they extract nectar from flowers. Example:

Mexican big-eared bat *Macrotus mexicanus*: ranges through western and southern Mexico to Guatemala

FAMILY DESMODONTIDAE

Vampires; 3 species

Members of this family have no nose-leaf but have instead a naked pad with U-shaped grooves at the tip. The teeth are specialized for cutting, and these are the true vampires which feed on fresh blood. They bite their prey where hair or feathers are scanty, usually without disturbing the sleeping victim. Example:

Vampire bat *Desmodus rotundus*: found from northern Mexico to Chile, central Argentina and Uruguay

FAMILY NATALIDAE

Funnel-eared bats; about 15 species

These slim bats have large, funnel-shaped ears. Example:

Natalus stramineus: a funnel-eared bat found from northern Mexico to Panama; also in Brazil, the Guianas and the Lesser Antilles

FAMILY FURIPTERIDAE

Smoky bats; 2 species

A tropical South American family of small funnel-eared bats with truncated snouts ending in a disc or pad. Example:

Smoky bat *Furipterus horrens*: occurs from Panama southwards to Brazil

PHYLUM CHORDATA	Animals with notochords
SUB-PHYLUM VERTEBRATA	Animals with backbones
CLASS MAMMALIA	Mammals
INFRA-CLASS EUTHERIA	Placental mammals
ORDER CHIROPTERA	Bats
ORDER PRIMATES	Primates

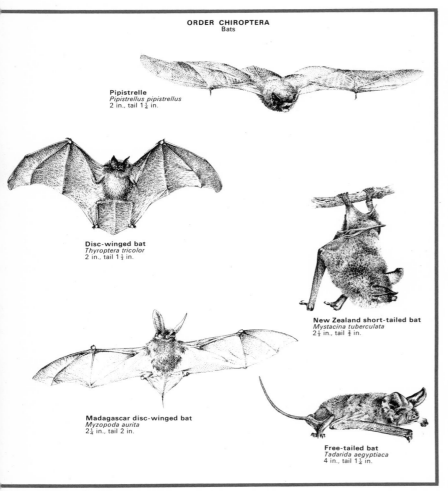

ORDER CHIROPTERA
Bats

Pipistrelle
Pipistrellus pipistrellus
2 in., tail 1¼ in.

Disc-winged bat
Thyroptera tricolor
2 in., tail 1¼ in.

New Zealand short-tailed bat
Mystacina tuberculata
2¼ in., tail ¾ in.

Madagascar disc-winged bat
Myzopoda aurita
2¼ in., tail 2 in.

Free-tailed bat
Tadarida aegyptiaca
4 in., tail 1¼ in.

Philippine tree-shrew
Urogale everetti
8 in., tail 6 in.

Indri
Indri indri
2 ft 6 in., tail 2½ in.

Slender loris
Loris tardigradus
10 in.

Aye-aye
Daubentonia madagascariensis
16 in., tail 24 in.

FAMILY THYROPTERIDAE
Disc-winged bats; 2 species
These bats from central and northern South America have circular suction discs or cups on the wrists and ankles, and claws on the thumbs. Example:
Thyroptera tricolor: found in tropical forests from British Honduras south-eastwards to Trinidad

FAMILY MYZOPODIDAE
There is one species:
Madagascar disc-winged bat *Myzopoda aurita*: similar to the true disc-winged bats, but with larger ears and the thumb-claw is shorter

FAMILY VESPERTILIONIDAE
Typical insect-eating bats; 275 species
The four previous families are probably specialized off-shoots of the Vespertilionidae, a family of very small bats with tiny eyes, and generally without a nose-leaf. Some have glands in the snout and some have long ears. Examples:
Noctule *Nyctalus noctula* (3 in., tail 2½ in.): found in Europe and Asia. It is red-brown, and it flies with many quick turns, often before sunset. It often roosts in very large colonies
Long-eared bat *Plecotus auritus* (2 in., tail 2 in.): found in Europe and Asia. Except in summer, when females form colonies, it roosts singly. It flies only after dark and can hover
Pipistrelle *Pipistrellus pipistrellus*: occurs in Europe and Asia. Generally dark brown in color, it usually appears about sunset. Its flight is jerky and erratic, and it roosts in cave entrances, under rocks, in trees and in buildings

FAMILY MYSTACINIDAE
There is one species:
New Zealand short-tailed bat *Mystacina tuberculata*: today found only on Solomon Island, off Stewart Island. It has needle-sharp claws, those of the thumbs and feet bearing small subsidiary talons. The wings are rolled up under a leathery membrane when the bat is not flying; this allows the arms to be used in running

FAMILY MOLOSSIDAE
Mastiff or free-tailed bats; 80 species
Most members of this family, found in most warm parts of the world, have tails which project beyond the edge of the tail membrane, narrow wings, velvety fur and no nose-leaf. Example:
Tadarida aegyptiaca: a free-tailed bat found in Africa and western Asia. It sleeps by day in hollow trees and crevices in caves and rocks

ORDER PRIMATES

Most primates are relatively unspecialized, tree-dwelling mammals, having limbs with five digits but showing a tendency towards the development of grasping hands and feet. They generally have nails instead of claws. The eyes are near the front of the head and set close together so that both look in the same direction—providing stereoscopic vision and judgment of distances—and the sense of smell is less important than the senses of vision, hearing and touch. Apart from man, whose distribution is worldwide, most primates live in tropical and sub-tropical regions. There are two sub-orders:

SUB-ORDER PROSIMII
This sub-order contains the more primitive primates, which have long snouts and eyes which do not face directly forwards. There are six families:

FAMILY TUPAIIDAE
Tree-shrews; 20 species
This ancient family is sometimes included with the insect-eating mammals. Tree-shrews outwardly look like long-nosed squirrels. The scrotum, unlike that of other primates, lies in front of the penis. They have long and supple digits with sharp, moderately curved claws. All live in tropical forests in Asia. Example:
Philippine tree-shrew *Urogale everetti*: found only on Mindanao Island

FAMILY LEMURIDAE
Lemurs; 15 species
They are the most abundant of the primates of Madagascar. Their lower incisor teeth are modified to form a fur-grooming comb, unlike those of the tree-shrews. The fingers and toes bear nails, but there is a long grooming claw on each second toe. The thumb and big toe are opposable to the other digits. Examples:
Ruffed lemur *Varecia variegata*: lives in forests of north-eastern Madagascar. It has a ruff of long hair on its neck and the sides of its head. There are three differently colored races
Gray mouse lemur *Microcebus murinus* (5 in., tail 6½ in.): occurs in the forests of western Madagascar. Mouse lemurs, the smallest primates, are agile and active at night, preying on insects. It is possible that they are related to the bush-babies of Africa and many aspects of their behavior are similar

FAMILY INDRIIDAE
Indri and sifakas; 4 species
Members of this family are similar to lemurs except that they climb with a hand-over-hand movement, cling in an erect position to vertical branches, and move on the ground by hopping because their legs are much longer than their arms. Strictly vegetarian, they feed on leaves and fruit. Example:
Indri *Indri indri*: now very rare, it is confined to the forests of eastern Madagascar. Active by day, it has a mournful, wailing territorial call

FAMILY DAUBENTONIIDAE
There is one species:
Aye-aye *Daubentonia madagascariensis*: found in forests of northern Madagascar. The aye-aye has a single rodent-like incisor on each side of each jaw, and gnaws a hole in bark where its sensitive ears have located an insect; it then inserts its wiry middle finger and impales a grub

FAMILY LORISIDAE
Lorises, pottos and bush-babies; 11 species
Lorises and pottos are well adapted for slow movement, so that they can creep up undetected on birds. Their hands and feet are specialized for grasping; the first digit is opposable and very strong. Bush-babies have long tails, large eyes, and large mobile ears which can be folded. They are vertical clingers, and they tend to hop on their hind legs when on the ground. All are nocturnal. Like lemurs they have a tooth comb. Example:
Slender loris *Loris tardigradus*: found in southern India and Ceylon. It is a slender animal and has no tail

PHYLUM CHORDATA	Animals with notochords
SUB-PHYLUM VERTEBRATA	Animals with backbones
CLASS MAMMALIA	Mammals
INFRA-CLASS EUTHERIA	Placental mammals
ORDER PRIMATES	Primates

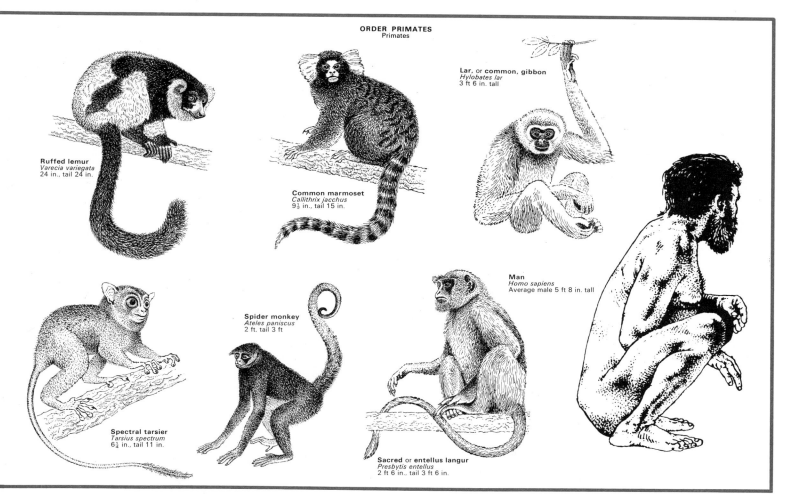

ORDER PRIMATES
Primates

Ruffed lemur
Varecia variegata
24 in., tail 24 in.

Common marmoset
Callithrix jacchus
9½ in., tail 15 in.

Lar, or **common, gibbon**
Hylobates lar
3 ft 6 in. tall

Man
Homo sapiens
Average male 5 ft 8 in. tall

Spider monkey
Ateles paniscus
2 ft. tail 3 ft

Spectral tarsier
Tarsius spectrum
6¾ in., tail 11 in.

Sacred or **entellus langur**
Presbytis entellus
2 ft 6 in., tail 3 ft 6 in.

FAMILY TARSIIDAE
Tarsiers; 3 species
Tarsiers have flattened faces, very large eyes, round skulls and no tooth comb. The legs are elongated, especially the tarsus bones, and the scaly, naked underside of the tail is used to provide support. Tarsiers are active only at night, when they leap through the trees from trunk to trunk. All live in south-east Asia. Example:
Spectral tarsier *Tarsius spectrum*: found in scrub jungle in Celebes and neighboring islands

SUB-ORDER ANTHROPOIDEA
This sub-order includes the higher primates, which possess a short snout and full stereoscopic vision. It is divided into two infra-orders: the Platyrrhini (the first two families) and the Catarrhini (the three other families), which may have evolved independently from prosimians. The platyrrhines, with wide-apart, sideways-facing nostrils, are entirely South American, whereas the catarrhines, with close-together, downward-facing nostrils, are found in Africa and Asia

FAMILY CALLITRICHIDAE
Marmosets and tamarins; 21 species
These small monkeys have claws on all digits except the great toe, and do not use their tails for clinging. All are active by day. Examples:
Goeldi's marmoset *Callimico goeldii* (8½ in., tail 12½ in.): found in the upper tributaries of the Amazon. It is black with a cape of long hair
Common marmoset *Callithrix jacchus*: found in the tropical and sub-tropical forests of Brazil and Bolivia

FAMILY CEBIDAE
Cebid monkeys; 26 species
These monkeys, which have nails on all their fingers and toes, are larger than marmosets, and tend to move less jerkily. Some species have prehensile tails. Examples:
Douroucouli or **night monkey** *Aotus trivirgatus* (18 in., tail 16 in.): the only nocturnal higher primate, it occurs in forests from Nicaragua to Argentina, and from the Guianas to Peru and Ecuador. It has large, owl-like eyes emphasized by the white areas around them
Spider monkey *Ateles paniscus*: found in the topmost branches in tropical forests from southern Mexico to Brazil. It has very long legs, and moves swiftly, using its tail as a fifth limb

FAMILY CERCOPITHECIDAE
Old World monkeys; 60 species
This is the first family of the catarrhine infra-order. Old World monkeys walk on all fours, have some facial expression, and the males have dagger-like canine teeth. The family includes two distinct groups: the colobines, with complex stomachs for feeding on leaves, and the omnivorous cercopithecines, which have simple stomachs and large cheek pouches in which food can be stored. Examples:
Black-and-white colobus *Colobus polykomos* (2 ft, tail 3 ft): found in the middle layers of the African forest. It has a coat of long glossy black hair with white markings
Sacred or **entellus langur** *Presbytis entellus*: colobine monkey found in the forests of India and Pakistan. Unlike other langurs, it lives mainly on the ground
Grivet, or **vervet monkey,** *Cercopithecus aethiops* (2 ft 8 in., tail 2 ft): lives in wooded savanna regions of Africa. It spends much of its time on the ground
Drill *Mandrillus leucophaeus* (2 ft 4 in., tail 5 in.): this forest-dwelling cercopithecine from western equatorial Africa has a black face, with prominent ridges on the sides of the nose, and red and blue buttocks
Gelada *Theropithecus gelada* (2 ft 5 in., tail 1 ft 8 in.): a cercopithecine found on the Ethiopian plateau. The gelada has a rounded muzzle, a bright red patch of naked skin on the chest, a long tufted tail and powerful jaws. The male has a mane
Rhesus monkey *Macaca mulatta* (24 in., tail 12 in.): a cercopithecine found in northern India, southern China and Indo-China. The Rh (from Rhesus) blood factor was first discovered in these monkeys

FAMILY PONGIDAE
Apes; 9 species
Like man and unlike other primates, apes have no tail, long arms and highly developed brains; they are man's closest living relatives. Examples:
Lar, or **common, gibbon** *Hylobates lar*: found in the rain forests of Burma, Thailand, Malaya, Borneo, Sumatra and Java. This slender, swift-moving animal lives almost entirely in the trees where it swings by its long arms from branch to branch; when on the ground it walks upright with its arms held high for balance. These gibbons live in pairs and make loud territorial calls
Orang-utan *Pongo pygmaeus* (up to 5 ft 6 in. tall): found in the forests of Borneo and northern Sumatra. The orang-utan has sparse, shaggy red hair and its hands and feet are similar to each other. The male has a huge goiter-like throat-sac and two fatty swellings in the cheeks
Gorilla *Gorilla gorilla* (up to 6 ft tall): found in the forests of equatorial Africa. Together with chimpanzees, gorillas, which are the largest living primates, are the animal species closest to man. The limbs are more human in proportion than those of the orang-utan, although the arms are longer than the legs. The feet are man-like, with the big toe larger than the others. Gorillas generally walk on all fours, arms supported by the backs of the middle part of the fingers, and are almost entirely ground-dwelling. They live in groups of up to 30 headed by an adult male, and are more quiet and retiring than chimpanzees. They have short dense black hair
Chimpanzee *Pan troglodytes* (about 3 ft 6 in.): found in the rain forests of tropical Africa; more widespread than the gorilla. Chimpanzees have large ears and long, scant black hair. They live in trees and on the ground in loose communities of up to 80, without fixed leaders

FAMILY HOMINIDAE
There is one species.
Man *Homo sapiens*: ranges throughout the world because of his ability to modify or create environments. The family evolved from ape-like ancestors about 26 million years ago, although modern man did not appear until about 40,000 years ago. Man is distinguished from other primates by his highly developed brain (enabling him to have a complex spoken language), his erect posture (involving considerable modification of the skeleton and muscles so that the body can be balanced on two legs), and sparse body hair

Mammals

PHYLUM CHORDATA	Animals with notochords
SUB-PHYLUM VERTEBRATA	Animals with backbones
CLASS MAMMALIA	Mammals
SUB-CLASS THERIA	Mammals that do not lay eggs
INFRA-CLASS EUTHERIA	Placental mammals
ORDER CETACEA	Whales

ORDER CETACEA

Whales

Cetaceans, the mammals most completely adapted to life in the water, have streamlined bodies tapering towards the tail. They cannot move about on land, their skin needs moisture continuously and, since they have no breastbone, most of them die if stranded on land because of the pressure on their lungs. Whales have no hind limbs. Their forelimbs are modified into broad flippers, and the tail has a horizontal fluke projecting on each side. A layer of blubber covers the whole body beneath the skin and helps to conserve heat. There are no external ears. The horizontal tail immediately distinguishes whales from fish. There are two distinct sub-orders of whales:

SUB-ORDER ODONTOCETI

Toothed whales

Generally much smaller than the whalebone whales, toothed whales have conical, pointed teeth in the lower or both jaws, or only one tusk-like tooth in the upper jaw. The lower jaw is narrow, not bowed outwards as in the baleen whales, and the tongue is small. Toothed whales feed mainly on fish. There are five families:

FAMILY PLATANISTIDAE
River dolphins; 4 species

All freshwater dolphins have long, almost bird-like beaks which may contain as many as 200 teeth. They live in the Amazon, Orinoco, Yangtse and Ganges rivers. Example:
Susu, or **Ganges dolphin**, *Platanista gangetica*: lives in the Ganges, Brahmaputra and perhaps Indus rivers. It has tiny eyes but is blind and probes in the mud for shellfish

FAMILY ZIPHIIDAE
Beaked whales; 15 species

These medium-sized whales have a beak, one or two pairs of functional teeth in the lower jaw, and two to four throat furrows converging to form a V-pattern at the chin. Example:
Cuvier's beaked whale *Ziphius cavirostris*: found in all seas, but it is rare. It has only one pair of teeth

FAMILY PHYSETERIDAE
Sperm whales; 2 species

These whales have no dorsal fin and have functional teeth in the lower jaw, which is much shorter than the upper. The larger species has a barrel-shaped head, which is a third of the total body length and is filled with spermaceti oil, used in industry as a lubricant. It feeds mainly on squids. The pygmy sperm whale has a porpoise-like body. Example:
Sperm whale *Physeter catodon*: common in warm oceans; the males migrate to colder waters in summer

FAMILY MONODONTIDAE
White whales; 2 species

White whales are closely related to the dolphins but have fewer teeth and no dorsal fin. The species are:
Beluga, or **white whale**, *Delphinapterus leucas* (up to 18 ft): found in Arctic waters; it has 18 teeth in each jaw
Narwhal *Monodon monoceros*: found in Arctic waters. The male has teeth in the upper jaw, one (or rarely two) of which develops into a long twisted tusk, projecting forwards through the upper lip to a length of up to 8 ft; in the female these teeth remain undeveloped

FAMILY DELPHINIDAE
Dolphins and porpoises; 50 species

These mammals, generally small compared with other whales, have no throat grooves; they have teeth in both jaws, and most have a dorsal fin in the centre of the back. Examples:

Killer whale *Orcinus orca* (male up to 30 ft, female up to 15 ft): found in oceans throughout the world. This black-backed whale has a white underside, and a tall, narrow dorsal fin. Killer whales' stomachs have been found to contain dolphins up to 10 ft long
Atlantic bottle-nosed dolphin *Tursiops truncatus*: found in the North Atlantic and the Mediterranean Sea. It has a short snout with 20–26 teeth on each side of each jaw. Bottle-nosed dolphins, known as porpoises in North America, can be taught to give complex performances
Common or **harbor porpoise** *Phocaena phocaena* (up to 6 ft): found in the North Atlantic and adjacent seas; it commonly swims up rivers. It has no beak

SUB-ORDER MYSTICETI

Whalebone whales

Most species of whalebone whales are large—there is none less than 17 ft long when fully grown. There are no teeth in either jaw; instead, the V-shaped upper jaw has plates of baleen (whalebone), which act as sieves or strainers for plankton and are enclosed by the two halves of the lower jaw when the whale is not feeding. There are three families:

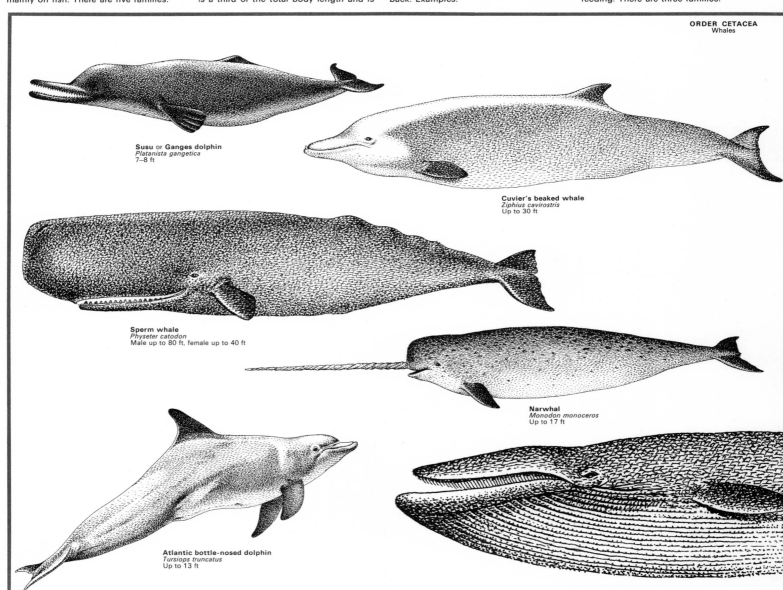

ORDER CETACEA
Whales

Susu or **Ganges dolphin**
Platanista gangetica
7–8 ft

Cuvier's beaked whale
Ziphius cavirostris
Up to 30 ft

Sperm whale
Physeter catodon
Male up to 80 ft, female up to 40 ft

Narwhal
Monodon monoceros
Up to 17 ft

Atlantic bottle-nosed dolphin
Tursiops truncatus
Up to 13 ft

PHYLUM CHORDATA	Animals with notochords	INFRA-CLASS EUTHERIA	Placental mammals
SUB-PHYLUM VERTEBRATA	Animals with backbones	ORDER CETACEA	Whales
CLASS MAMMALIA	Mammals	ORDER EDENTATA	Anteaters, sloths and armadillos
SUB-CLASS THERIA	Mammals that do not lay eggs	ORDER PHOLIDOTA	Pangolins

FAMILY ESCHRICHTIIDAE

There is one species:

California gray whale *Eschrichtius gibbosus*: this whale migrates from Arctic waters to shallows off the Californian coast to breed. It has a very broad mouth, 2–4 ft deep furrows on the throat, and no dorsal fin but a series of low bumps on the back near the tail. The baleen is short and thick with coarsely frayed inner edges to strain the small bottom-living creatures on which this whale feeds

FAMILY BALAENOPTERIDAE

Rorquals; 6 species

Also called fin whales, the rorquals are distinguished from the right whales by a dorsal fin, narrow ridges on the throat, a smaller head (generally a quarter or a fifth of the body length), only slightly curved jaws, and shorter and less flexible baleen. Examples:

Blue whale *Balaenoptera musculus* (record length 108 ft): feeds in Arctic and Antarctic waters and migrates to sub-tropical waters to breed. It is the largest mammal that has ever lived

Common rorqual or **fin whale** *Balaenoptera physalus*: found in all oceans, feeding on herrings and cod as well as on plankton

FAMILY BALAENIDAE

Right whales; 3 species

These whales have long mouths—the head is more than a quarter of the total body length—and the lower jaw scoops down at the front so that it encloses the upper jaw only at the sides. There are no throat grooves and no dorsal fin. The baleen plates are long, narrow and very elastic, and these whales feed only on microscopic plankton. Example:

Greenland right whale *Balaena mysticetus*: found in the Arctic Ocean. It is black, except for a white chin and a gray area near the tail

ORDER EDENTATA

Anteaters, sloths and armadillos

These rather primitive New World mammals have on the forelimbs two or three fingers much longer than the others. These long fingers are used as hooks by sloths, to break open anthills by anteaters, and to burrow by armadillos. All lack front teeth, and cheek teeth, if present, have no enamel. There are three families:

FAMILY MYRMECOPHAGIDAE

Anteaters; 3 species

Anteaters have long, tapering snouts, tubular mouths with no teeth, and long sticky tongues. Example:

Tamandua or **lesser anteater** *Tamandua tetradactyla*: found in tropical forests from southern Mexico to Brazil. This tree-dwelling anteater has a non-bushy prehensile tail

FAMILY BRADYPODIDAE

Sloths; 5 species

The slow-moving tree sloths have short, rounded heads, inconspicuous ears, and forward-facing eyes. The hand has two or three fingers with which sloths suspend themselves upside-down from branches. The hairs hang downwards so that rainwater runs down to the back. Algae often grow on the surface of the straw-like hairs, giving the fur a green color and camouflaging the animal among the leaves. Example:

Two-toed sloth *Choloepus didactylus*: lives in the forests of Venezuela, the Guianas and northern Brazil

FAMILY DASYPODIDAE

Armadillos; 20 species

Members of this family have a covering of horny plates or bands connected by flexible skin, so that most species can roll up into a ball for defense. They have three

to five strong claws on the front feet which are used for burrowing, and up to 90 peg-like teeth. They roam in open country from the southern U.S.A. to the Argentine pampas. Example:

Nine-banded armadillo *Dasypus novemcinctus*: found in South and Central America, and in southern North America, where it is still extending its range. Its chief food includes insects and other invertebrates; it also eats birds' eggs

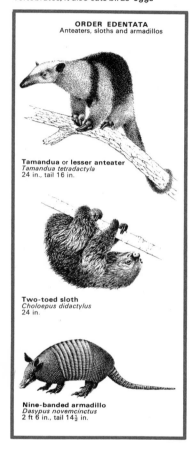

ORDER EDENTATA
Anteaters, sloths and armadillos

Tamandua or **lesser anteater**
Tamandua tetradactyla
24 in., tail 16 in.

Two-toed sloth
Choloepus didactylus
24 in.

Nine-banded armadillo
Dasypus novemcinctus
2 ft 6 in., tail 14½ in.

ORDER PHOLIDOTA

The mammals of this order are the Old World counterparts of the New World edentates. There is only one family:

FAMILY MANIDAE

Pangolins; 7 species

This family, found in the Old World tropics, consists of animals with long tapering bodies, covered above with overlapping scales but with no scales on the snout, sides of the face or undersides. The tongue has muscular roots which pass down through the chest and attach to the pelvis; the five strong front claws are used to tear open termites' nests and for burrowing. Ground-dwelling species roll themselves into a ball for defense Example:

Cape pangolin *Manis temminckii*: lives in dry savanna regions of southern and eastern Africa

Greenland right whale
Balaena mysticetus
Up to 70 ft

California gray whale
Eschrichtius gibbosus
Up to 45 ft

Common rorqual or **fin whale**
Balaenoptera physalus
Up to 85 ft

Cape pangolin
Manis temminckii
24 in., tail 18 in.

PHYLUM CHORDATA	Animals with notochords	INFRA-CLASS EUTHERIA	Placental mammals
SUB-PHYLUM VERTEBRATA	Animals with backbones	ORDER LAGOMORPHA	Pikas, hares and rabbits
CLASS MAMMALIA	Mammals	ORDER RODENTIA	Rodents
SUB-CLASS THERIA	Mammals that do not lay eggs		

ORDER LAGOMORPHA

Pikas, hares and rabbits

Although these animals resemble rodents, they have an additional pair of non-gnawing, chisel-shaped incisor teeth outside the normal pair. Their scrotum, unlike that of rodents, lies in front of the penis, which has no bone. They eat their feces the first time waste matter is passed from each meal, so making best use of plant food. There are two families:

FAMILY OCHOTONIDAE

Pikas or mouse hares; 14 species

Typical inhabitants of Arctic and alpine tundra, these animals are the most common small plant-eaters in Tibet and along the Siberian Arctic coast. They have short ears, no visible tail, long, dense, soft fur, and nostrils which can be closed in bad weather. The hind limbs are not very long, and the undersides of the feet are heavily furred. Example:

Rocky mountain pika *Ochotona princeps*: a pika found in the Rocky Mountains region of North America. Like other pikas, it dries grass in the sun and stores the hay as food for winter

FAMILY LEPORIDAE

Hares and rabbits; 50 species

The leporids are found throughout the world except in Australia, New Zealand, Madagascar and various oceanic islands (although some have been introduced to these places by man). They have short, furry, upturned tails and very long ears and hind limbs. They are most commonly active at dusk and dawn. Examples:

Brown hare *Lepus capensis*: a solitary animal, it rests in depressions in the ground among thick vegetation. Its powerful hind quarters and long back legs enable it to run at speeds of up to 40 mph

Eastern cottontail rabbit *Sylvilagus floridanus* (18 in.): lives in open or bushy country from southern Canada to Argentina, in old burrows of other animals

ORDER RODENTIA

Rodents

Rodents are the most successful of modern mammals, apart from man, and are found in all parts of the world. They are easily identified by the long pair of chisel-like incisor teeth (with enamel on the front surface only) projecting from each jaw at the front of the mouth; these teeth grow continuously and if for any reason they are not worn down by gnawing, the tips may grow past each other and perforate the palate. In some rodents the lips can be closed behind the incisors so that the animals can gnaw without dirt entering their mouths. The scrotum, unlike that of the lagomorphs, is behind the penis, which has a bone. Three sub-orders are recognized on the basis of the position and structure of the jaw muscles:

SUB-ORDER SCIUROMORPHA

Squirrel-like rodents

This sub-order includes squirrels, marmots, gophers and beavers. There are seven families:

FAMILY APLODONTIDAE

There is one species:

Sewellel *Aplodontia rufa*: a thick-set, heavy, burrowing animal, often called the mountain beaver; it lives in forests, near streams, in western North America

FAMILY SCIURIDAE

Squirrels; 250 species

Found all over the world except Australia, squirrels are active during the day and generally live in trees, although some species are ground-dwelling and dig burrows. They have large eyes, and many are brightly colored. Examples:

Eastern chipmunk *Tamias striatus*: found in deciduous forests and bush areas in the eastern U.S.A. and south-eastern Canada. It has black and yellow stripes down its back

Eurasian red squirrel *Sciurus vulgaris* (9 in., tail 7 in.): found in the coniferous forests of Europe and Asia; generally red-brown but sometimes black, it has conspicuous tufts on its ears

Alpine marmot *Marmota marmota* (20 in., tail 6 in.): this thick-set burrower lives in the Alps and Carpathians and is active during the day except from September to March when it hibernates

Red-and-white giant flying squirrel *Petaurista alborufa* (23 in., tail 25 in.): found in dense forests in southern Asia. This nocturnal animal lives in hollow trees during the day. A broad, furry gliding skin stretches from the wrist to the hind foot and to the base of the tail, enabling it to glide from tree to tree. It sometimes rides ascending air currents, and can bank and turn to control its glide

FAMILY GEOMYIDAE

Pocket gophers; 30 species

These North American burrowing rodents have strong digging claws and two long fur-lined external cheek pouches, used for carrying food, which the animal can turn inside-out for cleaning. They spend most of their lives underground. Example:

Plains pocket gopher *Geomys bursarius*: makes burrows up to 300 ft long in loose sandy soil in grasslands

FAMILY HETEROMYIDAE

Kangaroo rats and pocket mice; 70 species

Occurring from western North America to Venezuela, these animals have long hind limbs for jumping and cheek pouches like those of pocket gophers. They make burrows under bushes, and become torpid in cold weather. Example:

Merriam's kangaroo rat *Dipodomys merriami*: lives in arid areas of Mexico and western North America

FAMILY CASTORIDAE

There is one species:

Beaver *Castor fiber*: found in rivers and lakes in Europe, Asia and North America, the beaver is a water-dwelling rodent, with dense underfur overlaid with coarse guard hairs, ears and eyes which can be closed under water, webbed feet and a broad, paddle-shaped scaly tail. The dam-building activities of beavers can create large ponds and greatly change whole environments

FAMILY ANOMALURIDAE

Scaly-tailed squirrels; 9 species

Except for members of the genus *Zenkerella*, all scaly-tailed squirrels have a gliding skin or membrane between the limbs, extending to the tail. All scaly-tailed squirrels have two overlapping rows of scales on the underside of the tail which act as an 'anti-skid' device when they land on a tree-trunk. Example:

Pel's scaly-tailed squirrel *Anomalurus peli*: found in forests of West Africa

FAMILY PEDETIDAE

There is one species:

Springhaas, or **Cape jumping hare**, *Pedetes capensis*: lives in grasslands and open bush in eastern and southern Africa. Except for the bushy tail, the springhaas has a kangaroo-like appearance with long hind legs and ears, and a soft coat

SUB-ORDER MYOMORPHA

Mouse-like rodents

This large group contains more than 1000 species of rodents. There are nine families:

FAMILY CRICETIDAE

Hamsters and allies; 570 species

Most members of this family burrow. Many have thick-set bodies and short tails and legs. Examples:

White-footed deer mouse *Peromyscus leucopus* (4 in., tail 4 in.): extremely abundant in North and Central America. This rodent bears a striking resemblance in form, color and habits to the European long-tailed field-mouse of the family Muridae. It has a soft, sandy-colored coat, large ears, and a hairy tail as long as its body

Eastern wood rat *Neotoma floridana* (9 in., tail 8 in.): found in eastern North America. The wood rat makes a nest of twigs, rocks and bones, and picks up anything attractive—often a piece of shiny foil—as nest material. Related behavior accounts for other names, such as 'pack rat' and 'trade rat'

Common hamster *Cricetus cricetus* (10 in., tail 2 in.): found in the steppes of Europe and Asia and in ploughed land and along river banks. It has cheek pouches and broad feet with well-developed claws for burrowing

Brown lemming *Lemmus lemmus* (5 in., tail 1 in.): lives in tundra of Europe, Asia and North America. It is a heavily furred, stocky rodent with very short ears and tail. Lemmings burrow through the soil in summer and under the snow in winter; they make nests of grass and moss. Every 4–5 years, when the population cycle is at its peak and there are too many animals for the food available, they migrate in vast numbers in search of new territories

Muskrat or **musquash** *Ondatra zibethicus* (13 in., tail 10 in.): lives in marshes, lakes and rivers of North America and has been introduced into Europe. Its hind feet are partly webbed with a fringe of hairs, called the swimming fringe, along the edges; its tail is flattened. The musk rat builds mounds in swamps, connected with the land by long tunnels with underwater exits

Round-tailed musk rat *Neofiber alleni*: found in bogs and swamps in Florida and southern Georgia. It is a good swimmer and burrower, building mounds in moist soil. Its fur has long guard hairs and soft, short underfur

ORDER LAGOMORPHA
Pikas, hares and rabbits

Rocky mountain pika
Ochotona princeps
8 in.

Brown hare
Lepus capensis
24 in., tail 4 in.

Sewellel
Aplodontia rufa
17 in., tail 1 in.

Merriam's kangaroo rat
Dipodomys merriami
4 in., tail 6 in.

Beaver
Castor fiber
3 ft, tail 12 in.

Eastern chipmunk
Tamias striatus
6 in., tail 4 in.

Pel's scaly-tailed squirrel
Anomalurus peli
17 in., tail 18 in.

Plains pocket gopher
Geomys bursarius
9 in., tail 4 in.

Springhaas or **Cape**
Pedetes capensis
24 in., tail 21 in.

PHYLUM CHORDATA	Animals with notochords
SUB-PHYLUM VERTEBRATA	Animals with backbones
CLASS MAMMALIA	Mammals
SUB-CLASS THERIA	Mammals that do not lay eggs
INFRA-CLASS EUTHERIA	Placental mammals
ORDER RODENTIA	Rodents

Short-tailed vole *Microtus agrestris* (4 in., tail 1½ in.): found in moist meadows, moors and open woods in Europe and western Asia. The long loose fur nearly hides the short ears. It digs surface runways and sometimes shallow burrows

Lesser Egyptian gerbil *Gerbillus gerbillus* (4 in., tail 3 in.): a common desert rodent, ranging from Palestine southwards to Uganda and as far west as Nigeria. It has a sandy coat with white feet and underparts

FAMILY SPALACIDAE
Mediterranean mole-rats; 3 species
These rodents have long bodies; short legs; soft, dense, reversible fur; tactile bristles on the snout; no external eye openings and no external ears. They are found in eastern Europe and south-western Asia. Example:
Greater mole-rat *Spalax microphthalmus*: found in steppes of southern Russia; it is an extensive burrower

FAMILY RHIZOMYIDAE
Bamboo rats and African mole-rats; 18 species
With their compact bodies adapted for burrowing and their long incisor teeth uncovered by the lips, these rats resemble the American pocket gophers, except that they have no cheek pouches. Bamboo rats live in southern Asia. Example:
Splendid mole-rat *Tachyoryctes splendens* (8 in., tail 2⅛ in.): found in Ethiopia

FAMILY MURIDAE
Old World rats and mice; 500 species
Most of the rats and mice in this family are small animals with naked, scaly tails and long snouts. The structure of their teeth distinguishes them from the Cricetidae. Examples:
Black rat *Rattus rattus* (9 in., tail 10 in.): probably originated in south-eastern Asia, but is now found throughout the world in association with man. It is host to a flea which carries a bacterium causing plague, and is active mainly at night

House mouse *Mus musculus*: originated in the dry areas of Europe and Asia but is now common throughout the world, living in association with man in town and country; it is active mainly by night
Striped grass mouse *Lemniscomys striatus* (5 in., tail 5½ in.): found in various open habitats in Africa, this mouse has buff stripes on a dark brown background. It is a ground-dwelling rodent, active during the day
Giant pouched rat *Cricetomys gambianus* (15 in., tail 18 in.): this nocturnal African rat has short, thin fur, big ears, a long narrow head, cheek pouches, and a white tail-tip. It is unique in carrying parasitic cockroaches

FAMILY GLIRIDAE
Dormice; 10 species
Dormice, found in Europe, Asia and Africa, have rather bushy tails, soft coats, short bodies, short legs and toes, and curved claws for climbing. In the northern part of their range they become fat in autumn and are dormant from October to April. Example:
Hazel dormouse *Muscardinus avellanarius*: ranges from Britain to Asia Minor and Russia. It lives in dense undergrowth, hiding by day in a nest of vegetation built in the lower branches of trees

FAMILY PLATACANTHOMYIDAE
Spiny dormouse and Chinese pygmy dormouse; 2 species
These Asian rodents look like dormice except that the tail is scaly at the base and ends in a brush. They have large ears and long hind feet. Example:
Spiny dormouse *Platacanthomys lasiurus*: found in southern India. This rodent lives in trees and is found mainly in rocky hill country

FAMILY SELEVINIIDAE
There is one species:
Desert dormouse *Selevinia betpakdalaensis*: a rare animal discovered in 1938 in the clay and sandy deserts of

Kazakhstan, in the Soviet Union. It has a round body and long, non-bushy tail. It molts in an unusual way: the hair comes off in patches, along with the skin

FAMILY ZAPODIDAE
Birch mice and jumping mice; 11 species
These small, mouse-like animals are found in forests, meadows and swamps in northern Europe, Asia and North America. They have internal cheek pouches, long hind legs used for jumping and a long tail for balancing. Example:
Meadow jumping mouse *Zapus hudsonius*: inhabits meadows in the forested areas of North America

FAMILY DIPODIDAE
Jerboas; 25 species
These animals, found in Asia and northern Africa, are remarkably well adapted for jumping, with hind legs at least four times as long as the front legs, elongated feet with three central bones fused to form a single bone for strength and support, and long tails. Example:
Four-toed jerboa *Allactaga tetradactyla*: found only in Egypt, it burrows in sandy soils. It is the only jerboa with four toes on the hind feet

SUB-ORDER HYSTRICOMORPHA
Porcupine-like rodents
The 16 families in this sub-order of rodents range from the spine-bearing porcupines to the guinea-pigs and coypus

FAMILY HYSTRICIDAE
Old World porcupines; 20 species
These large, thick-set, short-legged rodents from Africa, Italy and southern Asia have long, sharp quills for defense in addition to hair on their bodies and tails. Example:
Indian crested porcupine *Hystrix indica*: lives in forests, rocky hills and ravines. It spends most of the day in its burrow and emerges at night to feed

FAMILY ERETHIZONTIDAE
New World porcupines; 23 species
These porcupines have shorter spines than their Old World counterparts; some of the spines are barbed. Their feet are modified for life in the trees—the sole is widened and the first toe on the hind foot is replaced by a broad, movable pad. Example:
North American porcupine *Erethizon dorsatum*: inhabits timbered regions of Alaska and other western states of the U.S.A., and Canada

FAMILY CAVIIDAE
Cavies or guinea-pigs; 23 species
Members of this South American family are found in rocky areas, savannas, forest edges and swamps. They have fairly coarse coats, large heads, long, thin limbs and rudimentary tails. Example:
Wild guinea-pig *Cavia tschudi*: digs its own burrows or occupies the deserted burrows of other animals

FAMILY HYDROCHOERIDAE
There is one species:
Capybara *Hydrochoerus hydrochaeris*: the largest living rodent. The capybara is semi-aquatic, living in groups by rivers and lakes in Central and South America. It has a broad head, short, rounded ears and webbed feet. There is a bare raised gland on the top of the snout in the adult male

FAMILY DINOMYIDAE
There is one species:
Pacarana *Dinomys branickii*: found in forests on the lower slopes of the Andes. It is thick-set, with a short stout furry tail, short ears and limbs, and long claws and whiskers

FAMILY DASYPROCTIDAE
Agoutis; 30 species
Members of this family have long legs, small, thick, hoof-like claws, and a coarse thick coat. Example:
Red-rumped agouti *Dasyprocta aguti*: found in forests in Brazil and the Guianas

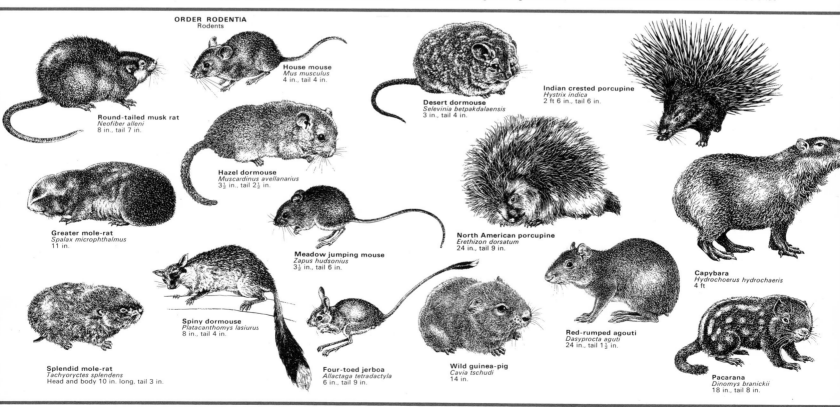

ORDER RODENTIA
Rodents

House mouse
Mus musculus
4 in., tail 4 in.

Desert dormouse
Selevinia betpakdalaensis
3 in., tail 4 in.

Indian crested porcupine
Hystrix indica
2 ft 6 in., tail 6 in.

Round-tailed musk rat
Neofiber alleni
8 in., tail 7 in.

Hazel dormouse
Muscardinus avellanarius
3½ in., tail 2½ in.

Greater mole-rat
Spalax microphthalmus
11 in.

Meadow jumping mouse
Zapus hudsonius
3½ in., tail 6 in.

North American porcupine
Erethizon dorsatum
24 in., tail 9 in.

Capybara
Hydrochoerus hydrochaeris
4 ft

Spiny dormouse
Platacanthomys lasiurus
8 in., tail 4 in.

Four-toed jerboa
Allactaga tetradactyla
6 in., tail 9 in.

Wild guinea-pig
Cavia tschudi
14 in.

Red-rumped agouti
Dasyprocta aguti
24 in., tail 1½ in.

Splendid mole-rat
Tachyoryctes splendens
Head and body 10 in. long, tail 3 in.

Pacarana
Dinomys branickii
18 in., tail 8 in.

PHYLUM CHORDATA	Animals with notochords	INFRA-CLASS EUTHERIA	Placental mammals
SUB-PHYLUM VERTEBRATA	Animals with backbones	ORDER RODENTIA	Rodents
CLASS MAMMALIA	Mammals	ORDER CARNIVORA	Flesh-eating mammals
SUB-CLASS THERIA	Mammals that do not lay eggs		

FAMILY CHINCHILLIDAE
Chinchillas and viscachas; 6 species
Most chinchillas are found in the foothills of the southern Andes. They have a large head, broad snout, large eyes and ears, and a long, fine coat. Their hind limbs are adapted for jumping, but they run, leap or creep on all fours. Example:
Chinchilla *Chinchilla laniger*: lives in barren, rocky mountain areas of Chile and Bolivia. It is farmed for its dense, silky, blue to pearl-gray fur

FAMILY CAPROMYIDAE
Coypus and hutias; 10 species
A family of robust, often aquatic, rodents; its members have small ears and eyes, short limbs, prominent claws, and a sparsely haired tail. Example:
Coypu *Myocastor coypus*: native to the streams and lakes of South America, but is farmed in Europe for its soft velvety fur, called nutria. It is active by day. All other species of capromyids are found in the West Indies

FAMILY OCTODONTIDAE
Octodonts; 8 species
These rat-like animals have long, silky body fur and coarsely haired tails which some species carry erect when running. They are found in South America from coastal regions up to 10,000 ft, and live in burrows. Example:
Degu *Octodon degus*: found in mountains of Peru and Chile

FAMILY CTENOMYIDAE
Tuco-tucos; 26 species
Tuco-tucos resemble pocket gophers but have no cheek pouches. They make their burrows in dry, sandy soil. Example:
Ctenomys peruanus: lives in South America

FAMILY ABROCOMIDAE
Chinchilla rats; 2 species
These rodents, which have long, dense underfur with fine guard hairs, are rat-like in appearance, with large eyes and ears, finely haired tails, short limbs, and weak claws which are hollow underneath. They live in crevices and burrows. Example:
Bennett's chinchilla rat *Abrocoma bennetti*: lives in the Andes and on the coastal hills of Chile

FAMILY ECHIMYIDAE
Spiny rats; 75 species
Rat-like in general appearance, these rodents of Central and South America generally have bristly fur. Example:
Guira *Euryzygomatomys spinosus*: found in Brazil and Paraguay in grassy and bushy areas

FAMILY THRYONOMYIDAE
Cane rats; 6 species
These rodents, widespread in Africa, have bristly hairs, flattened and grooved along their upper surfaces, growing in groups of five or six. Example:
Cutting grass *Thryonomys swinderianus*: inhabits reed beds and long grass

FAMILY PETROMYIDAE
There is one species:
Rock rat *Petromus typicus*: a squirrel-like rodent from south-western Africa. It has flexible ribs which enable it to squeeze through narrow crevices

FAMILY BATHYERGIDAE
African mole-rats; 50 species
Like other burrowing mammals, mole-rats have stocky bodies, strong feet, short tails and limbs, and small eyes and ears. Example:
Cape mole-rat *Georychus capensis*: lives in southern Africa in areas with loose, sandy soil

FAMILY CTENODACTYLIDAE
Gundis and Speke's pectinator; 8 species
The gundis of northern Africa look like guinea-pigs. They have soft fur, and comb-like brushes of bristles on two digits of the hind feet, for cleaning fur. Example:
Lataste's gundi *Massoutiera mzabi*: a gundi found in the western and central Sahara

ORDER CARNIVORA
Flesh-eating mammals
Most carnivores are well equipped for meat-eating, with powerful jaws, large canine teeth, cheek teeth used for shearing and crushing, and strong claws for gripping. Most have agile, graceful bodies; but some, like the almost omnivorous bears, are more heavily built. Carnivores are divided into two sub-orders, depending on the structure of the bones of the skull surrounding the middle and inner parts of the ear:

SUB-ORDER AELUROIDEA
Cats, hyenas and civets
This sub-order of generally cat-like mammals contains three families:

FAMILY FELIDAE
Cats; 34 species
Almost exclusively meat-eating, the cats are lightly built, with five digits on the front feet and four on the rear; almost all have strongly curved, retractile claws. They stalk their prey or lie in wait and spring on it with a short rush. Examples:
Cheetah *Acinonyx jubatus* (4 ft 6 in., tail 2 ft 6 in.): a swift-running, leanly built cat with non-retractile claws, found on the plains of Africa and south-western Asia
Wild cat *Felis silvestris* (2 ft 6 in., tail 14 in.): found wild in Europe, western Asia and Africa, it may be the ancestor of the domestic cat
Lion *Panthera leo*: lives in the grasslands of Africa and south-western Asia, where it is now rare. Tawny yellow in color, it hunts large grazing animals of the savanna, especially zebras and wildebeeste. The male has a ruff of hair—the mane—round the shoulders and neck

FAMILY HYAENIDAE
Hyenas and aardwolf; 4 species
Hyenas look rather like dogs, but their hindquarters are proportionally lower and less muscular. All have long limbs and large ears. Examples:
Spotted or **laughing hyena** *Crocuta crocuta*: lives on the African plains. It is a scavenger, especially on the remains of lions' prey, and a predator on wildebeeste, gazelles and zebras, among others. During the breeding season and when excited, it produces a characteristic laughing cry. It has four toes on the front feet
Aardwolf *Proteles cristatus* (2 ft 6 in., tail 10 in.): this small, striped animal with long, crest-like hair on its back is found on the savannas of southern and eastern Africa. It has very small teeth (unlike hyenas), and feeds almost entirely on termites and other insects. There are five toes on the front feet

FAMILY VIVERRIDAE
Civets and allies; about 75 species
These small and medium-sized carnivores of the warmer parts of the Old World have long, low bodies, short legs, long—generally bushy—tails, and pointed snouts. There are five toes on the front feet. Most of them are active at night. Nearly all have scent glands. Examples:
African civet *Civettictis civetta* (2 ft 6 in., tail 18 in.): found in forests and savanna; it has glands under the tail which produce a pungent oily secretion used in making perfume
Blotched genet *Genetta tigrina*: found in forests and thick grass in Africa. Genets have fine fur and are more clearly marked than civets
Binturong *Arctitis binturong* (3 ft, tail 2 ft 6 in.): a stockily built animal with a shaggy black coat, it can be distinguished from other members of its family by its long ear-tufts and bushy, prehensile tail. It feeds mainly on plants and lives in tropical forests in south-eastern Asia
Egyptian mongoose *Herpestes ichneumon* (24 in., tail 20 in.): this day-active animal lives in thick vegetation by rivers in African savanna. It was a sacred animal in ancient Egypt

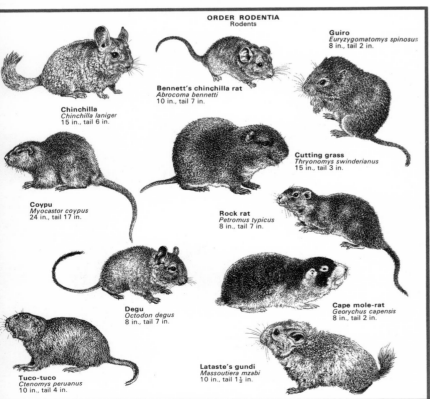

ORDER RODENTIA
Rodents

Chinchilla *Chinchilla laniger* 15 in., tail 6 in.

Bennett's chinchilla rat *Abrocoma bennetti* 10 in., tail 7 in.

Guiro *Euryzygomatomys spinosus* 8 in., tail 2 in.

Coypu *Myocastor coypus* 24 in., tail 17 in.

Cutting grass *Thryonomys swinderianus* 15 in., tail 3 in.

Rock rat *Petromus typicus* 8 in., tail 7 in.

Degu *Octodon degus* 8 in., tail 7 in.

Cape mole-rat *Georychus capensis* 8 in., tail 2 in.

Lataste's gundi *Massoutiera mzabi* 10 in., tail 1½ in.

Tuco-tuco *Ctenomys peruanus* 10 in., tail 4 in.

ORDER CARNIVORA
Flesh-eating mammals

Lion *Panthera leo* 6 ft 6 in., tail 2 ft 6 in.

Spotted or **laughing hyena** *Crocuta crocuta* 4 ft, tail 13 in.

Blotched genet *Genetta tigrina* 18 in., tail 18 in.

PHYLUM CHORDATA	Animals with notochords	INFRA-CLASS EUTHERIA	Placental mammals
SUB-PHYLUM VERTEBRATA	Animals with backbones	ORDER CARNIVORA	Flesh-eating mammals
CLASS MAMMALIA	Mammals	ORDER PINNIPEDIA	Seals, sea lions and walrus
SUB-CLASS THERIA	Mammals that do not lay eggs	ORDER PROBOSCIDEA	Elephants

SUB-ORDER ARCTOIDEA

Dogs, weasels, bears and raccoons
This sub-order of carnivores contains all the dog-like and bear-like mammals. There are four families:

FAMILY CANIDAE

Dogs; 37 species
These animals with long, slender limbs and bushy tails are generally good runners, moving on the tips of their toes. They have keen hearing and sight, but hunt mainly by scent and often run in packs of about 30. They can be divided broadly into dog-like and fox-like types. All have four toes on the front feet. Examples:
Black-backed jackal *Canis mesomelas*: found in eastern and southern Africa, it can run at about 35 mph, and is a pest in southern Africa
Cape hunting dog *Lycaon pictus* (3 ft 6 in., tail 16 in.): these dogs of the African plains range widely in packs, preying on any animals they can overpower
Fennec *Fennecus zerda* (16 in., tail 12 in.): this big-eared fox inhabits desert regions of northern Africa, living in burrows in the sand

FAMILY MUSTELIDAE

Weasels and their allies; about 70 species
Most mustelids are small animals; they have long, slender bodies and long tails. They walk on the soles of the feet rather than on the tips of the toes as dogs do. There are five digits on both the front and hind feet. Examples:
American mink *Mustela vison*: found in Canada and the U.S.A., it has dark brown fur adapted for an aquatic life, and yields the mink pelts highly valued by the fur trade. It nests in holes in banks, rocks and debris
Striped skunk *Mephitis mephitis* (18 in., tail 10 in.): found in North America. Two scent glands at the base of the tail contain a foul-smelling fluid which the animal can squirt at an aggressor up to distances of 10 ft

European badger *Meles meles* (2 ft 6 in., tail 8 in.): also found in Asia in grassland and wooded areas. This omnivorous mammal is active at night
Eurasian otter *Lutra lutra* (2 ft 6 in., tail 20 in.): this freshwater mammal has webbed feet and a tail thickened at the base
Pine marten *Martes martes* (24 in., tail 12 in.): found in wooded regions in northern Europe and western Asia, where it hunts small mammals and birds

FAMILY URSIDAE

Bears; 7 species
Except for the polar bear, which feeds mainly on seals, bears are omnivorous. They are the largest carnivores, and are heavily built with short, powerful legs and short tails, and they walk on the soles of their feet. Example:
Brown bear *Ursus arctos*: found in North America, Europe and Asia. The species is in danger of extinction in the western parts of the U.S.A. and its numbers in Europe have been greatly reduced

FAMILY PROCYONIDAE

Raccoons and pandas; 18 species
Raccoons are found in the Americas, and pandas in Asia. All closely resemble bears but are smaller, and they have two molar teeth instead of the bears' three on each side of the lower jaw. Examples:
Giant panda *Ailuropoda melanoleuca* (5 ft, tail 5 in.): a day-active panda found in a restricted region of Szechwan, China, on the slopes of the Tibetan plateau, feeding mainly on bamboo. It looks like a bear, but is almost certainly more closely related to the raccoons
Raccoon *Procyon lotor* (24 in., tail 12 in.): found in North and Central America. A nocturnal animal, it feeds on fruit, seeds, insects and crayfish which it crushes with its strong, back teeth
South American coati *Nasua nasua*: a day-active animal generally found in forest regions in groups of 6–40. It has a long, mobile snout

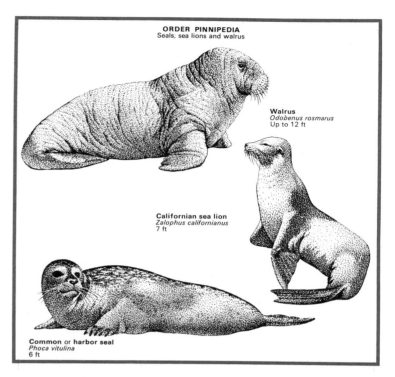

ORDER PINNIPEDIA
Seals; sea lions and walrus

Walrus
Odobenus rosmarus
Up to 12 ft

Californian sea lion
Zalophus californianus
7 ft

Common or **harbor seal**
Phoca vitulina
6 ft

ORDER PINNIPEDIA

Seals, sea lions and walrus
Pinnipeds are flesh-eating mammals with streamlined, torpedo-shaped bodies, limbs modified into flippers, and webbed feet—adaptations for life in the water. A thick layer of oily fat, or blubber, under the skin insulates them against the cold. They are closely related to the carnivores, from which they probably evolved about 30 million years ago. There are three families:

FAMILY ODOBENIDAE

There is one species:
Walrus *Odobenus rosmarus*: found in Arctic waters. Like the eared seals, the walrus can turn its hind flippers forwards to aid movement on land; but unlike them it has no external ears. The upper canines of the adult male grow downwards to form tusks up to 27 in. long

FAMILY OTARIIDAE

Sea lions or eared seals; 13 species
Unlike the walrus, the eared seals have conspicuous external ears; they can use all four limbs when moving on land. The family is divided into two groups, sea lions and fur seals. Examples:
Californian sea lion *Zalophus californianus*: found on the south-western coast of North America. It is the most abundant species, and the one commonly seen in zoos
Northern fur seal *Callorhinus ursinus* (7 ft): migrates in winter from the Bering Sea to California and Japan

FAMILY PHOCIDAE

Earless or true seals; 18 species
The true seals, which may have evolved from the same stock as did the otter (other pinnipeds may have evolved from a bear-like ancestor), have no obvious external ears, and their hind limbs or flippers cannot be swung forwards for moving on land. Examples:
Common or **harbor seal** *Phoca vitulina*: generally found on shores with sandbanks in the Northern Hemisphere
Southern Elephant seal *Mirounga leonina* (up to 20 ft): found in sub-Antarctic waters. The largest of all pinnipeds, it weighs up to 4 tons

ORDER PROBOSCIDEA

There is one family

FAMILY ELEPHANTIDAE

Elephants; 2 species
The elephant's most conspicuous external feature is its long flexible trunk, which is an elongation of the nose. The animal rests its weight on a fatty cushion beneath each of its broad feet. The single pair of upper incisors grow into large ivory tusks, and the cheek teeth replace each other throughout life
Asiatic elephant *Elephas maximus* (up to 10 ft tall at the shoulder): found in the tropical forests of southern Asia. This elephant has a flat forehead and small ears. Only the male has tusks, which may grow to 7 ft long
African elephant *Loxodonta africana*: found throughout Africa south of the Sahara. It is distinguished from the Asiatic elephant by its arched forehead, large ears, and two finger-like 'lips' at the end of the trunk. Males weigh up to $6\frac{1}{2}$ tons. Both sexes have tusks, which may grow to 11 ft long in the male and weigh more than 200 lb. each

Black-backed jackal
Canis mesomelas
2 ft 6 in., tail 15 in.

American mink
Mustela vison
21 in., tail 8 in.

Brown bear
Ursus arctos
Up to 8 ft

South American coati
Nasua nasua
24 in., tail 24 in.

African elephant
Loxodonta africana
Up to 11 ft 6 in. at shoulder

PHYLUM CHORDATA	Animals with notochords	ORDER HYRACOIDEA	Hyraxes
SUB-PHYLUM VERTEBRATA	Animals with backbones	ORDER SIRENIA	Sea-cows
CLASS MAMMALIA	Mammals	ORDER TUBULIDENTATA	Aardvark
SUB-CLASS THERIA	Mammals that do not lay eggs	ORDER PERISSODACTYLA	Odd-toed hoofed mammals
INFRA-CLASS EUTHERIA	Placental mammals	ORDER ARTIODACTYLA	Even-toed hoofed mammals

ORDER HYRACOIDEA

There is one family:

FAMILY PROCAVIIDAE
Hyraxes or dassies; 6 species
Sometimes mistaken for rabbits, hyraxes are very distantly related to elephants. They have a short snout, short ears, short, sturdy legs, and the toes bear flattened, hoof-like nails. Example:
Rock hyrax *Procavia capensis*: frequents rocky regions in Africa and the Near East. It makes a high whistling sound when alarmed

Rock hyrax
Procavia capensis
22 in.

ORDER SIRENIA

Sea-cows
These animals are distantly related to elephants and hyraxes, but are entirely adapted for life in the water, with a massive, cigar-shaped body, paddle-like forelimbs, no hind limbs, and a flattened tail. These slow-moving, plant-eating mammals are found in estuaries or near the coast. They either are solitary or associate in groups of up to six. There are two families:

FAMILY TRICHECHIDAE
Manatees; 3 species
Manatees have scattered hairs on their bodies. The upper lip is deeply split, each half moving independently, and the tail fin is rounded. Adults do not have incisor teeth. Example:
North American manatee *Trichechus manatus*: found along the coasts of Florida, Central America and the West Indian islands

FAMILY DUGONGIDAE
There is one species:
Dugong *Dugong dugon*: frequents the warm shores of the western Pacific and Indian Oceans. Dugongs have a deeply notched tail fin and no hair on their bodies. A pair of incisor teeth form tusks in the male

ORDER TUBULIDENTATA

There is one family:

FAMILY ORYCTEROPODIDAE
There is one species:
Aardvark *Orycteropus afer*: widespread in African grasslands. It has long ears, an elongated muzzle ending in wide nostrils, and a long, heavy tail. The tubular mouth contains a long, sticky tongue with which the animal picks up ants and termites; it has powerful claws, used for burrowing

Aardvark
Orycteropus afer
2 ft 6 in., tail 24 in.

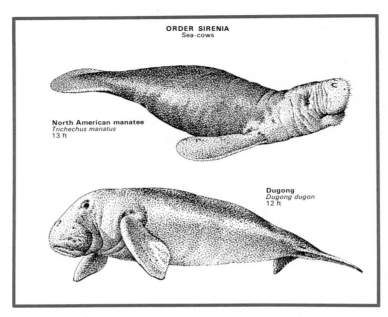

ORDER SIRENIA
Sea-cows

North American manatee
Trichechus manatus
13 ft

Dugong
Dugong dugon
12 ft

ORDER PERISSODACTYLA

Odd-toed hoofed mammals
These medium-sized to large animals, many of which are good runners, commonly have a reduced number of toes, each encased in a protective horny sheath, or hoof, and the weight is carried mainly by the middle digit of each foot. All are plant-eaters; their lips and incisor teeth are adapted for plucking plants, and their cheek-teeth for chewing. There are two sub-orders of odd-toed ungulates.

SUB-ORDER CERATOMORPHA
Tapirs and rhinoceroses
These stoutly built animals are found today only in the tropics and sub-tropics. There are two families:

FAMILY TAPIRIDAE
Tapirs; 4 species
Tapirs are heavy-bodied browsing ani-mals which live near water in forests in Central and South America and south-east Asia. A flexible proboscis overhangs the upper lip, and they have four toes on the front feet and three on the hind feet. Example:
Malayan tapir *Tapirus indicus*: found from Thailand to Sumatra, it has a striking black-and-white coat which probably acts as disruptive camouflage

FAMILY RHINOCEROTIDAE
Rhinoceroses; 5 species
Rhinoceroses, though heavily built and thick-skinned, can move swiftly over short distances. They have one or two fibrous horns on the nose, often a pro-truding upper lip, and three toes on all feet. They live in African grasslands and in the forests of southern Asia. Example:
Black rhinoceros *Diceros bicornis*: found from southern and eastern Africa westwards to northern Nigeria. It lives alone or in pairs, and has two horns, the larger front horn growing up to 3 ft long

SUB-ORDER HIPPOMORPHA
This sub-order, which contains the horses and extinct titanotheres, differs from the other sub-order of perissodactyls mainly in the structure of the teeth. There is only one family:

FAMILY EQUIDAE
Horses, asses and zebras; 6 species
All horses are swift runners with only one functional toe on each foot. They live in herds. The cheek-teeth are adapted for grinding plant food. Examples:
Przewalski's horse *Equus caballus przewalskii* (4 ft 6 in. at the shoulder): found in Mongolia, it is the only surviving race of the species from which domestic horses are descended
African wild ass *Equus asinus*: this wild ancestor of the donkey is found in the deserts of northern Africa

ORDER ARTIODACTYLA

Even-toed hoofed mammals
One of the most numerous groups of mammals today, the even-toed ungulates rest their weight equally on the third and fourth toes of each foot and have an even number of functional toes. There are three sub-orders:

SUB-ORDER SUIFORMES
This group of primitive even-toed hoofed mammals do not chew the cud. There are three families:

FAMILY SUIDAE
Pigs; 8 species
Pigs have a stocky body with a long head and mobile snout used for rooting, and sparse, bristly hair. They have a simple stomach, and eat both plant and animal food. Both their upper and lower tusk-like canine teeth point upwards. There are four toes on each foot, but the two central toes are the largest. Example:
Wild boar *Sus scrofa*: found in woodlands in Europe, northern Africa and nearly the whole of Asia, it is the ancestor of the domestic pig and has large powerful tusks

FAMILY TAYASSUIDAE
Peccaries; 2 species
Gregarious pig-like mammals from Central and South America, peccaries also have some ruminant characteristics: a fairly complex stomach, united third and fourth foot bones (these are separate in pigs), and tusk-like canines that point downwards and not upwards as in pigs. Example:
Collared peccary *Tayassu tajacu*: found in open forest and along forest edges in South and Central America and in the southern U.S.A.

FAMILY HIPPOPOTAMIDAE
Hippopotamuses; 2 species
These animals are good swimmers and divers. Their large, heavy, short-legged bodies have a thick layer of fat under the skin, and their slightly webbed feet have four toes. The bulls fight, using their tusk-like lower canines as weapons. Examples:
Common hippopotamus *Hippopotamus amphibius*: found in most African rivers; weighs 4 tons
Pygmy hippopotamus *Choeropsis liberiensis* (2 ft tall at the shoulder): found in forests near water in western Africa

SUB-ORDER TYLOPODA
The animals forming this sub-order have complex stomachs and chew the cud, but have been separate from the ruminant

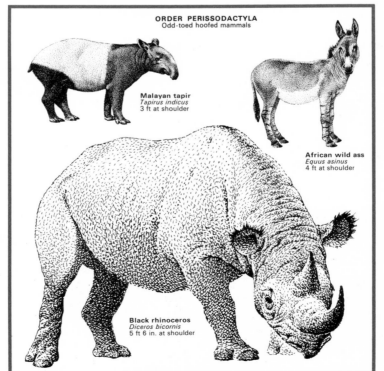

ORDER PERISSODACTYLA
Odd-toed hoofed mammals

Malayan tapir
Tapirus indicus
3 ft at shoulder

African wild ass
Equus asinus
4 ft at shoulder

Black rhinoceros
Diceros bicornis
5 ft 6 in. at shoulder

sub-order for about 55 million years. There is one family:

FAMILY CAMELIDAE
Camels; 4 wild species

Camels and llamas have only two functional toes, supported by expanded pads for walking on sand or snow. The slender snout bears a cleft upper lip. Examples:
Bactrian camel *Camèlus bactrianus*: found wild in the Gobi Desert and introduced elsewhere, it has two humps and shaggy hair
Guanaco *Lama guanicoe* (4 ft tall at the shoulder): found from sea level to 15,000 ft in the Andes and in central and southeastern South America. It may be the ancestor of the llama and the alpaca

SUB-ORDER RUMINANTIA
Ruminants

This is the most numerous and varied of the artiodactyl groups. All are ruminants (cud chewers) with three or, usually, four chambers in the stomach; their food is brought up from the first chamber and chewed while the animal is resting, before being swallowed a second time for complete digestion. Many have horns or antlers. There are five families:

FAMILY TRAGULIDAE
Chevrotains; 4 species

Chevrotains, also called mouse deer, are very small ruminants without horns. They have three-chambered stomachs, and the males have long, tusk-like canine teeth. They live in the tropical forests of Africa and southern Asia. Example:
Lesser Malay chevrotain *Tragulus javanicus*: it is uniformly brown, unlike

other species, which have spotted or striped coats.

FAMILY CERVIDAE
Deer; 40 species

Most male deer grow branched antlers— bony outgrowths of the skull covered with velvet (furry skin) during growth. Antler growth stops before the mating season and the velvet is then shed. Antlers are shed after the mating season. The smaller, more delicately built females do not generally have antlers. Examples:
Musk deer *Moschus moschiferus* (20 in. at the shoulder): found in the mountains of central Asia, it has tusk-like canine teeth but no antlers. A musk gland on the abdomen of the male secretes a brownish wax, used in the manufacture of perfume
Red deer *Cervus elaphus*: found in deciduous forests of Europe, Asia and North America. It has large antlers, often 3 ft long. The American race, known as the wapiti or American elk, is sometimes regarded as a separate species *Cervus canadensis*
Pudu *Pudu pudu* (16 in. tall at the shoulder): found in the temperate forests of Bolivia and Chile
Moose *Alces alces* (male more than 6 ft tall at the shoulder): the largest living deer, found in the coniferous forests of Europe and Asia (where it is called the elk) and North America. It is easily recognizable by its characteristic broad, overhanging muzzle
Chinese water deer *Hydropotes inermis* (24 in. tall at the shoulder): found in river valleys in China and Korea and introduced into England and France. It has no antlers but has long, curved tusks

FAMILY BOVIDAE
Cattle and antelopes; 110 species

Bovids have horns with bony cores which grow hard sheaths of horny material. The horns, which are unbranched, are never shed; the sheath is constantly renewed from inside. Most bovids live in grasslands. They vary widely in body form. Examples:
Yak *Bos grunniens* (5 ft 6 in. at shoulder): the wild cattle of the highest plateau of Tibet at altitudes of 15,000–16,500 ft. A smaller, often mottled form is used as a domesticated animal in China and India
Common eland *Taurotragus oryx* (6 ft at the shoulder): a large antelope with straight, spirally twisted horns; it lives on the plains of southern and eastern Africa
Four-horned antelope *Tetracerus quadricornis* (2 ft 6 in. tall at the shoulder): inhabits open woodland in India. The male, with four small horns, is the only living four-horned mammal
European bison *Bison bonasus* (6 ft at the shoulder): formerly widespread in European forests, it is now found only in a few small, protected herds. It has heavy forequarters, a hump on its shoulders and a massive head, but is not as heavily built as the related American species
Gray duiker *Sylvicapra grimmia*: found in open country south of the Sahara. Duikers are small, short-legged African antelopes with a tuft of hair between their short, sharply pointed horns
Defassa waterbuck *Kobus defassa* (4 ft 6 in. tall at the shoulder): a thick-set antelope which lives near water in African grasslands. It has long, coarse hair and large, corrugated horns curved slightly forwards at the tips

Arabian oryx *Oryx leucoryx* (up to 4 ft tall at the shoulder): formerly found in Arabia and Iraq in arid plains and deserts, it has been hunted almost to extinction in the wild. It has long, sharp horns
Hartebeest *Alcelaphus buselaphus* (4 ft 6 in. tall at the shoulder): ranges in large herds on the African plains, and runs swiftly when alarmed. It is an ungainly animal with shoulders higher than the rump. Its horns are lyre-shaped
Royal antelope *Neotragus pygmaeus* (12 in. tall at the shoulder): found in West African forests, it is the smallest ruminant. Its black horns are only about 1 in. long
Blackbuck *Antilope cervicapra* (2 ft 6 in. at the shoulder): the typical antelope of the Indian plains. The adult male is glossy black above, and the females are yellow-fawn; both are white underneath
Saiga antelope *Saiga tatarica* (2 ft 6 in. tall at the shoulder): formerly found throughout the steppes of Europe and Asia and once in danger of extinction, its numbers are now increasing as a result of careful conservation. It is a wary, sheep-like animal with a large swollen muzzle and downward-facing nostrils
Chamois *Rupicapra rupicapra* (2 ft 8 in. tall at the shoulder): found in the Alps, the Pyrénées and most of the other mountain ranges of Europe and Asia Minor; it is a goat-antelope with slender black horns set close together and bending back at the tips to form a hook. It lives in the alpine zone in the summer, descending into the forests in winter
Wild goat *Capra hircus* (3 ft at shoulder): inhabits hilly country in the Aegean islands, Turkey, Iran and Sind; it is the ancestor of the domestic goat. Both sexes have long horns and beards which vary in size according to the race
Musk-ox *Ovibos moschatus* (up to 5 ft at the shoulder): now confined to northern Canada and Greenland. It is more closely related to sheep than to true oxen, and looks like a large, long-coated ram. Its broad, downward-curving horns nearly meet in the middle of the skull
Bighorn sheep *Ovis canadensis* (up to 3 ft 6 in. at the shoulder): found in the mountains of Siberia and western North America, it is the only wild sheep in North America. The male has tightly curved horns with outward-pointing tips and thick bases; the female has very small horns or none at all. It belongs to the same genus as the domestic sheep

FAMILY ANTILOCAPRIDAE

There is one species:
Pronghorn *Antilocapra americana*: lives in North American grasslands. Both sexes have horns consisting of fused hairs sheathing a bony core; the sheath is shed each year

FAMILY GIRAFFIDAE
Giraffes; 2 species

The two or three horns of the giraffe and okapi (absent in the female okapi) are bony growths covered by skin
Giraffe *Giraffa camelopardalis*: lives in small herds on the African savanna, ranging into the arid zone in western Africa and the Sudan where acacia trees grow. A third horn generally develops on the forehead, and East African races often have an extra small pair of horns behind the main pair, making five in all. The giraffe's prehensile tongue can extend about 20 in. to strip leaves from trees
Okapi *Okapia johnstoni* (5 ft tall at the shoulder): found in rain forest in the eastern Congo, the okapi is a primitive member of the giraffe family, first discovered by Europeans in about 1900. It is like the giraffe in structure, but has a shorter neck and shorter legs

ORDER ARTIODACTYLA
Even-toed hoofed mammals

Wild boar
Sus scrofa
6 ft

Lesser Malay chevrotain
Tragulus javanicus
12 in. at shoulder

Collared peccary
Tayassu tajacu
3 ft, tail 2 in.

Pronghorn
Antilocapra americana
3 ft at shoulder

Common hippopotamus
Hippopotamus amphibius
5 ft at shoulder

Gray duiker
Sylvicapra grimmia
2 ft at shoulder

Red deer
Cervus elaphus
Up to 5 ft at shoulder

Giraffe
Giraffa camelopardalis
Male up to 18 ft tall

Bactrian camel
Camelus bactrianus
6 ft at shoulder

ACKNOWLEDGMENTS

General acknowledgments

Many people and organizations assisted in the preparation of this book. The editors wish to thank them all, in particular:

Anti-Locust Research Center; Dr. E. N. Arnold; J. Bleby (Laboratory Animal Center of the Medical Research Council); Dr. F. W. Braestrup; The Trustees of the British Museum (Natural History); Broadway Arts Limited; Roy Brown; Dr. Maurice Burton; Professor A. J. E. Cave; Dr. Malcolm J. Coe; Commonwealth Forestry Institute, Oxford; Dr. R. W. G. Dennis; Dr. V. S. Eastop; H. L. Edlin; Dr. W. M. Edmunds; Forestry Commission; L. Forman; Dr. Harold Fox; Daniel Freeman; Dr. Brian Gardiner; Dr. A. W. Gentry; Geological Society; Alice Grandison; Dr. P. H. Greenwood; Dr. J. Linsley Gressitt (Bernice P. Bishop Museum, Honolulu); Roger P. Harris; Charles Heller; T. G. Howarth; Dr. Devra Kleiman; J. R. Laundon; Michael J. Lawrence; The Library, Canada House; Ian MacPhail; Dr. K. G. McKenzie; P. T. McGovern; Dr. Arthur Mansfield; Dr. Sidnie Manton; Marine Biological Association of the United Kingdom; Dr. N. B. Marshall; Dr. Robert Martin; John L. Mason; Dr. A. Melderis; R. H. A. Merlin; Prue Napier; Clifford Owen; Dr. David Pye; Royal Botanic Gardens, Kew, England; The Royal Geographical Society; The Royal Horticultural Society; The Royal Veterinary College; The Scott Polar Research Institute; Nigel Sitwell; Dr. A. G. Smith; Dr. David Snow; A. F. Stimson; M. K. Swales; Richard I. Vane-Wright; Peter Wallace (Fisheries Research Laboratory, Lowestoft, England); A. C. Wheeler; Dr. Mary Whitear; Dr. D. P. Wilson; R. J. Wood (Fisheries Research Laboratory, Lowestoft); Sir Maurice Yonge; The Zoological Society of London, especially the librarian, Mr. R. A. Fish, and his staff.

Photographers

The credits for each page read in descending order. Where the tops or bases of photographs are on the same level, or where one photograph overlaps another at top and base, the credits read from left to right.

1. P. David. 2–3. J. Dominis/LIFE © Time Inc. 5. C. Rentmeester/LIFE © Time Inc. 6–7. I. Holmäsen. 8. N. Fox-Davies. 10–11. Philcarol/Monkmeyer. 12. S. Gillsäter/Tiofoto; N. Fox-Davies; J. Six; D. Botting; D. van Campen; E. Schulthess/Black Star; I. Virkkunen; N. Fox-Davies. 13. Okapia; J. and D. Bartlett; D. Botting; B. Leidmann/Bavaria Verlag; J. Linsley Gressitt; T. W. Hall; T. Myers; Ylla/Rapho-Guillumette. 14. Popperfoto; G. Laycock; A. Visage/Jacana; D. Faulkner. 15. NASA. 18. C. Ott/National Audubon Society. 21. W. Peterson; R. I. Lewis Smith; R. E. Longton; W. Luthy/Bavaria Verlag; S. and D. McCutcheon/F. W. Lane. 22. E. Schuhmacher. 23. J. P. Varin—F. Bel-G. Vienne/Jacana; M. C. T. Smith; B. Gemsbøl. 24. F. Bruemmer. 25. S. Gillsäter/Tiofoto. 26. F. Bruemmer. 27. T. Grant/National Film Board of Canada; T. Larsen/World Wildlife Fund; National Film Board of Canada; S. Gillsäter/B. Coleman. 28. F. Bruemmer; I. McLaren; Popperfoto; G. Quedens/F. W. Lane. 29. G. Hansson. 30. E. Zimen; S. Wayman/LIFE © Time Inc. 31. F. Bruemmer; J. and D. Bartlett. 32. A. Christiansen/F. W. Lane. 33. R. Harrington; R. P. Bille; R. P. Bille; E. Hosking. 34. M. Robert/Jacana; F. Massart/Jacana. 35. G. L. Kooyman; J. Calvert/B. Coleman; C. Ray/B. Coleman; M. C. T. Smith. 36. B. Stonehouse. 37. M. C. T. Smith; M. C. T. Smith; E. Schulthess/Black Star. 38. G. Holton/B. Coleman; E. Schulthess/Black Star; R. I. Lewis Smith; R. I. Lewis Smith. 39. M. C. T. Smith; R. I. Lewis Smith; R. I. Lewis Smith. 40. G. Hansson. 42. Trapp/Bavaria Verlag; Trapp/Bavaria Verlag; I. Virkkunen. 43. R. Freson; R. Hallensleben/Bavaria Verlag; I. Holmäsen. 44. W. Peterson; W. L. Miller; D. Bartlett/B. Coleman; J. and D. Bartlett. 45. Freelance Photographers Guild; W. Bonatti/Mondadori Press. 46. A. Christiansen/F. W. Lane; H. Engels. 47. R. P. Bille. 48. H. W. Silvester; R. P. Bille; J. A. Hancock. 49. S. Collins/National Audubon Society; L. Lee Rue III/F. W. Lane (sequence of four); Okapia. 50. Forestry Commission; A. B. Klots; R. P. Bille. 51. S. Dalton/N.H.P.A.; C. E. Mohr/National Audubon Society; G. Thompson; W. E. Ferguson; E. S. Ross; Forestry Commission. 52. L. D. Mech; W. Bonatti/Mondadori Press; Okapia. 53. L. D. Mech; R. P. Bille; R. P. Bille. 54. R. Austing/F. W. Lane. 55. J. Markham; R. P. Bille; H. H. Harrison/G. Heilman; E. Hosking; I. Virkkunen; I. Virkkunen. 56. S. Gillsäter/Tiofoto. 57. H. W. Silvester; D. Robinson/B. Coleman. 58. G. Kinns/A.F.A.; J. van Wormer/B. Coleman. 59. G. Quedens; T. McHugh/B. Coleman; F. Zwickel; F. Vollmar/World Wildlife Fund. 60. T. W. Martin/Rapho-Guillumette; I. Virkkunen; R. Austing/Camera Press. 61. A. Christiansen/F. W. Lane; S. Grossman/John Hillelson Agency; G. Quedens. 62. L. West/F. W. Lane. 64. S. T. Karlsson/Tiofoto; F. Erize; L. H. Newman/N.H.P.A. 65. Picturepoint; M. Andrews; C. McDermott/N.H.P.A.; T. W. Martin/Rapho-Guillumette; T. W. Martin/Rapho-Guillumette; H. Eisenbeiss/F. W. Lane; N. Fox-Davies. 66. J. and D. Bartlett; L. Quitt/National Audubon Society; G. Hyde; I. Virkkunen. 67. M. W. F. Tweedie; I. Virkkunen; I. Virkkunen; A. Christiansen/F. W. Lane. 68. W. Rohdich/F. W. Lane; I. Virkkunen; H. A. Thronhill/National Audubon Society; I. Virkkunen. 69. I. Holmäsen; J. H. Gerard; R. P. Bille; A. Margiocco. 70. D. Bartlett; G. Quedens/F. W. Lane; J. Burton/B. Coleman; W. Tilgner/Black Star; G. Koller. 71. R. P. Bille; A. D. Cruickshank/National Audubon Society; A. Christiansen/F. W. Lane; F. Bel-G. Vienne/Jacana. 72. R. P. Bille; J. A. L. Cooke; J. Burton/B. Coleman. 73. H. Schrempp/F. W. Lane; I. Virkkunen; J. Six; L. M. Chase/F. W. Lane. 74. B. Gemsbøl; T. Martin/Rapho-Guillumette; J. Markham. 75. G. Kinns/A.F.A.; J. Burton/B. Coleman; I. Virkkunen; I. Virkkunen. 76. J. Lindblad/B. Coleman; L. Yigael; A. Fatras. 77. A. Fatras; J. P. Varin/Jacana; J. Burton/B. Coleman. 78. R. P. Bille; J. and D. Bartlett; J. and D. Bartlett. 79. A. Margiocco; L. Lee Rue III/National Audubon Society; G. Koller; J. and D. Bartlett. 80. M. Robert/Jacana; Y. Lanceau/Jacana. 81. H. W. Silvester; W. Ferguson; A. Margiocco; R. P. Bille. 82. T. Iwago; K. Tanaka. 83. F. Bel-G. Vienne/Jacana; Fox Photos; P. Wayre; G. Kinns/A.F.A.; G. Kinns/A.F.A. 84. Photographic Library of Australia; M. K. Morcombe; P.L.A.; J. Goode. 85. P.L.A.; M. K. Morcombe; G. Pizzey/N.H.P.A.; P.L.A. 86. G. Pizzey; G. Pizzey/B. Coleman; P.L.A.; P.L.A.; J. Carnemolla. 87. J. Warham; E. Slater; E. Slater; J. Goode; J. R. Brownlie/B. Coleman. 88. E. Schuhmacher; M. F. Soper; M. F. Soper. 89. M. F. Soper; P. Morrison/N.Z. Wildlife Service; J. Warham; M. F. Soper; J. L. Kendrick/N.Z. Wildlife Service; M. F. Soper; M. F. Soper. 90. Okapia. 92. G. Cubitt. 93. F. Erize; E. Slater; Okapia; P. Hill. 94. F. Hartmann; N. Myers/Camera Press; D. Bartlett. 95. J. Dominis/LIFE © Time Inc.; D. Bartlett; G. Pizzey/N.H.P.A.; G. Pizzey/N.H.P.A. 96. E. Hosking; P. Johnson; C. Haagner. 97. P. Hill; M. Amin; K. B. Newman; C. Haagner. 98. N. Myers; N. Tinbergen. 99. N. Myers; N. Myers; D. Bartlett; D. and M. Zimmerman. 100. G. Heilman. 101. D. Hughes; W. T. Miller; C. Bavagnoli/ LIFE © Time Inc.; P. Johnson; M. J. Coe. 102. C. Haagner; N. Myers. 103. Okapia; V. Tomasyan/Camera Press (sequence of three); N. Myers. 104. F. Erize; N. Myers. 105. N. Myers; M. Quarishy/B. Coleman; N. Myers. 106. J. Dominis/LIFE © Time Inc.; D. Charman; C. Haagner. 107. J. Dominis/LIFE © Time Inc.; M. Amin; J. Dominis/LIFE © Time Inc. 108. J. Dominis/LIFE © Time Inc.; N. Myers; J. Dominis/LIFE © Time Inc. 109. G. Schaller/LIFE © Time Inc.; N. Myers. 110. F.P.G. 111. D. Bartlett; C. A. W. Guggisberg/B. Coleman. 112. John Visser; S. A. Thompson. 113. W. Gotz; W. Gotz; W. Gotz; J. Visser; J. Crook. 114. F. Hartmann; K. B. Newman; D. Botting; D. Bartlett. 115. D. Bartlett; A. Christiansen/F. W. Lane. 116. C. A. W. Guggisberg/B. Coleman; J. Pearson/B. Coleman; J. Pearson/B. Coleman. 117. C. Haagner; A. Christiansen/F. W. Lane; D. Bartlett; B. Campbell/B. Coleman; L. H. Brown. 118. A. Bannister/N.H.P.A.; E. S. Brown; J. A. L. Cooke; D. Bartlett. 119. B. Campbell/B. Coleman; A. Christiansen/F. W. Lane; J. Visser; A. Christiansen/F. W. Lane; S. Trevor/B. Coleman; D. Bartlett/B. Coleman. 120. G. Manson-Bahr; D. Bartlett; Colour Library International. 121. D. Bartlett; Okapia; D. Bartlett; W. D. Haacke (sequence of three); W. T. Miller; C. Haagner. 122. J. R. Simon. 123. J. van Wormer/B. Coleman; J. van Wormer/B. Coleman; H. Engels; H. Engels; M. P. Drazin. 124. J. R. Simon; W. L. Miller; D. and M. Zimmerman. 125. R. Austing/F. W. Lane; L. Lee Rue III/B. Coleman; J. R. Simon; J. R. Simon. 126. R. Frederick; G. Grandjean. 127. H. Schunemann/Bavaria Verlag; P. Montoya/Jacana; G. Nystrand/F. W. Lane. 128. Okapia. 129. L. Yigael; W. Ferguson; Popperfoto. 130. J. Juan Spillet; A. Margiocco; J. Juan Spillet. 131. P. Jackson/B. Coleman; A. Margiocco; A. Margiocco; D. Bartlett; A. Visage/Jacana; A. Margiocco. 132. F. Erize. 133. A. Margiocco; F. Erize; F. Erize; F. Erize. 134. Okapia; F. Erize; D. Botting. 135. D. Botting; F. Lazi; J. M. Cei; F. Erize; F. Erize; F. Erize. 136. E. Galloway; Australian News and Information Bureau; J. Goode. 137. G. Pizzey; Okapia; E. Slater (sequence of six). 138. G. Pizzey; G. Pizzey/B. Coleman. 139. P. Slater/B. Coleman; D. Hancock; P.L.A. 140. P.L.A. 141. E. Slater; V. Serventy/B. Coleman; P.L.A.; P.L.A. 142. J. Carnemolla; G. Pizzey/B. Coleman; G. Pizzey/B. Coleman. 143. G. Pizzey/N.H.P.A.; G. Pizzey; G. Pizzey/B. Coleman. 144. J. and D. Bartlett. 146. P. A. Pittet; Bavaria Verlag; G. DeLisle/Picturepoint. 147. W. E. Ferguson; S. A. Thompson; J. and D. Bartlett; W. Peterson. 148. H. D. Brown. 149. J. and D. Bartlett; J. and D. Bartlett; H. Hughes; J. and D. Bartlett; C. Gans (sequence of three). 150. S. Gillsäter/Tiofoto. 151. E. Hosking; J. Massey Stewart. 152. F. E. Blanc/World Wildlife Fund; M. Tomkinson/N.H.P.A.; C. Haagner. 153. C. Haagner; G. Rodger/Magnum; J. Juan Spillet. 154. W. Peterson; J. Burton/B. Coleman; A. Margiocco. 155. W. D. Haacke; W. Ferguson; D. and M. Zimmerman; W. Peterson. 156. J. and D. Bartlett; J. and D. Bartlett; C. Haagner. 157. L. Yigael; L. Yigael; K. B. Newman; J. and D. Bartlett; J. and D. Bartlett; J. and D. Bartlett. 158. J. and D. Bartlett; W. D. Haacke; D. and M. Zimmerman; W. E. Ferguson. 159. M. K. Morcombe; W. D. Haacke; C. Haagner; W. E. Ferguson. 160. P. Hill; W. D. Haacke; W. E. Ferguson; J. and D. Bartlett; Okapia. 161. W. Peterson; H. D. Brown. 162. G. Newlands. 163. A. Bannister/N.H.P.A.; W. E. Ferguson; A. Bannister/N.H.P.A.; A. Bannister/N.H.P.A.; J. Visser. 164. S. Dalton/N.H.P.A.; A. Bannister/N.H.P.A.; A. Bannister/N.H.P.A.; A. Bannister/N.H.P.A. 165. A. Bannister/N.H.P.A.; A. Bannister/N.H.P.A.; W. E. Ferguson; A. Bannister/N.H.P.A.; A. Bannister/N.H.P.A.; A. Bannister/N.H.P.A.; D. Bartlett; E. R. Degginger. 166. D. J. Chivers. 168. D. Botting. 169. Popperfoto. 170. C. W. Rettenmeyer; F. G. H. Allen; P. Hill; F. G. H. Allen; U. Rahm. 171. C. W. Rettenmeyer; K. Weidman; P. Hill; F. G. H. Allen; R. E. Hutchins; K. Weidman. 172. J. and D. Bartlett; C. P. Warner; H. Eisenbeiss/F. W. Lane; K. Weidman. 173. C. W. Rettenmeyer; K. Weidman; R. C. Hermes; J. Burton/B. Coleman. 174. L. Burrows/LIFE © Time Inc.; Lim Boo Liat. 175. M. P. L. Fogden; Zoological Society of London; F. G. H. Allen. 176. Okapia; A. Margiocco. 177. J. A. Kern; J. A. Kern; G. Holton/B. Coleman. 178. Okapia; I. DeVore. 179. Okapia; F. G. H. Allen. 180. P. Ward; T. Beamish; A. Margiocco. 181. E. Hanumantha Rao; W. Ferguson; J. Burton/B. Coleman. 182. H. Skafte; H. Skafte; B. N. S. Deo/Rapho-Guillumette. 183. San Diego Zoological Society (sequence of three); V. A. Wager; E. S. Ross; E. Hanumantha Rao. 184. M. Krishnan; J. Juan Spillet. 185. M. Krishnan; M. Hemple; Lim Boo Liat; J. Juan Spillet. 186. G. Lotti/Mondadori Press; S. Wayman/LIFE © Time Inc. 187. S. Wayman/LIFE © Time Inc. 188. Ylla/Rapho-Guillumette; M. Hemple. 189. Philcarol/F. W. Lane; E. Hosking; E. P. Gee from *The Wildlife of India* (Collins); E. P. Gee from *The Wildlife of India* (Collins). 190. Okapia; M. P. L. Fogden; Zoological Society of London. 191. M. Hemple; F. G. H. Allen. 192. L. McCombe/LIFE © Time Inc. 193. P. Jackson/B. Coleman; C. P. Warner; M. Hemple; M. Hemple. 194. I. Muul; Lim Boo Liat; Lim Boo Liat. 195. J. Burton/B. Coleman; C. P. Warner; C. P. Warner; P. M. Fogden; J. H. Gerard. 196. Okapia; C. Bavagnoli/LIFE © Time Inc. 197. D. Bartlett; U. Rahm; F.P.G.; D. Holberton; Okapia; A. R. Devez-MGB/Jacana; A. R. Devez-MGB/Jacana. 198. Baron Hugo van Lawick © National Geographic Society. 199. H. Albrecht; Baron Hugo van Lawick © National Geographic Society (sequence of four). 200. Okapia. 201. U. Rahm; U. Rahm; D. Bartlett; Okapia. 202. C. A. Spinage. 203. J. Burton/B. Coleman; D. Bartlett/B. Coleman; J. F. Oates; P. Ward; P. Ward. 204. D. Bartlett; Okapia; E. S. Ross. 205. Popperfoto; U. Rahm; Philcarol/Monkmeyer; Okapia. 206. D. Bartlett; Popperfoto; A. R. Devez-MGB/Jacana. 207. A. Walker; A. Walker; U. Rahm; A. R. Devez-MGB/Jacana. 208. Popperfoto; Okapia. 209. P. Johnson; Popperfoto; P. Johnson. 210. A. Margiocco; W. T. Miller; C. P. Warner. 211. S. A. Thompson; W. D. Haacke; M. J. Coe; H. D. Brown. 212. E. Gould; F. Goro/LIFE © Time Inc.; H. E. Uible. 213. S. Larrain/Magnum; D. Attenborough; D. Bartlett; D. Bartlett. 214. A. Jolly. 215. D. Attenborough; D. Attenborough; R. Martin; Popperfoto; C. Bavagnoli/LIFE © Time Inc.; R. Martin. 216. Okapia; M. D. Tuttle; C. W. Rettenmeyer. 217. D. Bartlett; Okapia; P. Morris; D. Pye; M. D. Tuttle; M. D. Tuttle; P. Morris; D. Pye. 219. Zoological Society of London; S. Grossman/F.P.G.; J. Burton/B. Coleman; N. Leen/LIFE © Time Inc. 220. D. Faulkner; C. W. Rettenmeyer; S. Grossman/F.P.G.; S. Grossman/F.P.G.; K. Severin. 221. D. J. Chivers; Hladik/Jacana. 222. K. Weidman; T. Morrison; C. W. Rettenmeyer. 223. D. Hibberd; C. W. Rettenmeyer; K. Weidman; C. Gans. 224. J. R. Simon/B. Coleman; P. Wayre; C. W. Rettenmeyer; D. Bartlett. 225. D. Faulkner; Keystone Press; K. Weidman. 226. W. Scheithauer. 227. D. Botting; R. Kinne/B. Coleman; J. A. Kern; Okapia; K. Weidman. 228. Okapia; Okapia; J. and D. Bartlett. 229. C. W. Rettenmeyer; C. P. Warner; C. W. Rettenmeyer; C. P. Warner; W. E. Duellman; C. Gans. 230. A. Root/Okapia. 230–31. S. Diczbalis (sequence of four). 231. G. Pizzey/B. Coleman. 232. G. Pizzey/B. Coleman; Okapia; Okapia; Okapia. 233. G. Pizzey/N.H.P.A.; P.L.A.; Okapia; J. Warham. 234. D. Bartlett; E. S. Ross; Lim Boo Liat; E. S. Ross. 235. J. Burton/B. Coleman. 236. M. Hemple; E. S. Ross; E. S. Ross; P. M. Fogden. 237. K. Weidman; F. Baillie/N.H.P.A.; K. Weidman; K. Weidman; G. Pizzey. 238. P. Verzier/Jacana. 240–41. J. Muench. 241. J. Crawford; H. Engels; M. Karwendel/Skyport Fotos. 242. D. Faulkner/B. Coleman. 243. A. Aichhorn; A. Christiansen/F. W. Lane; W. Braun; R. P. Bille. 244. R. Van Nostrand/National Audubon Society; T. W. Hall. 245. F. Erize; T. W. Hall; A. Root/B. Coleman. 246. V. Geist; C. Ott; T. W. Hall. 247. R. P. Bille; R. P. Bille; T. Iwago; R. P. Bille. 248. E. Hosking; J. Dominis/LIFE © Time Inc. 249. R. Allin/National Audubon Society; A. Aichhorn; J. Schuler. 250. R. P. Bille. 251. J. and D. Bartlett; T. Myers; R. P. Bille; M. J. Coe. 252. T. Morrison. 254–55. S. Thorarinsson. 255. S. Thorarinsson; K. Gillett; J. Muench; J. Linsley Gressitt. 256. E. R. Degginger. 257. P. Grubb © The Royal Society; F. Erize; S. Gillsäter/B. Coleman; S. Larrain/Magnum; P. Grubb © The Royal Society. 258. D. Merrie; S. Gillsäter/Tiofoto. 259. M. F. Soper; G. Holton/B. Coleman; G. Holton/B. Coleman; N. Bonner. 260. F. Erize; C. Weaver; F. Erize. 261. J. and D. Bartlett; G. Laycock; F. Erize. 262. F. Erize; D. R. Stoddart © The Royal Society. 263. R. Gaymer; R. Gaymer; M. Silverstone/Magnum; E. Schuhmacher. 264. C. Weaver. 265. G. Laycock; J. A. Hancock/B. Coleman; J. A. Hancock; J. A. Hancock; A. Root/Okapia; F. Erize. 266. B. Cropp. 268. R. Perron. 270. E. Bork/National Film Board of Canada; R. Carpenter; I. Holmäsen; G. Heilman. 271. I. Holmäsen; J. Clegg; Treat Davidson/F. W. Lane; J. Burton/B. Coleman. 272. G. Heilman; J. F. Oates; Mondadori Press. 273. Camera Press; H. Barnfather/B. Coleman; J. Burton/B. Coleman; W. E. Ferguson. 274. J. H. Gerard; W. H. Amos; I. Virkkunen. 275. J. Six; E. R. Degginger; P. Parks; J. Burton/B. Coleman; P. Parks. 276. A. Visage/Jacana; D. Faulkner; D. Faulkner. 277. D. Bartlett; Treat Davidson/F. W. Lane; A. Visage/Jacana. 278. J. H. Tashjian at Steinhart Aquarium. 279. H. Angel; H. Angel; H. Angel; R. Thompson/F. W. Lane. 280. A. Margiocco; A. Margiocco; Popperfoto. 281. F. Greenway/N.H.P.A.; J. Six; R. P. Bille; J. Burton/B. Coleman; J. Norris-Wood. 282. A. Margiocco; H. W. Silvester; K. Weidman; E. R. Degginger. 283. W. Bonatti/Mondadori Press; E. Hanumantha Rao; D. Bartlett; K. Weidman. 284. D. and M. Zimmerman; G. Kinns/A.F.A.; J. Finch/F. W. Lane; S. Dalton/N.H.P.A. 285. D. Botting; J. Burton/B. Coleman; S. A. Thompson; N. Myers/Camera Press. 286. P. Scott; D. Bartlett. 287. D. Bartlett; P. Slater; D. Hughes. 288. E. Hosking; T. Davidson/F. W. Lane; H. W. Silvester. 289. D. Hughes; D. Bartlett; E. R. Degginger; L. H. Brown. 290. J. Burton/B. Coleman; C. E. Mohr; A. Y. Owen/LIFE © Time Inc. 291. R. W. Mitchell; R. W. Mitchell; R. W. Mitchell; S. Gillsäter/Tiofoto. 292. J. Goode; J. S. Wightman; K. Gillett; E. Schuhmacher. 293. D. Botting; J. Burton/B. Coleman. 294. N. Fox-Davies. 295. J. Burton/B. Coleman; G. L. Kooyman; N. Fox-Davies. 296. P. Hill; W. Braun; P. Hill. 297. K. Gillett; A. Bannister/N.H.P.A.; D. Bartlett; A. Bannister/N.H.P.A. 298. W. Deas/Barnaby's Picture Library; D. P. Wilson; D. P. Wilson. 299. D. P. Wilson; D. P. Wilson; D. P. Wilson; D. P. Wilson; P. Hill; P. David; D. P. Wilson; P. Parks. 300. P. David; F. Schulke/Black Star; B. Cropp. 301. B. Cropp; T. Myers; B. Cropp. 302. B. Cropp. 303. P. David; D. Faulkner; D. Faulkner; P. David; T. Myers; D. Faulkner. 304. P. David/Photo Aquatics; A. Margiocco; A. Margiocco. 305. D. P. Wilson; P. David/F. W. Lane; K. Gillett. 306. D. Faulkner; D. Faulkner; P. Hill; D. Faulkner; D. Faulkner. 306–7. J. Burton/B. Coleman. 307. D. Faulkner; D. Faulkner; P. Hill. 308. P. David; P. David; P. David; P. David/Photo Aquatics. 309 P. David; P. David; P. David/Photo Aquatics; P. David/Photo Aquatics; P. David/Photo Aquatics. 310. K. Gillett; P. Hill; A. Bannister/N.H.P.A.; A. Bannister/N.H.P.A. 311. B. Cropp; B. Cropp; G. L. Kooyman; Barnaby's Picture Library. 312. D. Faulkner; W. Braun. 313. Okapia; B. Cropp; S. Gillsäter/Tiofoto; D. Faulkner; B. Cropp. 314. G. Leavens/B. Coleman; British Antarctic Survey. 315. J. Dominis/LIFE © Time Inc.; J. and D. Bartlett. 316. J. R. Simon/B. Coleman; Mondadori Press. 317. R. Kinne/B. Coleman; S. Myers; K. W. Kenyon/National Audubon Society; C. K. Bertram. 318. F. Bruemmer. 318–19. J. Linsley Gressitt; Mondadori Press. 319. F. Erize. 320. Crown Copyright, Institute of Geological Sciences; R. I. Lewis Smith. 320–21. E. Schuhmacher. 324–25. A. S. Romer. 342–43. A. Bannister/N.H.P.A.; C. P. Warner. 343. I. Holmäsen; O. Danesch; H. Angel. 344. A. Bannister/N.H.P.A.; J. Burton/B. Coleman; G. Pizzey/B. Coleman. 345. N. Myers/Bavaria Verlag. 346–47. A. Root. 347. E. Hosking. 349. T. Iwago; A. Bannister/N.H.P.A.; Philcarol/Monkmeyer. 350. A. T. Band; M. Amin. 351. T. Iwago. 352–53. J. and D. Bartlett; D. Kessel/LIFE © Time Inc. 353. R. Pinney/National Audubon Society. 354–55. L. Darling from *The Gull's Way*. 355. A. Bannister/N.H.P.A.; J. Burton/B. Coleman. 356. A. Margiocco. 356–57. Colorphoto Hinz, Basle. 357. Picturepoint; A. Bannister/N.H.P.A.; British Museum. 358. A. Poignant. 358–59. Japanese painting (about 1800), from the Japanese State Archives, photographed by Bradley Smith, New York. 361. Detail from a 13th-century manuscript, The Vatican Library. 362–63. Relief from the Tomb of Nefer, Sakkara, Egypt (2500–2300 B.C.), photographed by B. Brake/LIFE © Time Inc.; Detail from a Florentine painting (about 1417), The Cleveland Museum of Art, The Holden Collection. 363. P.-N. Nilsson/Tiofoto. 364. Bettmann Archive; D. Lees; Radio Times Hulton Picture Library. 365. From the Atkins Museum of Fine Arts, Kansas City, Missouri, photographed by H. Groskinsky/LIFE © Time Inc. 366. I. DeVore. 366–67. Copy of a 17th-century painting, Hachisuka Collection, Japan. 367. G. Biasi/Mondadori Press. 368–69. D. Plage/Anglia T.V.; J. Pearson/B. Coleman. 369. F. Bruemmer.

Artists

The drawings and diagrams throughout the book have been made by: P. L. Church, David Cook, Brian Craker, Barry Driscoll, Barry Evans, Ian Garrard, Roy Grubb, Vana Haggerty, Gillian Lockwood, Lesley Marshall, John Norris-Wood, Philip North-Taylor, Denys Ovenden, Josephine Rankin, Charles Raymond, Kathleen Smith, Tom Stalker Miller, Harry Titcombe, Norman Weaver, Michael Woods, Sidney Woods.

In the classification section, the drawings of invertebrates are by Norman Weaver; fish are by Lesley Marshall and Norman Weaver; amphibians and reptiles are by John Norris-Wood; birds are by Barry Driscoll and Harry Titcombe; mammals are by Barry Driscoll, John Norris-Wood, Charles Pickard, John Thomas, and Norman Weaver.

Charles Pickard painted the color illustrations for the evolution section.

Cartography by Fairey Surveys Limited.

Sources of reference

The editors also acknowledge their indebtedness to the following books and journals, which were consulted for reference:

Abyss by C. P. Idyll (T. Y. Crowell); *Adaptation to Desert Environment* by J. P. Kirmiz (Plenum); *Africa: A Natural History* by Leslie Brown (Random House); *African Wild Life* (Wild Life Protection and Conservation Society of South Africa); *The Age of Reptiles* by Edwin H. Colbert (Norton); *Animal Behavior* (Study of Behavior) by J. D. Carthy (St. Martin's Press); *Animal Ecology* by Charles Elton (Barnes & Noble); *Animal Ecology* by S. Charles Kendeigh (Prentice-Hall); *Animal Geography* 'by Wilma George (Dover); *Animal Locomotion* by Sir James Gray (Norton); *Animal Navigation* by R. M. Lockley (Hart); *Animal Worlds* by Marston Bates (Random House); *Animals; Animals and Birds in Australia* by Graham Pizzey (Dufour); *Animals in the Night* by J. H. Prince (Tri-Ocean); *Animals of Eastern Australia* by Stan and Kay Breeden (Harrap); *Annals* of the South African Museum; *The Apes* by Vernon Reynolds (Dutton); *Arachnida* by Theodore Savory (Academic Press); *Arctic* (Arctic Institute of North America); *Asia* by Pierre Pfeffer (Random House); *Aspects of Deep Sea Biology* by N. B. Marshall (Academic Press); *Audubon Magazine* (National Audubon Society); *Australia and the Pacific Islands* by Allen Keast (Random House); *An Australian Mammal Book* by C. Barrett (Oxford University Press); *Atlas of European Birds* by K. H. de Voous (Nelson); *A Biography of the Sea* by Richard Carrington (Chatto and Windus); *Biologie der Süsswasserinsekten* by C. Wesenberg-Lund (S-H Service Agency); *Biologie des Eaux Souterraines, Littorales et Continentales* by C. D. Deboutteville (Hermann, Paris); *The Biology of Estuarine Animals* by J. Green (University of Washington Press); *Bird Navigation* by G. V. T. Matthews (Cambridge University Press); *Birds and Mammals of the Sierra Nevada* by Lowell Sumner and Joseph S. Dixon (University of California Press); *Birds in the Balance* by Philip Brown (October House); *Birds of Paradise and Bower Birds* by E. T. Gilliard (Natural History Press); *Birds of North America* by Chandler S. Robbins, Bertel Bruun, and Herbert S. Zim (Golden Press); *Birds of the Antarctic* by E. Wilson (Humanities Press); *Birds of the Atlantic Ocean* by Keith Shackleton and Ted Stokes (Macmillan); *Birds of the World* by Hans Hvass (Dutton); *Birds of the World* by Oliver L. Austin, Jr. (Golden Press); *British Birds; British Freshwater Fishes* by Margaret E. Varley (Fishing News); *Bulletin* (Comité d'Etudes Historiques de l'Afrique Occidentale Francaise); *Bulletin* of the Museum of Comparative Zoology, Harvard; *Checklist of Birds of the World* by J. L. Peters (Harvard University Press); *Checklist of Palaearctic and Indian Mammals* by J. R. Ellerman and T. C. S. Morrison Scott (British Museum [Natural History]); *A Classification of Living Animals* by Lord Rothschild (Longmans); *Collins Pocket Guide to British Birds* by R. S. R. Fitter (W. Collins); *A Coloured Key to the Wildfowl of the World* by Peter Scott (Royle); *The Continent We Live On* by Ivan T. Sanderson (Random House); *Copeia* (American Society of Ichthyologists); *Coral Reefs and Atolls* by J. Stanley Gardiner (Macmillan); *Courtship: A Zoological (Ethological) Study* by Margaret Bastock (Aldine); *The Dancing Bees* by Karl von Frisch (Harcourt Brace Jovanovich); *The Deer and the Tiger* by George B. Schaller (University of Chicago Press); *Desert Animals* by Knut Schmidt-Nielsen (Oxford University Press); *The Dispersal of Plants throughout the World* by Henry N. Ridley (Reeve); *The Domestication and Exploitation of Plants and Animals* edited by Peter J. Ucko and G. W. Dimbleby (Gerald Duckworth); *East African Wildlife Journal* (East African Wildlife Society); *Ecological Monographs* (Ecological Society of America); *Ecology* (Ecological Society of America); *Ecology* by Eugene P. Odum (Holt, Rinehart & Winston); *Ecology of Intertidal Zones* by G. K. Reid (Rand McNally); *Endeavour* (Imperial Chemical Industries Ltd.); *Essays in Marine Biology* (Oliver and Boyd); *Ethology of Mammals* by R. F. Ewer (Plenum); *Europe* by Kai Curry-Lindahl (Random House); *Evolution of the Vertebrates* by Edwin H. Colbert (Wiley); *The Families and Genera of Living Rodents* by J. P. Ellerman and others (British Museum [Natural History]); *Fauna and Flora of the Rivers, Lakes and Reservoirs of the U.S.S.R.* by V. I. Zhadin and G. V. Gerd (Israel Program for Scientific Translations, Jerusalem); *A Field Guide to the Birds of Britain and Europe* by Roger Peterson, Guy Mountfort and P. A. D. Hollom (Houghton Mifflin); *A Field Guide to the Birds of East and Central Africa* by John G. Williams (Houghton Mifflin); *A Field Guide to the Birds of New Zealand* by R. A. Falla, R. B. Sibson, and E. G. Turbott (Houghton Mifflin); *A Field Guide to the Mammals* by William Henry Burt and Richard Philip Grossenheider (Houghton Mifflin); *A Field Guide to the Mammals of Britain and Europe* by F. H. van den Brink (Houghton Mifflin); *A Field Guide to the National Parks of East Africa* by John G. Williams (Houghton Mifflin); *A Field Guide to Western Reptiles and Amphibians* by R. C. Stebbins (Houghton Mifflin); *Folia Primatologica*, Basle; *Freshwater Invertebrates of the United States* by R. W. Pennak (Ronald Press); *Fundamentals of Ecology* by Eugene P. Odum (Saunders); *Fundamentals of Limnology* by Franz Ruttner (University of Toronto Press); *Fundamentals of Ornithology* by J. Van Tyne and A. J. Berger (Wiley); *The Galapagos* by R. Bowman (University of California Press); *Galapagos: Islands of Birds* by Bryan Nelson (Morrow); *A General Textbook of Entomology* by A. D. Imms (Barnes & Noble); *The Geographical Distribution of Animals* by Alfred Russel Wallace (Hafner); *The Geography of Flowering Plants* by R. Good (Wiley); *Great Waters* by Sir Alister Hardy (Harper & Row); *Grzimeks Tierleben* by B. Grzimek and others (Kindler Verlag AG, Zurich); *Hamlyn all-colour paperbacks* (Paul Hamlyn); *The Handbook of British Mammals* edited by H. N. Southern (Blackwell Davis); *A Handbook of Living Primates* by J. R. Napier and P. H. Napier (Academic Press); *Handbuch der Zoologie* by W. Kukenthal and T. Krumbach (Gruyter, Berlin); *A History of Domesticated Animals* by Frederick E. Zeuner (Harper & Row); *A History of Fishes* by J. R. Norman, second edition by P. H. Greenwood (Hill and Wang); *Hummingbirds* by Walter Scheithauer (T. Y. Crowell); *Ibis* (British Ornithologists' Union); *Insects and Physiology* by J. W. L. Beament and J. E. Treherne (American Elsevier); *'Instinct' and 'Intelligence'* by S. A. Barnett (Prentice-Hall); *Introduction to Biology* by D. G. Mackean (Arco); *Introduction to High Altitude Entomology* by M. S. Mani (Barnes & Noble); *Island Life* by Sherwin Carlquist (Doubleday); *The Invertebrata* by L. A. Borradaile and F. A. Potts, third edition revised by G. A. Kerkut (Cambridge University Press); *Invertebrate Zoology* by Robert D. Barnes (Saunders); *Invertebrates: Structure and Function* by E. J. W. Barrington (Houghton Mifflin); *Journal of Mammalogy* (American Society of Mammalogists); *Journal* of the Marine Biological Association of the United Kingdom; *Journal of Zoology* (Proceedings of The Zoological Society of London); *King Solomon's Ring* by Konrad Z. Lorenz (T. Y. Crowell); *Larousse Encyclopedia of Animal Life* (McGraw-Hill); *The Last of the Wild* by Eugen Schuhmacher (Doubleday); *Lemur Behavior* by Alison Jolly (University of Chicago Press); *Life in the Deserts* by J. L. Cloudsley-Thompson and M. J. Chadwick (Dufour); *The Life of Birds* by Joel Carl Welty (Knopf); *The Life of Fishes* by N. B. Marshall (World); *The Life of Insects* by Sir Vincent B. Wigglesworth (World); *Life in Lakes and Rivers* by T. T. Macan and E. B. Worthington (W. Collins); *The Life of Mammals* by L. Harrison Matthews (W. Collins); *Life Nature Library* (Time-Life International [Nederland] N.V.); *The Life of Plants* by E. J. H. Corner (World); *The Life of Primates* by Adolph H. Schultz (Universe); *The Life of Reptiles* by Angus Bellairs (American Elsevier); *The Life of Vertebrates* by J. Z. Young (Oxford University Press); *Limnology and Oceanography* (The American Society of Limnology and Oceanography); *A List of Land Mammals of New Guinea, Celebes and Adjacent Islands 1758–1953* by E. M. C. Laurie and J. E. Hill (British Museum [Natural History]); *Living Amphibians of the World* by Doris M. Cochran (Doubleday); *Living Birds of the World* by E. T. Gilliard (Doubleday); *Living Insects of the World* by A. B. and E. B. Klots (Doubleday); *Living Invertebrates of the World* by Ralph Buchsbaum and Lorus J. Milne (Hamish Hamilton); *Living Reptiles of the World* by K. P. Schmidt and R. F. Inger (Doubleday); *The Magic of the Senses* by Vitus B. Dröscher (Dutton); *Malayan Animal Life* by M. W. F. Tweedie and J. L. Harrison (International Publishers Service); *The Mammals* by Desmond Morris (Harper & Row); *Mammals of Britain: Their Tracks, Trails and Signs* by M. J. Lawrence and R. W. Brown (Blandford); *The Mammals of Eastern Canada* by Randolf L. Peterson (Oxford University Press); *Mammals of Nevada* by E. Raymond Hall (University of California Press); *The Mammals of North America* by E. Raymond Hall and Keith R. Kelson (Ronald Press); *Mammals of the U.S.S.R.* edited by N. Bobrinskii (State Publishing Office, Moscow); *Mammals of the U.S.S.R. and Adjacent Countries* by S. I. Ognev (Israel Program for Scientific Translations, Jerusalem); *Mammals of the World* by Ernest P. Walker (Johns Hopkins Press); *Man and Monkey* by L. Williams (Lippincott); *Marine Mammals* by Richard J. Harrison and Judith E. King (Hillary House); *Marsupials of Australia* by Basil J. Marlow (Jacaranda Press, Brisbane); *Mémoires* de l'Institut Scientifique de Madagascar; *Memoirs* of the Museum of Comparative Zoology, Harvard; *Memorias* de Museo de Historia Natural, "Javier Prado"; *The Migration of Birds* by Jean Dorst (Houghton Mifflin); *The Migratory Barren-ground Caribou of Canada* by John P. Kelsall (Canadian Wildlife Service); *Mimicry in Plants and Animals* by W. Wickler (McGraw-Hill); *Molluscs* by J. E. Morton (Hillary House); *National Geographic* (National Geographic Society); *Native Animals of New Zealand* by A. W. B. Powell (Auckland Museum); *Natural History* (American Museum of Natural History); *The Natural History of Mammals* by François Bourlière (Knopf); *Natural Selection and Heredity* by P. M. Sheppard (Hillary House); *Nature; The Neolithic Revolution* by Sonia Cole (British Museum [Natural History]); *A New Dictionary of Birds* by Sir A. Landsborough Thomson (McGraw-Hill); *New Scientist; Notes and Comments on Vertebrate Paleontology* by Alfred Sherwood Romer (University of Chicago Press); *Oceanic Birds of South America* by R. C. Murphy (Macmillan and American Museum of Natural History); *The Oceans: Their Physics, Chemistry and General Biology* by H. U. Sverdrup, Martin W. Johnson, and Richard H. Fleming (Prentice-Hall); *Oikos*, Copenhagen; *On Aggression* by Konrad Lorenz (Harcourt Brace Jovanovich); *The Open Sea* by Sir Alister C. Hardy (Houghton Mifflin); *The Origin of Life* by J. D. Bernal (World); *Oryx* (Journal of the Fauna Preservation Society); *Our Living World of Nature* series (McGraw-Hill); *Oxford Book of Insects* by J. Burton (Oxford University Press); *The Pattern of Animal Communities* by Charles S. Elton (Barnes & Noble); *Penguins* by John Sparks and Tony Soper (Taplinger); *Penguins* by Bernard Stonehouse (Golden Press); *Philosophical Transactions* of the Royal Society; *Physical Geography* by A. N. Strahler (Wiley); *The Physiological Effects of High Winds* edited by W. H. Weihe (Pergamon); *Pleistocene Extinctions* edited by P. S. Martin and H. E. Wright, Jr. (Yale University Press); *Primate Behavior* edited by Irven DeVore (Holt, Rinehart & Winston); *Primates* by W. C. Osman Hill (Wiley); *Primates* edited by Phyllis C. Jay (Holt, Rinehart & Winston); *Proceedings* of the California Academy of Science; *The Procession of Life* by Alfred S. Romer (World); *Purnell's Encyclopedia of Animal Life; The Red Book* by James Fisher, Noel Simon, and Jack Vincent (W. Collins); *Red Data Book* (International Union of Conservation of Nature and Natural Resources, Survival Service Commission, Morges, Switzerland); *Relationships of the Anoles* by R. E. Etheridge (University of Michigan); *Reptiles of Australia* by Eric Worrell (Tri-Ocean); *Die Säugetiere der Sowjetunion* by V. G. Heptener and A. G. Bannikov (Gustav Fischer); *Science* (American Association for the Advancement of Science); *Science Journal; The Science of Life* by Gordon Rattray Taylor (McGraw-Hill); *Scientific American; The Sea* by Rachel Carson (Macgibbon and Kee); *The Sea Shore* by C. M. Yonge (Warne); *Seals of the World* by Judith E. King (British Museum [Natural History]); *The Seas* by Sir Frederick S. Russell and C. M. Yonge (Warne); *The Shell Bird Book* by James Fisher (The Ebury Press and Michael Joseph); *Signals of the Animal World* by Dietrich Burkhardt, Wolfgang Schleidt, and Helmut Altner (McGraw-Hill); *Snakes of Southern Africa* by V. F. M. Fitzsimons (Tri-Ocean); *South America and Central America* by Jean Dorst (Random House); *Southern African Mammals* by J. R. Ellerman, T. C. S. Morrison Scott, and R. W. Hayman (British Museum [Natural History]); *The Stocks of Whales* by N. A. Mackintosh (Fishing News); *A Study of Bird Song* by Edward A. Armstrong (Oxford University Press); *Symposia* of The Zoological Society of London; *Systematic Dictionary of Mammals of the World* by Maurice Burton (Peter Smith); *The Terrestrial Mammals of Western Europe* by G. B. Corbet (Dufour); *A Textbook of Entomology* by Herbert H. Ross (Wiley); *A Textbook of Zoology* by T. J. Parker and W. A. Haswell (Macmillan and St. Martin's Press); *Tracks and Signs of British Animals* by A. Leutscher (Cleaver Hume Press); *Traité de Zoologie* by Pierre-P. Grassé (Masson, Paris); *Transactions* of The Zoological Society of London; *A Treatise of Limnology* by G. Evelyn Hutchinson (Wiley); *The Tropical Rain Forest* by P. W. Richards (Cambridge University Press); *The Tuatara, Lizards and Frogs of New Zealand* by Richard Sharell (Tri-Ocean); *The Unbelievable Land* edited by I. Norman Smith (The Queen's Printer, Canada); *Underwater Guide to Marine Life* by Carleton Ray and Elgin Ciampi (A. S. Barnes); *The University Atlas* (George Philip); *Vanishing Wild Animals of the World* by Richard Fitter (Franklin Watts); *Vertebrate Paleontology* by Alfred Sherwood Romer (University of Chicago Press); *Waterfowl of the World* by J. Delacour (Heineman); *The Whale* edited by Leonard Harrison Matthews (Allen and Unwin); *Where to Watch Birds* by John Gooders (Deutsch); *Wild Fox* by Roger Burrows (Taplinger); *Wildlife of the South Seas* by F. A. Rodelberger and Vera I. Groschoff (Viking Press); *The Wild Life of India* by E. P. Gee (W. Collins); *Die Wirbeltiere des Kamerungebirges* by Martin Eisentraut (Paul Parey, Hamburg); *The World of Birds* by James Fisher and Roger Tory Peterson (Doubleday); *The World of Spiders* by W. S. Bristowe (Johnson Reprint); *The World of the Polar Bear* by Richard Perry (University of Washington Press); *The World of the Walrus* by Richard Perry (Taplinger); *World Vegetation* by Denis Riley and Anthony Young (Cambridge University Press); *Zoogeography* by Philip J. Darlington, Jr. (Wiley); *Zoogeography of the Sea* by Sven Ekmon (Sidgwick and Jackson); *The Zoology of Tropical Africa* by J. L. Cloudsley-Thompson (Norton); *Zoo Quest to Madagascar* by David Attenborough (Lutterworth).

Drawings and diagrams are based on many sources. The editors acknowledge the following in particular:

20. Meeting of the waters—*The Oceans: Their Physics, Chemistry and General Biology* by Sverdrup, Johnson, and Fleming, © 1942. By permission of Prentice-Hall Inc., Englewood Cliffs, New Jersey. 22. Protection for the newborn—*Seals of Arctic and Eastern Canada* by A. W. Mansfield (Fisheries Research Board of Canada, Ottawa). 23. Cold feet give protection—adapted from *Adaptations to Cold* by Laurence Irving. Copyright © January 1966 by Scientific American, Inc. All rights reserved. Small ears reduce heat loss—*Principles of Animal Ecology* by W. C. Allee, Alfred E. Emerson, Orlando Park, Thomas Park, and Karl P. Schmidt (W. B. Saunders). 26. Powerful swimming stroke—frames from the film *Motor Patterns of Polar Bears* by Dr. Martin W. Schein (PCR 124K, Psychological Cinema Register, The Pennsylvania State University). 29. How the lemming population rises and falls—graph reproduced from *Some Aspects of Population Structure in the Short-term Cycle of the Brown Lemming* by Frank A. Pitelka, *Cold Spring Harbor Symposium on Quantitative Biology, XXII:* 248, 1957. 30. Danger signals—from a drawing by W. D. Berry by permission of Professor H. O. Pruitt, Jr. 56. Flat-footed walk—*Animal Locomotion* by Sir James Gray (Weidenfeld and Nicolson). 67. How an aphid feeds—*The Life of Insects* by V. B. Wigglesworth (Weidenfeld and Nicolson). 70. How antlers and horns differ—adapted from *Horns and Antlers* by Walter Modell. Copyright © April 1969 by Scientific American, Inc. All rights reserved. 72. In the grip of a fungus—*Predaceous Fungi and Nematodes* by C. L. Duddington, *Experientia* Vol. XVIII No. 12 (1962). 73. Building a nest with natural bricks and silken mortar—adapted from *False Scorpions* by Theodore H. Savory. Copyright © March 1966 by Scientific American, Inc. All rights reserved. 83. "Sixth finger" for gripping—*Men and Pandas* by Desmond and Ramona Morris (Hutchinson). 95. Two runners—*Animal Locomotion* by Sir James Gray (Weidenfeld and Nicolson). 110. Continuous growth—from *Age Criteria for the African Elephant, Loxodonta a. africana* by R. M. Laws: *East African Wildlife Journal,* Vol. 4 (1966). 111. New teeth to replace the old—from *Age Criteria for the African Elephant, Loxodonta a. africana* by R. M. Laws: *East African Wildlife Journal,* Vol. 4 (1966). 112. Baboons on the move—from *Baboon Social Behavior* by K. R. L. Hall and Irven DeVore, from *Primate Behavior: Field Studies of Monkeys and Apes* edited by Irven DeVore. Copyright © 1965 by Holt, Rinehart & Winston, Inc. Reprinted by permission of Holt, Rinehart & Winston, Inc. 114. Construction of a weaver's nest—*Nest Form and Construction of Certain West African Weaver Birds* by J. H. Crook, *Ibis* 102: 1-25. Parasites and hosts—*Der Brutparasitismus der Witwenvögel* by Jurgen Nicolai, *Naturwissenschaft und Medizin* Jahrgang 2 (1965) Heft 7, Seite 3. By courtesy of Boehringer Mannheim at Mannheim, West Germany. 119. *Macrotermes* termite mound—adapted from *Air-conditioned Termite Nests* by Martin Luscher. Copyright © July 1961 by Scientific American, Inc. All rights reserved. 127. Mole-rat burrow—*Mammals of the U.S.S.R. and Adjacent Countries* by S. I. Ognev. Translated by Israel Program for Scientific Translations. 131. Scale and hair—*Schuppentiere* by Dr. Erna Mohr, *Die Neue Brehm-Bücherei* Vol. 72, 1961 (A. Ziemsen Verlag, Wittenberg Lutherstadt). 134. Anteater's claws—*Mammals of the World* by Ernest P. Walker (Johns Hopkins Press, Baltimore). 135. Patterns of armor—*Mammals of the World* by Ernest P. Walker (Johns Hopkins Press, Baltimore); Field Museum of Natural History, Chicago; and Lloyd G. Ingles. 142. The cock that builds an incubator—*The Mallee Fowl* by H. J. Frith (Angus and Robertson). 147. Differing desert climates—*Life in Deserts* by J. L. Cloudsley-Thompson and M. J. Chadwick (G. T. Foulis & Co., 1964); *Physical Geography* by A. N. Strahler. Copyright © 1965 (Wiley); and adapted from *The North American Deserts* by Edmund C. Jaeger with the permission of the publisher (Stanford: Stanford University Press, 1957) p. 24. 148. Conserving water—adapted from *The Jerboa and Desert* by J. P. Kirmiz, *Science Journal* November 1965. Tolerance of furnacelike temperatures—adapted from *Desert Ground Squirrels* by George A. Bartholomew and Jack W. Hudson. Copyright © November 1961 by Scientific American, Inc. All rights reserved. 151. Chambered stomach—*Traité de Zoologie* by Pierre-P. Grassé, Vol. XVII, 1955 (Masson, Paris). Varying body temperature—adapted from *The Physiology of the Camel* by Knut Schmidt-Nielsen. Copyright © December 1959 by Scientific American, Inc. All rights reserved. Heat exchange—adapted from *The Physiology of the Camel* by Knut Schmidt-Nielsen. Copyright © December 1959 by Scientific American, Inc. All rights reserved. 159. Coping with the desert's temperature changes—redrawn from *Behavioural attitudes and regulation of temperature in Amphibolurus lizards* by S. D. Bradshaw and A. R. Main, *J. Zool., Lond.* (1968) 154, 193-221. 161. How the vipers and the rattlesnakes move their bodies by waves of muscular contractions—from diagrams in *Animal Locomotion* by Sir James Gray (Weidenfeld and Nicolson). 168. The five layers of the tropical forest—*The Tropical Rain Forest* by P. W. Richards (Cambridge University Press). Forest temperatures—*The Tropical Rain Forest* by P. W. Richards (Cambridge University Press). Forest humidity—*The Tropical Rain Forest* by P. W. Richards (Cambridge University Press). 174. Paws and hands—*A Handbook of Living Primates* by J. R. Napier and P. H. Napier (Academic Press, London and New York); and *Primates: Comparative Anatomy and Taxonomy,* Vol. 1, by W. C. Osman Hill (Edinburgh University Press). 177. Indications of maturity and status—from *The Common Langur of North India* by Phyllis Jay, from *Primate Behavior: Field Studies of Monkeys and Apes* edited by Irven DeVore. Copyright © 1965 by Holt, Rinehart & Winston, Inc. Reprinted by permission of Holt, Rinehart & Winston, Inc. 179. Swinging through the trees—Ralph Morse photograph, courtesy Animal Talent Scouts, Inc., and Time-Life Books. 187. Retracted claws and Extended claws—*The Mammalia of India* by Robert A. Sterndale, abridged edition 1929 (Thacker, Spink and Co., Calcutta); and *Der Tiger* by Vratislav Mazak, *Die Neue Brehm-Bücherei* Vol. 356, 1965 (A. Ziemsen Verlag, Wittenberg Lutherstadt). 203. Padded soles—*On peculiar structures in the feet of certain species of mammals which enable them to walk on smooth perpendicular surfaces* by G. E. Dobson, *Proceedings of The Zoological Society of London,* 1876: 526-534. 210. Muscular control—*The Chameleon* by Carl Gans, *Natural History,* April 1967. 226. Bills to suit different flowers—reprinted with permission from Josselyn Van Tyne and Andrew J. Berger, *Fundamentals of Ornithology*. Copyright © 1959 (Wiley); and *Hummingbirds* by Crawford H. Greenewalt (Doubleday, New York). How a hummingbird hovers—*Animal Locomotion* by Sir James Gray (Weidenfeld and Nicolson). Feather structure that gives iridescent plumage—*Hummingbirds* by Crawford H. Greenewalt (Doubleday). 229. How the anole changes color—*Colour Changes and Structure of the Skin of Anolis carolinensis* by Charles E. Von Geldern, *Proceedings of the California Academy of Sciences* Vol. X, No. 12, February 1921. 231. Male bower birds build and decorate several types of elaborate pavilions for display and mating—adapted from *Bower Birds* by A. J. Marshall. Copyright © June 1956 by Scientific American, Inc. All rights reserved; and *The Evolution of Bower Birds* by E. Thomas Gilliard. Copyright © August 1963 by Scientific American, Inc. All rights reserved. 259. Effortless soaring—*Flight of the Albatross* by William Jameson, *Natural History,* April 1960. 260. Strutting blue-footed boobies—*Galapagos, Islands of Birds* by Bryan Nelson (Longmans). 264. Shells from a common ancestor—*Island Life* by Sherwin Carlquist (Natural History Press). 270. Layers of lake water in summer—*Fundamentals of Ecology* by Eugene P. Odum (W. B. Saunders), after Deevey, 1951. 271. The food cycle in a lake—*Ecology of Inland Waters and Estuaries* by G. K. Reid. Copyright © 1961 by Litton Educational Publishing, Inc., by permission of Rheinhold Publishing Company. From *The Trophic-Dynamic Aspect of Ecology* by R. L. Lindeman, *Ecology* 23 (1942): 399-418. 273. Adaptations to torrents—*Ecology, Bionomics and Evolution of the Torrential Fauna* by Sunder L. Hora, *Philosophical Transactions of the Royal Society* Series B. 218, 171-282 (1930). 274. Methods of trapping prey—*Biologie der Süsswasserinsekten* by C. Wesenberg-Lund (Springer, Berlin). 275. How invertebrates swim (leech)—*Der Medizinische Blutegel und seine Verwandten* by K. Herter, *Die Neue Brehm-Bücherei* Vol. 381, 1968 (A. Ziemsen Verlag, Wittenberg Lutherstadt). 277. Navigation by electricity—adapted from *Electric Location by Fishes* by H. W. Lissman. Copyright © March 1963 by Scientific American, Inc. All rights reserved. 278. Cocooned fish—*On the Anatomy and Physiology of Protopterus annectens* by W. N. Parker, *Trans. R.I.A.,* Vol. 30, Part 3 (1892). 280. Stages toward an adult form—*Introduction to Biology* by D. G. Mackean (Murray). 289. Filter feeding—*Filter-feeding and Food of Flamingoes* by Penelope M. Jenkin, *Philosophical Transactions of the Royal Society* Series B. 240, 401 (1957). 292. Waders' bills—*The Biology of Estuarine Animals* by J. Green (Sidgwick and Jackson). 293. Graded habitats in a mangrove swamp—*A General Account of the Fauna and Flora of Mangrove Swamps and Forests in the Indo-West-Pacific Region* by William Macnae, *Advances in Marine Biology* Vol. 6, edited by Sir Frederick S. Russell and Sir Maurice Yonge (Academic Press). 294. Marine food cycle—adapted from *The Nature of Oceanic Life* by John D. Isaacs. Copyright © September 1969 by Scientific American, Inc. All rights reserved. 296. Rock-borers—*The New Zealand Seashore* by John Morton and Michael Miller (Collins); and *British Conchology* by John Gwyn Jeffreys (Gurney and Jackson). 297. Burrowing into the sand—*Seashore Life* by Gillian Matthews and Peter Parks (Penguin Books). 299. Food-sieving "house"—*The Nature of Oceanic Life* by John D. Isaacs. Copyright © September 1969 by Scientific American, Inc. All rights reserved. 300. Tearing and crushing teeth—*A History of Fishes* by J. R. Norman, second edition by P. H. Greenwood (Benn). 301. Senses that guide a shark—adapted from *The Behavior of Sharks* by Perry W. Gilbert. Copyright © July 1962 by Scientific American, Inc. All rights reserved. 303. Takeoff—from a photograph by Dr. Wolfgang Klausewitz in *Der Flug der Tiere* by Herta Schmidt (Verlag Dr. Waldemar Kramer, Frankfurt). 305. Mating arm—by permission of Kaye & Ward Limited, London, and A. S. Barnes & Company, Inc., Cranbury, New Jersey, from *The Underwater Guide to Marine Life* by C. Ray and E. Ciampi. Copyright © 1956; and *Die Cephalopoden* by Professor Dr. Adolf Naef, *Fauna e Flora del Golfo di Napoli,* 35A Monografia (R. Friedländer & Sohn, Berlin). Highly developed eyes—*A History of Fishes* by J. R. Norman, second edition by P. H. Greenwood (Benn), and *Invertebrate Zoology* by Robert D. Barnes (W. B. Saunders), after Wells. 309. A male that lives on its mate—*The Ceratioid Fishes* by E. Bertelsen, *Dana Reports* 1928-30, Vol. 7, No. 39 (Oxford University Press; A/S Import Lager, Copenhagen). 314. Toothed whale and Whalebone whale—*The Seas* by Sir Frederick S. Russell and Sir Maurice Yonge (Warne); *The Whale* edited by Dr. Leonard Harrison Matthews (Allen and Unwin; Tre Tryckare, Cagner & Co., Gothenburg); American Museum of Natural History; and *On the Osteology of the Cachalot or Sperm-whale* by W. H. Flower, *Transactions of The Zoological Society of London,* Vol. 6. 318. Reproductive cycle—*Tracking the Grey Seals* by E. A. Smith, *Natural History,* March 1962. 322. The plates on which the continents rest are moving—continental drift map based on a map by Dr. A. G. Smith. 323. Adjoining continents—adapted from *Confirmation of Continental Drift* by P. M. Hurley. Copyright © April 1968 by Scientific American, Inc. All rights reserved. Former land link—from *Atlas of Evolution* by Sir Gavin de Beer (Nelson, London; Elsevier Nederland, Amsterdam; Bayerischer Landwirtshafts Verlag, Germany; Ediciones Omega, Spain). Sea barrier—*Pleistocene Extinctions* edited by P. S. Martin and H. E. Wright, Jr. (Yale University Press). From *Unterartengliederung und Nacheiszeitliche Ausbreitung des Maulwurfs, Talpa europaea L.* by G. Stein: Berlin, *Mitteil, zool. Mus.,* 39, 379-402 (Akademie-Verlag, Berlin). 325. Evolution shown by evidence (*Tyrannosaurus* and mammal reconstruction)—*Vertebrate Paleontology* by Alfred S. Romer (University of Chicago Press). The evolution of the horse—*The Procession of Life* by Alfred S. Romer (Weidenfeld and Nicolson). 326. The cell—the smallest unit of life (animal cell)—adapted from *The Living Cell* by Jean Brachet. Copyright © September 1961 by Scientific American, Inc. All rights reserved; (bacterium)—F. A. Eislerling and W. R. Romig, *Journal of Ultrastructure Research,* Vol. 6, 540 (Academic Press, New York); (virus)—adapted from *Building a Bacterial Virus* by William B. Wood and R. S. Edgar. Copyright © July 1967 by Scientific American, Inc. All rights reserved; (mycoplasma)—adapted from *The Smallest Living Cells* by Harold J. Morowitz and Mark E. Tourtellotte. Copyright © March 1962 by Scientific American, Inc. All rights reserved. 338. From jaw to ear—*Vertebrate Paleontology* by Alfred S. Romer (University of Chicago Press); and *The Life of Mammals* by L. Harrison Matthews (Weidenfeld and Nicolson). 347. How bees give directions—*The Dancing Bees* by Karl von Frisch (Methuen).